D0874034

SPECIAL EDITION #642
The Keswick Story

Bill and Ruth Raws

"THE KESWICK STORY"

How the Victorious Life Bible Conferences Began:

The history of the Victorious Life Conferences dates back to 1913 when this emphasis was incorporated into a conference held at Oxford, Pa. An outgrowth of a denominational missionary conference for youth, these annual gatherings soon became interdenominational and administered by an independent committee. A summer conference was held for the first several years, but the sense of urgency for the spreading of the message of "The Life That is Christ" resulted in conferences at other seasons and in widely-scattered centers throughout the country.

Much of the impetus in establishing the movement is traceable to the work of God in the life of Charles G. Trumbull, Editor of "The Sunday School Times." While attending the Keswick Convention in England in 1910, he was brought into a new appropriation of God's resources for Christian living. He shared his testimony with a large group of young people assembled at a missionary conference in 1911. Among those who heard this report was Robert C. McQuilken. He, in turn, was transformed through the message brought by Trumbull. Through McQuilken's influence it was arranged that the same message should be stressed in the annual missionary conference of his denomination. Later he was instrumental in organizing independent conferences where the truths of triumphant living and missions were stressed.

"The Sunday School Times" publication became the printed voice of this movement and greatly aided the establishment of the work. A permanent committee was formed to plan for conferences, and the facilities of Princeton Seminary and Stonybrook School for Boys were rented for summer use. Outstanding Bible teachers, Christian Life speakers and missionaries brought Spirit-directed messages which resulted in transformed and rechanneled lives.

From the earliest days there were Christian leaders who feared the terminology of the message of victory, associating it with "perfectionism." However, keen theologians and dedicated Bible teachers such as Drs. W. H. Griffith-Thomas, W. B. Anderson and C. I. Scofield were active in the group and helped it maintain a balanced biblical position in the conferences. Instead of teaching perfectionism the group maintained the truth of the believer's sanctification being on the one hand perfect through his position in Christ, but progressive as to his personal experience.

Gradually it became apparent that a permanent home site for holding the conferences would be an advantage over the use of rented facilities. After much prayer, the Lord directed the group to accept an offer from Addison C. Raws to make the property of Kes-

Addison C. Raws

wick Colony of Mercy, Keswick Grove, N.J., the site for future conferences. The board of the Victorious Life Testimony became the legal body to administer the property. Since 1924 the two works have been conducted simultaneously on the same property with the use of separate facilities. The number of summer conferences has increased from four to eight weeks with weekend sessions being conducted at various times throughout the year. In addition to those speakers mentioned earlier, the list of those whose ministry was especially blessed in the earlier years of the conferences includes: L. L. Legters, D. B. Dinwiddie, Reginald Wallis, Graham Scroggie, Will Houghton, William Culbertson, F. J. Miles and R. A. Torrey.

Although the messages have been particularly directed to Christians, many people have been led to Christ while attending Keswick conferences. Multitudes have appropriated in a new way the fullness of God's salvation and entered into a life of maintained fullness of the Holy Spirit. Hundreds have been called of the Lord into vocational service through the missionary ministry of the conferences. One church alone traces the call of 40 of its young people into the Lord's service to their conference attendance at Keswick.

In the 1920's it was placed upon the hearts of the Keswick board to establish a mission division called The Pioneer Mission Agency. Originally its purpose was to stimulate existing mission boards to reach indigenous tribal groups. Information derived through exploratory surveys was passed on to these boards, and a change in strategy resulted in some instances. In other cases, new, independent missions took up this responsibility. An all-night prayer meeting for access to Mexico led to the formation of a special department of the Pioneer Mission Agency which was to be known as the Wycliffe Bible Translators. It later became a separate organization. In more recent years the mission division has acted in a supervisory and sponsoring role for independent missionaries. In addition, special projects have been funded through offerings received at the Keswick conferences. In this way the missionary vision of the founders has been maintained and worldwide responsibility for reaching the unreached has been presented as a vital part of the normal Christian Life.

The Keswick Colony of Mercy

Behind the vital ministry of Keswick Colony of Mercy with its life-transforming message to hopeless alcoholics lies a chain of miracles. The first link took place in the life of William Raws, Keswick's founder. At death's door a

Mr. William Raws
Founder

a result of the bondage of alcoholism, Raws cried out to his mother's God for salvation. He received the Lord Jesus Christ while all alone in his small art studio. God performed a regenerating and liberating work in his life.

Immediately Raws sought to share the message of this victory with others. After establishing two rescue missions in the city of Philadelphia, he was led to a new concept in work with alcoholics—a rural, residential, spiritual program of rehabilitation designed to help the whole man. The Lord led him to take a step of faith and agree to purchase a 600 acre tract of land in the pine area of New Jersey, calling it Keswick after one of his favorite painting sites in his native England. At the time he was unaware of God's plan to bring a Bible conference ministry, patterned after the English Keswick Convention, held at that same painting site, to this property.

Settling in the White-frame farm house on the property, William Raws, his family and some men from the mission, gathered for a service of dedication and devotion. They decided

First Colony Chapel

Early Keswick Colony Scenes

1. William Raws Memorial Building 2. Saw Mill 3. Homestead Cottage
4. Lakeside Cottage 5. Farm Project

to count the available funds for the project and found that they had just $1.87 capital. From its inception the work was established on faith in the promises of God rather than on the apparent resources. Since its founding in 1897 God has fully provided for all the needs of Keswick Colony using Spirit-directed Christians and churches to provide the thousands of dollars needed annually for the maintaining of the ministry. Specific and perservering prayer has been answered with definite provision from the Lord. Requests in prayer for such things as cows, horses, vehicles and buildings, have been met in a divinely-directed manner. On more than one occasion when a specific amount of money was prayed for, the next mail would contain a gift in that amount. The property has also been miraculously protected from several devastating forest fires through God's intervention in turning the direction of the wind.

Through the years of its history Keswick Colony of Mercy has received well over 15,000 men from nearly every state of the union and from all walks of life. Hundreds have trusted Jesus Christ for salvation and have been set free from sin's power through yielding to Him. Homes have been restored and churches supplied with active workers as a result of what the Lord has done in former slaves of alcohol.

The leadership of the Colony was passed on from the founder, who was called home in 1910, to his son Addison. He led the work for more than 50 years. A third generation has carried on the ministry following the death of Addison C. Raws in 1970.

William A. "Bill" Raws

Having served along with his father for 20 years, William Raws was able to assume the full leadership of the work when his father was called Home.

During the prohibition era, the Colony work became inactive. Few applications were received. It was during those years that the conference ministry was established at Keswick. Soon, however, the repeal of prohibition brought rapid increase in the need for the Colony. As a result, the two ministries have grown in parallel fashion.

Accommodations for 44 men for a recommended stay of at least three months has enabled Keswick to care for nearly 200 men each year. There is no charge for any man's stay since the work is supported by the unsolicited gifts from interested friends. The cost of operation has been substantially reduced by involving the men in its maintenance program. This serves as a therapy for body and mind. The key to Keswick's approach to the alcoholic is II Corinthians 5:17, "Therefore if any man be in Christ, he is a new creature: old things are passed away; behold, all things are become new." Bringing men into relationship to Jesus Christ results in a changed set of desires, behavior patterns and personality.

Shortly after Keswick Colony was founded, a minister brought his son for help. He was in desperate condition both physically and spiritually. His overcoat had been sold for more booze prior to his coming to Keswick even though the weather was bitter cold. It was a triumphant day for him when William Raws was able to lead him to Christ in the little chapel. A gifted musician, this young man began to use his talents for the Lord. After leaving Keswick he became part of the Billy Sunday team, playing the piano and organ for large campaigns. Much of his time and talent was devoted to composing music for hymns and gospel songs. His name appears in the composers' lists of nearly every hymnal because B. D. Ackley was the author of more than 3600 pieces.

Multitudes of other men have been just as gloriously redeemed through the years of Keswick's history. Many have become leaders in their home churches and some have been directed into the ministry and mission work. Only Eternity itself will reveal the full story of God's redeeming grace through the ministry of Keswick Colony of Mercy.

"where God speaks to hearts"
AUDITORIUM

1.

2.

3.

4.

1. *(Outside) Keswick Auditorium*
2. *Present Chapel at Colony*
3. *Colony Mens Building*
4. *Raws Memorial Building*

VICTORIOUS LIFE HYMNS

A Bible centered compilation of the most singable Psalms, hymns and Spiritual Songs obtainable. Carefully selected to provide encouragement, enjoyment, strength and Spiritual growth to Christian believers, with the hope that through their continued use they may be led to "Sing with the spirit . . . . and with the understanding also" (I Cor. 14:15).

Compilation Committee

William A. Raws – Warren Whitney

ALFRED B. SMITH

Chairman

Music Editors

DONNA AND CONRAD KRIEGER

FIRST EDITION

America's Keswick

Keswick Grove

Whiting, New Jersey 08759

Introduction

It was over 50 years ago that Charles M. Alexander, of the world-renowned team of Torrey and Alexander, compiled the first "Victorious Life Hymnal". That it has continued in use until this present day is proof that its ideas and contents were certainly worthwhile and useful.

Through the years thousands of young and old alike have made important spiritual and life-affecting decisions as they sang from this inspired instrument.

I count it a great honor and privilege to have a part in compiling this new edition of VICTORIOUS LIFE HYMNS. Those of you acquainted with the first hymnal will see that this is larger and covers a much wider range of subjects. This was done to enable this edition to be used not only as a special conference hymnal but also for general church use. For in so many present-day hymnals, the older songs with a real spiritual content are being omitted and more recent songs, which are entertaining but often containing less spiritual emphasis, are being substituted. In VICTORIOUS LIFE HYMNS we have endeavored to present only the best of standard hymns and gospel songs and of the newer songs, only those which are scripturally sound and musically acceptable have been added.

VICTORIOUS LIFE HYMNS has been kept simple in its makeup, biographies, forms of service, listings of authors and composers, metrical indexes, etc., have all been omitted feeling that these should be in a special church service and music handbook and not in a hymnal predominately used for congregational participation. This also has allowed more room to include an additional gospel chorus section. As much as possible all of the songs have been grouped together according to dominate themes but sectional headings have been deliberately omitted feeling that these tend to limit a song to one particular category. The topical index with its extensive listings will prove invaluable and the general index with its listings of titles and first lines of both the verse and the chorus will prove a great help in finding your favorite selection.

My prayer is that hearts will be blessed and lives spiritually refreshed and strengthened through the use of this book and that VICTORIOUS LIFE HYMNS will become a treasured possession and constant companion to many a singing pilgrim around the world.

> "Sing unto the Lord oh ye saints of His and give thanks to the remembrance of His holiness." [Psalms 30:4]
>
> "Thanks be to God, who giveth us the Victory through our Lord Jesus Christ." [I Cor. 15:57]

Melody Manor
Montrose, Pa., 1975

"Sing"cerely yours,

Alfred B. Smith, Mus. Doc.

 Printed in U.S.A.
2 3 4 5 6 7 8 9

VICTORIOUS LIFE HYMNS

My Hope Is in the Lord

1

Norman J. Clayton — Norman J. Clayton

1. My hope is in the Lord Who gave Him - self for me,
2. No mer - it of my own His an - ger to sup - press,
3. And now for me He stands Be - fore the Fa - ther's throne,
4. His grace has planned it all, 'Tis mine but to be - lieve,
And paid the price of all my sin at Cal - va - ry.
My on - ly hope is found in Je - sus' right - eous - ness.
He shows His wound - ed hands, and names me as His own.
And rec - og - nize His work of love and Christ re - ceive.
CHORUS
For me He died, For me He lives,
For me He died, For me He lives,
And ev - er - last - ing life and light He free - ly gives.

2

Hallelujah, Praise Jehovah!

Psalm 16-A.B.S.

William J. Kirkpatrick
& Alfred B. Smith

1. Hal-le - lu - jah, praise Je - ho - vah! From the heav-ens praise his name;
2. Let them prais-es give Je - ho - vah, They were made at his com - mand;
3. All ye fruit - ful trees and ce - dars, All ye hills and moun-tains high,

Praise Je - ho - vah in the high - est, All his an - gels praise pro - claim.
Them for - ev - er he es - tab - lished, His de - cree shall ev - er stand.
Creep-ing things and beasts and cat - tle, Birds that in the heav - ens fly.

All his hosts to - geth - er praise him, Sun, and moon, and stars on high;
From the earth, O praise Je - ho - vah, All ye floods, ye crea - tures all;
Kings of earth and all ye peo - ple, Princ-es great, earth's judg-es all;

Praise him, O ye heav'n of heav - ens, And ye floods a - bove the sky.
Fire, and hail, and snow, and va - pors, Storm - y winds that hear him call.
Praise his name, young men and maid - ens, A - ged men, and chil - dren small.

Chorus

Let them prais - es give Je - ho - vah, For his name a - lone is high,
Let them prais - es

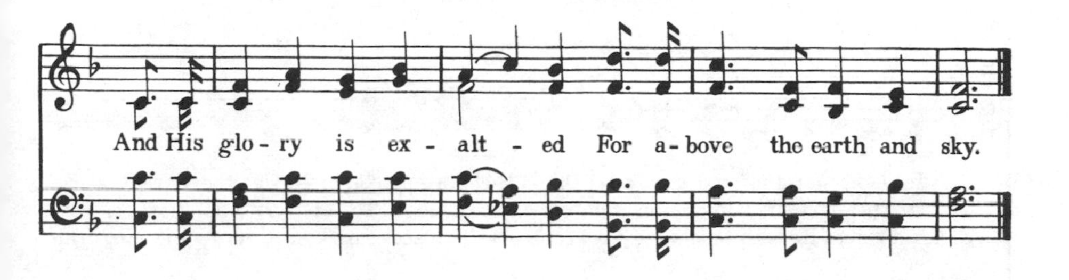
And His glo - ry is ex - alt - ed For a - bove the earth and sky.

Bless the Lord, My Soul

3

E. A. Barnes, Edit. A.B.S.
Psalm 103:1

William J. Kirkpatrick
Arr. By Donna Krieger

1. O bless the Lord, my soul, As the Friend who died for thee; And bless him for the sav-ing grace, So rich, so full and free.
2. O bless the Lord, my soul, As the Rock in which we hide; And bless him for the sense of peace, A-mid the surg-ing tide.
3. O bless the Lord, my soul, As the Hope so sure and sweet; And bless him for the lov-ing call To wor-ship at his feet.
4. O bless the Lord, my soul, As the Guide in days to come; And bless him for the crown of life And heav'ns e-ter-nal home.
Chorus
Bless the Lord, my soul,
(Bless the Lord,) (my soul,)
Bless the Lord, my soul;
(Bless the Lord,) (my soul,)
And all that is with-in me, Bless His ho-ly name.

4 To God Be the Glory

Fanny J. Crosby William H. Doane

1. To God be the glo - ry, great things He hath done, So loved He the world that He
2. O per-fect re - demp-tion, the pur-chase of blood, To ev - ery be - liev - er the
3. Great things He hath taught us, great things He hath done, And great our re-joic - ing thro'

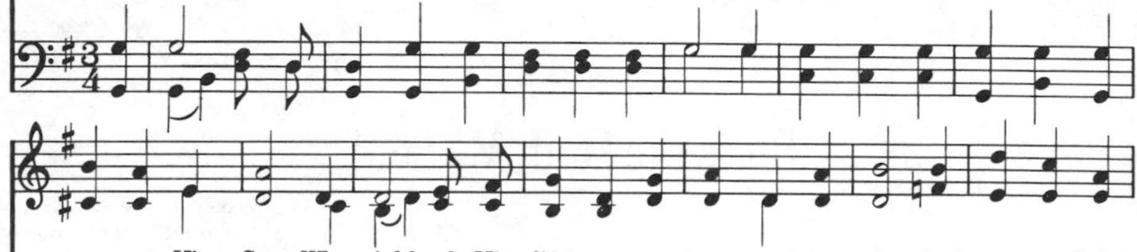

gave us His Son, Who yield-ed His life an a - tone-ment for sin, And o-pened the
prom-ise of God; The vil - est of - fend - er who tru - ly be-lieves, That mo-ment from
Je - sus the Son; But pur - er, and high - er, and great - er will be Our won-der, our

Refrain

Life-gate that all may go in.
Je - sus a par-don re-ceives. Praise the Lord, praise the Lord, Let the earth hear His
trans-port, when Je - sus we see.

voice! Praise the Lord, praise the Lord, Let the peo - ple re-joice! O come to the

Fa - ther thro' Je - sus the Son, And give Him the glo - ry, great things He hath done.

Be Thou Exalted

Fanny J. Crosby & A. B. S.

Alfred B. Smith

1. Be Thou ex - alt - ed, for ev-er and ev-er, God of e - ter - ni - ty, The Ancient of
2. Be Thou ex - alt - ed, O Son of the Highest Gra-cious Re - deem - er Our Sav-iour and
3. Be Thou ex - alt - ed, O Spir-it e - ter-nal! Dwell in our hearts, keep us Ho-ly with-
Days! Won-drous in Maj - es - ty, so might-y in wis-dom, per-fect in
King! One with the Fa - ther, co - e-qual in glo - ry, Here at Thy
in; Feed us each day with Thy Heav-en-ly Man-na "Heal-er of
Chorus
ho - li-ness, and wor-thy of praise.
foot - stool our homage we bring.
wound-ed hearts" Thy praises we sing.
Be thou ex - alt - ed by ser-aphs and
an-gels, Be thou ex - alt - ed with harp and with song; Saints in their
an-thems of rap-ture a - dore thee, Thine be the glo-ry for-ev-er A - men!

6 Arise, My Soul, Arise

Charles Wesley

Old Norman Melody

1. A - rise, my soul, a - rise! Shake off thy guilt - y fears;
2. He ev - er lives a - bove, For me to in - ter - cede;
3. Five bleed - ing wounds He bears, Re - ceived on Cal - va - ry;
4. The Fa - ther hears Him pray, His dear a - noint - ed One;
5. My God is rec - on - ciled, His par - doning voice I hear;
The bleed - ing Sac - ri - fice In my be - half ap - pears.
His all - re - deem - ing love, His pre - cious blood to plead;
They pour ef - fec - tual prayers, They strong - ly plead for me;
He can - not turn a - way The pres - ence of His Son:
He owns me for His child, I can no long - er fear:
Be - fore the throne my Sure - ty stands; My name is writ - ten
His blood a - toned for all our race, And sprin - kles now the
"For - give him, O for - give," they cry, "Nor let that ran - somed
His Spir - it an - swers to the blood, And tells me I am
With con - fi - dence I now draw nigh, And "Fa - ther, Ab - ba,
on His hands, My name is writ - ten on His hands.
throne of grace, And sprin - kles now the throne of grace.
sin - ner die! Nor let that ran - somed sin - ner die!"
born of God, And tells me I am born of God.
Fa - ther!" cry, And "Fa - ther, Ab - ba, Fa - ther" cry. A - MEN.

Crown Him With Many Crowns 7

Matthew Bridges
Alt. By John Rippon

Oliver Holden

1. Crown Him with man - y crowns, The Lamb up - on His throne;
2. Crown Him the Son of God Be - fore the worlds be - gan,
3. Crown Him the Lord of life, Who tri - umphed o'er the grave,
4. Crown Him the Lord of peace, Whose power a scep - ter sways
5. Crown Him the Lord of love! Be - hold His hands and side,
Hark! how the heaven-ly an - them drowns All mu - sic but its own!
And ye, who tread where He hath trod, Crown Him the Son of man,
And rose vic - to - rious in the strife For those He came to save.
From pole to pole, that wars may cease, And all be prayer and praise!
Rich wounds, yet vis - i - ble a - bove, In beau - ty glo - ri - fied.
A - wake, my soul, and sing Of Him who died for thee,
Who ev - ery grief hath known That wrings the hu - man breast,
His glo - ries now we sing Who died, and rose on high,
His reign shall know no end, And round His pierc - ed feet
All hail, Re - deem - er, hail! For Thou hast died for me:
And hail Him as thy match-less King Through all e - ter - ni - ty.
And takes and bears them for His own, That all in Him may rest.
Who died, e - ter - nal life to bring, And lives that death may die.
Fair flowers of Par - a - dise ex - tend Their fra-grance ev - er sweet.
Thy praise shall nev - er, nev - er fail Through-out e - ter - ni - ty.
A-MEN.

8 All Hail the Power

CORONATION
Edward Perronet
Alt. John Rippon
Oliver Holden
1. All hail the power of Je - sus' name! Let an - gels pros - trate fall;
2. Ye cho - sen seed of Is - rael's race, Ye ran - somed from the fall,
3. Let ev - ery kin - dred, ev - ery tribe, On this ter - res - trial ball,
4. O that with yon - der sa - cred throng We at His feet may fall!
Bring forth the roy - al di - a - dem, And crown Him Lord of all;
Hail Him who saves you by His grace, And crown Him Lord of all;
To Him all maj - es - ty as - cribe, And crown Him Lord of all;
We'll join the ev - er - last - ing song, And crown Him Lord of all;
Bring forth the roy - al di - a - dem, And crown Him Lord of all!
Hail Him who saves you by His grace, And crown Him Lord of all!
To Him all maj - es - ty as - cribe, And crown Him Lord of all!
We'll join the ev - er - last - ing song, And crown Him Lord of all!
MILES LANE
(Second Tune)
William Shrubsole
1. All hail the power of Je - sus' name! Let angels pros-trate fall; Bring forth the roy - al
di - a - dem, And crown Him, crown Him, crown Him, Crown Him Lord of all!

All Hail the Power

DIADEM
Edward Perronet
Adapt. By John Rippon
James Ellor
1. All hail the pow'r of Je - sus' name! Let an - gels pros-trate
2. Ye cho - sen seed of Is - rael's race, Ye ran-somed of the
3. Let ev - ery kin - dred, ev - ery tribe, On this ter - res - trial
4. O that with yon - der sa - cred throng We at His feet may
fall, Let an - gels pros-trate fall; Bring forth the roy - al di - a-
fall, Ye ran - somed of the fall; Hail Him who saves you by His
ball, On this ter - res - trial ball; To Him all maj - es - ty as-
fall, We at His feet may fall! We'll join the ev - er - last - ing
dem,
grace, And crown .... Him, crown Him,
cribe,
song, And crown Him, crown Him, crown Him, crown Him, crown Him,
crown ....
crown Him, crown Him, And crown Him Lord of all. A-men.
......................Him, And crown Him Lord of all!

10 And Can It Be

Charles Wesley

Thomas Campbell

1. And can it be that I should gain An in - terest in the
2. 'Tis mys - tery all! Th Im-mor - tal dies! Who can ex - plore His
3. He left His Fa - ther's throne a - bove, So free, so in - fi -
4. Long my im-pris - oned spir - it lay Fast - bound in sin and
5. No con - dem-na - tion now I dread; Je - sus, and all in

Sav - iour's blood? Died He for me, who caused His pain, For me, who
strange de - sign? In vain the first - born ser - aph tries To sound the
nite His grace; Emp - tied Him - self of all but love, And bled for
na - ture's night; Thine eye dif - fused a quick-ening ray. I woke, the
Him, is mine! A - live in Him, my liv - ing Head, And clothed in

Him to death pur-sued? A - maz - ing love! How can it be That
depths of love di - vine! 'Tis mer - cy all! Let earth a - dore; Let
A - dam's help - less race. 'Tis mer - cy all, im - mense and free! For,
dun - geon flamed with light; My chains fell off, my heart was free; I
right - eous - ness di - vine, Bold I ap - proach th' e - ter - nal throne, And

Thou, my God, shouldst die for me?
an - gel minds in - quire no more.
O my God, it found out me.
rose, went forth, and fol - lowed Thee.
claim the crown through Christ, my own.

REFRAIN

A - maz - ing love! How

A - maz-ing love!

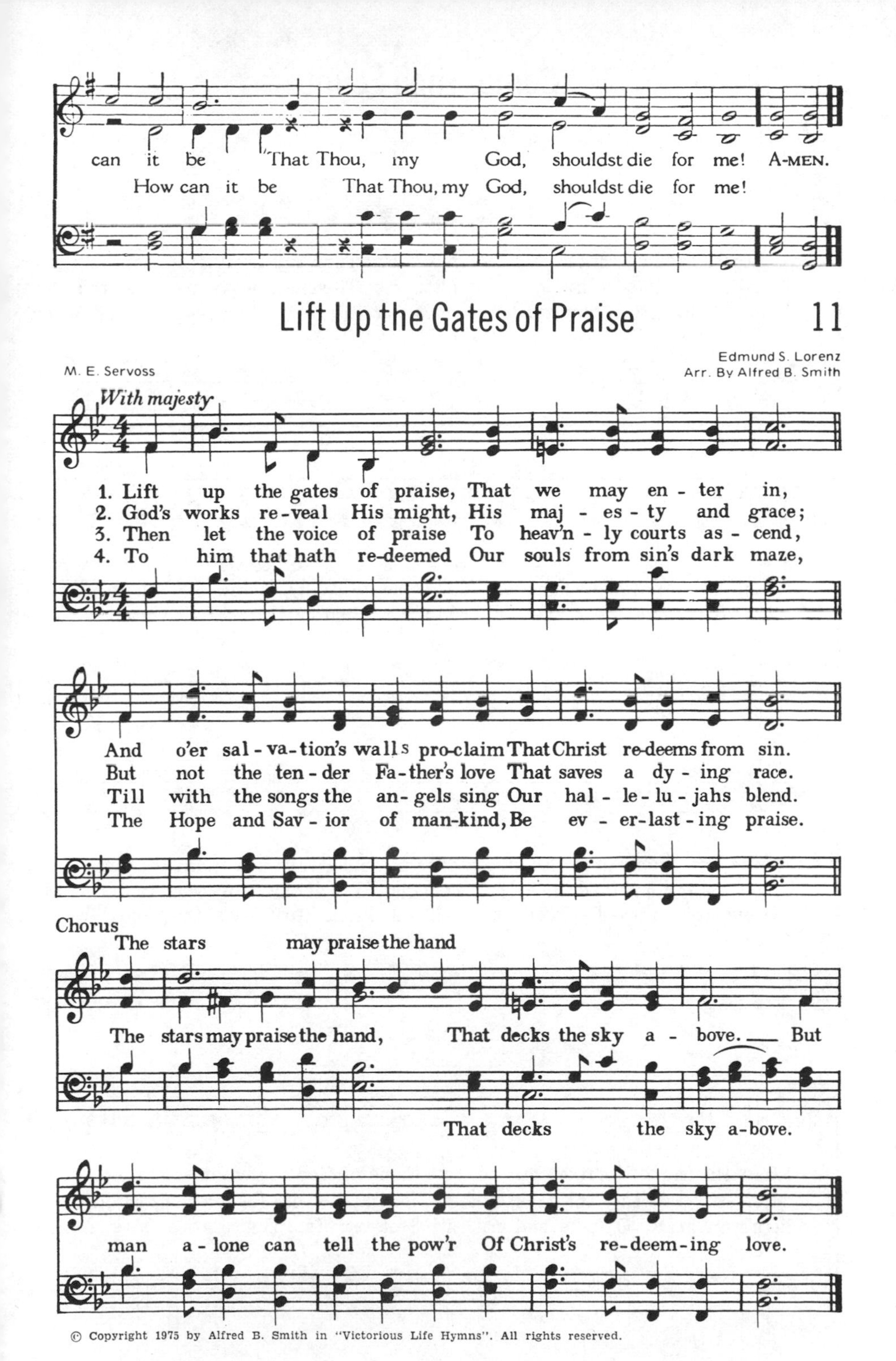
can it be That Thou, my God, shouldst die for me! A-MEN.
How can it be That Thou, my God, shouldst die for me!
Lift Up the Gates of Praise
11
M. E. Servoss
Edmund S. Lorenz
Arr. By Alfred B. Smith
With majesty
1. Lift up the gates of praise, That we may en - ter in,
2. God's works re-veal His might, His maj - es - ty and grace;
3. Then let the voice of praise To heav'n - ly courts as - cend,
4. To him that hath re-deemed Our souls from sin's dark maze,
And o'er sal - va - tion's walls pro-claim That Christ re-deems from sin.
But not the ten - der Fa - ther's love That saves a dy - ing race.
Till with the songs the an - gels sing Our hal - le - lu - jahs blend.
The Hope and Sav - ior of man-kind, Be ev - er-last - ing praise.
Chorus
The stars may praise the hand
The stars may praise the hand, That decks the sky a - bove. But
That decks the sky a-bove.
man a - lone can tell the pow'r Of Christ's re-deem-ing love.
© Copyright 1975 by Alfred B. Smith in "Victorious Life Hymns". All rights reserved.

12 Come, Thou Fount

Robert Robinson
Edited by E. M. Clarkson

Traditional American Melody
Arr. by John Wyeth

1. Come, Thou Fount of ev - ery bless - ing, Tune my heart to sing Thy grace;
2. Hith - er - to Thy love has blest me; Thou hast bro't me to this place;
3. O to grace how great a debt - or Dai - ly I'm con-strained to be!
Streams of mer - cy, nev - er ceas - ing, Call for songs of loud - est praise.
And I know Thy hand will bring me Safe - ly home by Thy good grace.
Let Thy good - ness, like a fet - ter, Bind my wan-dering heart to Thee:
Teach me some me - lo - dious son - net, Sung by flam - ing tongues a - bove;
Je - sus sought me when a stran - ger, Wan-dering from the fold of God;
Prone to wan - der, Lord, I feel it, Prone to leave the God I love;
Praise His name—I'm fixed up - on it—Name of God's re - deem-ing love.
He, to res - cue me from dan - ger, Bought me with His pre-cious blood.
Here's my heart, O take and seal it; Seal it for Thy courts a - bove. A-men.

O Could I Speak the Matchless Worth 13

Samuel Medley

Wolfgang A. Mozart
Arr. by Lowell Mason

1. O could I speak the match - less worth,
2. I'd sing the pre - cious blood He spilt,
3. I'd sing the char - ac - ters He bears,
4. Soon the de - light - ful day will come

O could I sound the glo - ries forth Which in my Sav - iour shine,
My ran - som from the dread-ful guilt Of sin and wrath di - vine!
And all the forms of love He wears, Ex - alt - ed on His throne:
When my dear Lord will bring me home, And I shall see His face;

I'd soar and touch the heav'nly strings, And vie with Ga-briel while he sings
I'd sing His glo - rious right-eous-ness, In which all-per - fect heavenly dress
In loft - iest songs of sweet-est praise, I would to ev - er - last - ing days
Then with my Sav - iour, Brother, Friend, A blest e - ter - ni - ty I'll spend,

In notes al - most di - vine, In notes al - most di - vine.
My soul shall ev - er shine, My soul shall ev - er shine.
Make all His glo - ries known, Make all His glo - ries known.
Tri - um - phant in His grace, Tri - um-phant in His grace. A-MEN.

14 O Day of Rest and Gladness

Christopher Wordsworth

German Melody
Arr. by Lowell Mason

1. O day of rest and glad-ness, O day of joy and light,
2. On thee, at the cre - a - tion, The light first had its birth;
3. To - day on wea - ry na - tions The heav'n - ly man - na falls;
4. New grac - es ev - er gain - ing From this our day of rest,
O balm of care and sad - ness, Most beau - ti - ful, most bright;
On thee, for our sal - va - tion, Christ rose from depths of earth;
To ho - ly con - vo - ca - tions The sil - ver trump - et calls,
We reach the rest re - main - ing To spir - its of the blest;
On thee the high and low - ly, Through a - ges joined in tune, Sing
On thee our Lord vic - to - rious The Spir - it sent from heav'n; And
Where gos - pel light is glow - ing With pure and ra - diant beams, And
To Ho - ly Ghost be prais - es, To Fa - ther and to Son; The
"Ho - ly, ho - ly, ho - ly," To the great God Tri - une.
thus on thee most glo - rious A tri - ple light was giv'n.
liv - ing wa - ter flow - ing With soul - re - fresh - ing streams.
Church her voice up - rais - es To Thee, blest Three in One. A - men.

Immortal, Invisible, God Only Wise

Walter C. Smith

Welsh Hymn Melody

1. Im - mor - tal, in - vis - i - ble, God on - ly wise,
2. Un - rest - ing, un - hast - ing, and si - lent as light,
3. To all, life Thou giv - est, to both great and small,
4. Great Fa - ther of glo - ry, pure Fa - ther of light,
In light in - ac - ces - si - ble hid from our eyes,
Nor want - ing, nor wast - ing, Thou rul - est in might;
In all life Thou liv - est, the true life of all.
Thine an - gels a - dore Thee, all veil - ing their sight;
Most bless - ed, most glo - rious, the An - cient of Days,
Thy jus - tice like moun - tains high soar - ing a - bove
We blos - som and flour - ish as leaves on the tree,
All praise we would ren - der; O help us to see
Al - might - y, vic - to - rious, Thy great name we praise.
Thy clouds, which are foun - tains of good - ness and love.
And with - er and per - ish— but naught chang-eth Thee.
'Tis on - ly the splen - dor of light hid - eth Thee! A - men.

16 Glory Be to Him Who Loved Us

Horatius Bonar

Suggested by Stamford
Alfred B. Smith

1. Glo - ry be to Him who loved us, Washed us from each
2. "Glo - ry, wor - ship, laud, and bless - ing" Thus the choir tri -
3. Glo - ry to the King of an - gels, Glo - ry to the
4. Glo - ry be to Thee, O Fa - ther, Glo - ry be to

sin - ful stain; Glo - ry be to Him who made us
um - phant sings; "Hon - or, rich - es, power, do - min - ion"
Church's King, Glo - ry to the King of na - tions,
Thee, O Son, Glo - ry be to Thee, O Spir - it,

Priests and kings with Him to reign; Glo - ry, wor - ship,
Thus its praise cre - a - tion brings; Thou art wor - thy,
Heaven and earth His prais - es sing: Glo - ry ev - er
Glo - ry be to God a - lone, As it was, is

laud, and bless - ing To the Lamb who once was slain.
Thou art wor - thy, Lord of lords and King of kings.
and for - ev - er To the King of glo - ry bring.
now, and shall be While the end - less a - ges run.

Broaden out
Glo - ry wor-ship, laud, and bless-ing To the Lamb who once was slain.
Thou art wor-thy, Thou art wor-thy, Lord of Lords and King of kings.
Glo - ry ev - er and for - ev - er To the King of glo - ry bring.
As it was, is now, and shall be While the end-less a - ges run.
© Copyright 1975 by Alfred B. Smith in "Victorious Life Hymns". All rights reserved.
Worthy Is the Lamb
17
W. P. MacKay
Alfred B. Smith
1. Wor - thy, wor-thy is the Lamb— Wor - thy, wor-thy is the Lamb—
2. He re-deemed our souls to God— He re-deemed our souls to God—
3. He has made us kings and priests— He has made us kings and priests—
4. We shall ev - er reign with Him— We shall ev - er reign with Him—
Refrain
Wor - thy, wor-thy is the Lamb— That was slain!
He re-deemed our souls to God— By His blood.
He has made us kings and priests,— To our God.
We shall ev - er reign with Him,— The Lamb of God.
Praise Him, and a - dore Him

Praise Him and a - dore Him Praise Him and a - dore Him Praise the Lamb!

18 O My Soul, Bless Thou Jehovah

Reuben A. Torrey
Psalm 34:1

Alfred B. Smith

1. O my soul, bless thou Je - ho - vah, God of love and grace art Thou:
Thou a - lone art wise and ho - ly; At thy feet I hum - bly bow.

2. Thou Thy Son hast free - ly giv - en, All our sins to bear a - way;
On the cross He made a - tone-ment, Then to glo - ry led the way.

3. He for us re-ceived the Spir - it, Pre-cious gift of love di - vine;
Shed Him forth up - on Thy chil - dren; Now for - ev - er He is mine.

4. Je - sus soon a-gain re - turn-eth, Ev - er - more with Him I'll be,
Like Him thro' the end-less a - ges, Saved for all e - ter - ni - ty.

Chorus

O my soul, bless thou Je - ho - vah! O my soul, bless thou Je - ho - vah!
O my soul, bless thou Je - ho - vah! And crown Him Lord of all.

The Spacious Firmament on High 19

Psa. 19
Joseph Addison

Franz Joseph Haydn

1. The spa - cious fir - ma - ment on high, With all the
2. Soon as the eve - ning shades pre - vail, The moon takes
3. What though in sol - emn si - lence all Move round this
blue e - the - re-al sky, And span - gled heavens, a shin - ing frame,
up the won - drous tale, And night - ly to the lis - tening earth
dark ter - res - tri-al ball? What though no re - al voice nor sound
Their great O - rig - i - nal pro - claim. Th'un-wea - ried sun, from
Re - peats the sto - ry of her birth; Whilst all the stars that
A - midst their ra - diant orbs be found? In rea - son's ear they
day to day, Does his Cre - a - tor's power dis - play, And pub - lish -
round her burn, And all the plan - ets in their turn, Con - firm the
all re-joice, And ut - ter forth a glo - rious voice; For - ev - er
es to ev - ery land The work of an al-might - y hand.
ti - dings as they roll, And spread the truth from pole to pole.
sing - ing, as they shine, "The hand that made us is di - vine." A-MEN.

20 Great God of Wonders

Samuel Davies

John Newton

1. Great God of won-ders! all Thy ways Are match-less, God-like, and di-vine; But the fair glo-ries of Thy grace More God-like and un-ri-valed shine, More God-like and un-ri-valed shine.
2. In won-der lost, with trem-bling joy, We take the par-don of our God: Par-don for crimes of deep-est dye, A par-don bought with Je-sus' blood, A par-don bought with Je-sus' blood.
3. O may this strange, this match-less grace, This God-like mir-a-cle of love, Fill the whole earth with grate-ful praise, And all th'an-gel-ic choirs a-bove, And all th'an-gel-ic choirs a-bove.
CHORUS
Who is a par-d'ning God like Thee? Or who has grace so rich and free? Or who has grace so rich and free? free?
1
2

This Is My Father's World

Franklin L. Sheppard
Arr. by Norman Johnson

Maltbie D. Babcock

1. This is my Fa - ther's world, And to my list-'ning ears
2. This is my Fa - ther's world– The birds their car - ols raise;
3. This is my Fa - ther's world– O let me ne'er for - get

All na - ture sings, and round me rings The mu - sic of the spheres.
The morn - ing light, the lil - y white, De - clare their Mak - er's praise.
That tho the wrong seems oft so strong God is the Rul - er yet.

This is my Fa - ther's world! I rest me in the thought Of
This is my Fa - ther's world! He shines in all that's fair; In the
This is my Fa - ther's world! The bat - tle is not done; Je -

rocks and trees, of skies and seas– His hand the won - ders wrought.
rus - tling grass I hear Him pass– He speaks to me ev - 'ry - where.
sus who died shall be sat - is - fied, And earth and heav'n be one.

22 Holy, Holy, Holy!

Reginald Heber | John B. Dykes

1. Ho-ly, Ho-ly, Ho-ly! Lord God Al-might-y! Ear-ly in the morn-ing our song shall rise to Thee; Ho-ly, Ho-ly, Ho-ly! Mer-ci-ful and Might-y! God in Three Per-sons, bless-ed Trin-i-ty!
2. Ho-ly, Ho-ly, Ho-ly! All the saints a-dore Thee, Cast-ing down their gold-en crowns a-round the glass-y sea; Cher-u-bim and ser-a-phim fall-ing down be-fore Thee, Which wert and art, and ev-er-more shalt be.
3. Ho-ly, Ho-ly, Ho-ly! Tho' the darkness hide Thee, Tho' the eye of sin-ful man Thy glo-ry may not see, On-ly Thou art ho-ly; there is none be-side Thee Per-fect in power, in love, and pu-ri-ty.
4. Ho-ly, Ho-ly, Ho-ly! Lord God Al-might-y! All Thy works shall praise Thy name, in earth, and sky, and sea; Ho-ly, Ho-ly, Ho-ly! Mer-ci-ful and Might-y! God in Three Per-sons, bless-ed Trin-i-ty! A-MEN.

23 O for a Thousand Tongues

Charles Wesley | Arr. by Lowell Mason

1. O for a thou-sand tongues to sing My great Re-deem-er's praise,
2. My gra-cious Mas-ter and my God, As-sist me to pro-claim,
3. Je-sus! the name that charms our fears, That bids our sor-rows cease;
4. He breaks the power of can-celed sin, He sets the pris-oner free;
5. Hear Him, ye deaf; His praise, ye dumb, Your loos-ened tongues em-ploy;

The glo-ries of my God and King, The tri-umphs of His grace.
To spread through all the earth a-broad, The hon-ors of Thy name.
'Tis mu-sic in the sin-ner's ears, 'Tis life, and health, and peace.
His blood can make the foul-est clean; His blood a-vailed for me.
Ye blind, be-hold your Sav-iour come; And leap, ye lame, for joy. A-MEN.
O Worship the King
24
Robert Grant
J. Michael Haydn
1. O wor-ship the King, all-glo-rious a-bove, O grate-ful-ly sing His power and His love; Our Shield and De-fend-er, the An-cient of Days, Pa-vil-ioned in splen-dor, and gird-ed with praise.
2. O tell of His might, O sing of His grace, Whose robe is the light, whose can-o-py space. His char-iots of wrath the deep thun-der-clouds form, And dark is His path on the wings of the storm.
3. Thy boun-ti-ful care what tongue can re-cite? It breathes in the air, it shines in the light, It streams from the hills, it de-scends to the plain, And sweet-ly dis-tills in the dew and the rain.
4. Frail chil-dren of dust, and fee-ble as frail, In Thee do we trust, nor find Thee to fail; Thy mer-cies how ten-der! how firm to the end! Our Mak-er, De-fend-er, Re-deem-er and Friend. A-MEN.

Love Divine, All Loves Excelling

Charles Wesley

John Zundel

1. Love di - vine, all loves ex - cell - ing, Joy of heaven, to earth come down;
2. Breathe, oh, breathe Thy lov - ing Spir - it In - to ev - ery trou - bled breast;
3. Come, Al - might - y, to de - liv - er, Let us all Thy life re - ceive;
4. Fin - ish, then, Thy new cre - a - tion, Pure and spot - less let us be;

Fix in us Thy hum - ble dwell - ing, All Thy faith - ful mer - cies crown.
Let us all in Thee in - her - it, Let us find the prom - ised rest;
Sud - den - ly re - turn, and nev - er, Nev - er more Thy tem - ples leave.
Let us see Thy great sal - va - tion Per - fect - ly re-stored in Thee;

Je - sus, Thou art all com - pas - sion, Pure, un - bound-ed love Thou art—
Take a - way the love of sin - ning; Al - pha and O - me - ga be;
Thee we would be al - ways bless - ing, Serve Thee as Thy hosts a - bove,
Changed from glo - ry in - to glo - ry Till in heaven we take our place,

Vis - it us with Thy sal - va - tion, En - ter ev - ery trem-bling heart.
End of faith, as its be - gin-ning, Set our hearts at lib - er - ty.
Pray, and praise Thee with-out ceas-ing, Glo - ry in Thy per- fect love.
Till we cast our crowns be - fore Thee, Lost in won-der, love, and praise. A-MEN.

O the Deep, Deep Love of Jesus

S. Trevor Francis

Thomas J. Williams

1. O the deep, deep love of Je-sus– Vast, un-meas-ured, bound-less, free!
2. O the deep, deep love of Je-sus– Spread His praise from shore to shore!
3. O the deep, deep love of Je-sus– Love of ev-'ry love the best!
Roll-ing as a might-y o-cean In its full-ness o-ver me,
How He lov-eth, ev-er lov-eth, Chang-eth nev-er, nev-er-more.
'Tis an o-cean vast of bless-ing, 'Tis a ha-ven sweet of rest.
Un-der-neath me, all a-round me, Is the cur-rent of Thy love–
How He watch-es o'er His loved ones, Died to call them all His own;
O the deep, deep love of Je-sus– 'Tis a heav'n of heav'ns to me;
Lead-ing on-ward, lead-ing home-ward, To my glo-rious rest a-bove.
How for them He in-ter-ced-eth, Watch-eth o'er them from the throne!
And it lifts me up to glo-ry, For it lifts me up to Thee.

27 How Great Thou Art

William F. Sherwin
Arr. by A. B. S.
Psalm 8 Circa 1880
1. Lord, our Lord, thro' earth's vast frame How ex - alt - ed is Thy name!
2. When Thy heav - ens I sur - vey, Which Thy fin-gers' work dis-play,
3. What is man that in Thy mind He a con-stant place should find?
Who hast set Thy glo - ry bright Far a - bove the heav-en's height; How
When the moon and stars I see Or - dered all by Thy de - cree; How
What the son of man that he Should be vis - it - ed by Thee? How
great Thou art!
Chorus
Lord, our Lord, we praise Thee How great Thou art! Who hast
set Thy glo-ry bright Far a-bove the heav-en's height, How great Thou art!

Great Is Thy Faithfulness

Thomas O. Chisholm — William M. Runyan

1. Great is Thy faith-ful-ness, O God my Fa-ther, There is no shad-ow of
2. Sum-mer and win-ter, and springtime and har-vest, Sun, moon and stars in their
3. Par-don for sin and a peace that en-dur-eth, Thy own dear pres-ence to

turn-ing with Thee; Thou chang-est not, Thy com-pas-sions they fail not;
cours-es a-bove Join with all na-ture in man-i-fold wit-ness
cheer and to guide; Strength for to-day and bright hope for to-mor-row,

Refrain

As Thou hast been Thou for-ev-er wilt be.
To Thy great faith-ful-ness, mer-cy and love. Great is Thy faith-ful-ness!
Bless-ings all mine, with ten thou-sand be-side!

Great is Thy faith-ful-ness! Morn-ing by morn-ing new mer-cies I see; All I have

need-ed Thy hand hath pro-vid-ed—Great is Thy faith-ful-ness, Lord, un-to me!

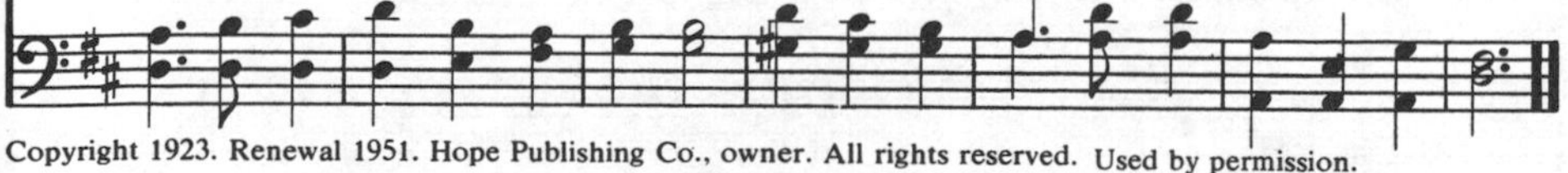

29 A Mighty Fortress

Psalm 46
Martin Luther
Trans. by Frederick H. Hedge
Martin Luther
1. A might - y for - tress is our God, A bul - wark nev - er fail - ing;
2. Did we in our own strength con-fide, Our striv - ing would be los - ing,
3. And though this world, with dev - ils filled, Should threat - en to un - do us,
4. That word a - bove all earth - ly powers, No thanks to them, a - bid - eth;
Our help - er He, a - mid the flood Of mor - tal ills pre - vail - ing:
Were not the right Man on our side, The man of God's own choos - ing:
We will not fear, for God hath willed His truth to tri - umph through us:
The Spir - it and the gifts are ours Through him who with us sid - eth:
For still our an - cient foe Doth seek to work us woe; His craft and power are
Dost ask who that may be? Christ Je - sus, it is He; Lord Sab - a - oth His
The Prince of Dark - ness grim, We trem - ble not for him; His rage we can en-
Let goods and kin - dred go, This mor - tal life al - so; The bod - y they may
great, And, armed with cru - el hate, On earth is not his e - qual.
name, From age to age the same, And He must win the bat - tle.
dure, For lo, his doom is sure; One lit - tle word shall fell him.
kill: God's truth a - bid - eth still; His king - dom is for - ev - er. A-men.

Our Great Saviour

J. Wilbur Chapman
Rowland H. Prichard
Arr. by Robert Harkness
1. Je - sus! what a Friend for sin - ners! Je - sus! Lov - er of my soul;
2. Je - sus! what a Strength in weak - ness! Let me hide my - self in Him;
3. Je - sus! what a Help in sor - row! While the bil - lows o'er me roll,
4. Je - sus! what a Guide and Keep - er! While the tem - pest still is high,
5. Je - sus! I do now re - ceive Him, More than all in Him I find,
Friends may fail me, foes as - sail me, He, my Sav - ior, makes me whole.
Tempt-ed, tried, and some-times fail - ing, He, my Strength, my vic-t'ry wins.
E - ven when my heart is break-ing, He, my Com-fort, helps my soul.
Storms a - bout me, night o'er - takes me, He, my Pi - lot, hears my cry.
He hath grant - ed me for - give - ness, I am His, and He is mine.
Refrain
Hal - le - lu - jah! what a Sav - ior! Hal - le - lu - jah! what a Friend!
Sav - ing, help - ing, keep - ing, lov - ing, He is with me to the end.

31 Praise Him! Praise Him!

Fanny J. Crosby | Chester G. Allen

1. Praise Him! praise Him! Je - sus, our bless - ed Re - deem - er! Sing, O Earth, His
2. Praise Him! praise Him! Je - sus, our bless - ed Re - deem - er! For our sins He
3. Praise Him! praise Him! Je - sus, our bless - ed Re - deem - er! Heav'n-ly por - tals

won-der - ful love pro - claim! Hail Him! hail Him! high-est arch-an - gels in glo - ry;
suf-fered, and bled and died; He our Rock, our hope of e - ter - nal sal - va - tion,
loud with ho - san - nas ring! Je - sus, Sav - ior, reign-eth for - ev - er and ev - er;

Strength and hon - or give to His ho - ly name! Like a shep-herd Je - sus will
Hail Him! hail Him! Je - sus the Cru - ci - fied. Sound His prais - es! Je - sus who
Crown Him! crown Him! Proph-et and Priest and King! Christ is com - ing! o - ver the

Refrain

guard His chil-dren, In His arms He car-ries them all day long:
bore our sor-rows; Love un-bound-ed, won-der-ful, deep and strong: Praise Him! praise Him
world vic - to-rious, Pow'r and glo - ry un-to the Lord be - long:

tell of His ex-cel-lent great-ness; Praise Him! praise Him! ev-er in joy-ful song!
Love, Life, and Everlasting Joy
32
Unknown
Alfred B. Smith
1. O Christ, in Thee my soul has found, And found in Thee a-lone,
2. I sighed for rest and hap-pi-ness, I yearned for them, not Thee;
3. I tried the brok-en cis-terns, Lord, But how the wa-ters failed!
4. The pleas-ures lost I sad-ly mourned, But nev-er wept for Thee,
The peace, the joy I sought so long, The life till now un-known.
But while I passed my Sav-iour by, His love laid hold on me.
For as I stooped to drink they fled, And mocked me as I wailed.
Till grace my sight-less eyes re-ceived, Thy love-li-ness to see.
Chorus
Now none but Christ can sat-is-fy, No oth-er name for me;
There is love, and life, and last-ing joy, Lord Je-sus, found in Thee.
© Copyright 1975 by Alfred B. Smith in "Victorious Life Hymns". All rights reserved.

33 Jesus, Wondrous Saviour!

D. A. McGregor
Thomas Hastings & Alfred B. Smith

1. Je - sus, won-drous Sav - iour! Christ, of kings, the King!
2. All earth's flow - ing pleas - ures Were a win - try sea,
3. Life is death, if sev - ered From Thy throb - bing heart.
4. Je - sus! all per - fec - tions Rise and end in Thee;
An - gels fall be - fore Thee, Pros - trate, wor - ship - ping;
Heav'n it - self with - out Thee Dark as night would be.
Death with life a - bund - ant At Thy touch would start.
Bright - ness of God's glo - ry Thou, e - ter - nal - ly.
Fair - est they con - fess Thee In the Heav'n a - bove.
Lamb of God! Thy glo - ry Is the light a - bove.
Worlds and men and an - gels All con - sist in Thee:
Fav - our'd be - yond meas - ure They Thy face who see;
We would sing Thee fair - est Here in hymns of love;
Lamb of God! Thy glo - ry Is the life of love.
Yet Thou cam - est to us In hu - mil - i - ty.
May we, gra - cious Sav - iour, Share this ec - sta - sy.

Wonderful Saviour

J. M. Harris

J. M. Harris
Rev. by Alfred B. Smith

1. Je - sus, my King, my won-der-ful Sav-iour, All of my life is
2. Par-don for sin, oh, won-der-ful sto - ry! All of its stains washed
3. Je - sus, my Lord, I'll ev - er a - dore Thee, Lay at Thy feet my
4. When in that bright and beau-ti - ful cit - y I shall be hold Thy
giv - en to Thee. I am re - joic - ing in Thy sal - va - tion.
whit - er than snow! Je - sus has come to live in His tem - ple,
treas-ures of love. Lead me in ways to show forth Thy glo - ry,
glo - ries un - told, I shall be like Thee, won-der-ful Sav - iour,
Thy pre-cious blood has made me free.
And with His love my heart is a - glow.
Ways that will end in heav-en a - bove.
And I will sing while a - ges un - fold.
Chorus
Won-der-ful Sav-iour, won-der-ful
Sav - iour, Thou art so near, so pre-cious to me! Won-der-ful
Sav - iour, won-der-ful Sav-iour, My heart is filled with prais-es to Thee.

35

I Will Praise Him!

Margaret J. Harris

Margaret J. Harris

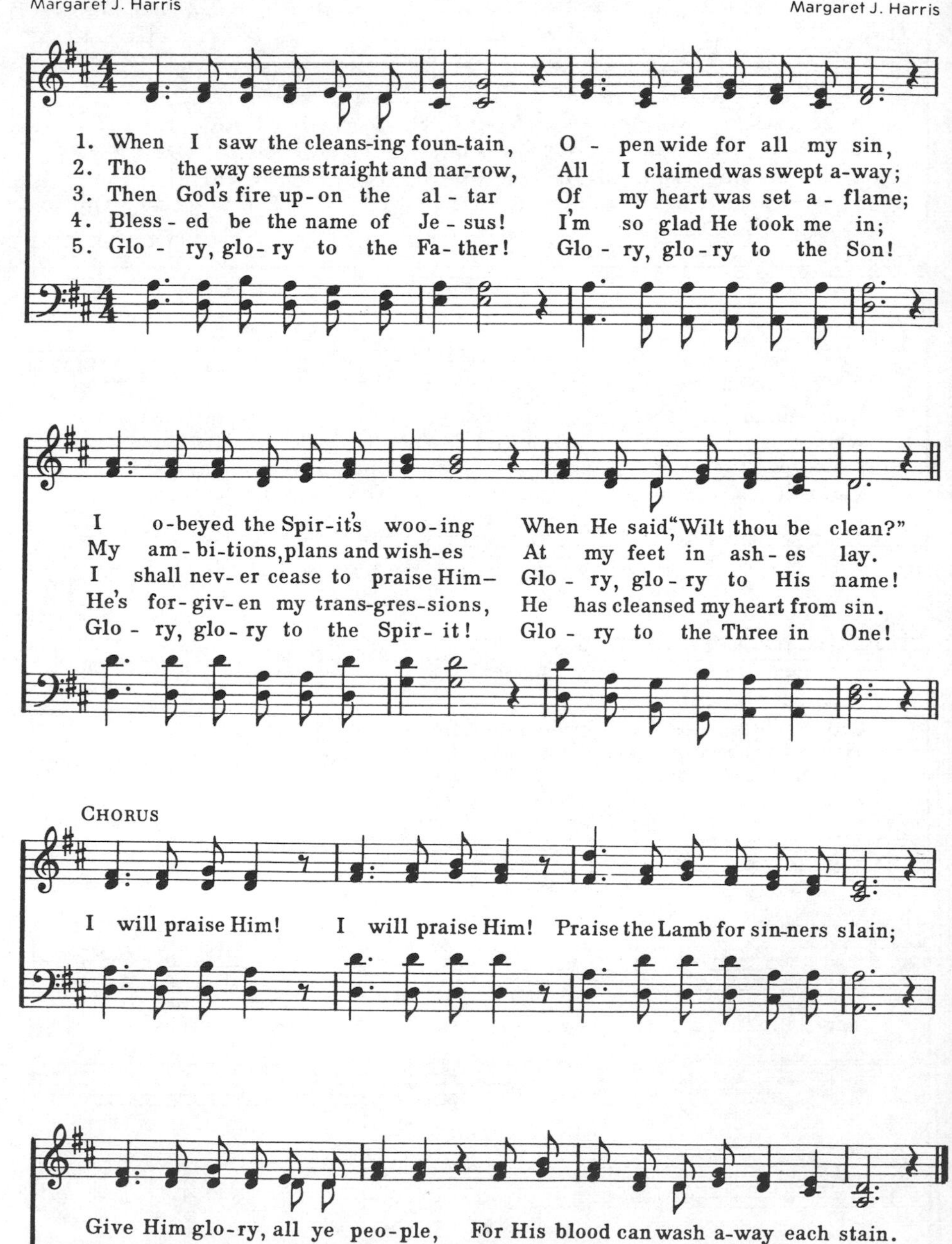
1. When I saw the cleans-ing foun-tain, O - pen wide for all my sin,
2. Tho the way seems straight and nar-row, All I claimed was swept a-way;
3. Then God's fire up-on the al - tar Of my heart was set a - flame;
4. Bless - ed be the name of Je - sus! I'm so glad He took me in;
5. Glo - ry, glo - ry to the Fa - ther! Glo - ry, glo - ry to the Son!
I o-beyed the Spir-it's woo-ing When He said, "Wilt thou be clean?"
My am - bi-tions, plans and wish-es At my feet in ash - es lay.
I shall nev - er cease to praise Him— Glo - ry, glo - ry to His name!
He's for-giv - en my trans-gres-sions, He has cleansed my heart from sin.
Glo - ry, glo - ry to the Spir - it! Glo - ry to the Three in One!
CHORUS
I will praise Him! I will praise Him! Praise the Lamb for sin-ners slain;
Give Him glo-ry, all ye peo-ple, For His blood can wash a-way each stain.

Lord, With Glowing Heart

Francis Scott Key

Alfred B. Smith

1. Lord, with glow - ing heart I'd praise thee For the bliss thy love be - stows,
2. Praise, my soul, the God that sought thee, Wretch-ed wan-d'rer far a - stray;
3. Praise thy Sav - iour God that drew thee To that cross, new life to give,
4. Lord, this bos - om's ar - dent feel - ing Vain - ly would my lips ex - press:
For the par-d'ning grace that saves me, And the peace that from it flows:
Found thee lost, and kind - ly brought thee From the paths of death a - way:
Held a blood-sealed par - don to thee, Bade thee look to him and live:
Low be - fore thy foot-stool kneel - ing, Deign thy sup-pliant's pray'r to bless:
Help, O God, my weak en - deav - or; This dull soul to rap - ture raise:
Praise, with love's de - vout - est feel - ing, Him who saw thy guilt-born fear,
Praise the grace whose threats a-larmed thee, Roused thee from thy fa - tal ease,
Let thy love, my soul's chief treas - ure, Love's pure flame with - in me raise;
Thou must light the flame, or nev - er Can my love be warmed to praise.
And, the light of hope re-veal - ing, Bade the blood-stain'd cross ap-pear.
Praise the grace whose prom-ise warm'd thee, Praise the grace that whis-pered peace.
And, since words can nev - er meas-ure, Let my life show forth thy praise.

37 Praise God from Whom All Blessings Flow

Thomas Ken (Original rhythm)* From the Genevan Psalter, 1551

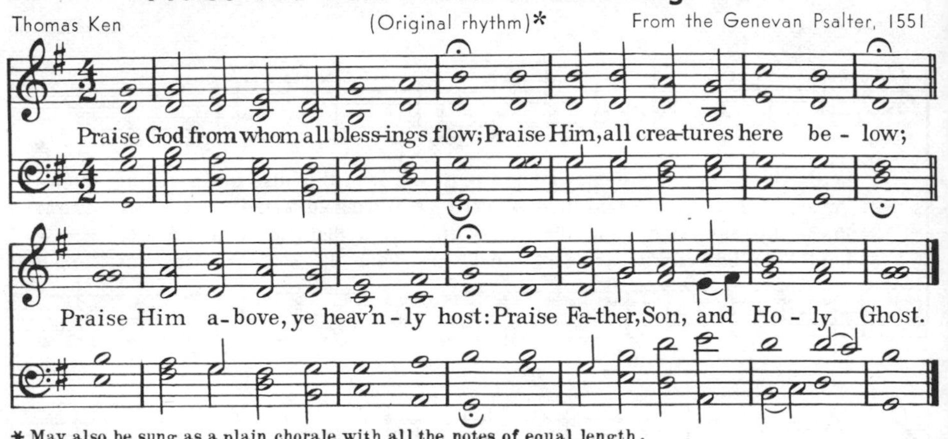
Praise God from whom all bless-ings flow; Praise Him, all crea-tures here be - low;
Praise Him a-bove, ye heav'n - ly host: Praise Fa-ther, Son, and Ho - ly Ghost.

* May also be sung as a plain chorale with all the notes of equal length.

38 Keswick Doxology

Unison "Geistliche Kirchengesange," 1623

Praise God from whom all bless-ings flow; Praise Him all creatures here be-low;
Harmony
Unison
Al - le - lu - jah, Al - le - lu - jah! Praise Him a - bove, ye heav'n-ly
Harmony
host; Praise Fa-ther, Son, and Ho-ly Ghost. Al - le - lu - jah, Al - le-
Unison
lu - jah, Al - le - lu - jah, Al - le - lu - jah, Al - le - lu - jah!

The God of Abraham Praise

Thomas Olivers

Jewish Melody
Arr. by Meyer Lyon

1. The God of A-braham praise, Who reigns en-throned a - bove;
2. The God of A-braham praise, At whose su - preme com - mand
3. He by Him - self hath sworn, I on His oath de - pend,
4. The whole tri - um - phant host Give thanks to God on high;

An - cient of ev - er - last - ing days, And God of love.
From earth I rise, and seek the joys At His right hand.
I shall, on ea - gles wings up - borne, To heaven as - cend;
"Hail, Fa - ther, Son and Ho - ly Ghost!" They ev - er cry.

Je - ho - vah, great I AM, By earth and heaven con - fessed;
I all on earth for - sake, Its wis - dom, fame, and power;
I shall be - hold His face, I shall His power a - dore,
Hail, A-braham's God and mine! I join the heaven - ly lays;

I bow and bless the sa - cred name, For - ev - er blest.
And Him my on - ly por - tion make, My shield and tower.
And sing the won - ders of His grace For - ev - er - more.
All might and ma - jes - ty are Thine, And end - less praise. A-MEN.

40 Since the Fullness of His Love Came in

Eliza E. Hewitt — B. D. Ackley

1. Once my way was dark and dreary, For my heart was full of sin,
But the sky is bright and cheery, Since the fullness of His love came in.

2. There is grace for all the lowly, Grace to keep the trusting soul,
Power to cleanse and make me holy; Jesus shall my yielded life control.

3. Let me spread abroad the story, Other souls to Jesus win;
For the cross is now my glory, Since the fullness of His love came in.

REFRAIN

I can never tell how much I love Him, I can never tell His love for me;
For it passeth human measure Like a deep, unfathomed sea; deep, unfathomed sea;
'Tis redeeming love in Christ my Saviour, In my soul the heavenly joys begin;

And I live for Je - sus on - ly, Since the full-ness of His love came in.

May Jesus Christ Be Praised

41

Trans. by Edward Caswall

Joseph Barnby

1. When morn - ing gilds the skies, My heart a - wak - ing cries:
2. Does sad - ness fill my mind, A sol - ace here I find:
3. In heaven's e - tei - nal bliss The love - liest strain is this,
4. Be this, while life is mine, My can - ti - cle di - vine,
May Je - sus Christ be praised; A - like at work or prayer
May Je - sus Christ be praised; Or fades my earth - ly bliss,
May Je - sus Christ be praised; The powers of dark - ness fear,
May Je - sus Christ be praised; Be this th' e - ter - nal song,
To Je - sus I re - pair: May Je - sus Christ be praised.
My com - fort still is this: May Je - sus Christ be praised.
When this sweet chant they hear: May Je - sus Christ be praised.
Through all the a - ges long: May Je - sus Christ be praised. AMEN.

42 Heavenly Father, I Glorify You

Rewritten by Richard A. Bennett
Anon.
Arr. Donna J. Krieger
1. Heav'n-ly Fa-ther, I glo-ri-fy You. Heav'n-ly Fa-ther, I glo-ri-fy You. I love you, a-dore You, and bow down be-fore You; Heav'n-ly Fa-ther, I glo-ri-fy You.
2. Son of God, I mag-ni-fy You. Son of God, I mag-ni-fy You. You loved me, re-deemed me; Your blood has now freed me; Son of God, I mag-ni-fy You.
3. Ho-ly Spir-it, You're a com-fort to me. Ho-ly Spir-it, You're a com-fort to me. You teach me and guide me, and live now in-side me; Ho-ly Spir-it, You're a com-fort to me.
4. Three in One, I do wor-ship You now. Be-fore God in Heav-en I bow. I wor-ship in truth as I wor-ship in spir-it, Three in One, I do wor-ship You now.

43 God Is So Good!
Author Unknown
Arr. by John Moore
1. God is so good! God is so good
2. He ans-wers pray'r! He ans-wers pray'r
3. God loved the world! God loved the world

God is so good! He's so good to me.
God is so good! And He ans - wers pray'r.
God loved the world, And He gave His Son.
© Copyright 1975 by Alfred B. Smith in "Victorious Life Hymns". All rights reserved.
Jesus Has Loved Me
44
J. W. MacGill
C.W. & E. M.
1. Je - sus has loved me— won-der - ful Sav - ior! Je - sus has loved me, I can - not tell why; Came He to res - cue sin-ners all worth-less, My heart He conqured— for Him I would die.
2. Je - sus has saved me— won-der - ful Sav - ior! Je - sus has saved me, I can - not tell how; All that I know is, He was my ran-som, Dy - ing on Cal-v'ry with thorns on His brow.
3. Je - sus will lead me— won-der - ful Sav - ior! Je - sus will lead me, I can - not tell where; But I will fol - low, thro' joy or sor - row, Sun-shine or tem-pest, sweet peace or de - spain.
4. Je - sus will crown me— won-der - ful Sav - ior! Je - sus will crown me, I can - not tell when; Great throne of splen-dor hail I with glad-ness, Crown'd 'mid the plau-dits of an - gels and men.
Chorus— Glo - ry to Je - sus— won - der - ful Sav - ior! Glo - ry to Je - sus, the One I a - dore; Glo - ry to Je - sus— won-der - ful Sav - ior! Glo - ry to Je - sus, and praise ev - er - more.
D. C. for Chorus

45 Rejoice, the Lord Is King

Charles Wesley

John Darwall

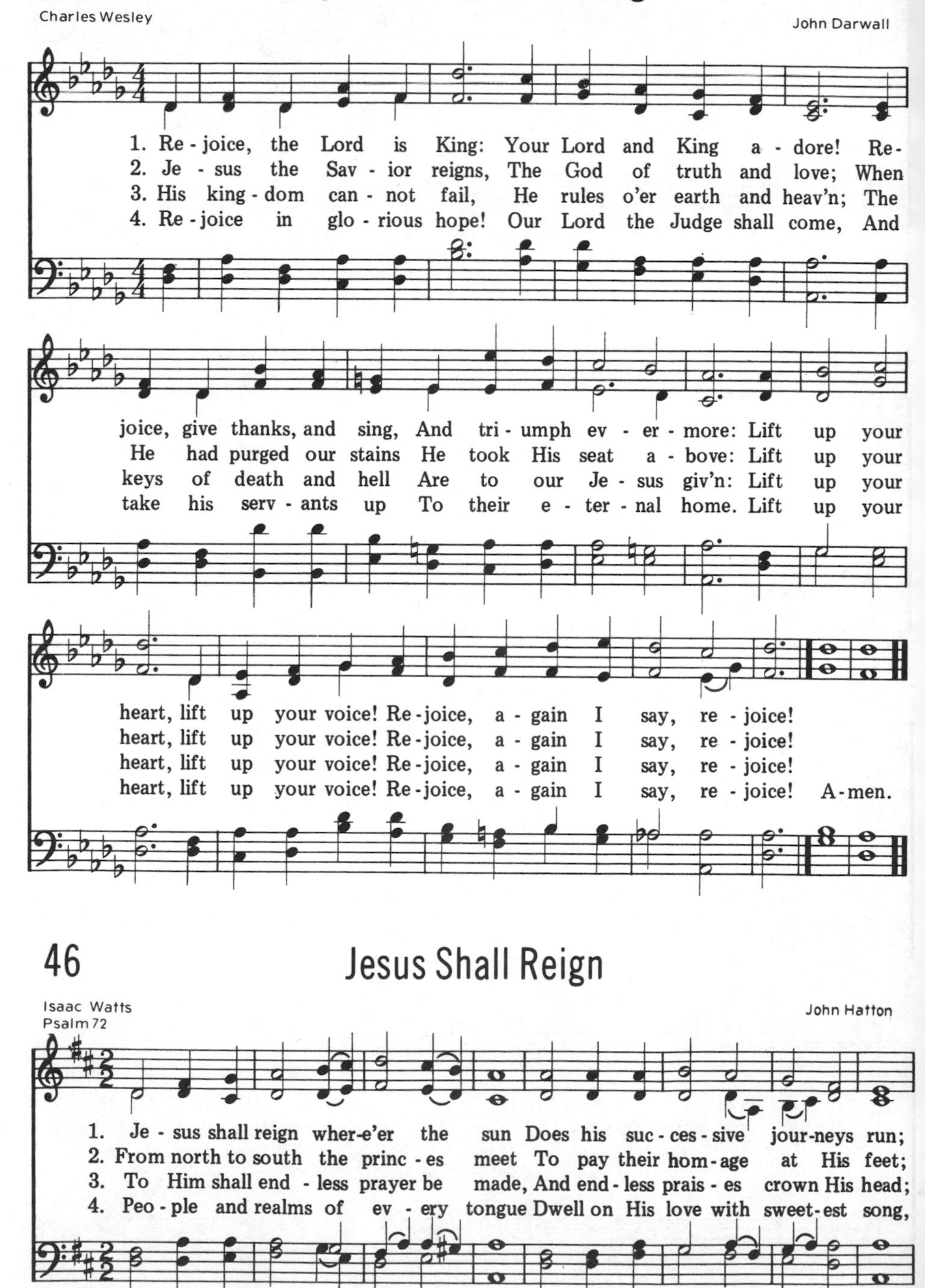

1. Re - joice, the Lord is King: Your Lord and King a - dore! Re-
2. Je - sus the Sav - ior reigns, The God of truth and love; When
3. His king - dom can - not fail, He rules o'er earth and heav'n; The
4. Re - joice in glo - rious hope! Our Lord the Judge shall come, And
joice, give thanks, and sing, And tri - umph ev - er - more: Lift up your
He had purged our stains He took His seat a - bove: Lift up your
keys of death and hell Are to our Je - sus giv'n: Lift up your
take his serv - ants up To their e - ter - nal home. Lift up your
heart, lift up your voice! Re - joice, a - gain I say, re - joice!
heart, lift up your voice! Re - joice, a - gain I say, re - joice!
heart, lift up your voice! Re - joice, a - gain I say, re - joice!
heart, lift up your voice! Re - joice, a - gain I say, re - joice! A - men.
46
Jesus Shall Reign
Isaac Watts
Psalm 72
John Hatton
1. Je - sus shall reign wher-e'er the sun Does his suc - ces - sive jour-neys run;
2. From north to south the princ - es meet To pay their hom - age at His feet;
3. To Him shall end - less prayer be made, And end - less prais - es crown His head;
4. Peo - ple and realms of ev - ery tongue Dwell on His love with sweet - est song,

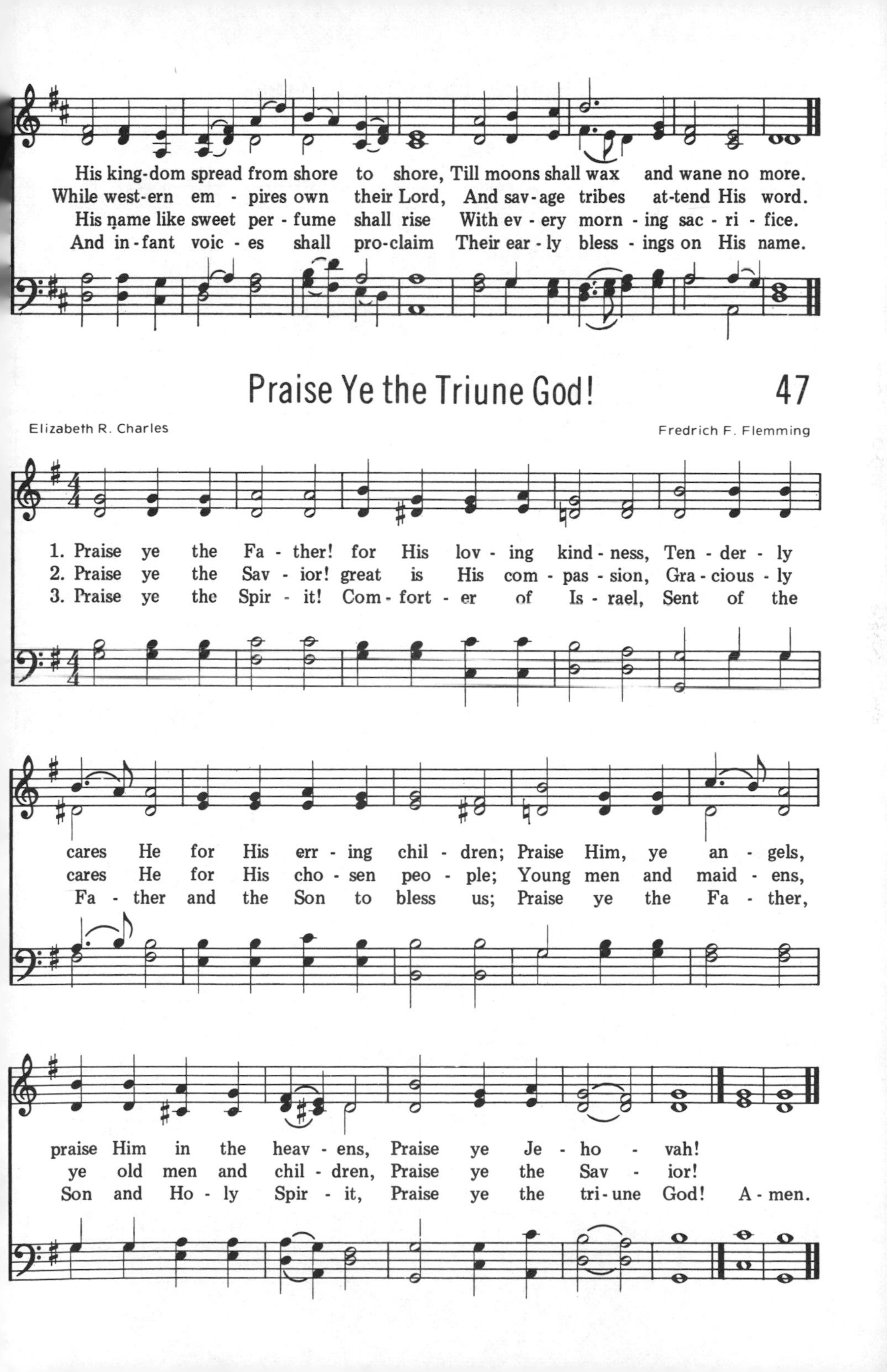
His king-dom spread from shore to shore, Till moons shall wax and wane no more.
While west-ern em - pires own their Lord, And sav-age tribes at-tend His word.
His name like sweet per - fume shall rise With ev - ery morn - ing sac - ri - fice.
And in-fant voic - es shall pro-claim Their ear - ly bless - ings on His name.
Praise Ye the Triune God!
47
Elizabeth R. Charles
Fredrich F. Flemming
1. Praise ye the Fa - ther! for His lov - ing kind - ness, Ten - der - ly cares He for His err - ing chil - dren; Praise Him, ye an - gels, praise Him in the heav - ens, Praise ye Je - ho - vah!
2. Praise ye the Sav - ior! great is His com - pas - sion, Gra - cious - ly cares He for His cho - sen peo - ple; Young men and maid - ens, ye old men and chil - dren, Praise ye the Sav - ior!
3. Praise ye the Spir - it! Com - fort - er of Is - rael, Sent of the Fa - ther and the Son to bless us; Praise ye the Fa - ther, Son and Ho - ly Spir - it, Praise ye the tri - une God! A - men.

48 Hallelujah to the Lamb

Isaac Watts

Unknown
Revised & Arr. by Alfred B. Smith

1. Come, let us join our cheer-ful songs With an-gels round the throne;
Ten thou-sand thou-sand are their tongues, But all their joys are one.

2. "Wor - thy the Lamb that died," they cry, "To be ex - alt - ed thus!"
"Wor - thy the Lamb!" our hearts re - ply; "For He was slain for us."

3. Je - sus is worth-y to re - ceive Hon - our and pow'r Di - vine;
And bless-ings, more than we can give, Be, Lord, for ev - er Thine.

4. Let all that dwell a - bove the sky, And air, and earth, and seas,
In - spire to lift Thy glo - ries high, And speak Thine end-less praise.

5. The whole cre - a - tion join in one To bless the sac - red name
Of Him that sits up - on the throne, And to a - dore the Lamb.

Chorus

Hal-le - lu-jah to the Lamb who died on Mount Cal - va - ry!
Hal - le - lu - jah, hal - le - lu - jah, hal - le - lu - jah! A - men.

We're Marching to Zion

Isaac Watts

Robert Lowry

1. Come, we that love the Lord, And let our joys be known, Join
2. Let those re - fuse to sing Who nev - er knew our God; But
3. The hill of Zi - on yields A thou - sand sa - cred sweets Be -
4. Then let our songs a-bound, And ev - ery tear be dry, We're

in a song with sweet ac - cord, Join in a song with sweet ac - cord, And
chil - dren of the heaven - ly King, But chil - dren of the heaven - ly King, May
fore we reach the heaven - ly fields, Be - fore we reach the heaven - ly fields, Or
marching thro' Im-man-uel's ground, We're marching thro' Im - man-uel's ground, To

thus sur - round the throne, And thus sur - round the throne.
speak their joys a - broad, May speak their joys a - broad.
walk the gold - en streets, Or walk the gold - en streets.
fair - er worlds on high, To fair - er worlds on high.

thus sur-round the throne, And thus sur - round the throne.

CHORUS

We're march - ing to Zi - on, Beau - ti - ful, beau - ti - ful Zi - on; We're
We're march - ing on to Zi - on,

march-ing up-ward to Zi - on, the beau - ti - ful cit - y of God. A-MEN.
Zi - on, Zi - on,

50 In My Heart There Rings a Melody

Elton M. Roth

Elton M. Roth

1. I have a song that Je - sus gave me, It was sent from heav'n a - bove; There nev - er was a sweet - er mel - o - dy, 'Tis a mel - o - dy of love.
2. I love the Christ who died on Cal - v'ry, For He washed my sins a - way; He put with - in my heart a mel - o - dy, And I know it's there to stay.
3. 'Twill be my end - less theme in glo - ry, With the an - gels I will sing; 'Twill be a song with glo - rious har - mo - ny, When the courts of heav - en ring.
Refrain
In my heart there rings a mel - o - dy, There rings a mel - o - dy with heav - en's har - mo - ny; In my heart there rings a mel - o - dy; There rings a mel - o - dy of love.

Why Do I Sing About Jesus? 51

Albert A. Ketchum
Albert A. Ketchum
1. Deep in my heart there's a glad - ness, Je - sus has saved me from sin! Praise to His name—what a Sav - ior! Cleans - ing with- out and with - in.
2. On - ly a glimpse of His good - ness, That was suf - fi - cient for me; On - ly one look at the Sav - ior, Then was my spir - it set free.
3. He is the fair - est of fair ones, He is the Lil - y, the Rose; Riv - ers of mer - cy sur - round Him, Grace, love and pit - y He shows.
Refrain – Unison or Two Parts
Why do I sing a - bout Je - sus? Why is He pre-cious to me? He is my Lord and my Sav - ior, Dy - ing! He set me free!
(set me free!)

52 Verily, Verily

James McGranahan James McGranahan

1. Oh, what a Sav - iour that He died for me! From con - dem -
2. All my in - i - qui - ties on Him were laid, All my in-
3. Though poor and need - y, I can trust my Lord; Though weak and
4. Though all un - wor - thy, yet I will not doubt; For him that
na - tion He hath made me free; "He that be - liev - eth on the
debt - ed - ness by Him was paid; All who be - lieve on Him, the
sin - ful, I be - lieve His word; O glad mes - sage! Ev - ery
com - eth He will not cast out: "He that be - liev - eth," oh, the
REFRAIN
Son," saith He, "Hath ev - er - last - ing life."
Lord hath said, "Have ev - er - last - ing life." "Ver - i - ly, ver - i - ly,
child of God "Hath ev - er - last - ing life."
good news shout! "Hath ev - er - last - ing life."
I say un - to you; Ver - i - ly, ver - i - ly," mes - sage ev - er new!

"He that be - liev - eth on the Son"–'tis true!–"Hath ev - er - last - ing life!"
Revive Us Again
53
William P. Mackay
John J. Husband
1. We praise Thee, O God, for the Son of Thy love, For Je - sus who died and is now gone a - bove.
2. We praise Thee, O God, for Thy Spir - it of light, Who has shown us our Sav - iour and scat-tered our night.
3. All glo - ry and praise to the Lamb that was slain, Who has borne all our sins and has cleansed ev - ery stain.
4. Re - vive us a - gain, fill each heart with Thy love; May each soul be re - kin - dled with fire from a - bove.
Refrain
Hal - le - lu - jah! Thine the glo - ry, Hal-le - lu - jah! A - men; Hal - le - lu - jah! Thine the glo - ry; Re - vive us a - gain.

54 Still Sweeter Every Day

W. C. Martin

C. Austin Miles

1. To Je - sus ev - 'ry day I find my heart is clos - er drawn,
2. His glo - ry broke up - on me when I saw Him from a - far,
3. My heart is some - times heav - y but He comes with sweet re - lief,
He's fair - er than the glo - ry of the gold and pur - ple dawn;
He's fair - er than the lil - y, bright - er than the morn - ing star;
He folds me to His bos - om when I droop with blight - ing grief;
He's all my fan - cy pic - tures in its fair - est dreams, and more —
He fills and sat - is - fies my long - ing spir - it o'er and o'er —
I love the Christ who all my bur - dens in His bod - y bore —
Each day He grows still sweet - er than He was the day be - fore.
Each day He grows still sweet - er than He was the day be - fore.
Each day He grows still sweet - er than He was the day be - fore.
CHORUS
The half can - not be fan - cied this
The half can - not be fan - cied on this side the gold - en shore, The

side the gold-en shore; O there
half can-not be fan-cied on this side the gold-en shore; O there He'll be still
He'll be still sweet - er than He ev- er was be- fore.
sweet-er than He ev-er was be-fore, than He ev- er was be - fore.
Unsearchable Riches
55
Fanny J. Crosby
John R. Sweney
1. O the un-search-a-ble rich-es of Christ! Wealth that can nev-er be told!
2. O the un-search-a-ble rich-es of Christ! Who shall their great-ness de - clare!
3. O the un-search-a-ble rich-es of Christ! Free-ly, how free-ly they flow,
4. O the un-search-a-ble rich-es of Christ! Who would not glad-ly en - dure
Fine
Rich- es ex-haust-less of mer- cy and grace, Pre-cious, more pre-cious than gold!
Jew-els whose lus-ter our lives may a- dorn, Pearls that the poor-est may wear!
Mak-ing the souls of the faith-ful and true Hap-py wher- ev- er they go!
Tri - als, af- flic-tions, and cross-es on earth, Rich-es like these to se - cure!
D.S. – O the un-search-a-ble rich-es of Christ – Pre-cious, more precious than gold!
CHORUS
D.S.
Pre - cious, more pre - cious – Wealth that can nev- er be told;

56 My Redeemer

Philip P. Bliss

Rowland H. Prichard

1. I will sing of my Re - deem - er And His won-drous love to me;
2. I will tell the won-drous sto - ry, How my lost es - tate to save,
3. I will praise my dear Re - deem - er, His tri-umph-ant power I'll tell,
4. I will sing of my Re - deem - er And His heaven-ly love for me;
On the cru - el cross He suf - fered, From the curse to set me free.
In His bound-less love and mer - cy, He the ran - som free - ly gave.
How the vic - to - ry He giv - eth O - ver sin, and death, and hell.
He from death to life hath brought me, Son of God with Him to be.
Refrain
Sing, oh, sing of my Re - deem - er, With His blood He pur-chased me,
On the cross He sealed my par - don, Paid the debt, and made me free.

Redeemed

Fanny J. Crosby

William J. Kirkpatrick

1. Re-deemed–how I love to pro-claim it! Re-deemed by the blood of the Lamb;
2. Re-deemed and so hap-py in Je - sus; No lan-guage my rap - ture can tell.
3. I think of my bless-ed Re-deem - er, I think of Him all the day long;
4. I know I shall see in His beau - ty The King in whose law I de - light,
Re-deemed through His in - fi - nite mer - cy, His child, and for - ev - er, I am.
I know that the light of His pres - ence With me doth con - tin - ual - ly dwell.
I sing, for I can-not be si - lent; His love is the theme of my song.
Who lov - ing - ly guard-eth my foot - steps And giv - eth me songs in the night.
Refrain
Re - deemed, re - deemed, Re-deemed by the blood of the Lamb;
re-deemed, re-deemed,
Re - deemed, re - deemed, His child, and for - ev - er, I am.
re-deemed, re-deemed,

58 He's a Wonderful Saviour to Me

Virgil P. Brock

Blanche Kerr Brock

1. I was lost in sin but Je - sus res-cued me;
2. He's a Friend so true, so pa-tient, and so kind;
3. He is al - ways near to com-fort and to cheer;
4. Dear-er grows the love of Je - sus day by day;
He's a won-der-ful Sav-iour to me.
So won-der-ful!
I was bound by fear but Je - sus set me free;
Ev-'ry- thing I need in Him I al - ways find;
He for-gives my sins; He dries my ev -'ry tear.
Sweeter is His grace while pressing on my way;
REFRAIN
He's a won-der - ful Sav-iour to me.
So wonderful!
For He's a won-der-ful Sav-iour to me;
wonderful!
He's a won-der-ful Sav-iour to me.
wonderful!
I was lost in sin, but Je - sus took me in; He's a won-der-ful Sav-iour to me.

Then Jesus Came

Oswald J. Smith

Homer Rodeheaver

1. One sat a - lone be - side the high-way beg - ging, His eyes were blind, the
2. From home and friends the e - vil spir - its drove him, A - mong the tombs he
3. "Un - clean! un-clean!" the le - per cried in tor - ment, The deaf, the dumb, in
4. Their hearts were sad as in the tomb they laid him, For death had come and
5. So men to - day have found the Sav-iour a - ble, They could not con - quer
light he could not see; He clutched his rags and shiv-ered in the shad - ows,
dwelt in mis - er - y; He cut him - self as de - mon pow'rs pos-sessed him,
help - less-ness stood near; The fe - ver raged, dis - ease had gripped its vic - tim,
tak - en him a - way; Their night was dark and bit - ter tears were fall - ing,
pas - sion, lust and sin; Their bro - ken hearts had left them sad and lone - ly,
Then Je - sus came and bade his dark-ness flee.
Then Je - sus came and set the cap - tive free.
Then Je - sus came and cast out ev - 'ry fear.
Then Je - sus came and night was turned to day.
Then Je - sus came and dwelt, Him-self, with - in.
REFRAIN
When Je - sus comes the tempt-er's pow'r is bro-ken; When Je-sus comes the tears are wiped a - way. He takes the gloom and fills the life with glo - ry, For all is changed when Je-sus comes to stay.

60 I Will Sing The Wondrous Story

Francis H. Rowley
Peter P. Bilhorn
1. I will sing the won-drous sto - ry Of the Christ who died for me,
2. I was lost but Je - sus found me, Found the sheep that went a - stray,
3. I was bruised but Je - sus healed me; Faint was I from man - y a fall;
4. Days of dark - ness still come o'er me, Sor-row's paths I oft - en tread,
How He left His home in glo - ry For the cross of Cal - va - ry.
Threw His lov - ing arms a - round me, Drew me back in - to His way.
Sight was gone, and fears pos-sessed me, But He freed me from them all.
But the Sav - ior still is with me; By His hand I'm safe - ly led.
CHORUS
Yes, I'll sing the won-drous sto ry Of the
Yes, I'll sing the won-drous sto - ry
Christ who died for me, Sing it with the saints in
Of the Christ who died for me, Sing it with
glo - ry Gath-ered by the crys-tal sea.
the saints in glo - ry, Gath-ered by the crys-tal sea.

Singing I Go

Eliza E. Hewitt

William J. Kirkpatrick

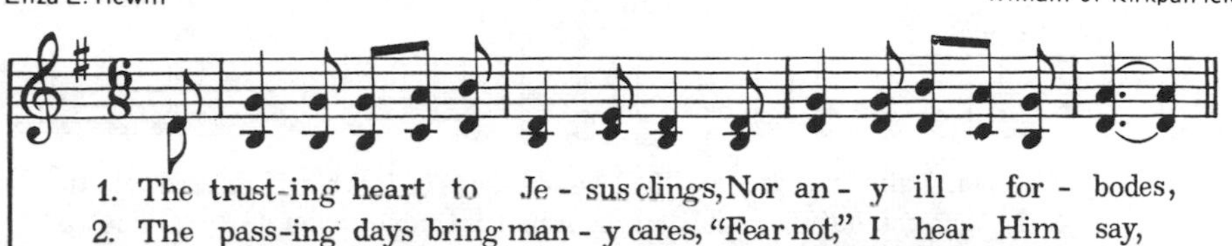

1. The trust-ing heart to Je - sus clings, Nor an - y ill for - bodes,
2. The pass-ing days bring man - y cares, "Fear not," I hear Him say,
3. He tells me of my Fa-ther's love And nev - er slumb'-ring eye;
4. When to the throne of grace I flee, I find the prom - ise true,

But at the cross of Cal - v'ry sings, Praise God for lift - ed loads!
And when my fears are turned to pray'rs, The bur-dens slip a - way.
My ev - er - last - ing King a-bove Will all my needs sup - ply.
The might-y arms up-hold - ing me Will bear my bur-dens too.

Chorus

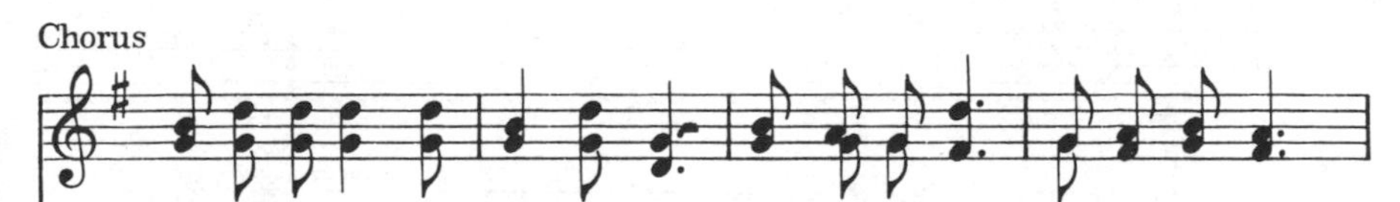

Sing-ing, I go a - long life's road, Prais-ing the Lord, prais-ing the Lord;

rit. ad lib.

Sing-ing, I go a - long life's road, For Je-sus has lift-ed my load.

62 Oh, It Is Wonderful

C.H.G.
Charles H. Gabriel
DUET
1. I stand all amazed at the love Je-sus of-fers me, Confused at the grace that so ful-ly He proffers me; I tremble to know that for me He was cru-ci-fied—That for me, a sin-ner, He suf-fered, He bled, and died.
2. I mar-vel that He would descend from His throne divine, To res-cue a soul so re-bel-lious and proud as mine; That He should extend His great love unto such as I; Suf-fi-cient to own, to re-deem, and to jus-ti-fy.
3. I think of his hands pierced and bleeding to pay the debt! Such mercy, such love and de-vo-tion can I forget? No, no! I will praise and a-dore at the mer-cy-seat, Until at the glo-ri-fied throne I kneel at His feet.
rit.
Chorus-4 Parts
rit.
Oh, it is won-der-ful that He should care for me! E-nough to die for me!
won-der-ful!
won-der-ful!
Broaden
Oh, it is won-der-ful, won-der-ful to me!

Sweet Name Come Down From Heaven 63

Author Unknown Alt. ABS

Arthur S. Sullivan

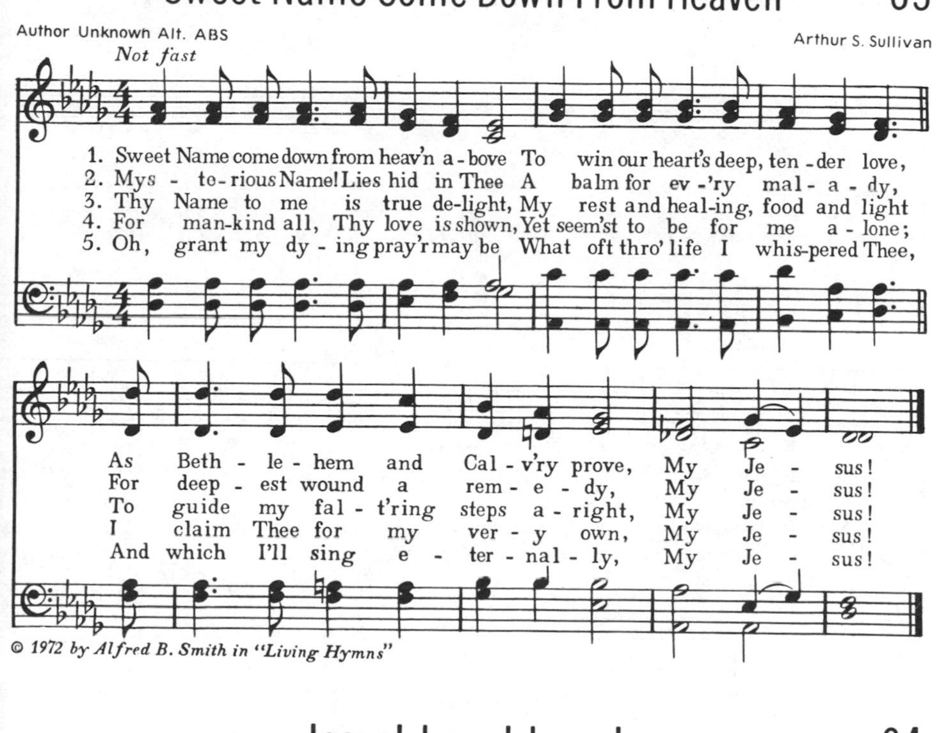
Not fast
1. Sweet Name come down from heav'n a - bove To win our heart's deep, ten - der love,
2. Mys - te - rious Name! Lies hid in Thee A balm for ev - 'ry mal - a - dy,
3. Thy Name to me is true de-light, My rest and heal-ing, food and light
4. For man-kind all, Thy love is shown, Yet seem'st to be for me a - lone;
5. Oh, grant my dy - ing pray'r may be What oft thro' life I whis-pered Thee,
As Beth - le - hem and Cal - v'ry prove, My Je - sus!
For deep - est wound a rem - e - dy, My Je - sus!
To guide my fal - t'ring steps a - right, My Je - sus!
I claim Thee for my ver - y own, My Je - sus!
And which I'll sing e - ter - nal - ly, My Je - sus!

Jesus! Jesus! Jesus! 64

Source Unknown

Abbey Hymns

1. Je - sus! Je - sus! Je - sus! Sing a - loud the Name;
2. Je - sus! Name of cleans - ing, Wash - ing all our stains;
3. Je - sus! Name of bold - ness, Mak - ing cow - ards brave;
4. Je - sus! Name of beau - ty, Beau - ty far too bright
5. Je - sus! be our joy - note In this vale of tears;
Till it soft - ly, slow - ly, Sets all hearts a - flame.
Je - sus! Name of heal - ing, Balm for all our pains.
Name! that in the bat - tle, Cer - tain - ly must save.
For our earth-born fan - cy, For our mor - tal sight.
Till we reach the home - land, And th' e - ter - nal years.
A-MEN.

65 My Jesus, I Love Thee

William R. Featherstone | Adoniram J. Gordon

1. My Je - sus, I love Thee, I know Thou art mine; For Thee all the
2. I love Thee, be - cause Thou hast first lov - ed me, And pur-chased my
3. I'll love Thee in life, I will love Thee in death, And praise Thee as
4. In man - sions of glo - ry and end - less de - light, I'll ev - er a-
fol - lies of sin I re - sign; My gra-cious Re - deem - er, my Sav - ior art
par - don on Cal - va - ry's tree; I love Thee for wear - ing the thorns on Thy
long as Thou lend-est me breath; And say when the death - dew lies cold on my
dore Thee in heav - en so bright; I'll sing with the glit - ter - ing crown on my
Thou; If ev - er I loved Thee, my Je - sus, 'tis now.
brow; If ev - er I loved Thee, my Je - sus, 'tis now.
brow; If ev - er I loved Thee, my Je - sus, 'tis now.
brow; If ev - er I loved Thee, my Je - sus, 'tis now. A-men.

66 Praise The Savior, Ye Who Know Him

Thomas Kelly | Traditional German Melody

1. Praise the Sav - ior, ye who know Him! Who can tell how much we owe Him'
2. Je - sus is the name that charms us; He for con - flict fits and arms us;
3. Trust in Him, ye saints, for - ev - er; He is faith - ful, chang-ing nev - er;
4. Keep us, Lord, O keep us cleav - ing To Thy - self and still be - liev - ing,
5. Then we shall be where we would be, Then we shall be what we should be;

Glad - ly let us ren - der to Him All we are and have.
Noth - ing moves and noth - ing harms us While we trust in Him.
Nei - ther force nor guile can sev - er Those He loves from Him.
Till the hour of our re - ceiv - ing Prom - ised joys with Thee.
Things that are not now, nor could be, Soon shall be our own. A - men.
We Come, O Christ, to Thee
67
E. Margaret Clarkson
John Darwall
1. We come, O Christ, to Thee, True Son of God and man, By Whom all things con-
2. Thou art the Way to God, Thy blood our ran - som paid; In Thee we face our
3. Thou art the liv - ing Truth! All wis - dom dwells in Thee, Thou Source of ev - ery
4. Thou on - ly art true Life, To know Thee is to live The more a - bund-ant
5. We wor - ship Thee, Lord Christ, Our Sav - ior and our King, To Thee our youth and
sist, In Whom all life be - gan: In Thee a - lone we
Judge And Mak - er un - a - fraid. Be - fore the throne ab -
skill, E - ter - nal Ver - i - ty! Thou great I Am! In
life That earth can nev - er give: O ris - en Lord! We
strength A - dor - ing - ly we bring: So fill our hearts, that
live and move, And have our be - ing in Thy love.
solved we stand, Thy love has met Thy law's de - mand.
Thee we rest, True an - swer to our ev - ery quest.
live in Thee, And Thou in us e - ter - nal - ly.
men may see Thy life in us, and turn to Thee. A - men.
'ords taken from "Hymns". © Inter-Varsity Christian Fellowship. Used by permission of InterVarsity Press,

68 He Is So Precious To Me

Charles H. Gabriel — Charles H. Gabriel

1. So pre-cious is Je-sus, my Sav-ior, my King, His praise all the day
2. He stood at my heart's door 'mid sun-shine and rain, And pa-tient-ly wait-
3. I stand on the moun-tain of bless-ing at last, No cloud in the heav-
4. I praise Him be-cause He ap-point-ed a place Where some day, thru faith
long with rap-ture I sing; To Him in my weak-ness for strength I can cling,
ed an en-trance to gain; What shame that so long He en-treat-ed in vain,
ens a shad-ow to cast; His smile is up-on me, the val-ley is past,
in His won-der-ful grace, I know I shall see Him—shall look on His face,
For He is so pre-cious to me.
CHORUS
For He is so pre-cious to me, For He is so pre-cious to me; 'Tis heav-en
so pre-cious to me, so pre-cious to me;
be-low my Re-deem-er to know, For He is so pre-cious to me.

That's Why I Love Him

S. L. Scott Lawrence

1. Je - sus has prom - ised my Shep - herd to be, That's why I
2. He the weak lambs to His bo - som will take, That's why I
3. He has in heav - en pre - pared me a place, That's why I
love Him so;...... And to the chil - dren He said, "Come to Me,"
love Him so;...... Nev - er will He for a mo - ment for - sake,
love Him so;...... Where I may dwell, by His won - der - ful grace,
That's why I love Him so.......
CHORUS
That's why I love Him, That's why I
love Him, Be-cause He first loved me;............ When I'm tempt-ed and
loved me;
tried, He is close by my side, That's why I love Him so.......

70 What a Wonderful Saviour

Elisha A. Hoffman Elisha A. Hoffman

1. Christ has for sin a-tone-ment made, What a won-der-ful Sav-iour!
2. I praise Him for the cleans-ing blood, What a won-der-ful Sav-iour!
3. He cleansed my heart from all its sin, What a won-der-ful Sav-iour!
4. He walks be-side me all the way, What a won-der-ful Sav-iour!
5. He gives me o-ver-com-ing power, What a won-der-ful Sav-iour!
6. To Him I've giv-en all my heart, What a won-der-ful Sav-iour!
We are re-deemed! The price is paid! What a won-der-ful Sav-iour!
That rec-on-ciled my soul to God; What a won-der-ful Sav-iour!
And now He reigns and rules there-in; What a won-der-ful Sav-iour!
And keeps me faith-ful day by day; What a won-der-ful Sav-iour!
And tri-umph in each try-ing hour; What a won-der-ful Sav-iour!
The world shall nev-er share a part; What a won-der-ful Sav-iour!
Chorus
What a won-der-ful Sav-iour is Je-sus, my Je-sus!
What a won-der-ful Sav-iour is Je-sus, my Lord!

Since Jesus Came Into My Heart

R. H. McDaniel — Charles H. Gabriel

1. What a won-der-ful change in my life has been wrought Since Je-sus came
2. I have ceased from my wandering and go-ing a-stray, Since Je-sus came
3. There's a light in the val-ley of death now for me, Since Je-sus came
4. I shall go there to dwell in that Cit-y, I know, Since Je-sus came
in-to my heart! I have light in my soul for which long I have sought,
in-to my heart! And my sins, which were man-y, are all washed a-way,
in-to my heart! And the gates of the Cit-y be-yond I can see,
in-to my heart! And I'm hap-py, so hap-py, as on-ward I go,
Since Je-sus came in-to my heart!
CHORUS
Since Je-sus came in-to my heart,
Since Je-sus came in, came in-to my heart,
Since Je-sus came in-to my heart,
Since Je-sus came in, came in-to my heart,
Floods of joy o'er my soul like the sea bil-lows roll, Since Je-sus came in-to my heart.

72 Saved by the Blood

S. J. Henderson | Daniel B. Towner

1. Saved by the blood of the Cru - ci - fied One! Now ran - somed from
2. Saved by the blood of the Cru - ci - fied One! The an - gels re -
3. Saved by the blood of the Cru - ci - fied One! The Fa - ther— He
4. Saved by the blood of the Cru - ci - fied One! All hail to the

sin and a new work be - gun, Sing praise to the Fa - ther and
joic - ing be - cause it is done; A child of the Fa - ther, joint
spake, and His will— it was done; Great price of my par - don, His
Fa - ther, all hail to the Son, All hail to the Spir - it, the

praise to the Son, Saved by the blood of the Cru - ci - fied One!
heir with the Son, Saved by the blood of the Cru - ci - fied One!
own pre - cious Son; Saved by the blood of the Cru - ci - fied One!
great Three in One! Saved by the blood of the Cru - ci - fied One!

CHORUS

Saved! Saved! My sins are all par-doned, my guilt is all gone!
Saved, I'm saved! glo - ry, I'm saved!

Saved! saved! I am saved by the blood of the Cru - ci - fied One!
Saved, I'm saved! glo - ry, I'm saved!

Saved, Saved!

Jack P. Schofield — Jack P. Schofield

1. I've found a Friend who is all to me; His love is ev - er true. I love to tell how He lift - ed me, And what His grace can do for you.
2. He saved me from ev - 'ry sin and harm, Se- cures my soul each day. I'm lean - ing strong on His might - y arm; I know He'll guide me all the way.
3. When poor and need - y and all a - lone, In love He said to me, "Come un - to Me and I'll lead you home, To live with Me e - ter - nal - ly."
REFRAIN
Saved by His pow'r di-vine! Saved to new life sub-lime!
Saved by His pow'r, Saved to new life,
Life now is sweet and my joy is com-plete, For I'm saved, saved, saved!

74 Saved! Saved! Saved!

Oswald J. Smith

Roger M. Hickman

Unison
1. Saved! saved! saved! my sins are all for - giv'n; Christ is mine! I'm on my way to heav'n; Once a guilt - y sin - ner, lost, un - done, Now a child of God, saved thro' His Son.
2. Saved! saved! saved! by grace and grace a - lone; O, what won - drous love to me was shown, In my stead Christ Je - sus bled and died, Bore my sins, for me was cru - ci - fied.
3. Saved! saved! saved! O, joy be - yond com - pare! Christ my life and I His con - stant care; Yield - ing all and trust - ing Him a - lone, Liv - ing now each mo-ment as His own.
CHORUS - parts
Saved! I'm saved thro' Christ, my all in all; Saved! I'm saved, what
my all in all;
ev - er may be - fall; He died up - on the cross for me, He bore the aw - ful

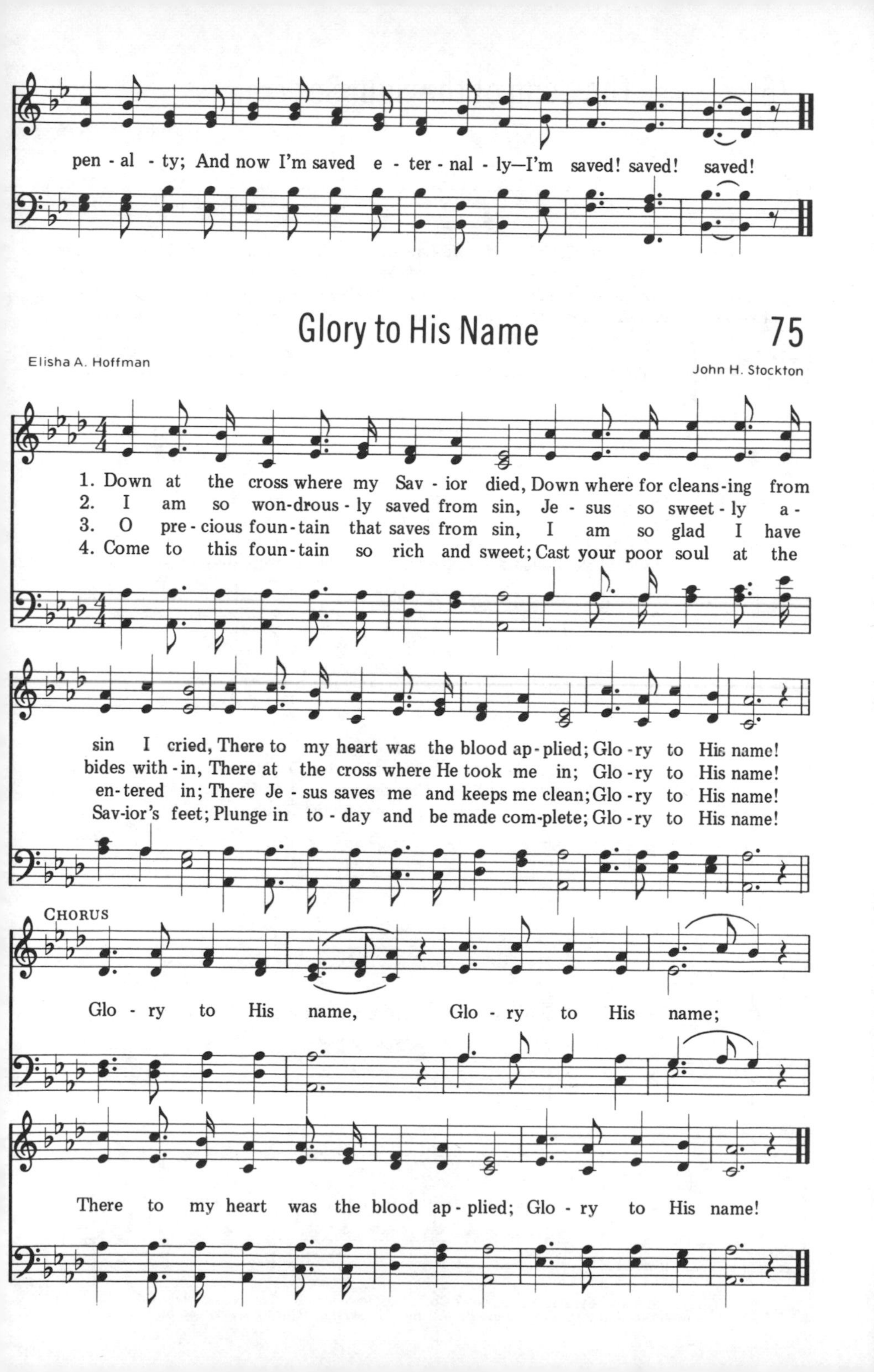
pen - al - ty; And now I'm saved e - ter - nal - ly—I'm saved! saved! saved!
Glory to His Name
75
Elisha A. Hoffman
John H. Stockton
1. Down at the cross where my Sav - ior died, Down where for cleans-ing from sin I cried, There to my heart was the blood ap-plied; Glo - ry to His name!
2. I am so won-drous - ly saved from sin, Je - sus so sweet - ly a - bides with - in, There at the cross where He took me in; Glo - ry to His name!
3. O pre - cious foun - tain that saves from sin, I am so glad I have en - tered in; There Je - sus saves me and keeps me clean; Glo - ry to His name!
4. Come to this foun - tain so rich and sweet; Cast your poor soul at the Sav-ior's feet; Plunge in to - day and be made com-plete; Glo - ry to His name!
CHORUS
Glo - ry to His name, Glo - ry to His name;
There to my heart was the blood ap - plied; Glo - ry to His name!

76 The Song of the Soul Set Free

Oswald J. Smith — Alfred H. Ackley

1. Fair-est of ten thousand Is Je-sus Christ, my Sav-iour, The Lil-y of the Val-ley, The Bright and Morn-ing Star. He is all my glo-ry, And in this heart of mine For-ev-er-more I'm sing-ing A song of love di-vine.
2. Once my heart was burdened, But now I am for-giv-en, And with a song of glad-ness, I'm on my way to heav'n. Christ is my Re-deem-er; My Song of Songs is He; My Saviour, Lord, and Mas-ter. To Him my praise shall be.
3. When He came to save me, He set the joy bells ring-ing, And now I'm ev-er sing-ing, For Christ has ran-somed me. Once I lived in dark-ness; The light I could not see. But now I sing His prais-es, For He has set me free.
4. An-gels can-not sing it, This song of joy and free-dom, For mor-tals on-ly know it, The ran-somed and the free. Slaves were they in bond-age, And deep-est mis-er-y; But now they sing tri-um-phant, Their song of lib-er-ty.

REFRAIN

'Tis the song of the soul set free (set free); And its mel-o-dy is ring-ing. 'Tis the song of the soul set free (set free); Joy and peace to me it's bring-ing.

'Tis the song of the soul set free (set free); And my heart is ev - er sing-ing, Hal-le-
lu - jah! Hal - le - lu - jah! The song of the soul set free!
Hal - le - lu - jah! Hal - le - lu - jah!
rit.
Amazing Grace
77
John Newton
Early American Melody
1. A - maz - ing grace! how sweet the sound! That saved a wretch like me!
2. 'Twas grace that taught my heart to fear, And grace my fears re-lieved.
3. Thro' man-y dan - gers, toils, and snares I have al - read - y come.
4. When we've been there ten thou-sand years, Bright, shining as the sun,
I once was lost, but now am found; Was blind, but now I see.
How pre - cious did that grace ap - pear The hour I first be-lieved!
'Tis grace hath bro't me safe thus far, And grace will lead me home.
We've no less days to sing God's praise Than when we first be - gun.

78 Jesus Is All The World To Me

Will L. Thompson

Will L. Thompson

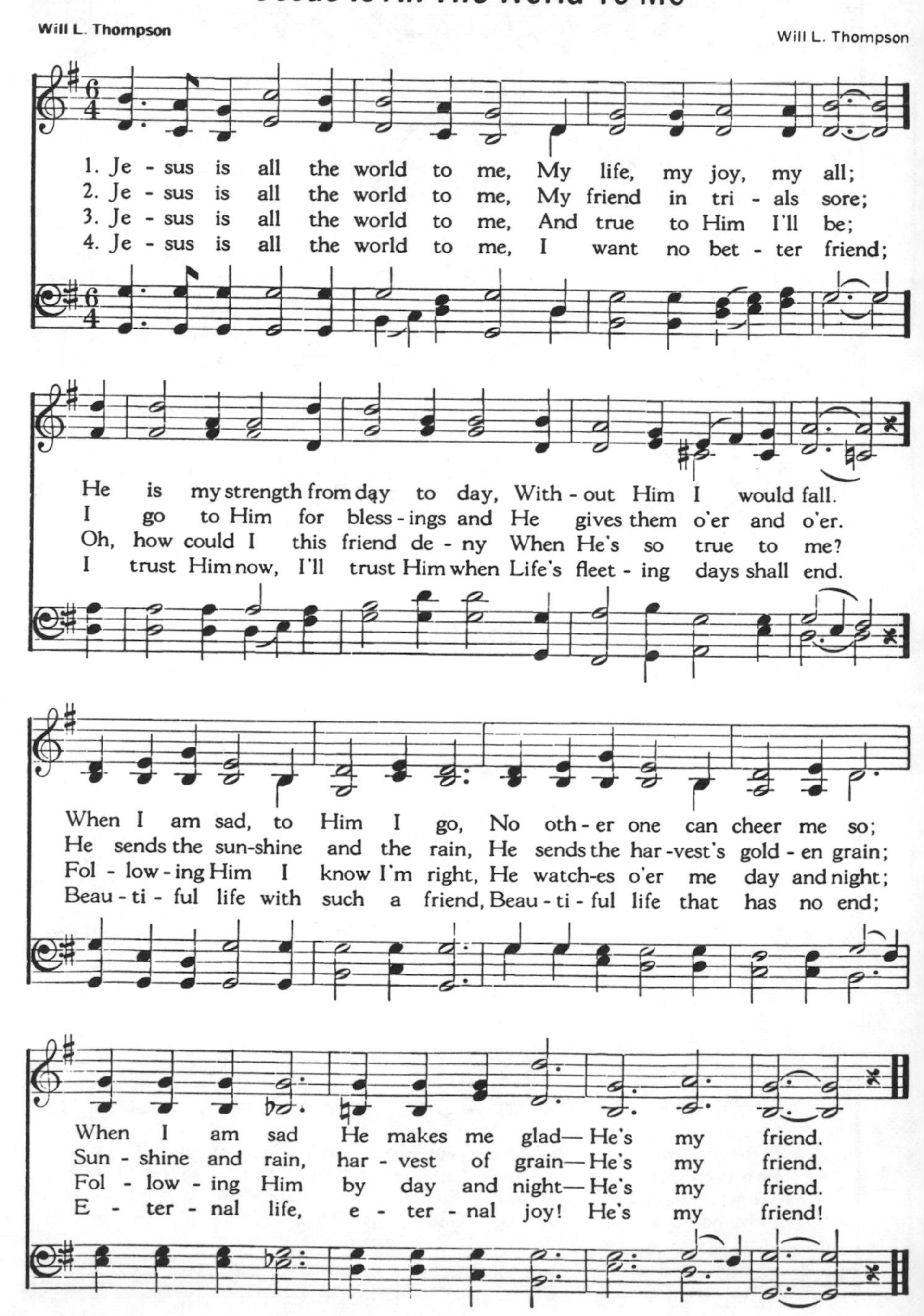
1. Je - sus is all the world to me, My life, my joy, my all;
2. Je - sus is all the world to me, My friend in tri - als sore;
3. Je - sus is all the world to me, And true to Him I'll be;
4. Je - sus is all the world to me, I want no bet - ter friend;
He is my strength from day to day, With - out Him I would fall.
I go to Him for bless - ings and He gives them o'er and o'er.
Oh, how could I this friend de - ny When He's so true to me?
I trust Him now, I'll trust Him when Life's fleet - ing days shall end.
When I am sad, to Him I go, No oth - er one can cheer me so;
He sends the sun-shine and the rain, He sends the har - vest's gold - en grain;
Fol - low - ing Him I know I'm right, He watch-es o'er me day and night;
Beau - ti - ful life with such a friend, Beau - ti - ful life that has no end;
When I am sad He makes me glad— He's my friend.
Sun - shine and rain, har - vest of grain— He's my friend.
Fol - low - ing Him by day and night— He's my friend.
E - ter - nal life, e - ter - nal joy! He's my friend!

Join All The Glorious Names

Isaac Watts

John Darwall

1. Join all the glo - rious names Of wis - dom, love, and power,
2. Great Pro - phet of my God, My tongue would bless Thy name:
3. Je - sus, my great High Priest, Of - fered His blood, and died;
4. Thou art my Coun - sel - lor, My Pat - tern, and my Guide,
5. My Sav - iour and my Lord, My Con - quer'r and my King,
That ev - er mor - tals knew, That an - gels
By Thee the joy - ful news Of our sal-
My guilt - y con - science seeks No sac - ri-
And Thou my Shep - herd art; Oh, keep me
Thy scep - tre and Thy sword, Thy reign - ing
ev - er bore: All are too poor to speak His worth,
va - tion came, The joy - ful news of sins for - giv'n,
fice be - side: His pow'r - ful blood did once a - tone
near Thy side; Nor let my feet e'er turn a - stray,
grace I sing: Thine is the pow'r; be - hold I sit
Too poor to set my Sav - iour forth.
Of hell sub - dued and peace with heav'n.
And now. it pleads be - fore the throne.
To wan - der in the crook - ed way.
In will - ing bonds be - neath Thy feet.
A - MEN.

Blessed Be The Name

William H. Clark
Refrain, Ralph E. Hudson

Arr. by Ralph E. Hudson
William J. Kirkpatrick

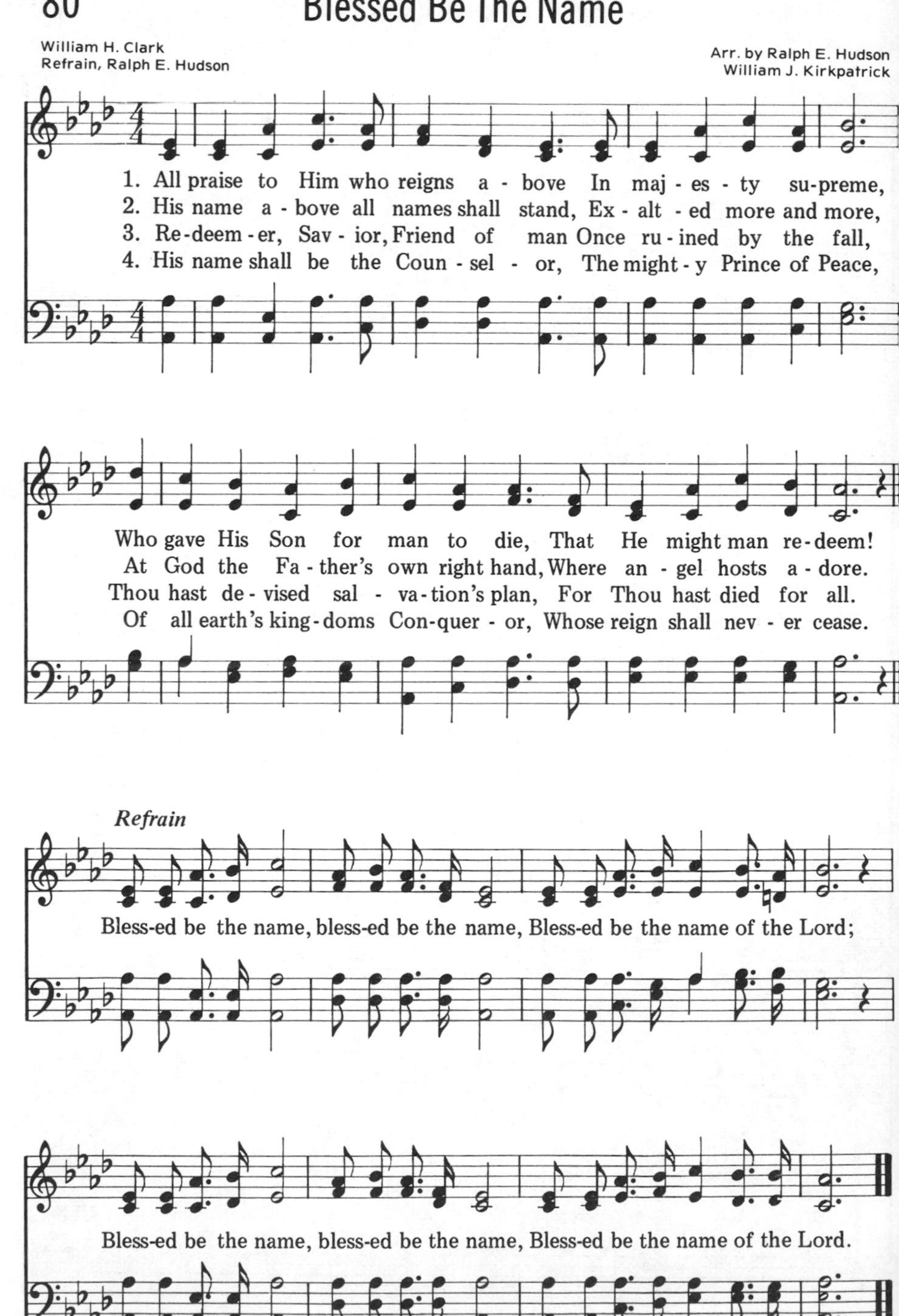
1. All praise to Him who reigns a - bove In maj - es - ty su-preme,
2. His name a - bove all names shall stand, Ex - alt - ed more and more,
3. Re-deem - er, Sav - ior, Friend of man Once ru - ined by the fall,
4. His name shall be the Coun - sel - or, The might - y Prince of Peace,
Who gave His Son for man to die, That He might man re-deem!
At God the Fa - ther's own right hand, Where an - gel hosts a - dore.
Thou hast de - vised sal - va - tion's plan, For Thou hast died for all.
Of all earth's king - doms Con-quer - or, Whose reign shall nev - er cease.
Refrain
Bless-ed be the name, bless-ed be the name, Bless-ed be the name of the Lord;
Bless-ed be the name, bless-ed be the name, Bless-ed be the name of the Lord.

Jesus Is the Sweetest Name I Know

Lela Long — Lela Long

1. There have been names that I have loved to hear, But nev - er has there been a name so dear To this heart of mine As the name di-vine, The pre-cious, pre-cious name of Je - sus.
2. There is no name in earth or heav'n a - bove That we should give such hon - or and such love As the bless-ed name; Let us all acclaim That wondrous, glorious name of Je - sus.
3. And some-day I shall see Him face- to - face To thank and praise Him for His won-drous grace Which He gave to me When He made me free, The bless-ed Son of God called Je - sus.
(1) to hear
(1) so dear
REFRAIN
Je - sus is the sweet- est name I know, And He's just the same as His love - ly name, And that's the rea- son why I love Him so. Oh, Je - sus is the sweet - est name I know!
rall.

82 Wonderful, Wonderful Jesus!

Anna B. Russell

Ernest O. Sellers

1. There is nev-er a day so drear-y, There is nev-er a night so
2. There is nev-er a cross so heav-y, There is nev-er a weight of
3. There is nev-er a care or bur-den, There is nev-er a grief or
4. There is nev-er a guilt-y sin-ner, There is nev-er a wan-d'ring
long, But the soul that is trust-ing Je-sus Will some-where
woe, But that Je-sus will help to car-ry Be-cause He
loss, But that Je-sus in love will light-en When car-ried
one, But that God can in mer-cy par-don Thru Je-sus
find a song.
lov-eth so.
to the cross.
Christ, His Son.
CHORUS
Won-der-ful, won-der-ful Je-sus! In the
heart He im-plant-eth a song; A song of de-liv-'rance,
im-plant-eth a song;
of cour-age, of strength– In the heart He im-plant-eth a song.

Take the Name of Jesus With You

Lydia Baxter

William H. Doane

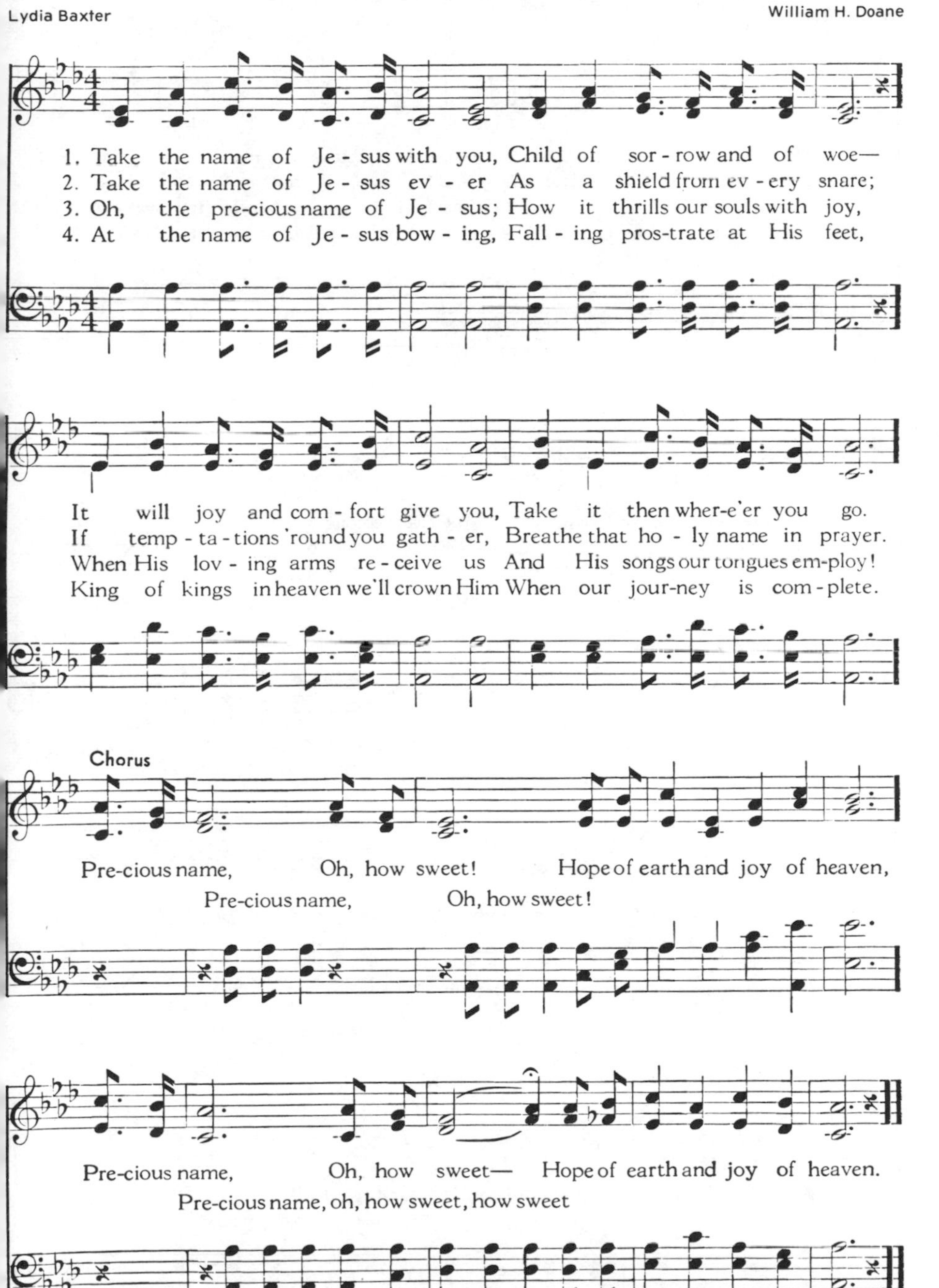
1. Take the name of Je-sus with you, Child of sor-row and of woe—
2. Take the name of Je-sus ev-er As a shield from ev-ery snare;
3. Oh, the pre-cious name of Je-sus; How it thrills our souls with joy,
4. At the name of Je-sus bow-ing, Fall-ing pros-trate at His feet,
It will joy and com-fort give you, Take it then wher-e'er you go.
If temp-ta-tions 'round you gath-er, Breathe that ho-ly name in prayer.
When His lov-ing arms re-ceive us And His songs our tongues em-ploy!
King of kings in heaven we'll crown Him When our jour-ney is com-plete.
Chorus
Pre-cious name, Oh, how sweet! Hope of earth and joy of heaven,
Pre-cious name, Oh, how sweet!
Pre-cious name, Oh, how sweet— Hope of earth and joy of heaven.
Pre-cious name, oh, how sweet, how sweet

84 The Name of Jesus

W. C. Martin | Edmund S. Lorenz

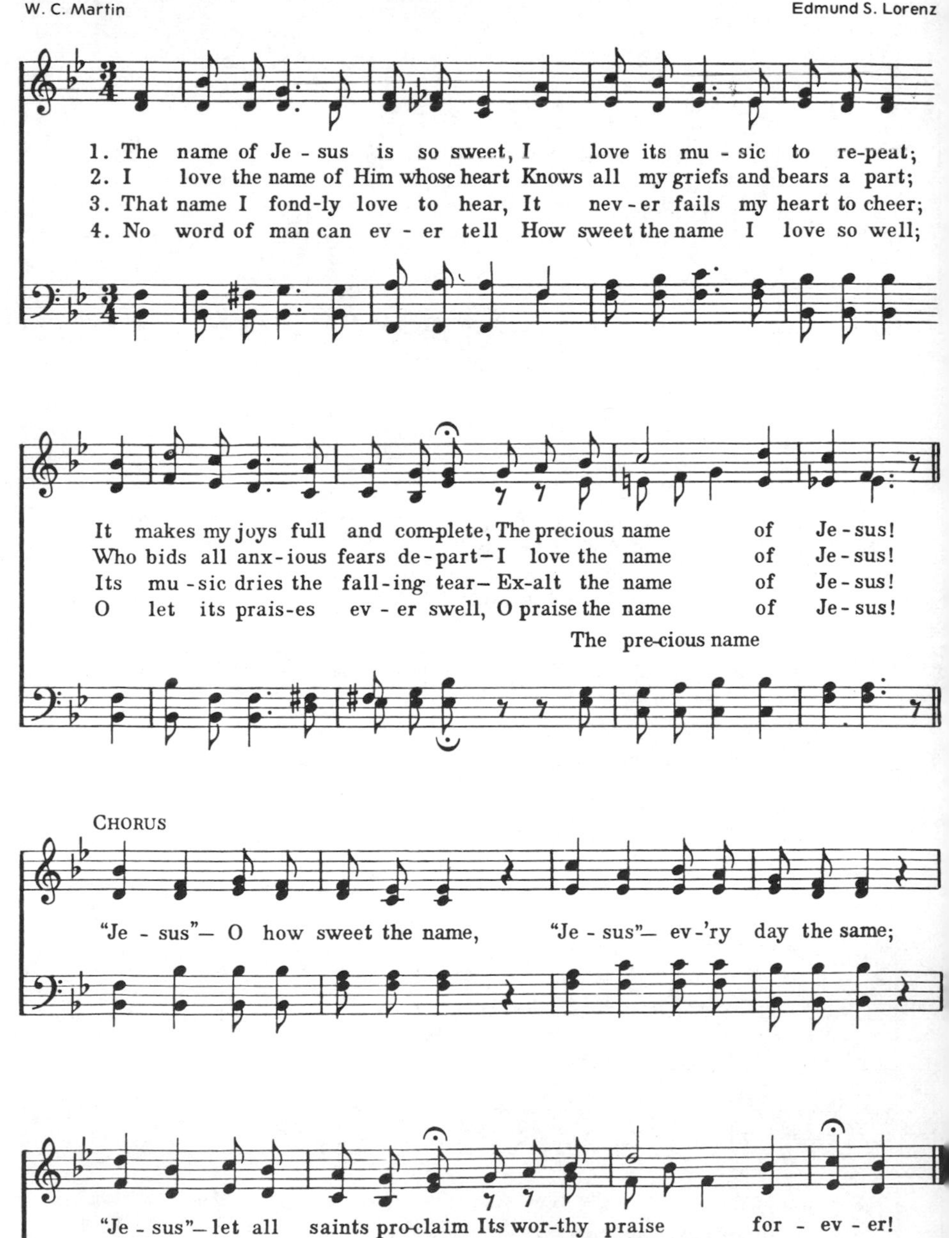
1. The name of Je - sus is so sweet, I love its mu - sic to re-peat;
2. I love the name of Him whose heart Knows all my griefs and bears a part;
3. That name I fond-ly love to hear, It nev - er fails my heart to cheer;
4. No word of man can ev - er tell How sweet the name I love so well;
It makes my joys full and com-plete, The precious name of Je - sus!
Who bids all anx - ious fears de - part – I love the name of Je - sus!
Its mu - sic dries the fall - ing tear – Ex-alt the name of Je - sus!
O let its prais-es ev - er swell, O praise the name of Je - sus!
The pre-cious name
CHORUS
"Je - sus" – O how sweet the name, "Je - sus" – ev - 'ry day the same;
"Je - sus" – let all saints pro-claim Its wor-thy praise for - ev - er!
Its wor-thy praise

That Beautiful Name

Jean Perry

Mabel Johnston Camp

1. I know of a Name, A beau-ti-ful Name, That an-gels brought down to earth; They whis-pered it low, One night long a-go, To a maid-en of low-ly birth.
2. I know of a Name, A beau-ti-ful Name, That un-to a Babe was giv'n; The stars glit-tered bright Thru-out that glad night, And an-gels praised God in heav'n.
3. The One of that Name My Sav-ior be-came, My Sav-ior of Cal-va-ry; My sins nailed Him there, My bur-dens He bare, He suf-fered all this for me.
4. I love that blest Name, That won-der-ful Name, Made high-er than all in heav'n; 'Twas whis-pered, I know, In my heart long a-go— To Je-sus my life I've giv'n.
CHORUS
That beau-ti-ful Name, That beau-ti-ful Name From sin has pow'r to free us! That beau-ti-ful Name, That won-der-ful Name, That match-less Name is Je-sus!

86 Tell Me the Story of Jesus

Fanny J. Crosby

John R. Sweney

1. Tell me the sto - ry of Je - sus, Write on my heart ev - ery word;
2. Fast - ing a - lone in the des - ert, Tell of the days that are past,
3. Tell of the cross where they nailed Him, Writhing in an-guish and pain;
Ref. Tell me the sto - ry of Je - sus, Write on my heart ev - ery word;
Fine
Tell me the sto - ry most pre - cious, Sweet-est that ev - er was heard.
How for our sins He was tempt - ed, Yet was tri - um-phant at last.
Tell of the grave where they laid Him, Tell how He liv - eth a - gain.
Tell me the sto - ry most pre - cious, Sweet-est that ev - er was heard.
Tell how the an-gels in cho - rus Sang as they wel-comed His birth,
Tell of the years of His la - bor, Tell of the sor - row He bore,
Love in that sto-ry so ten - der Clear - er than ev - er I see:
D.C. for Refrain
"Glo - ry to God in the high - est! Peace and good ti - dings to earth."
He was de-spised and af - flict - ed, Home-less, re - ject - ed and poor.
Stay, let me weep while you whis - per, Love paid the ran - som for me.

Seeking for Me

Author Unknown

Edward Hasty
Arr. Donna Krieger

1. Je-sus my Sav-iour, to Beth-le-hem came, Born in a man-ger to sor-row and
2. Je-sus my Sav-iour, on Cal-va-ry's tree, Paid the great debt and my soul He set
3. Je-sus my Sav-iour, the same as of old, While I was wan-d'ring a - far from the
4. Je-sus my Sav-iour shall come from on high- Sweet is the prom-ise as wea-ry years

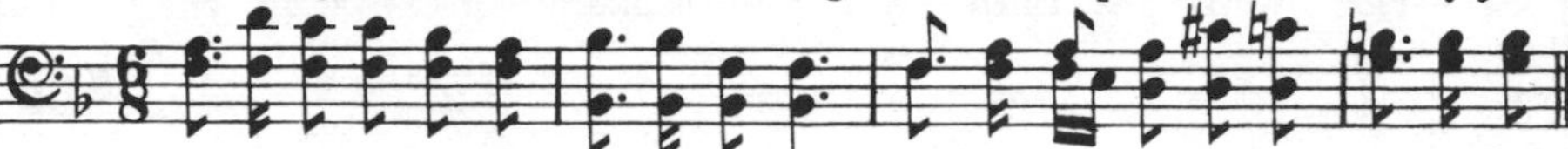

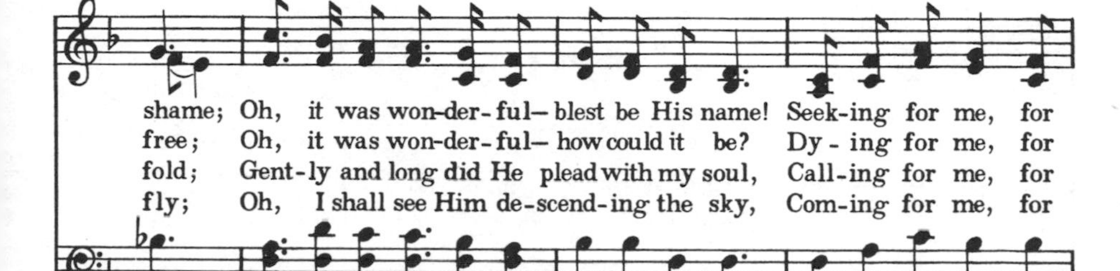

shame; Oh, it was won-der-ful- blest be His name! Seek-ing for me, for
free; Oh, it was won-der-ful- how could it be? Dy - ing for me, for
fold; Gent-ly and long did He plead with my soul, Call-ing for me, for
fly; Oh, I shall see Him de-scend-ing the sky, Com-ing for me, for

Refrain
me! Seek-ing for me! for me! Seek-ing for me, for me!
me! Dy - ing for me! for me! Dy - ing for me, for me!
me! Call-ing for me! for me! Call-ing for me, for me!
me! Com-ing for me! for me! Com-ing for me, for me!

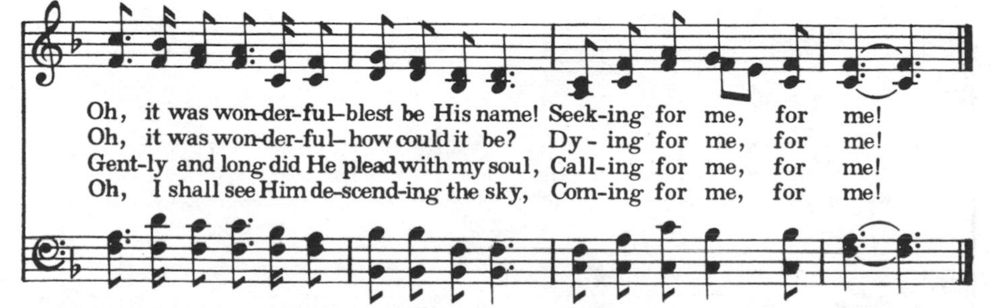

Oh, it was won-der-ful-blest be His name! Seek-ing for me, for me!
Oh, it was won-der-ful- how could it be? Dy - ing for me, for me!
Gent-ly and long did He plead with my soul, Call-ing for me, for me!
Oh, I shall see Him de-scend-ing the sky, Com-ing for me, for me!

88 Joy to the World

Isaac Watts

Origin Uncertain

1. Joy to the world! The Lord is come; Let earth re -
2. Joy to the earth! The Sav - iour reigns; Let men their
3. No more let sins and sor - rows grow, Nor thorns in -
4. He rules the earth with truth and grace, And makes the
ceive her King; Let ev - ery heart pre - pare Him room,
songs em - ploy; While fields and floods, rocks, hills, and plains
fest the ground. He comes to make His bless - ings flow
na - tions prove The glo - ries of His right - eous - ness,
And heaven and na - ture sing, And heaven and na - ture
Re - peat the sound - ing joy, Re - peat the sound - ing
Far as the curse is found, Far as the curse is
And won - ders of His love, And won - ders of His
And heaven and na - ture sing, And
sing, And heaven, and heaven and na - ture sing.
joy, Re - peat, re - peat the sound - ing joy.
found, Far as, far as the curse is found.
love, And won - ders, won - ders of. His love.
heaven and na-ture sing,

O Little Town of Bethlehem

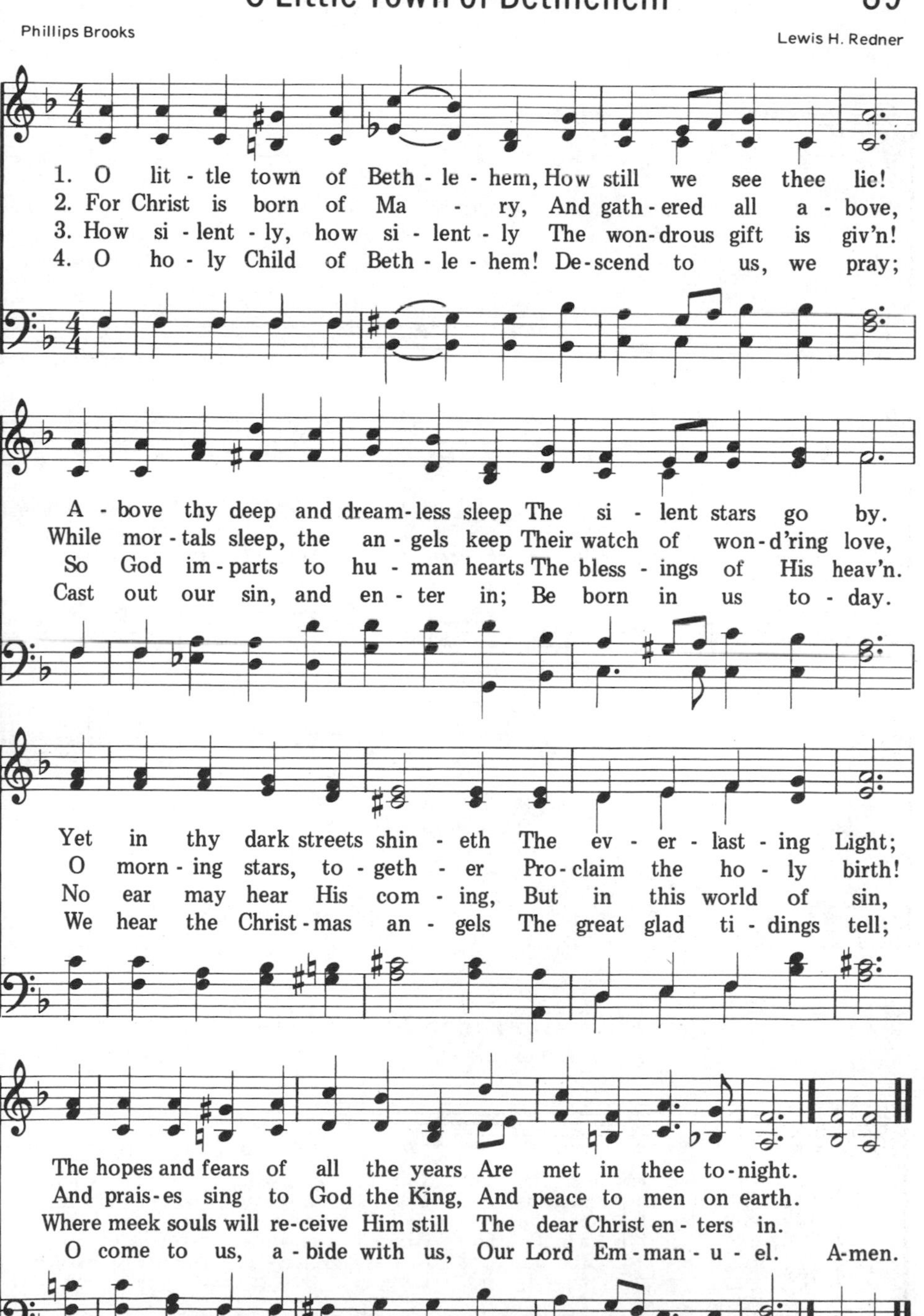
Phillips Brooks
Lewis H. Redner
1. O lit - tle town of Beth - le - hem, How still we see thee lie!
2. For Christ is born of Ma - ry, And gath - ered all a - bove,
3. How si - lent - ly, how si - lent - ly The won-drous gift is giv'n!
4. O ho - ly Child of Beth - le - hem! De-scend to us, we pray;
A - bove thy deep and dream-less sleep The si - lent stars go by.
While mor - tals sleep, the an - gels keep Their watch of won - d'ring love,
So God im - parts to hu - man hearts The bless - ings of His heav'n.
Cast out our sin, and en - ter in; Be born in us to - day.
Yet in thy dark streets shin - eth The ev - er - last - ing Light;
O morn - ing stars, to - geth - er Pro - claim the ho - ly birth!
No ear may hear His com - ing, But in this world of sin,
We hear the Christ - mas an - gels The great glad ti - dings tell;
The hopes and fears of all the years Are met in thee to - night.
And prais - es sing to God the King, And peace to men on earth.
Where meek souls will re - ceive Him still The dear Christ en - ters in.
O come to us, a - bide with us, Our Lord Em - man - u - el. A-men.

90 Silent Night! Holy Night!

Joseph Mohr
Trans. by John F. Young

Franz Gruber

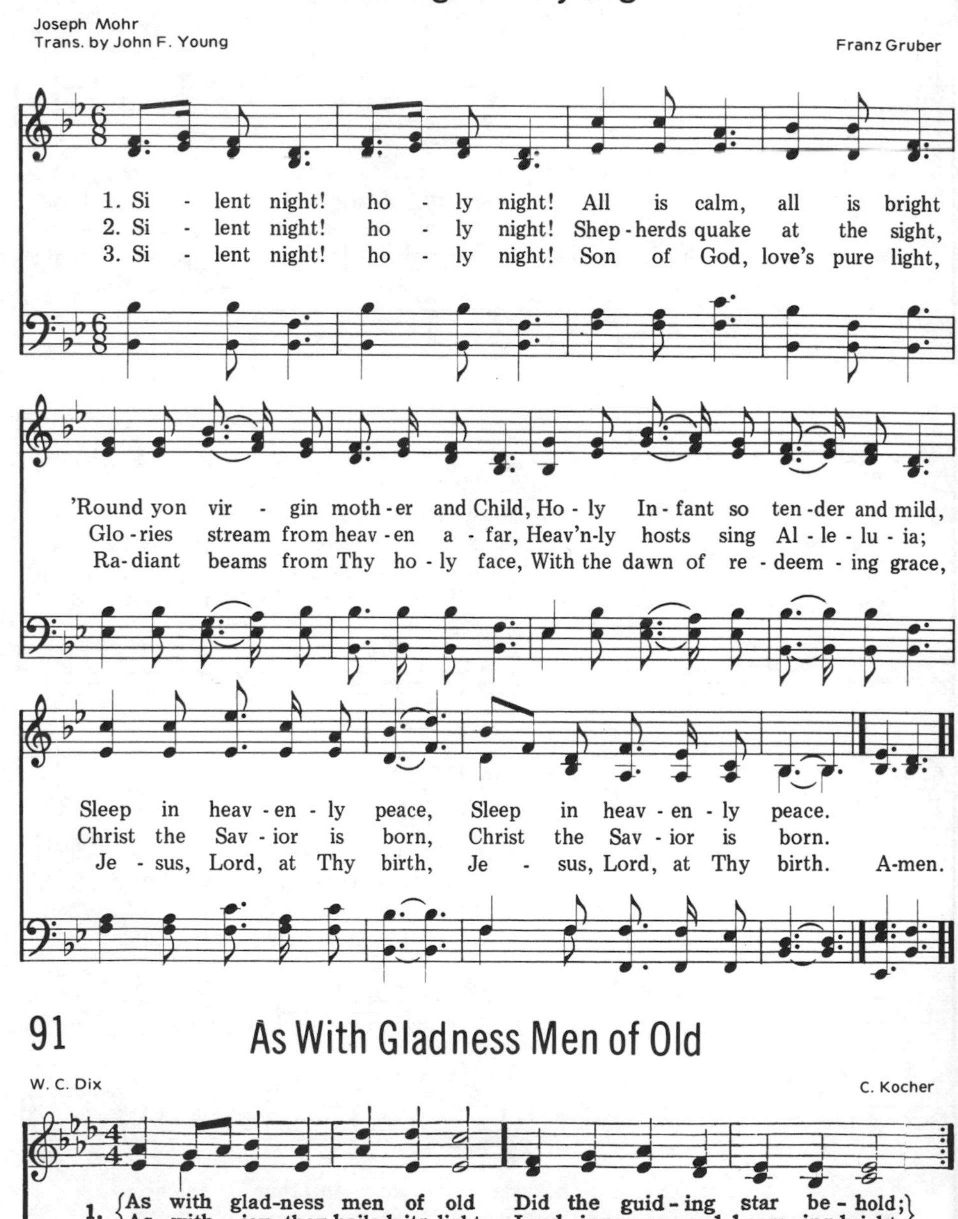

1. Si - lent night! ho - ly night! All is calm, all is bright
2. Si - lent night! ho - ly night! Shep - herds quake at the sight,
3. Si - lent night! ho - ly night! Son of God, love's pure light,
'Round yon vir - gin moth - er and Child, Ho - ly In - fant so ten - der and mild,
Glo - ries stream from heav - en a - far, Heav'n-ly hosts sing Al - le - lu - ia;
Ra - diant beams from Thy ho - ly face, With the dawn of re - deem - ing grace,
Sleep in heav - en - ly peace, Sleep in heav - en - ly peace.
Christ the Sav - ior is born, Christ the Sav - ior is born.
Je - sus, Lord, at Thy birth, Je - sus, Lord, at Thy birth. A-men.

91 As With Gladness Men of Old

W. C. Dix

C. Kocher

1. As with glad-ness men of old Did the guid - ing star be - hold;
As with joy they hailed its light, Lead - ing on - ward, beam - ing bright;
2. As with joy - ful steps they sped To that low - ly man - ger - bed,
There to bend the knee be - fore Him whom heav'n and earth a - dore:
3. As they of-fered gifts most rare At that man - ger rude and bare;
So may we with ho - ly joy, Pure, and free from sin's al - loy,

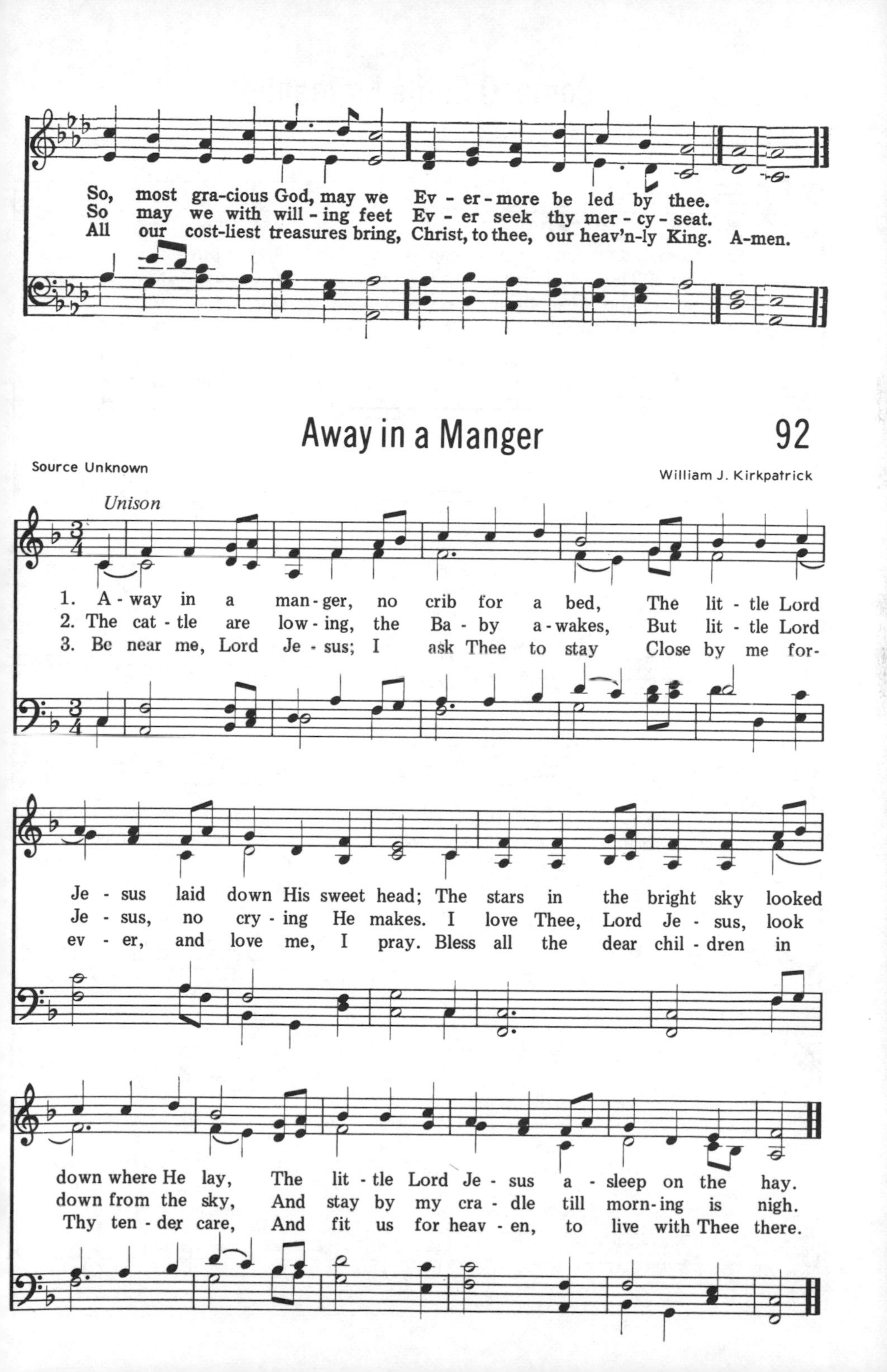
So, most gra-cious God, may we Ev - er - more be led by thee.
So may we with will - ing feet Ev - er seek thy mer - cy - seat.
All our cost-liest treasures bring, Christ, to thee, our heav'n-ly King. A-men.
Away in a Manger
92
Source Unknown
William J. Kirkpatrick
Unison
1. A - way in a man - ger, no crib for a bed, The lit - tle Lord
2. The cat - tle are low - ing, the Ba - by a - wakes, But lit - tle Lord
3. Be near me, Lord Je - sus; I ask Thee to stay Close by me for-
Je - sus laid down His sweet head; The stars in the bright sky looked
Je - sus, no cry - ing He makes. I love Thee, Lord Je - sus, look
ev - er, and love me, I pray. Bless all the dear chil - dren in
down where He lay, The lit - tle Lord Je - sus a - sleep on the hay.
down from the sky, And stay by my cra - dle till morn-ing is nigh.
Thy ten - der care, And fit us for heav - en, to live with Thee there.

93 O Come, O Come Emmanuel

Latin Hymn
Trans. by John M. Neale

Thomas Helmore

1. O come, O come, Em - man - u - el, And ran - som cap - tive
2. O come, Thou Rod of Jes - se, free Thine own from Sa - tan's
3. O come, Thou Day-spring, come and cheer Our spir - its by Thine
4. O come, Thou Key of Da - vid, come, And o - pen wide our
Is - ra - el, That mourns in lone - ly ex - ile here
tyr - an - ny; From depths of hell Thy peo - ple save
ad - vent here; And drive a - way the shades of night,
heaven - ly home; Make safe the way that leads on high,
Un - til the Son of God ap - pear. Re - joice! Re - joice! Em -
And give them vic - tory o'er the grave. Re - joice! Re - joice! Em -
And pierce the clouds and bring us light! Re - joice! Re - joice! Em -
And close the path to mis - er - y. Re - joice! Re - joice! Em -
man - u - el Shall come to thee, O Is - ra - el!
man - u - el Shall come to thee, O Is - ra - el!
man - u - el Shall come to thee, O Is - ra - el!
man - u - el Shall come to thee, O Is - ra - el! A-MEN.

O Come, All Ye Faithful

Anon. Latin
Trans. by Frederick Oakeley

John Wade's Cantus Divers

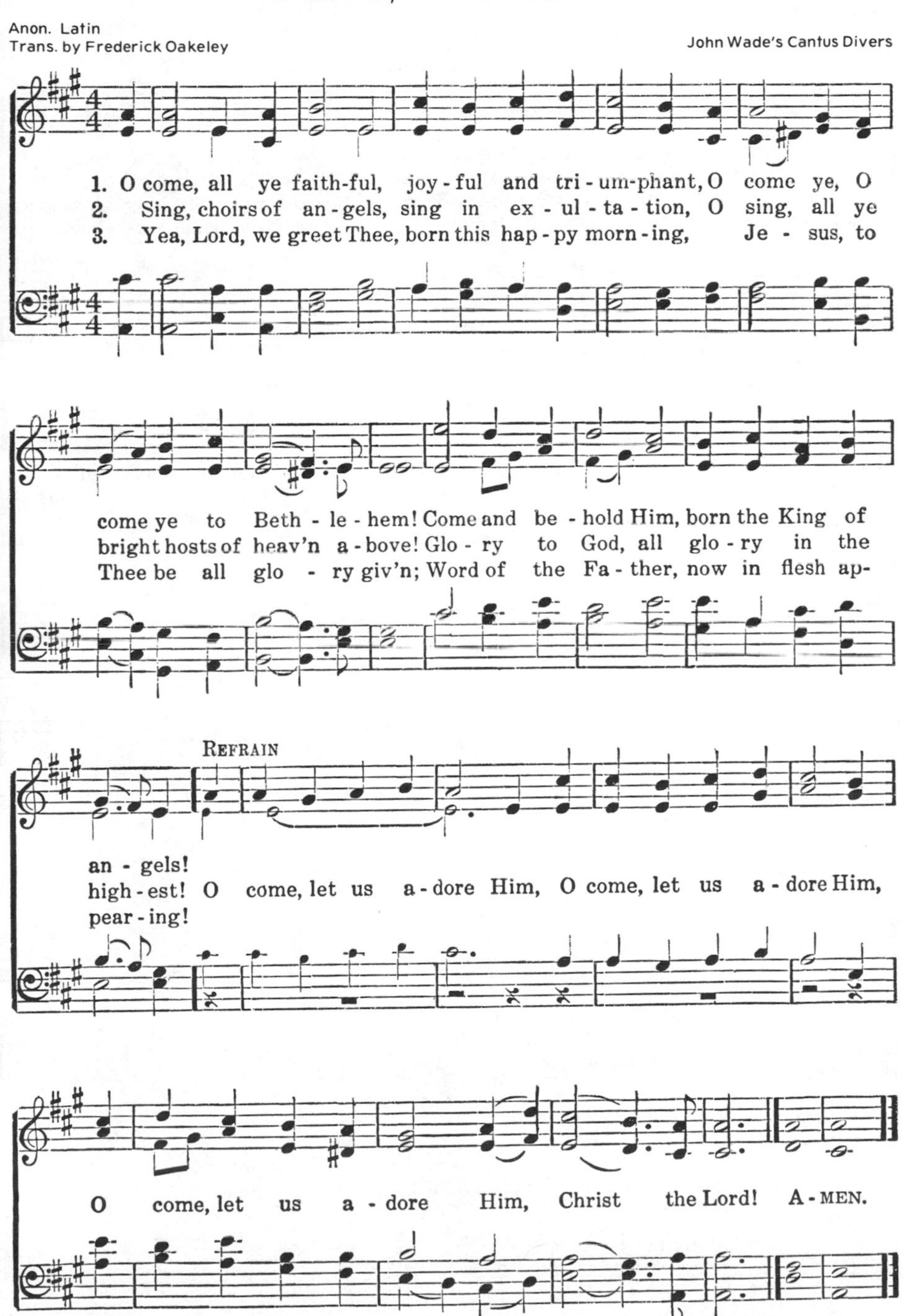
1. O come, all ye faith-ful, joy-ful and tri-um-phant, O come ye, O come ye to Beth-le-hem! Come and be-hold Him, born the King of an-gels!
2. Sing, choirs of an-gels, sing in ex-ul-ta-tion, O sing, all ye bright hosts of heav'n a-bove! Glo-ry to God, all glo-ry in the high-est!
3. Yea, Lord, we greet Thee, born this hap-py morn-ing, Je-sus, to Thee be all glo-ry giv'n; Word of the Fa-ther, now in flesh ap-pear-ing!
Refrain
O come, let us a-dore Him, O come, let us a-dore Him, O come, let us a-dore Him, Christ the Lord! A-men.

95 It Came Upon the Midnight Clear

Edmund H. Sears

Richard S. Willis

1. It came up-on the mid-night clear, That glo-rious song of old,
2. Still through the clo-ven skies they come, With peace-ful wings un-furled,
3. And ye, be-neath life's crush-ing load, Whose forms are bend-ing low,
4. For lo, the days are has-tening on, By proph-et-bards fore-told,

From an-gels bend-ing near the earth To touch their harps of gold:
And still their heaven-ly mu-sic floats O'er all the wea-ry world:
Who toil a-long the climb-ing way With pain-ful steps and slow,
When, with the ev-er-cir-cling years, Comes round the age of gold:

"Peace on the earth, good-will to men, From heaven's all-gra-cious King": The
A-bove its sad and low-ly plains They bend on hov-ering wing: And
Look now! for glad and gold-en hours Come swift-ly on the wing; O
When peace shall o-ver all the earth Its an-cient splen-dors fling, And

world in sol-emn still-ness lay To hear the an-gels sing.
ev-er o'er its Ba-bel sounds The bless-ed an-gels sing.
rest be-side the wea-ry road, And hear the an-gels sing.
the whole world give back the song Which now the an-gels sing. A-MEN.

Angels We Have Heard on High

Source Unknown
Old French Carol
1. An - gels we have heard on high, Sweet - ly sing - ing o'er the plains,
2. Shep-herds, why this ju - bi - lee? Why your joy - ous strains pro - long?
3. Come to Beth - le - hem and see Him whose birth the an - gels sing;
4. See with - in a man - ger laid Je - sus, Lord of heaven and earth!
And the moun-tains in re - ply Ech - o back their joy - ous strains.
Say what may the ti - dings be, Which in - spire your heaven - ly song?
Come, a - dore on bend - ed knee Christ the Lord, the new - born King.
Ma - ry, Jo - seph, lend your aid, With us sing our Sav - iour's birth.
Refrain
Glo - - - - - - - - - - - - - ri - a
in ex - cel - sis De - o,
Glo - - - - - - - - - ri - a in ex - cel - sis De - o.
A-men.

97 What Child Is This?

William C. Dix
English Melody
1. What Child is this, who, laid to rest,. On Ma-ry's lap is sleep-ing?
2. Why lies He in such mean es-tate Where ox and ass are feed-ing?
3. So bring Him in-cense, gold and myrrh—Come, rich and poor, to own Him;
Whom an-gels greet with an-thems sweet, While shep-herds watch are keep-ing?
Good Christian, fear— for sin-ners here The si-lent Word is plead-ing.
The King of kings sal-va-tion brings—Let lov-ing hearts en-throne Him.
REFRAIN
This, this is Christ the King, Whom shep-herds guard and an-gels sing:
Haste, haste to bring Him laud— The Babe, the Son of Ma-ry.
98
There's a Wonderful Name
N. J. C
Norman J. Clayton
Not fast
There's a won-der-ful name,— 'Tis Je-sus, It is

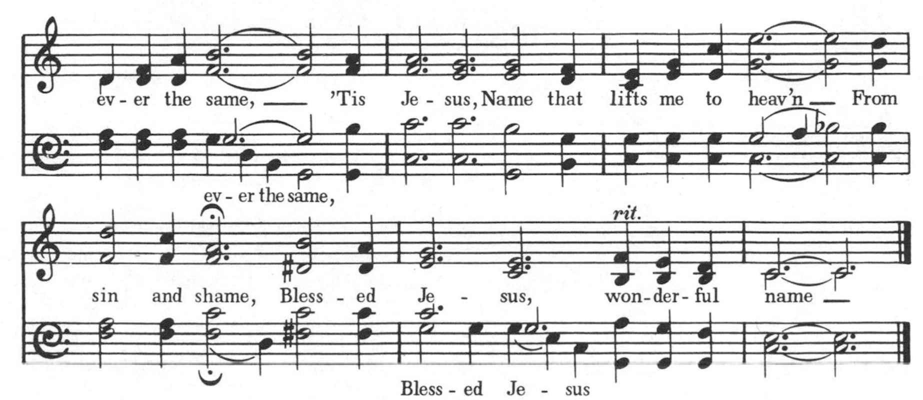
ev - er the same, 'Tis Je - sus, Name that lifts me to heav'n From
ev - er the same,
rit.
sin and shame, Bless - ed Je - sus, won-der-ful name
Bless - ed Je - sus

There's a Song in the Air! 99

Josiah G. Holland

Karl P. Harrington
Arr. by John Willard

1. There's a song in the air! There's a star in the sky! There's a moth-er's deep prayer And a ba - by's low cry! And the star rains its fire while the beau - ti - ful sing, For the man-ger of Beth-le-hem cra-dles a King!
2. There's a tu-mult of joy O'er the won-der-ful birth, For the Vir-gin's sweet Boy Is the Lord of the earth. Ay! the star rains its fire while the beau - ti - ful sing, For the man-ger of Beth-le-hem cra-dles a King!
3. In the light of that star Lie the a - ges im-pearled, And that song from a - far Has swept o - ver the world. Ev - 'ry hearth is a - flame — and the beau - ti - ful sing In the homes of the na-tions that Je - sus is King!
4. We re - joice in the light, And we ech - o the song That comes down thru the night From the heav - en - ly throng. Ay! we shout to the love - ly e - van - gel they bring, And we greet in His cra - dle our Sav - ior and King!

100

Hosanna, Loud Hosanna

Jennette Threlfall

Gesangbuch, Wirtemberg

1. Ho - san - na, loud ho - san - na The lit - tle chil - dren sang;
2. From Ol - i - vet they fol - lowed 'Mid an ex - ult - ant crowd,
3. "Ho - san - na in the high - est!" That an - cient song we sing,

Through pil - lared court and tem - ple The love - ly an - them rang;
The vic - tor palm branch wav - ing, And chant - ing clear and loud;
For Christ is our Re - deem - er, The Lord of heav'n, our King;

To Je - sus, who had blessed them Close fold - ed to His breast,
The Lord of men and an - gels Rode on in low - ly state,
O may we ev - er praise Him With heart and life and voice,

The chil - dren sang their prais - es, The sim - plest and the best.
Nor scorned that lit - tle chil - dren Should on His bid - ding wait.
And in His bliss - ful pres - ence E - ter - nal - ly re - joice! A-men

'Tis Midnight; and on Olive's Brow

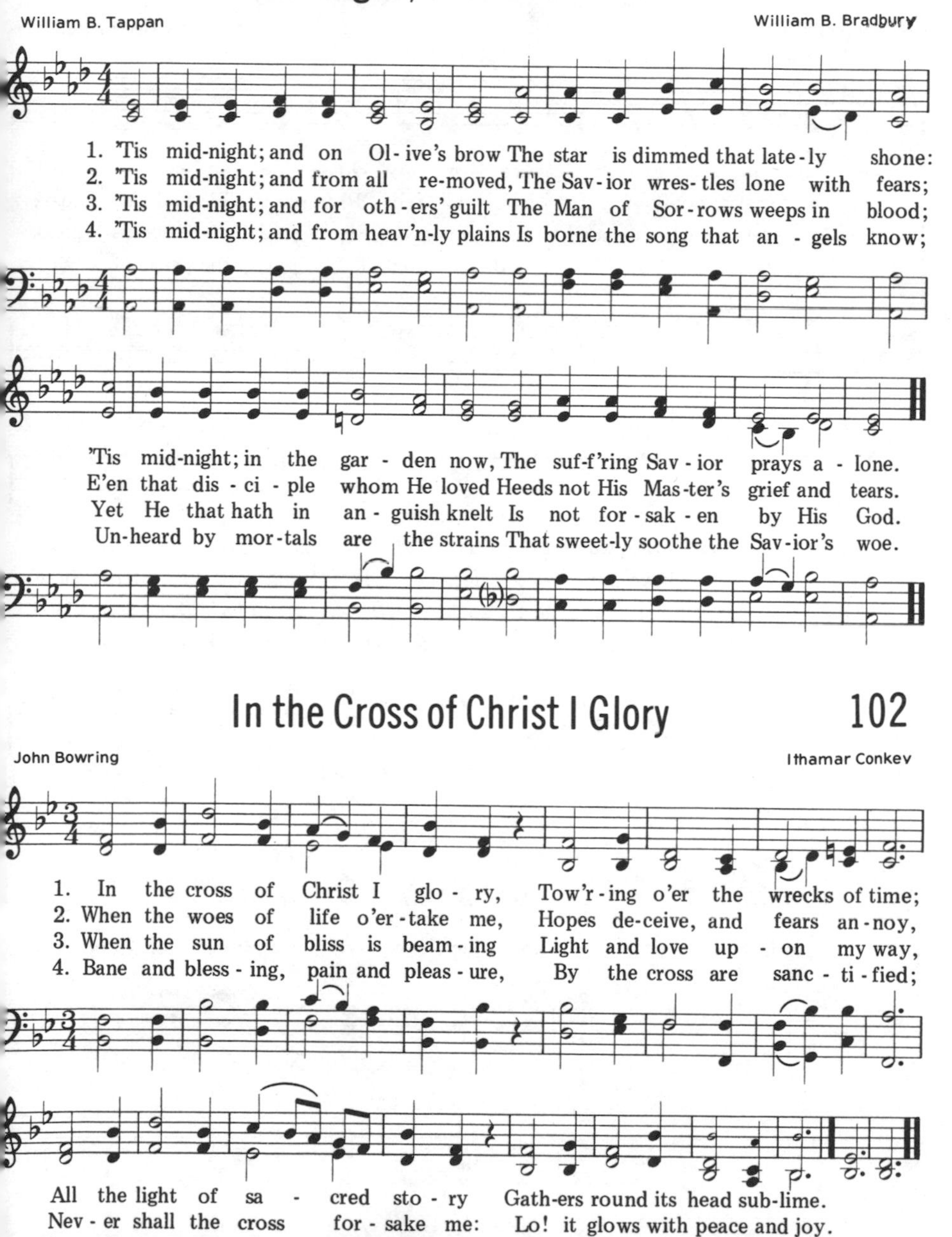
William B. Tappan
William B. Bradbury
1. 'Tis mid-night; and on Ol-ive's brow The star is dimmed that late-ly shone:
2. 'Tis mid-night; and from all re-moved, The Sav-ior wres-tles lone with fears;
3. 'Tis mid-night; and for oth-ers' guilt The Man of Sor-rows weeps in blood;
4. 'Tis mid-night; and from heav'n-ly plains Is borne the song that an-gels know;
'Tis mid-night; in the gar-den now, The suf-f'ring Sav-ior prays a-lone.
E'en that dis-ci-ple whom He loved Heeds not His Mas-ter's grief and tears.
Yet He that hath in an-guish knelt Is not for-sak-en by His God.
Un-heard by mor-tals are the strains That sweet-ly soothe the Sav-ior's woe.
(♭)
In the Cross of Christ I Glory 102
John Bowring
Ithamar Conkey
1. In the cross of Christ I glo-ry, Tow'r-ing o'er the wrecks of time;
2. When the woes of life o'er-take me, Hopes de-ceive, and fears an-noy,
3. When the sun of bliss is beam-ing Light and love up-on my way,
4. Bane and bless-ing, pain and pleas-ure, By the cross are sanc-ti-fied;
All the light of sa-cred sto-ry Gath-ers round its head sub-lime.
Nev-er shall the cross for-sake me: Lo! it glows with peace and joy.
From the cross the ra-diance stream-ing Adds more lus-ter to the day.
Peace is there that knows no meas-ure, Joys that thro' all time a-bide. A-men.

103 There Is a Green Hill Far Away

Cecil F. Alexander | George C. Stebbins

1. There is a green hill far a - way, Out - side a cit - y wall,
2. We may not know, we can - not tell What pains He had to bear;
3. He died that we might be for-given, He died to make us good,
4. There was no oth - er good e-nough To pay the price of sin;

Where the dear Lord was cru - ci - fied, Who died to save us all.
But we be - lieve it was for us He hung and suf - fered there.
That we might go at last to heaven, Saved by His pre - cious blood.
He on - ly could un - lock the gate Of heaven, and let us in.

CHORUS

Oh, dear - ly, dear - ly has He loved, And we must love Him too,
And trust in His re - deem-ing blood, And try His works to do.

The Old Rugged Cross

George Bennard

George Bennard

1. On a hill far a-way stood an old rug-ged cross, The em-blem of
2. Oh, that old rug-ged cross, so de-spised by the world, Has a won-drous at-
3. In the old rug-ged cross, stained with blood so di-vine, A won-drous
4. To the old rug-ged cross I will ev-er be true, Its shame and re-
suf-fering and shame; And I love that old cross where the dear-est and best
trac-tion for me; For the dear Lamb of God left His glo-ry a-bove
beau-ty I see; For 'twas on that old cross Je-sus suf-fered and died
proach glad-ly bear; Then He'll call me some day to my home far a-way,
CHORUS
For a world of lost sin-ners was slain.
To bear it to dark Cal-va-ry.
To par-don and sanc-ti-fy me.
Where His glo-ry for-ev-er I'll share.
So I'll cher-ish the old rug-ged cross, the
cross, ... Till my tro-phies at last I lay down; I will cling to the
old rug-ged cross,
old rug-ged cross, ... And ex-change it some day for a crown.
cross, the old rug-ged cross,

105 Behold the Lamb of God

J. Hoskins, Alt. A.B.S.
A.P. Gibbs Vs.4
Arr. by Alfred B. Smith
1. Be - hold! be-hold the Lamb of God, On the cross! On the cross! For us He shed His pre - cious blood, On the cross! On the cross! O hear His cry for those near by "O Fa-ther for-give; they know not why."
2. By faith we see Him lift - ed up, On the cross! On the cross! He drinks for us the bit - ter cup, On the cross! On the cross! The rocks do rend, the moun-tains quake, While Je - sus doth a - tone-ment make,
3. And now the might-y deed is done, On the cross! On the cross! The bat - tle fought, the vic - t'ry won, On the cross! On the cross! To heav'n He turns tri - umph-ant eyes: "'Tis fin - ished" now, the con - qu'ror cries,
4. But now He's ris'n, as - cend - ed, crowned, On the throne! On the throne! Heav'n's high - est place for Him is found, On the throne! On the throne! Our hearts we low in wor - ship bow, And join, as one, to hail Him now:
* We thank Thee Lord for this our food, God is love, God is love. But most for Je - sus, kind and good, God is love, God is love. These mer - cies bless and grant that we may live in peace and hon - or Thee.

* This makes an excellent *blessing* at mealtime.

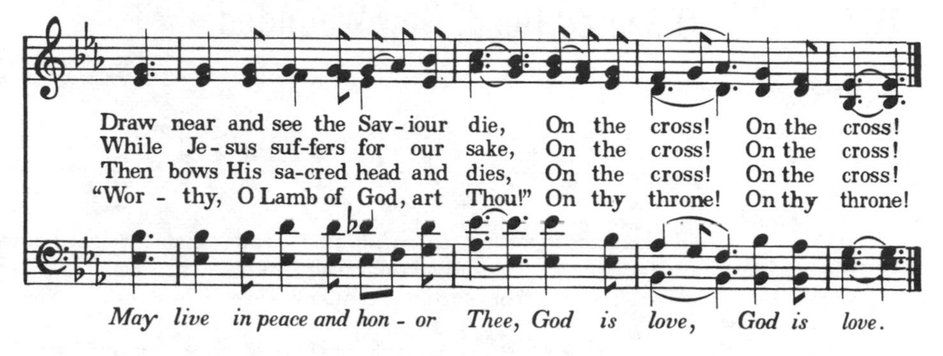
Draw near and see the Sav-iour die, On the cross! On the cross!
While Je-sus suf-fers for our sake, On the cross! On the cross!
Then bows His sa-cred head and dies, On the cross! On the cross!
"Wor - thy, O Lamb of God, art Thou!" On thy throne! On thy throne!
May live in peace and hon - or Thee, God is love, God is love.

I Know a Fount

106

O. C. Vs. 1
Cora Brockhuizen Vs. 2,3,4,
O. Cooke
Arr. by Alfred B. Smith
1. I know a fount where sins are wash'd a - way (a-way), I know a place where night is turned to day (to day); Bur - dens are lift - ed, blind eyes made to see; There's a won - der work - ing pow'r, In the blood of Cal - va - ry.
2. I have a Sav - iour, He's a faith-ful friend (a friend), One who is with me, will be to the end (the end). He now in glo - ry in - ter-cedes for me, 'Twas His pre-cious cleans-ing blood, that once flowed on Cal - va - ry.
3. I have a peace, this world could nev-er give (not give), Won - der - ful peace, for now in Christ I live (I live). From con-dem-na-tion He hath made me free, What a won - der work - ing pow'r, In the blood of Cal - va - ry.
4. I have a hope, My Lord will sure-ly come (will come), All His re - deemed ones shall be gathered home (be home). With Him in glo - ry ev - er-more to be, Then we'll praise Him for the blood, That was shed on Cal - va - ry.

107 O Sacred Head, Now Wounded

Hans Leo Hassler
Arr. by J. S. Bach
Attr. to Bernard of Clairvaux
1. O sa - cred Head, now wound - ed, With grief and shame weighed down,
2. What Thou, my Lord, hast suf - fered Was all for sin - ners' gain;
3. What lan - guage shall I bor - row To thank Thee, dear - est friend,
Now scorn - ful - ly sur - round - ed With thorns, Thine on - ly crown:
Mine, mine was the trans - gres - sion, But Thine the dead - ly pain.
For this Thy dy - ing sor - row, Thy pit - y with - out end?
O sa - cred Head, what glo - ry, What bliss till now was Thine!
Lo, here I fall, my Sav - ior! 'Tis I de - serve Thy place;
O make me Thine for - ev - er; And should I faint - ing be,
Yet, though de - spised and go - ry, I joy to call Thee mine.
Look on me with Thy fa - vor, Vouch - safe to me Thy grace.
Lord, let me nev - er, nev - er Out - live my love to Thee.
A - men.

He Was Wounded for Our Transgressions 108

Thomas O. Chisholm

Merrill Dunlop

1. He was wound - ed for our trans - gress - ions, He bore our
2. He was num-bered a - mong trans - gress - ors, We did es-
3. We had wan-dered, we all had wan-dered Far from the
4. Who can num - ber His gen - er - a - tion? Who shall de-

sins in His bod - y on the tree; For our guilt He
teem Him for - sak - en by His God; As our sac - ri-
fold of "the Shep-herd of the sheep;" But He sought us
clare all the tri - umphs of His cross? Mil - lions dead now

gave us peace, From our bond-age gave re - lease, And with His
fice He died, That the law be sat - is - fied, And all our
where we were, On the moun-tains bleak and bare, And brought us
live a - gain, Myr - iads fol - low in His train! Vic - to - rious

stripes, and with His stripes, And with His stripes our souls are healed.
sin, and all our sin, And all our sin was laid on Him.
home, and brought us home, And brought us safe - ly home to God.
Lord, vic - to - rious Lord, Vic - to - rious Lord and com - ing King!

109 Opened for Me

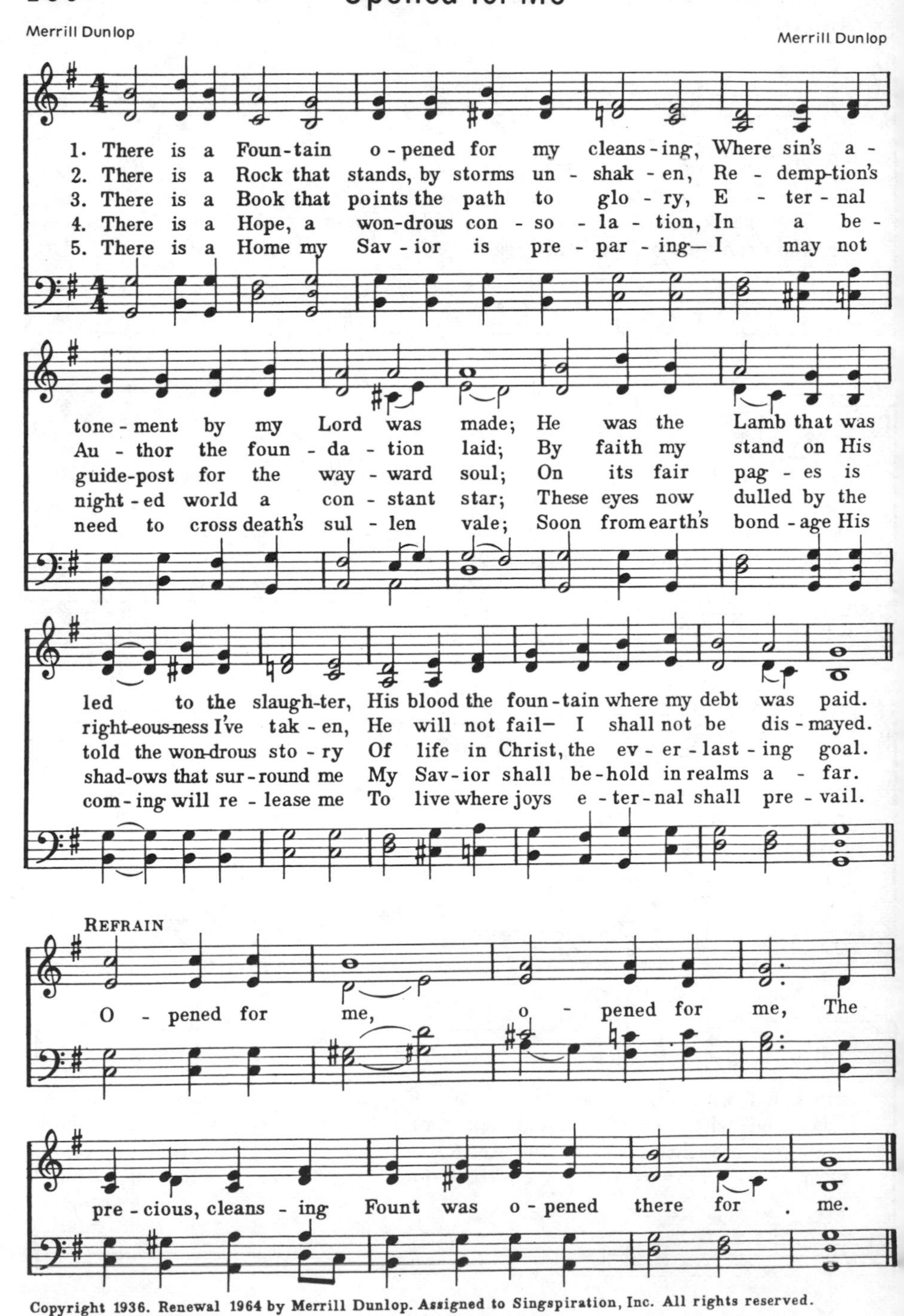

Merrill Dunlop
Merrill Dunlop
1. There is a Foun-tain o-pened for my cleans-ing, Where sin's a-
2. There is a Rock that stands, by storms un-shak-en, Re-demp-tion's
3. There is a Book that points the path to glo-ry, E-ter-nal
4. There is a Hope, a won-drous con-so-la-tion, In a be-
5. There is a Home my Sav-ior is pre-par-ing— I may not
tone-ment by my Lord was made; He was the Lamb that was
Au-thor the foun-da-tion laid; By faith my stand on His
guide-post for the way-ward soul; On its fair pag-es is
night-ed world a con-stant star; These eyes now dulled by the
need to cross death's sul-len vale; Soon from earth's bond-age His
led to the slaugh-ter, His blood the foun-tain where my debt was paid.
right-eous-ness I've tak-en, He will not fail— I shall not be dis-mayed.
told the won-drous sto-ry Of life in Christ, the ev-er-last-ing goal.
shad-ows that sur-round me My Sav-ior shall be-hold in realms a-far.
com-ing will re-lease me To live where joys e-ter-nal shall pre-vail.
REFRAIN
O-pened for me, o-pened for me, The
pre-cious, cleans-ing Fount was o-pened there for me.

When I Survey the Wondrous Cross 110

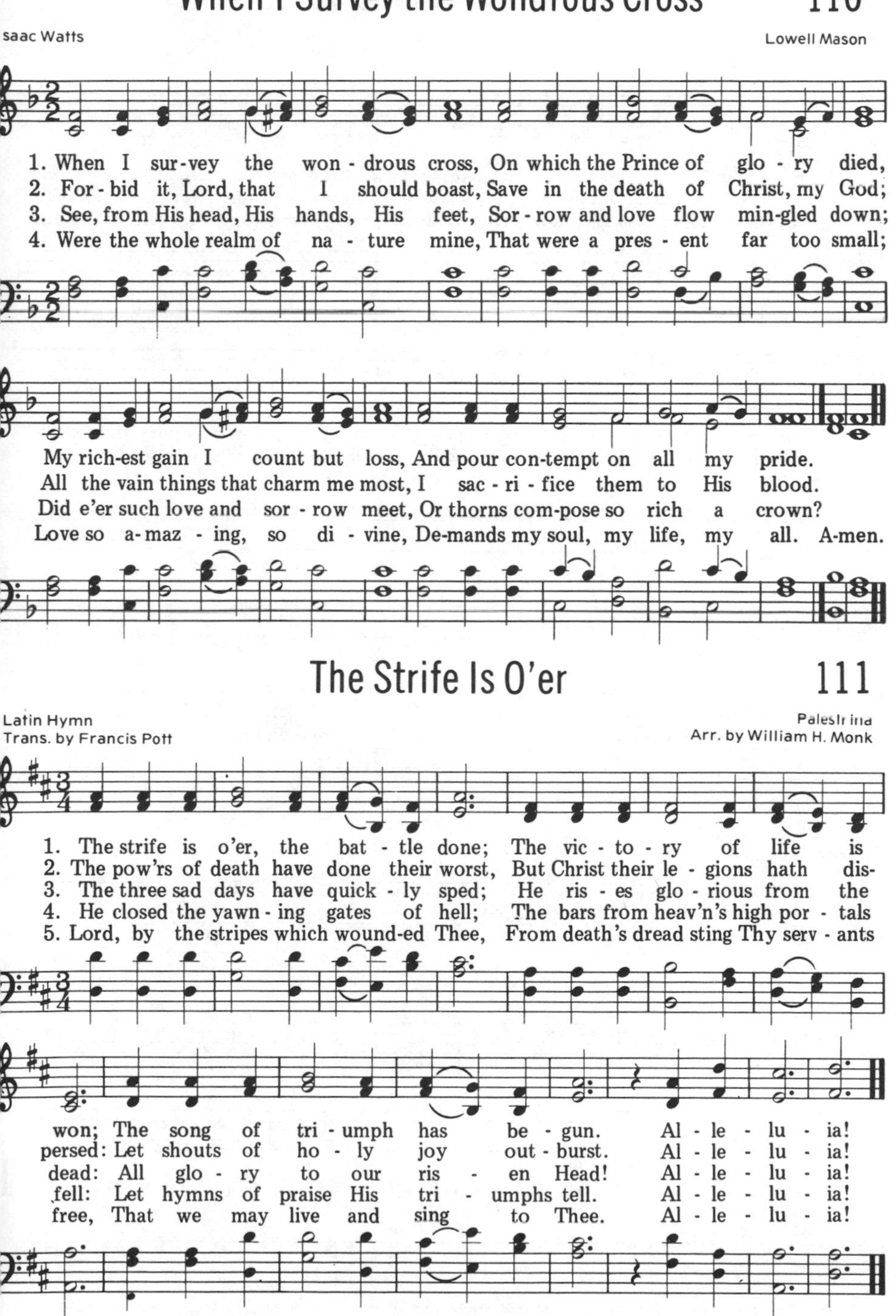
saac Watts
Lowell Mason
1. When I sur-vey the won - drous cross, On which the Prince of glo - ry died,
2. For - bid it, Lord, that I should boast, Save in the death of Christ, my God;
3. See, from His head, His hands, His feet, Sor - row and love flow min-gled down;
4. Were the whole realm of na - ture mine, That were a pres - ent far too small;
My rich-est gain I count but loss, And pour con-tempt on all my pride.
All the vain things that charm me most, I sac - ri - fice them to His blood.
Did e'er such love and sor - row meet, Or thorns com-pose so rich a crown?
Love so a-maz - ing, so di - vine, De-mands my soul, my life, my all. A-men.
The Strife Is O'er
111
Latin Hymn
Trans. by Francis Pott
Palestrina
Arr. by William H. Monk
1. The strife is o'er, the bat - tle done; The vic - to - ry of life is won; The song of tri - umph has be - gun. Al - le - lu - ia!
2. The pow'rs of death have done their worst, But Christ their le - gions hath dis- persed: Let shouts of ho - ly joy out - burst. Al - le - lu - ia!
3. The three sad days have quick - ly sped; He ris - es glo - rious from the dead: All glo - ry to our ris - en Head! Al - le - lu - ia!
4. He closed the yawn - ing gates of hell; The bars from heav'n's high por - tals fell: Let hymns of praise His tri - umphs tell. Al - le - lu - ia!
5. Lord, by the stripes which wound-ed Thee, From death's dread sting Thy serv - ants free, That we may live and sing to Thee. Al - le - lu - ia!

112 I Love Thee, Lord Jesus

I Pet. 2:7a

Alfred B. Smith

Solo or unison
1. Peace like a riv-er is flood-ing my soul, Since Christ, the Sav-iour has made my life whole; Sweet peace a-bid-ing my por-tion shall be– Je-sus, my Sav-iour is pre-cious to me.
2. Joy is a-bound-ing my heart glad-ly sings Climb-ing t'ward heav-en on eag-le strong wings; Christ has re-deemed me my soul He set free– Je-sus, my Sav-iour is pre-cious to me.
3. Oh, prec-ious Je-sus, how love-ly thou art! Come in thy full-ness and rule in my heart, Break ev-'ry fet-ter thy face let-me see, Thou shalt for-ev-er be pre-cious to me.
Chorus- 4 parts
I love Thee, Lord Je-sus with all of my heart I love Thee, Lord Je-sus with all of my heart for dy-ing on Cal-v'ry For

"I love Thee, Lord Jesus, with all of my heart" these simple words spoken by a little girl in a testimony service marked the beginning of the great Welsh revival.

giv-ing me vic-t'ry, I love Thee, Lord Je-sus with all of my heart.
Fairest Lord Jesus
113
From the German
17th Century
Silesian Folk Song
Arr. by James Hopkirk
1. Fair - est Lord Je - sus, Rul - er of all na - ture, O Thou of God and man the Son; Thee will I cher - ish, Thee will I hon - or, Thou my soul's glo - ry, joy, and crown.
2. Fair are the mead-ows, Fair - er still the wood-lands, Robed in the bloom - ing garb of spring; Je - sus is fair - er, Je - sus is pur - er, Who makes the woe - ful heart to sing.
3. Fair is the sun-shine, Fair - er still the moon-light, And fair the twink - ling, star - ry host; Je - sus shines bright - er, Je - sus shines pur - er, Than all the an - gels heaven can boast.
4. All fair - est beau - ty Heav - en - ly and earth - ly, Won-drous-ly, Je - sus, is found in Thee; None can be near - er, fair - er or dear - er, Than Thou, my Sav - iour, art to me. A-MEN.

114 Covered by the Blood

Nellie Edwards

Ran C. Story
Alt. Alfred B. Smith

1. Once in sin's dark-est night I was wan-d'ring a-lone; A stran-ger to mer-cy I stood. But the Sav-iour came nigh When He heard my faint cry, And He put my sins un-der the Blood.
2. From the bur-den I car-ried now I am set free, For Je-sus has lift-ed my load. Oh, the love and the grace I re-ceived in its place When He put my sins un-der the Blood.
3. I can ne'er un-der-stand why He sought e-ven me, Why His life-blood on Cal-va-ry flowed. But suf-fi-cient for me, Since He died on the tree, He hath put my sins un-der the Blood.
4. Now He comes to my heart and re moves ev-'ry care; He bears all my cum-ber-ing load. In a path-way re-plete With His love are my feet, Since He put my sins un-der the Blood.
Refrain
They are cov-ered by the Blood; They are cov-ered by the Blood. My sins are all cov-ered by the Blood. My in-iq-ui-ties so vast
(pre-cious Blood)

have been blot - ted out at last. For my sins are all cov-ered by the Blood.
(by the Blood)
I Know No Other Jesus
115
James M. Gray
Alfred B. Smith
1. I know no oth - er Je - sus Than He who died for me;
2. That hu-man Christs could save me Is in - ad - mis - si - ble;
3. The In-fant of the man - ger, The vil-lage Car - pen - ter,
The Sav-iour of lost sin - ners, The Christ of Cal - va - ry.
My Je - sus is the im - age Of God in - vis - i - ble.
The Teach - er sent from heav - en To men to min - is - ter;
I know no "i - deal" Je - sus That hu - man minds in - vent;
My Christ be-came in - car - nate And of the Vir - gin born;
The true his - tor - ic Je - sus, Who died and rose a - gain,
The on - ly Christ I wor - ship Is whom the Fa - ther sent.
He left a crown of glo - ry To wear the plat - ted thorn.
He on - ly is the Je - sus That I pro-claim to men.

116 It Cleanseth Me

A. F. Myers
F. L. Snyder
Alt. & Arr. by Alfred B. Smith
1. There is a stream that flows from Cal - va - ry, A crim - son tide so
2. Its sav - ing vir-tues ev - er are the same. It cleans - eth still, and
3. No oth - er foun-tain can for sin a - tone But Je - sus' blood, O
deep and wide. It wash - es whit - er than the pur - est snow; It
al - ways will. Poor sin - ners who will seek the Sav - iour's face Shall
pre - cious flood! And who - so - ev - er will may plunge there - in, And
cleans - eth me, I know.
know His won-drous grace.
be made free from sin.
Refrain
Hal - le - lu-jah! 'tis His blood that cleans-eth
me, 'Tis His grace that makes me free; And, my broth - er, 'tis for thee. Oh,
hal - le - lu-jah! 'tis sal - va-tion full and free; And it cleans-eth, yes, it cleans-eth me.

Nailed to the Cross

Mrs. Frank A. Breck

Grant Colfax Tuller
Arr. by Donna Krieger

1. There was One who was will-ing to die in my stead, That a
2. He is ten-der and lov-ing and pa-tient with me, While He
3. I will cling to my Sav-iour and nev-er de-part— I will

soul so un-wor-thy might live; And the path to the cross He was will-ing to tread,
cleans-es my heart of the dross; But "there's no con-dem-na-tion"-I know I am free,
joy-ful-ly jour-ney each day. With a song on my lips and a song in my heart,

All the sins of my life to for-give.
For my sins are all nailed to the cross.
That my sins have been tak-en a-way.

Refrain

They are nailed to the cross, They are nailed to the cross, O how much He was will-ing to bear! With what an-guish and loss Je-sus went to the cross! But He car-ried my sins with Him there.

118 Hallelujah for the Blood

Mrs. C. H. M.
Mrs. C. H. Morris
Arr. & Rev. by Alfred B. Smith
1. Hal-le-lu-jah for the Blood, for the sin-cleans-ing foun-tain! For the Lamb has been slain, and the ran-som price paid. Ful-ly can-celed was the debt when on Cal-va-ry's moun-tain All the sins of this world up-on Je-sus were laid.
2. Hal-le-lu-jah for the Blood! Sing for joy, all ye na-tions, And re-joice that the work of re-demp-tion is done. Here is par-don free for all, and a per-fect sal-va-tion Thro' the sin-cleans-ing blood of the Cru-ci-fied One.
3. Hal-le-lu-jah for the Blood! Hal-le-lu-jah for-ev-er! We shall sing it a-new in the king-dom of God, Where the an-thems of de-light shall be si-lent, no, nev-er. Ev-er-more hal-le-lu-jah for Christ and the Blood!
p Chorus
There was no arm to save, there was no eye to pit-y,
cresc.
Un-til Je-sus, our Sav-iour, from glo-ry came down.
f
He was might-y to

save; He was strong to de - liv - er. He has brot us sal - va-tion, a
Coda-after last chorus
robe, and a crown. Hal-le - lu-jah, hal-le - lu-jah! Sing the tri-um-phant
rit.
strain. Hal-le - lu-jah for the Blood and the Lamb that was slain!
Hallelujah, What a Saviour!
119
Philip P. Bliss
Philip P. Bliss
1. "Man of Sor-rows!" what a name For the Son of God, who came
2. Bear-ing shame and scoff-ing rude, In my place con-demned He stood—
3. Guilt-y, vile and help-less we, Spot-less Lamb of God was He;
4. Lift-ed up was He to die, "It is fin-ished," was His cry;
5. When He comes, our glo-rious King, All His ran-somed home to bring,
Ru-ined sin-ners to re-claim! Hal-le-lu-jah, what a Sav-ior!
Sealed my par-don with His blood: Hal-le-lu-jah, what a Sav-ior!
Full a-tone-ment! can it be? Hal-le-lu-jah, what a Sav-ior!
Now in heav'n ex-alt-ed high: Hal-le-lu-jah, what a Sav-ior!
Then a-new this song we'll sing: Hal-le-lu-jah, what a Sav-ior!

120 Wounded for Me

W. G. Ovens &
Gladys Watkin Roberts
W. G. Ovens
1. Wound - ed for me, wound - ed for me, There on the cross
2. Dy - ing for me, dy - ing for me, There on the cross
3. Ris - en for me, ris - en for me, Up from the grave
4. Liv - ing for me, liv - ing for me, Up in the skies
5. Com - ing for me, com - ing for me, One day to earth
He was wound - ed for me; Gone my trans - gres - sions, and
He was dy - ing for me; Now in His death my re-
He has ris - en for me; Now ev - er - more from death's
He is liv - ing for me; Dai - ly He's plead - ing and
He is com - ing for me; Then with what joy His dear
now I am free, All be-cause Je - sus was wound-ed for me.
demp-tion I see, All be-cause Je - sus was dy - ing for me.
sting I am free, All be-cause Je - sus has ris - en for me.
pray - ing for me, All be-cause Je - sus is liv - ing for me.
face I shall see, Oh, how I praise Him, He's com - ing for me.
121 Alas, and Did My Saviour Bleed
Isaac Watts
Hugh Wilson
1. A - las, and did my Sav - iour bleed? And did my Sov - ereign die?
2. Was it for sins that I had done He groaned up - on the tree?
3. Well might the sun in dark - ness hide, And shut His glo - ries in,
4. Thus might I hide my sham - ed face While His dear cross ap - pears,
5. But drops of grief can ne'er re - pay The debt of love I owe:

Would He devote that sacred head For such an one as I?
Amazing pity! Grace unknown! And love beyond degree!
When Christ, the mighty Maker, died For man, the creature's sin.
Dissolve my heart in thankfulness, And melt mine eyes to tears.
Here, Lord, I give myself to Thee; 'Tis all that I can do. A-MEN.
Nothing But the Blood
122
Robert Lowry
Robert Lowry
1. What can wash away my sin? Nothing but the blood of Jesus;
2. For my pardon this I see—Nothing but the blood of Jesus;
3. Nothing can for sin atone—Nothing but the blood of Jesus;
4. This is all my hope and peace—Nothing but the blood of Jesus;
What can make me whole again? Nothing but the blood of Jesus.
For my cleansing, this my plea—Nothing but the blood of Jesus.
Naught of good that I have done—Nothing but the blood of Jesus.
This is all my righteousness—Nothing but the blood of Jesus.
Refrain
O! precious is the flow That makes me white as snow;
No other fount I know, Nothing but the blood of Jesus.

123 Blessed Be the Fountain

Eden R. Latta
Henry S. Perkins
1. Bless-ed be the foun-tain of Blood, To a world of sin-ners re-vealed.
2. Thor-ny was the crown that He wore, And the Cross His bod-y o'er-came;
3. Fa-ther, I have wandered from Thee; Of-ten has my heart gone a-stray.
Bless-ed be the dear Son of God— On-ly by His stripes we are healed.
Griev-ous were the sor-rows He bore, But He suf-fered thus not in vain.
Crim-son do my sins seem to me— Wa-ter can-not wash them a-way.
Tho' I've wandered far from His fold, Bring-ing to my heart pain and woe,
May I to that foun-tain be led, Made to cleanse my sins here be-low;
Je-sus, to that foun-tain of Thine, Lean-ing on Thy prom-ise I go;
Wash me in the blood of the Lamb,
Wash me in the blood that He shed, And I shall be whit-er than snow.
Cleanse me by Thy wash-ing di-vine,
REFRAIN
Whit - er than the snow,
Whit-er than the snow, whit-er than the snow,
Whit - er
Whit-er than the snow,

than the snow; Wash me in the blood of the
whit - er than the snow;

rit.
Lamb, And I shall be whit - er than snow.
of the Lamb,

Must Jesus Bear the Cross Alone? 124

Thomas Shepherd

George N. Allen

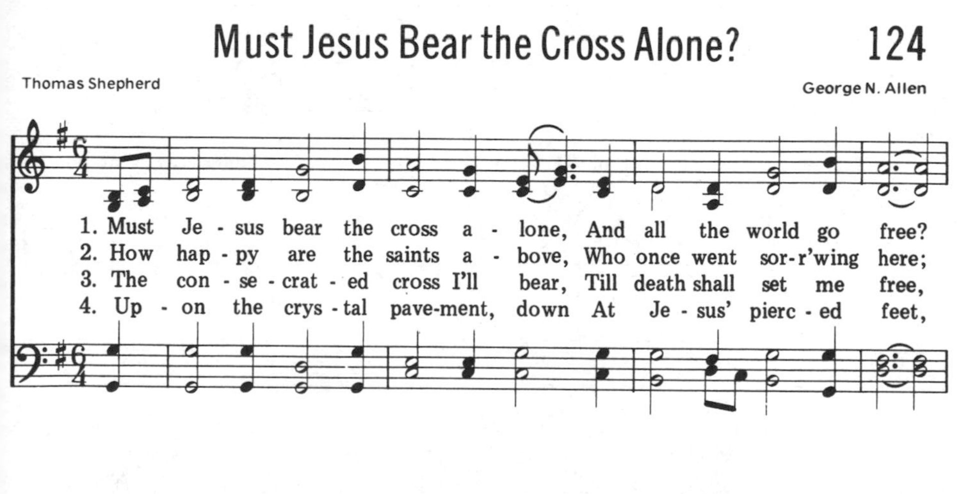
1. Must Je - sus bear the cross a - lone, And all the world go free?
2. How hap - py are the saints a - bove, Who once went sor-r'wing here;
3. The con - se - crat - ed cross I'll bear, Till death shall set me free,
4. Up - on the crys - tal pave-ment, down At Je - sus' pierc - ed feet,

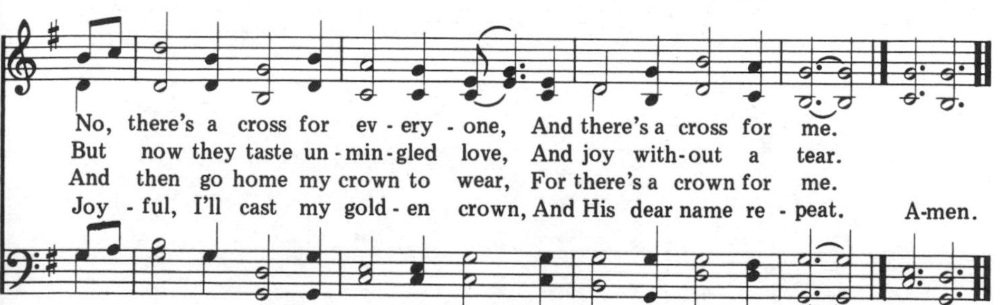
No, there's a cross for ev - ery - one, And there's a cross for me.
But now they taste un - min - gled love, And joy with - out a tear.
And then go home my crown to wear, For there's a crown for me.
Joy - ful, I'll cast my gold - en crown, And His dear name re - peat. A-men.

125 Power in the Blood

Lewis E. Jones | Lewis E. Jones

1. Would you be free from the bur - den of sin? There's pow'r in the blood,
2. Would you be free from your pas - sion and pride? There's pow'r in the blood,
3. Would you be whit - er, much whit - er than snow? There's pow'r in the blood,
4. Would you do serv - ice for Je - sus your King? There's pow'r in the blood,

pow'r in the blood; Would you o'er e - vil a vic - to - ry win? There's
pow'r in the blood; Come for a cleans - ing to Cal - va - ry's tide; There's
pow'r in the blood; Sin - stains are lost in its life - giv - ing flow; There's
pow'r in the blood; Would you live dai - ly His prais - es to sing? There's

won - der-ful pow'r in the blood.

REFRAIN

There is pow'r, pow'r, Wonder-working pow'r
there is

In the blood of the Lamb; There is pow'r, pow'r,
In the blood of the Lamb; there is

Won - der - work - ing pow'r In the pre - cious blood of the Lamb.

The Blood Will Never Lose Its Power 126

Civilla D. Martin
W. Stillman Martin
1. The blood that Je-sus once shed for me, As my Re-deem-er up-
2. It gives us ac-cess to God on high; From far - off plac-es it
3. It is a shel-ter for rich and poor; It is to heav-en the
4. And when with all the Blood-washed throng We sing in glo - ry re-
on the tree; The Blood that setteth the pris -'ner free Will nev - er lose its
brings us nigh To pre-cious blessings that nev - er die. It will nev - er lose its
o - pen door, The sin - ner's mer-it for - ev - er-more. It will nev - er lose its
demption's song, We'll pass the glo-ri-ous truth a-long: It has nev - er lost its
pow'r.
REFRAIN
It will nev- er lose its pow'r. It will nev - er lose its pow'r.
ho - ly pow'r.
ho-ly pow'r.
The Blood that cleans -es from all sin Will nev-er lose its pow'r.

127 Nor Silver, Nor Gold

James M. Gray

Daniel B. Towner

1. Nor sil - ver nor gold hath ob-tained my re-demp-tion; No rich - es of earth could have saved my poor soul. The blood of the cross is my on - ly foun-da - tion; The death of my Sav-iour now mak - eth me whole.
2. Nor sil - ver nor gold hath ob-tained my re-demp-tion; The guilt on my con - science too heav - y had grown. The blood of the cross is my on - ly foun-da - tion; The death of my Sav-iour could on - ly a - tone.
3. Nor sil - ver nor gold hath ob-tained my re-demp-tion; The ho - ly com - mand - ment for - bade me draw near. The blood of the cross is my on - ly foun-da - tion; The death of my Sav-iour re - mov - eth my fear.
4. Nor sil - ver nor gold hath ob-tained my re-demp-tion; The way in - to heav - en could not thus be bought. The blood of the cross is my on - ly foun-da - tion; The death of my Sav-iour re-demp-tion hath wrought.
REFRAIN
I am re - deemed, but not with sil - ver;
I am re-deemed, I am re - deemed, but not with sil - ver;
I am bought, but not with gold; Bought with a
I am bought, I am bought, but not with gold;

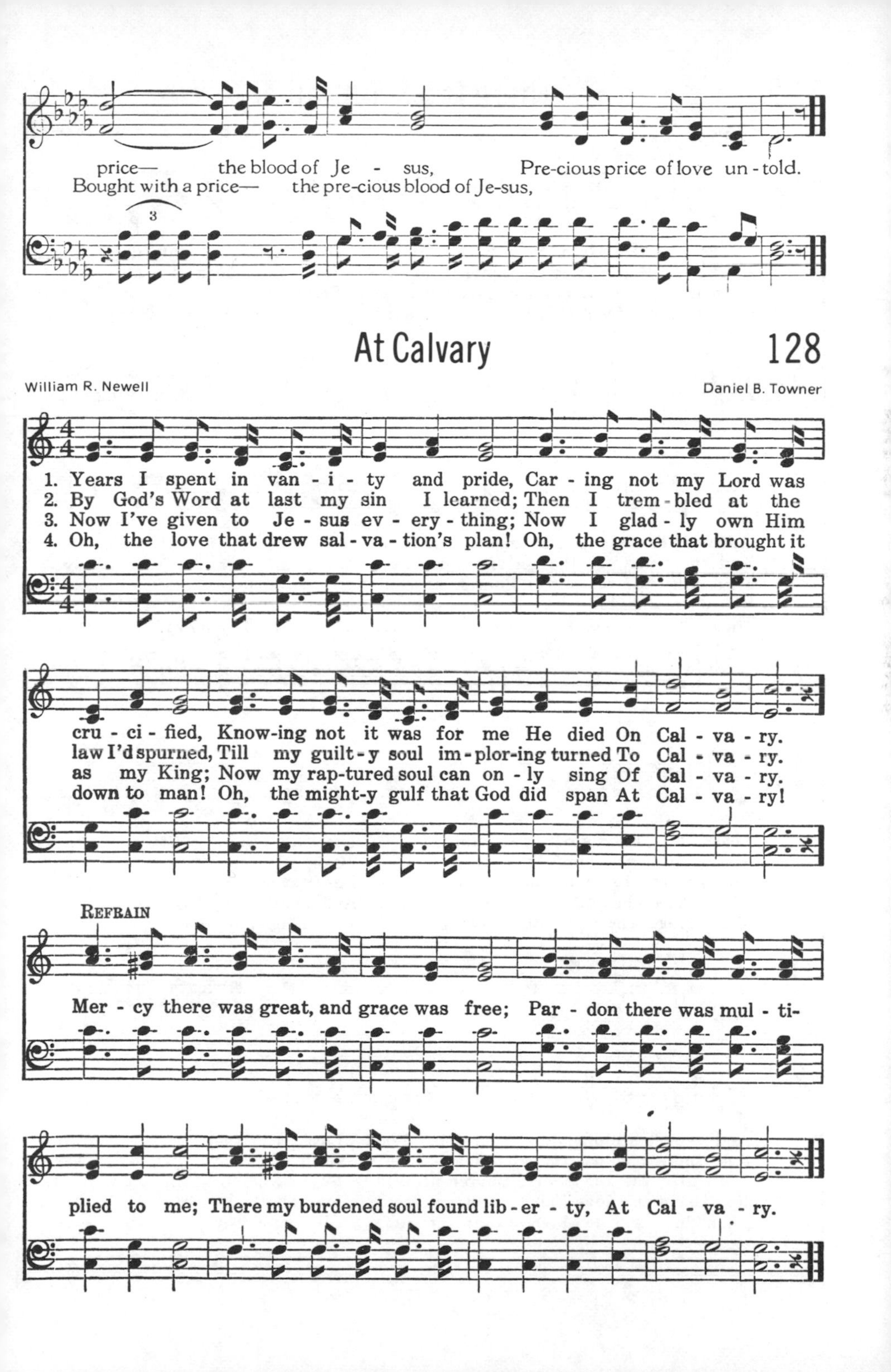
price— the blood of Je - sus, Pre-cious price of love un - told.
Bought with a price— the pre-cious blood of Je-sus,
3
At Calvary
128
William R. Newell
Daniel B. Towner
1. Years I spent in van - i - ty and pride, Car - ing not my Lord was cru - ci - fied, Know-ing not it was for me He died On Cal - va - ry.
2. By God's Word at last my sin I learned; Then I trem - bled at the law I'd spurned, Till my guilt - y soul im - plor-ing turned To Cal - va - ry.
3. Now I've given to Je - sus ev - ery - thing; Now I glad - ly own Him as my King; Now my rap-tured soul can on - ly sing Of Cal - va - ry.
4. Oh, the love that drew sal - va - tion's plan! Oh, the grace that brought it down to man! Oh, the might-y gulf that God did span At Cal - va - ry!
Refrain
Mer - cy there was great, and grace was free; Par - don there was mul - ti - plied to me; There my burdened soul found lib - er - ty, At Cal - va - ry.

129 There Is a Fountain

William Cowper — American Melody

1. There is a foun-tain filled with blood Drawn from Im-man-uel's veins,
2. The dy-ing thief re-joiced to see That foun-tain in his day,
3. Dear dy-ing Lamb, Thy pre-cious blood Shall nev-er lose its pow'r,
4. E'er since by faith I saw the stream Thy flow-ing wounds sup-ply,
5. When this poor lisp-ing, stam-m'ring tongue Lies si-lent in the grave,
And sin-ners plunged be-neath that flood Lose all their guilt-y stains:
And there may I, though vile as he, Wash all my sins a-way:
Till all the ran-somed Church of God Be saved to sin no more:
Re-deem-ing love has been my theme And shall be till I die:
Then in a no-bler, sweet-er song, I'll sing Thy pow'r to save:
Lose all their guilt-y stains, Lose all their guilt-y stains;
Wash all my sins a-way, Wash all my sins a-way;
Be saved to sin no more, Be saved to sin no more;
And shall be till I die, And shall be till I die;
I'll sing Thy pow'r to save, I'll sing Thy pow'r to save;
And sin-ners plunged be-neath that flood Lose all their guilt-y stains.
And there may I, though vile as he, Wash all my sins a-way.
Till all the ran-somed Church of God Be saved to sin no more.
Re-deem-ing love has been my theme And shall be till I die.
Then in a no-bler, sweet-er song, I'll sing Thy pow'r to save.

No Blood, No Altar Now

Horatius Bonar

Anon
& Alfred B. Smith

1. No blood, no al - tar now The sac - ri - fice is o'er!
2. We thank thee for the blood, The blood of Christ, Thy Son:
3. We thank thee for the grace, Des - cend - ing from a - bove,
4. We thank thee for the hope, So glad, and sure, and clear;
5. We thank thee for the crown Of glo - ry and of life;
No flame, no smoke as - cends on high. The Lamb is slain no more;
The blood by which our peace is made, Our vic - to - ry is won:
That ov - er-flows our wid - est guilt E - ter - nal Fa - ther's love.
It holds the droop - ing spir - it up Till the long dawn ap - pear;
'Tis no poor with - 'ring wreath of earth, Man's prize in mor - tal strife;
But rich - er blood has flowed from no - bler veins,
Great vic - to - ry o'er hell, and sin and woe
Love of the Fa - ther's ev - er - last - ing Son,
Fair hope! with what a sun - shine does it cheer
'Tis in - cor - rup - ti - ble as is the throne,
To purge the soul from guilt, and cleanse the red - est stains.
That needs no sec - ond fight, and leaves no sec - ond foe.
Love of the Ho - ly Ghost, Je - ho - vah, Three in One.
Our rough - est path on earth, our drear - iest de - sert here.
The king - dom of our God and His In - car - nate Son.

131 At the Cross

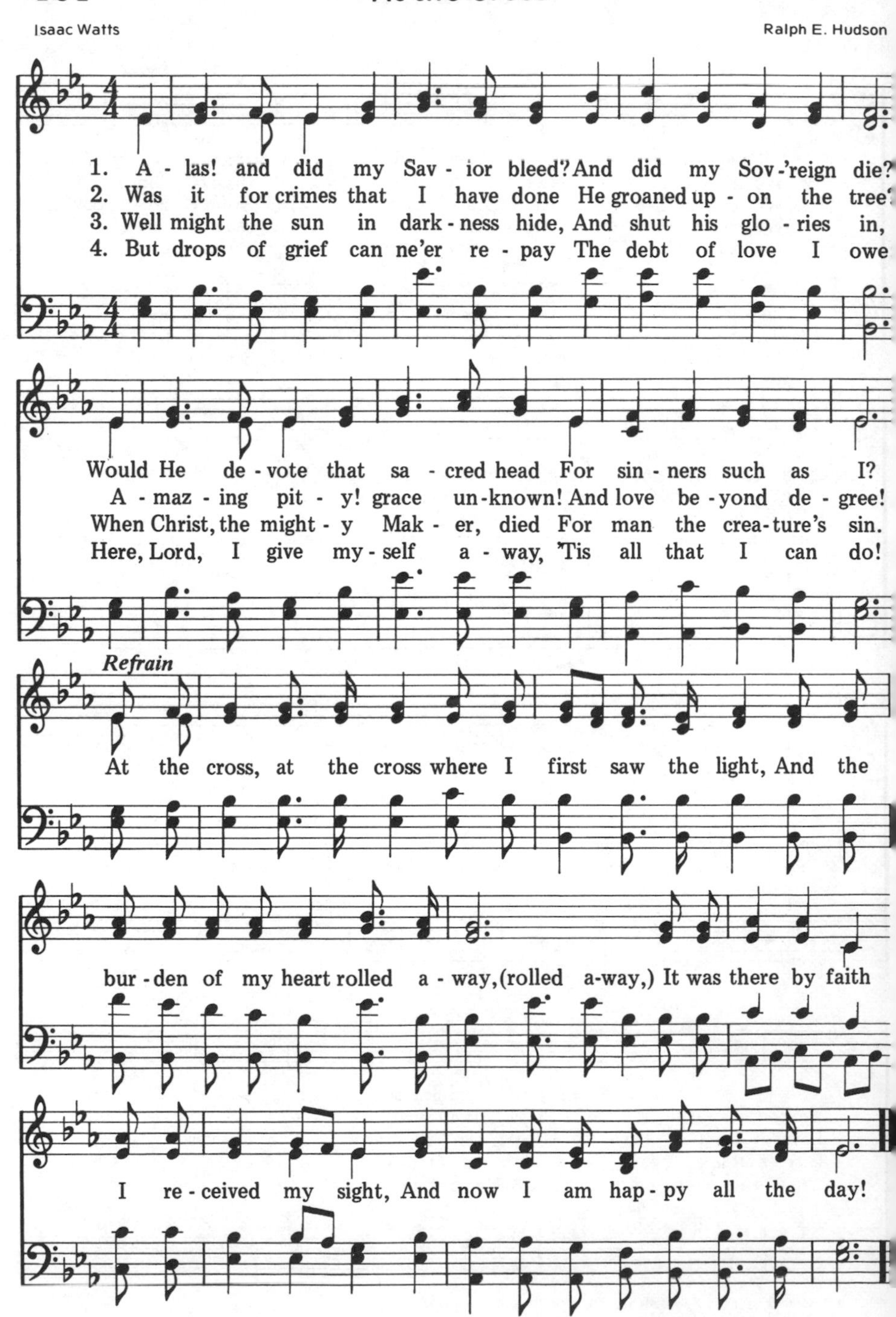

Isaac Watts
Ralph E. Hudson
1. A - las! and did my Sav - ior bleed? And did my Sov-'reign die?
2. Was it for crimes that I have done He groaned up - on the tree?
3. Well might the sun in dark - ness hide, And shut his glo - ries in,
4. But drops of grief can ne'er re - pay The debt of love I owe
Would He de - vote that sa - cred head For sin - ners such as I?
A - maz - ing pit - y! grace un - known! And love be - yond de - gree!
When Christ, the might - y Mak - er, died For man the crea - ture's sin.
Here, Lord, I give my - self a - way, 'Tis all that I can do!
Refrain
At the cross, at the cross where I first saw the light, And the
bur - den of my heart rolled a - way, (rolled a - way,) It was there by faith
I re - ceived my sight, And now I am hap - py all the day!

Christ the Lord is Risen Today

Charles Wesley

Arr. from "Lyra Davidica"

1. Christ the Lord is risen to - day, Al - - - - - le - lu - ia!
2. Love's re - deem - ing work is done, Al - - - - - le - lu - ia!
3. Lives a - gain our glo - rious King; Al - - - - - le - lu - ia!
4. Soar we now where Christ has led, Al - - - - - le - le - ia!

Sons of men and an - gels say: Al - - - - - le - lu - ia!
Fought the fight, the bat - tle won; Al - - - - - le - lu - ia!
Where, O death, is now thy sting? Al - - - - - le - lu - ia!
Fol - lowing our ex - alt - ed Head; Al - - - - - le - lu - ia!

Raise your joys and tri - umphs high, Al - - - - - le - lu - ia!
Death in vain for - bids Him rise; Al - - - - - le - lu - ia!
Dy - ing once, He all doth save: Al - - - - - le - lu - ia!
Made like Him, like Him we rise; Al - - - - - le - lu - ia!

Sing, ye heavens, and earth re - ply, Al - - - - - le - lu - ia!
Christ has o - pened Par - a - dise. Al - - - - - le - lu - ia!
Where thy vic - to - ry, O grave? Al - - - - - le - lu - ia!
Ours the cross, the grave, the skies. Al - - - - - le - lu - ia! A-MEN.

133 Christ Arose

Robert Lowry

Robert Lowry

1. Low in the grave He lay—Je-sus my Sav-ior! Wait-ing the com-ing day— Je-sus my Lord!
2. Vain-ly they watch His bed—Je-sus my Sav-ior! Vain-ly they seal the dead— Je-sus my Lord!
3. Death can-not keep his prey—Je-sus my Sav-ior! He tore the bars a-way— Je-sus my Lord!

Refrain

Up from the grave He a-rose, He a-rose, With a might-y tri-umph o'er His foes; He a-rose! He a-rose a vic-tor from the dark do-main, And He lives for-ev-er with His saints to reign. He a-rose! He a-rose! He a-rose! He a-rose! Hal-le-lu-jah! Christ a-rose!

Thine is the Glory

Edmond L. Budry
Trans. by Richard B. Hoyle
George Frederick Handel
1. Thine is the glo - ry, Ris - en, con-qu'ring Son; End - less is the
2. Lo! Je - sus meets us, Ris - en, from the tomb; Lov - ing - ly He
3. No more we doubt Thee, Glo-rious Prince of Life! Life is naught with-
vic - t'ry Thou o'er death hast won. An - gels in bright rai - ment
greets us, Scat - ters fear and gloom; Let His church with glad - ness
out Thee; Help us in our strife; Make us more than con-qu'rors,
Rolled the stone a - way, Kept the fold - ed grave-clothes
Hymns of tri - umph sing, For her Lord now liv - eth;
Through Thy death - less love; Bring us safe through Jor - dan
Refrain
Where Thy bod - y lay.
Death hath lost its sting. Thine is the glo - ry, Ris - en, con-qu'ring Son;
To Thy home a - bove.
End - less is the vic - t'ry Thou o'er death hast won. A - men.

135 Welcome, Happy Morning!

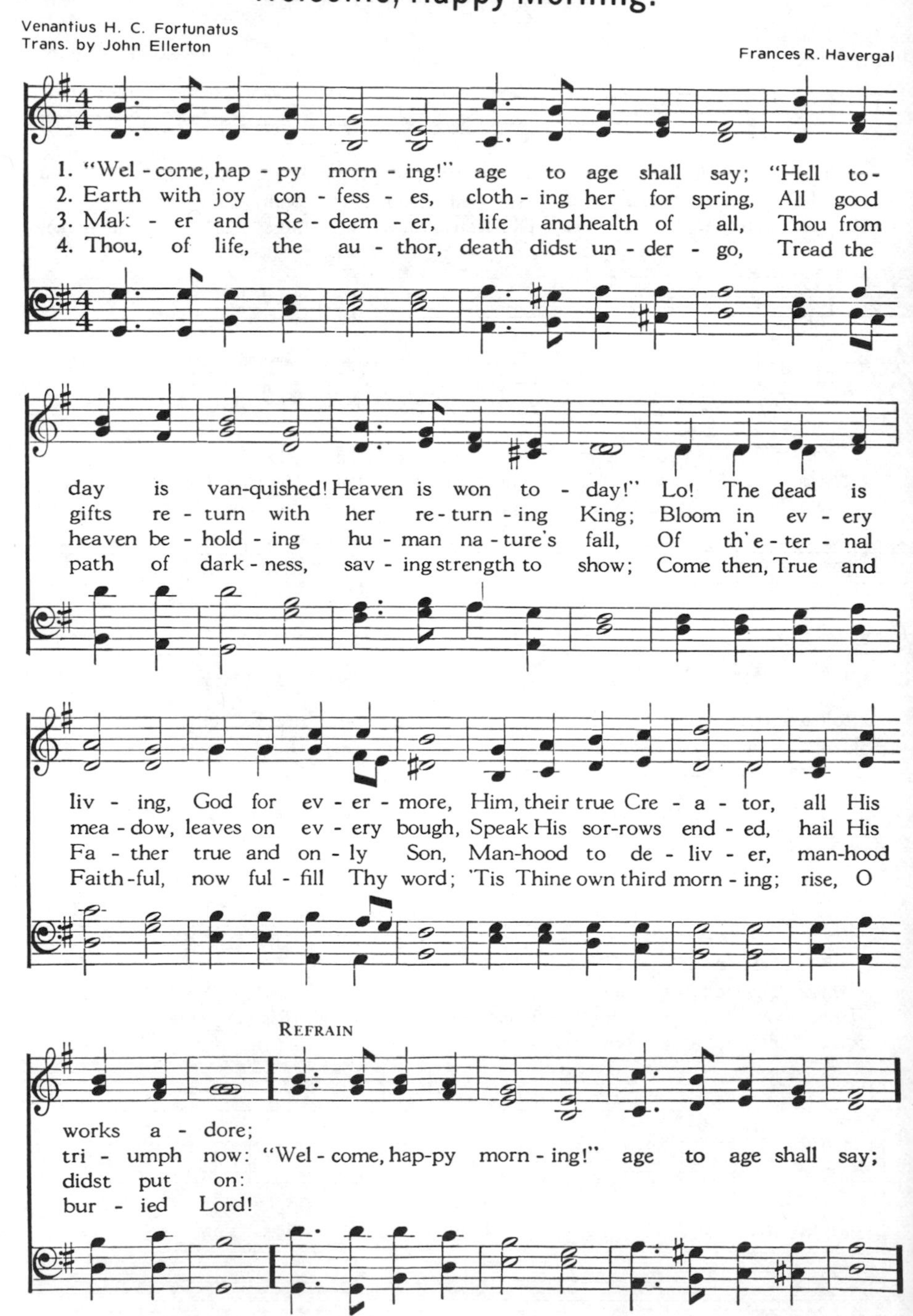
Venantius H. C. Fortunatus
Trans. by John Ellerton
Frances R. Havergal
1. "Wel - come, hap - py morn - ing!" age to age shall say; "Hell to-
2. Earth with joy con - fess - es, cloth - ing her for spring, All good
3. Mak - er and Re - deem - er, life and health of all, Thou from
4. Thou, of life, the au - thor, death didst un - der - go, Tread the
day is van-quished! Heaven is won to - day!" Lo! The dead is
gifts re - turn with her re - turn - ing King; Bloom in ev - ery
heaven be - hold - ing hu - man na - ture's fall, Of th' e - ter - nal
path of dark - ness, sav - ing strength to show; Come then, True and
liv - ing, God for ev - er - more, Him, their true Cre - a - tor, all His
mea - dow, leaves on ev - ery bough, Speak His sor-rows end - ed, hail His
Fa - ther true and on - ly Son, Man-hood to de - liv - er, man-hood
Faith-ful, now ful - fill Thy word; 'Tis Thine own third morn - ing; rise, O
works a - dore;
tri - umph now:
didst put on:
bur - ied Lord!
REFRAIN
"Wel - come, hap-py morn - ing!" age to age shall say;

"Hell to - day is van-quished! Heaven is won to - day!" A-MEN.
The Lord is Risen
136
William P. MacKay
Alfred B. Smith
1. The Lord is ris'n; and death's dark judg-ment flood I passed, in Him who bo't us with His blood. The Lord is ris'n: we stand be-yond the doom Of all our sin, thro' Je - sus' emp - ty tomb.
2. The Lord is ris'n; with Him we al - so rose, And in His grave see vanquished all our foes. The Lord is ris'n: be-yond the judg-ment land, In Him, in res - ur - rec - tion - life we stand.
3. The Lord is ris'n; and is gone on be - fore. We long to see Him, and to sin no more. The Lord is ris'n: our tri-umph-shout shall be, "Thou hast pre-vailed! Thy peo - ple, Lord are free!"

137 He Lives

Alfred H. Ackley Alfred H. Ackley

1. I serve a ris - en Sav-iour, He's in the world to -day; I know that He is
2. In all the world a-round me I see His lov- ing care, And tho' my heart grows
3. Rejoice, rejoice, O Christian, lift up your voice and sing E - ter - nal hal - le-

liv - ing, what-ev - er men may say; I see His hand of mer - cy, I
wea-ry, I nev - er will de - spair; I know that He is lead - ing thro'
lu - jahs to Je - sus Christ the King! The Hope of all who seek Him, the

hear His voice of cheer, And just the time I need Him He's al - ways near.
all the storm-y blast, The day of His ap - pear - ing will come at last.
Help of all who find, None oth-er is so lov - ing, so good and kind.

REFRAIN

He lives, He lives, Christ Je - sus lives to - day! He walks with me and
He lives, He lives,

talks with me a - long life's nar - row way. He lives, He lives, sal-
He lives, He lives,

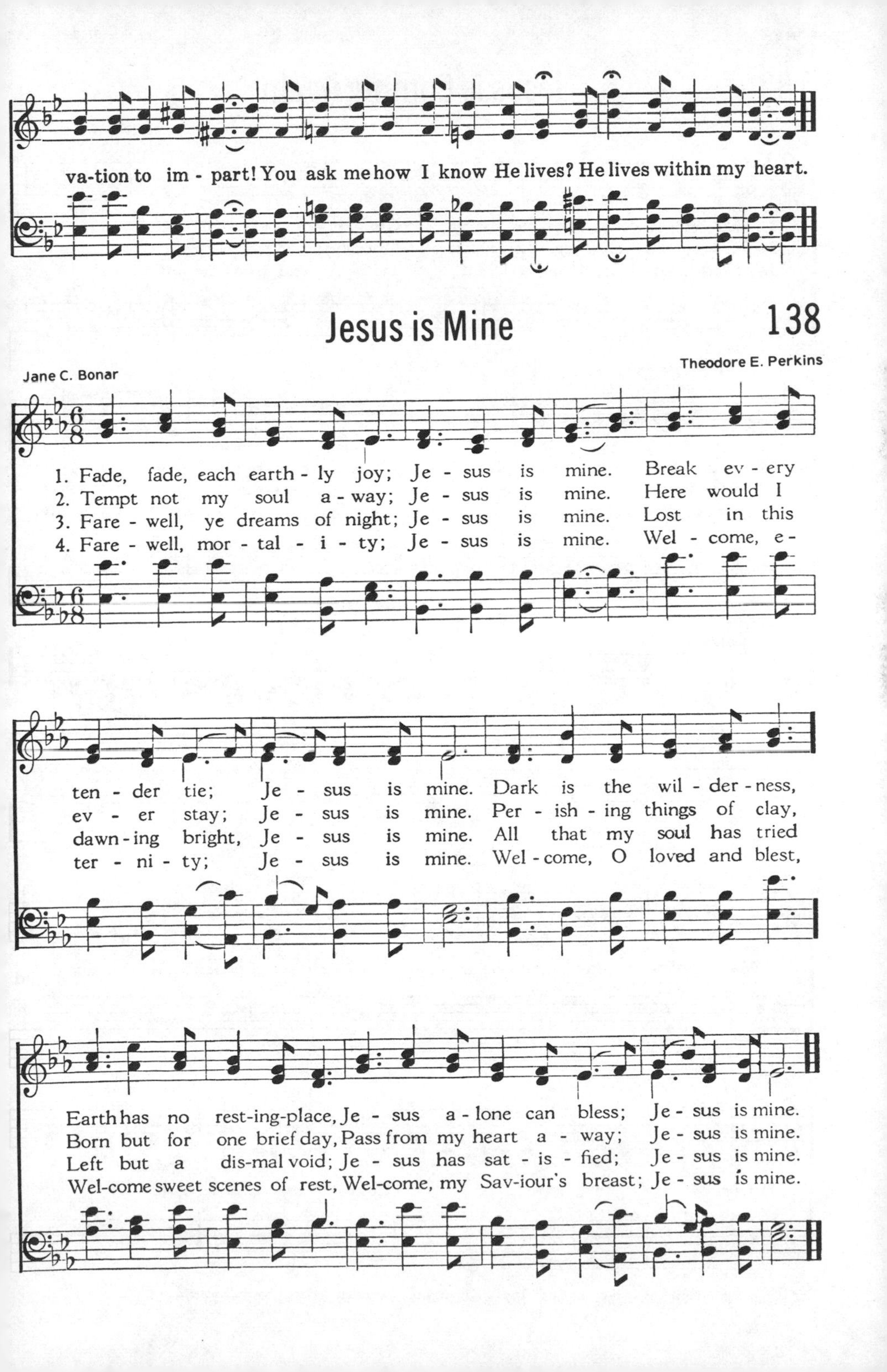
va-tion to im - part! You ask me how I know He lives? He lives within my heart.
Jesus is Mine
138
Jane C. Bonar
Theodore E. Perkins
1. Fade, fade, each earth - ly joy; Je - sus is mine. Break ev - ery
2. Tempt not my soul a - way; Je - sus is mine. Here would I
3. Fare - well, ye dreams of night; Je - sus is mine. Lost in this
4. Fare - well, mor - tal - i - ty; Je - sus is mine. Wel - come, e -
ten - der tie; Je - sus is mine. Dark is the wil - der - ness,
ev - er stay; Je - sus is mine. Per - ish - ing things of clay,
dawn - ing bright, Je - sus is mine. All that my soul has tried
ter - ni - ty; Je - sus is mine. Wel - come, O loved and blest,
Earth has no rest-ing-place, Je - sus a - lone can bless; Je - sus is mine.
Born but for one brief day, Pass from my heart a - way; Je - sus is mine.
Left but a dis-mal void; Je - sus has sat - is - fied; Je - sus is mine.
Wel-come sweet scenes of rest, Wel-come, my Sav-iour's breast; Je - sus is mine.

139 Jesus is Coming Again

John W. Peterson | John W. Peterson

1. Mar-vel-ous mes-sage we bring, Glo - ri-ous car - ol we sing,
2. For - est and flow-er ex-claim, Moun-tain and mead-ow the same,
3. Stand-ing be-fore Him at last, Tri - al and trou-ble all past,
Won-der-ful word of the King: Je-sus is com-ing a - gain! (a-gain!)
All earth and heav-en pro - claim: Je-sus is com-ing a - gain! (a-gain!)
Crowns at His feet we will cast: Je-sus is com-ing a - gain! (a-gain!)
CHORUS
Unison
Com - ing a - gain, Com - ing a - gain;
May - be morn - ing, may - be noon, May - be eve-ning and may-be soon!
Com - ing a - gain, Com - ing a - gain;

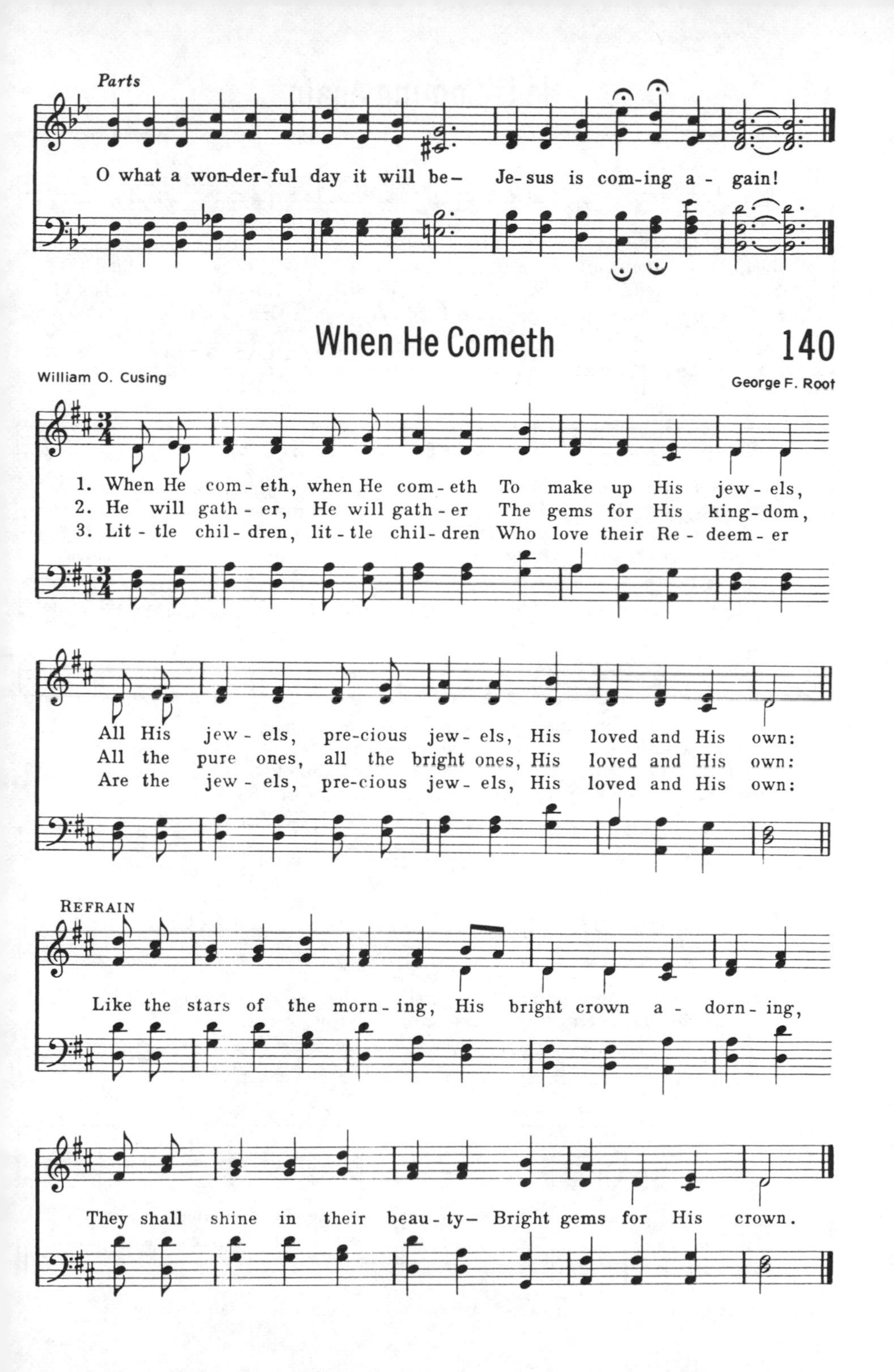
Parts
O what a won-der-ful day it will be- Je-sus is com-ing a-gain!
When He Cometh
140
William O. Cusing
George F. Root
1. When He com-eth, when He com-eth To make up His jew-els,
2. He will gath-er, He will gath-er The gems for His king-dom,
3. Lit-tle chil-dren, lit-tle chil-dren Who love their Re-deem-er
All His jew-els, pre-cious jew-els, His loved and His own:
All the pure ones, all the bright ones, His loved and His own:
Are the jew-els, pre-cious jew-els, His loved and His own:
REFRAIN
Like the stars of the morn-ing, His bright crown a-dorn-ing,
They shall shine in their beau-ty- Bright gems for His crown.

141 He is Coming Again

Mabel Johnston Camp | Mebel Johnston Camp

1. Lift up your heads, pil-grims a - wea-ry! See day's ap-proach now
2. Dark was the night— sin warred a-gainst us! Heav-y the load of
3. O bless-ed hope! O bliss-ful prom-ise! Fill-ing our hearts with
4. E - ven so, come, pre-cious Lord Je - sus! Cre - a - tion waits re -
crim-son the sky; Night shad-ows flee, and your Be-lov-ed, A -
sor - row we bore; But now we see signs of His com-ing— Our
rap - ture di - vine; O day of days! hail Thy ap-pear-ing! Thy
demp-tion to see; Caught up in clouds, soon we shall meet Thee— O
wait-ed with long-ing, at last draw-eth nigh.
hearts glow with-in us, joy's cup run-neth o'er!
tran-scend-ent glo-ry for - ev - er shall shine!
bless-ed as - sur-ance, for - ev - er with Thee!
CHORUS
He is com-ing a - gain, He is com-ing a-gain, The ver-y same Je-sus re - ject-ed of men;
He is com-ing a - gain, He is com-ing a-gain, With pow'r and great glo-ry, He is com-ing a-gain!

Is It the Crowning Day

Henry Ostrom

Charles H. Marsh

1. Je - sus may come to - day, Glad day! Glad day! And I would see my Friend; Dan - gers and trou - bles would end If Je - sus should come to - day.
2. I may go home to - day, Glad day! Glad day! Seem - eth I hear their song; Hail to the ra - di - ant throng! If I should go home to - day.
3. Why should I anx - ious be? Glad day! Glad day! Lights ap - pear on the shore, Storms will af - fright nev - er - more, For He is "at hand" to - day.
4. Faith - ful I'll be to - day, Glad day! Glad day! And I will free - ly tell Why I should love Him so well, For He is my all to - day.

Refrain

Glad day! Glad day! Is it the crown-ing day? I'll live for to - day, nor anx - ious be, Je - sus my Lord I soon shall see; Glad day! Glad day! Is it the crown - ing day?

143 Christ Is Coming Back Again

Oswald J. Smith

Alfred B. Smith

1. He will come the Lord of Glo - ry, From His home be-yond the skies;
2. With the trump of God re sound-ing, And a shout of vic - to - ry,
3. Day of days, we wait with long-ing, 'Mid a world of sin and woe,
He will come, oh, won-drous sto - ry! For His prom-ise nev - er dies;
He will burst the clouds a sun - der, Sweep-ing on tri - um-phant-ly;
Watch-ing for the blest ap - pear - ing Of the One who loves us so;
And we'll hail Him "Blest re - deem - er, Lamb of God for sin-ners slain,"
And the saints will quick-ly gath - er, As the dead in Christ a - rise,
Home at last and re - u - nit - ed, Far a - bove the things of time,
And we'll bow in ad - o - ra - tion, While we sing the glad re - frain.
With a shout of joy-ful greet-ing, To the Sav-iour in the skies.
'Twill be glo-ry, glo-ry, glo - ry, 'Mid the realms of light sub - lime.

Chorus
Hal - le - lu - jah! Hal - le - lu - jah! Prince of
Hal-le-lu-jah! Hal-le-lu - jah!
Peace and King of Kings! Hal - le - lu - jah! Hal-le -
Prince of Peace and King of Kings! Hal-le-lu-jah!
lu - jah! Let the courts of heav - en ring! Laud and
Hal - le - lu-jah! the courts of heav - en ring!
hon- or, praise and glo - ry To the Lamb for sin-ners slain; Hal-le-
lu - jah, Hal - le - lu - jah! Christ is com - ing back a - gain!

144 Christ Returneth!

H. L. Turner

James McGranahan

1. It may be at morn, when the day is a - wak - ing, When
2. It may be at mid - day, it may be at twi - light, It
3. While hosts cry Ho - san - na, from heav - en de - scend - ing, With
4. O joy! O de - light! should we go with - out dy - ing, No
sun-light thru dark-ness and shad-ow is break-ing, That Je - sus will
may be, per-chance, that the black-ness of mid - night Will burst in - to
glo - ri - fied saints and the an - gels at - tend - ing, With grace on His
sick-ness, no sad-ness, no dread and no cry - ing, Caught up thru the
come in the full - ness of glo - ry To re-ceive from the world His own.
light in the blaze of His glo - ry, When Je - sus re - ceives His own.
brow, like a ha - lo of glo - ry, Will Je - sus re - ceive His own.
clouds with our Lord in - to glo - ry, When Je - sus re - ceives His own.
Chorus
O Lord Je-sus, how long, how long Ere we shout the glad song–Christ re-
turn-eth! Hal-le-lu-jah! Hal-le-lu-jah! A - men, Hal-le-lu-jah! A - men.

Lo, He Comes, With Clouds Descending

John Cennick
Alfred B. Smith

1. Lo, He comes, with clouds de - scend - ing, Once for our sal - va - tion slain; Thou - sand an - gel - hosts at - tend - ing Swell the tri - umph of His train: Al - le - lu - ia! Al - le - lu - ia! Christ, the Lord, re - turns to reign.
2. Ev - 'ry eye shall then be - hold Him Robed in might- y maj - es - ty; Those who set at naught and sold Him, Pierced, and nailed Him to the Tree, Al - le - lu - ia! Al - le - lu - ia! Shall the true Mes - si - ah see.
3. Now re - demp - tion, long ex - pect - ed, See in sol - emn pomp ap - pear: All His saints, by men re - ject - ed, Now shall meet Him in the air: Al - le - lu - ia! Al - le - lu - ia! See the day of God ap - pear.
4. Yea, A - men; let all a - dore Thee, High on Thine e - ter - nal throne; Sav - ior, take the pow'r and glo - ry; Claim the king - doms for Thine own: Al - le - lu - ia! Al - le - lu - ia! Thou shalt reign, and Thou a - lone.

146 Coming Soon

Alfred B. Smith
Avis B. Christiansen
Chorus M. T. MacPhearson
1. The signs of the times tell of Christ's soon re-turn-ing! The tho't stirs our hearts with a deep sense of yearn-ing. How long 'til the trump shall re - sound thro the skies, And we shall be called to a - rise.
2. A place up in Hea-ven He now is pre-par-ing, And soon in His glo - ry His saints shall be shar - ing. Per - haps the glad sum-mons to - day we shall hear, To meet our dear Lord in the air!
3. The night is far spent, how we long for the dawn-ing! Our hearts thrill with joy at the hope of His com-ing Be read - y, be watch-ing this may be the day That Je - sus will catch us a - way!
Chorus M.T.M.
Unison
Com - ing soon; yes, He's com - ing soon.
Parts
He went a-way to pre - pare us a place, and we'll all gath-er there saved by

Unison
His match-less grace; For He's com - ing soon; yes, He's
Parts
com - ing soon. He'll shout from the air and we'll
all meet Him there, for He's com - ing soon.
the Sav-iour is com - ing soon, com-ing soon.
In a Moment
147
From "Our Hope"
Alt. by A. B. S.
Lewis S. Chafer
1. A mo-ment more, and I may be Caught up in glo - ry, Lord, with Thee;
2. A mo-ment more! earth left be-hind; Our bod-ies their re-demp-tion find;
3. A mo-ment more! what joy to wear Thy like-ness, Sav - iour, and to share
4. A mo-ment more! up - on Thy throne; Thy place by right then made Thine own;
5. A mo-ment more! Oh, can it be? One mo-ment bring such joy to me?
Oh, rap-tured sight! Thy face to see For - ev - er - more.
Our souls, the prize for which they pined With great de - sire!
With Thee, the peace pre-pared us there Where Thou are gone!
Thou wilt not fill that seat a - lone, But with Thy saints.
O joy of joys, to be with Thee! Our Sav - iour Lord!
© Copyright 1975 by Alfred B. Smith in "Victorious Life Hymns". All rights reserved.

148 The Comforter Has Come

Frank Bottome

William J. Kirkpatrick

1. O spread the ti-dings 'round, wher-ev - er man is found, Wher-ev - er hu-man
2. The long, long night is past, the morn-ing breaks at last, And hushed the dreadful
3. Lo, the great King of kings, with heal-ing in His wings, To ev - 'ry cap-tive
4. O bound-less love di - vine! how shall this tongue of mine To wond'ring mor-tals
hearts and hu - man woes a-bound; Let ev-'ry Christian tongue pro-claim the joy-ful
wail and fu - ry of the blast, As o'er the gold-en hills the day ad-vanc-es
soul a full de-liv'rance brings; And thro' the va-cant cells the song of tri-umph
tell the matchless grace di-vine—That I, a child of hell, should in His im - age
sound: The Com-fort - er has come!
fast! The Com-fort - er has come!
rings; The Com-fort - er has come!
shine! The Com-fort - er has come!
Chorus
The Com-fort-er has come, the Com-fort-er has
come! The Ho - ly Ghost from Heav'n, the Fa-ther's promise giv'n; O spread the
ti-dings 'round, wher-ev - er man is found—The Com - fort - er has come!

'Tis the Blessed Holy Spirit 149

H. J. Zelly
Ed. by A.B.S.

M. L. McPhail
Arr. by Alred B. Smith

1. Who is this that, like the sun - shine, Warms my
2. Who is this that fills with glad - ness, Drives a -
3. Who is this that gives me free - dom For my
4. Who is this that burns with - in me Like a
trust - ing heart to - day, Fills my soul with light and
way all anx - ious care, Scat - ters dark - ness, gives me
Lord to work and speak, Sends me out on lov - ing
flame of ho - ly fire, Pur - i - fies my will - ing
beau - ty, Drives the shad - ows far a - way?
com - fort, And a new de - light in pray'r?
er - rands, As the wan - d'ring ones I seek?
spir - it, Gives me now my one de - sire?
Chorus
'Tis the bless - ed Ho - ly Spir - it, Prom - ised by the Lord di - vine;
'Tis the pen - te - cos - tal bless - ing, Fill - ing this glad heart of mine.

150 Spirit of God, Descend Upon My Heart

George Croly

Frederick C. Atkinson

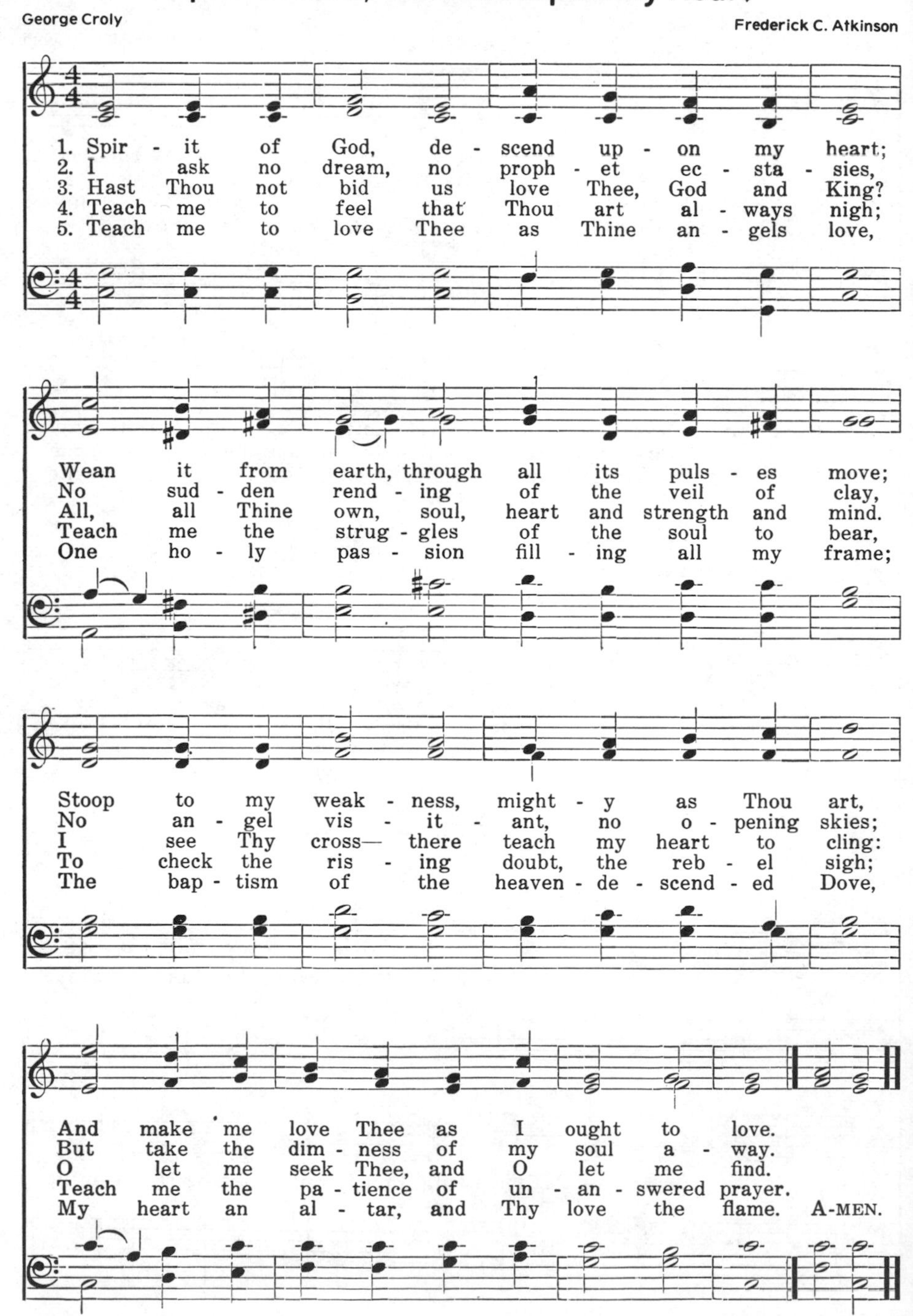
1. Spir - it of God, de - scend up - on my heart;
2. I ask no dream, no proph - et ec - sta - sies,
3. Hast Thou not bid us love Thee, God and King?
4. Teach me to feel that Thou art al - ways nigh;
5. Teach me to love Thee as Thine an - gels love,
Wean it from earth, through all its puls - es move;
No sud - den rend - ing of the veil of clay,
All, all Thine own, soul, heart and strength and mind.
Teach me the strug - gles of the soul to bear,
One ho - ly pas - sion fill - ing all my frame;
Stoop to my weak - ness, might - y as Thou art,
No an - gel vis - it - ant, no o - pening skies;
I see Thy cross— there teach my heart to cling:
To check the ris - ing doubt, the reb - el sigh;
The bap - tism of the heaven - de - scend - ed Dove,
And make me love Thee as I ought to love.
But take the dim - ness of my soul a - way.
O let me seek Thee, and O let me find.
Teach me the pa - tience of un - an - swered prayer.
My heart an al - tar, and Thy love the flame. A-MEN.

God Is Here

J. L. Black
Alfred B. Smith
& John R. Sweney
1. God is here, and that to bless us With the Spir - it's quick-'ning pow'r!
2. God is here! we feel His pres-ence In this con - se-crat - ed place;
3. God is here! oh, then be-liev - ing, Bring to Him our one de - sire,
4. Sav-iour, grant the pray'r we of - fer, While in sim-ple faith we bow;
See, the cloud, al-read- y bend-ing, Waits to drop the grate-ful show'r.
But we need the soul re - fresh-ing Of His free, un-bound-ed Grace.
That His love may now be kin-dled, Till its flame each heart in - spire.
From the win-dows of Thy mer - cy Pour us out a bless-ing now.
Chorus
Let it come, O Lord, we pray thee; Let the show'r of bless-ing fall;
We are wait - ing, we are wait - ing, Oh, re - vive the hearts of all.

152 Blessed Quietness

W. S. Marshall
Arr. by James M. Kirk
Manie P. Ferguson
1. Joys are flow-ing like a riv - er, Since the Com-fort - er has come;
2. Bring-ing life and health and glad - ness, All a - round this heav'n-ly Guest,
3. Like the rain that falls from heav - en, Like the sun - light from the sky,
4. See, a fruit-ful field is grow-ing, Bless-ed fruit of right-eous-ness;
5. What a won-der-ful sal - va - tion, Where we al - ways see His face!
He a - bides with us for - ev - er, Makes the trust - ing heart His home.
Ban-ished un - be - lief and sad-ness, Changed our wea - ri - ness to rest.
So the Ho - ly Ghost is giv - en, Com-ing on us from on high.
And the streams of life are flow-ing In the lone - ly wil - der - ness.
What a per-fect hab - i - ta - tion, What a qui - et rest - ing place!
Refrain
Bless - ed qui - et - ness, ho-ly qui - et - ness, What as - sur-ance in my soul!
On the storm - y sea He speaks peace to me, How the bil - lows cease to roll!

Thou Art Calling Me, Lord Jesus

Lewis Sperry Chafer

Alfred B. Smith

1. Thou art call - ing me, Lord Je - sus, As Thy liv - ing wit-ness here;
2. Thou art call - ing me, Lord Je - sus, To be work-ing one with Thee;
3. Thou art call - ing me, Lord Je - sus, To pre - vail - ing pow'r in pray'r;
4. Thou art call - ing me, Lord Je - sus, To a Vic - tor's ho - ly life;

On - ly by Thy life with - in me Can I a - ny wit - ness bear.
On - ly by Thy life with - in me Can there a - ny serv - ice be.
On - ly by Thy life with - in me I Thy in - ter - ces - sion share.
On - ly by Thy life with - in me Is there con-quest in the strife.

Chorus

Fill me, Ho - ly Spir - it, fill me. More than full - ness I would know;

I'm the small - est of Thy ves - sels, Yet I much can o - ver-flow.

154 Holy Spirit, Faithful Guide

Marcus M. Wells — Marcus M. Wells

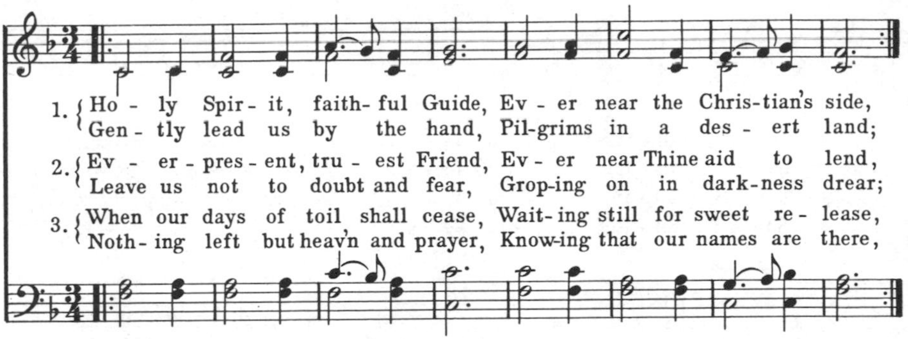

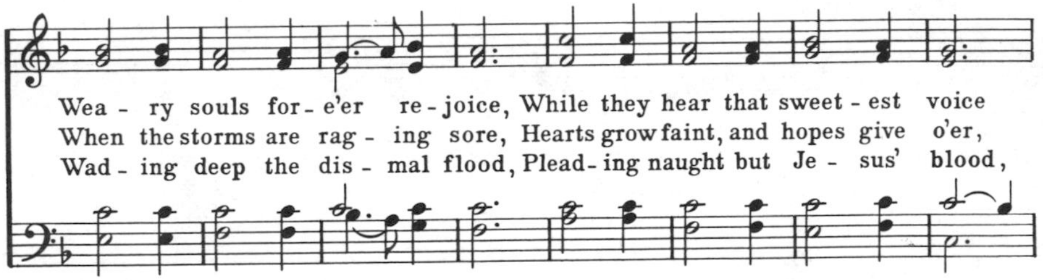

1. Holy Spirit, faithful Guide, Ever near the Christian's side,
Gently lead us by the hand, Pilgrims in a desert land;
Weary souls fore'er rejoice, While they hear that sweetest voice
Whisp'ring softly, "Wand'rer come! Follow Me, I'll guide thee home."

2. Ever-present, truest Friend, Ever near Thine aid to lend,
Leave us not to doubt and fear, Groping on in darkness drear;
When the storms are raging sore, Hearts grow faint, and hopes give o'er,
Whisper softly, "Wand'rer come! Follow Me, I'll guide thee home."

3. When our days of toil shall cease, Waiting still for sweet release,
Nothing left but heav'n and prayer, Knowing that our names are there,
Wading deep the dismal flood, Pleading naught but Jesus' blood,
Whisper softly, "Wand'rer come! Follow Me, I'll guide thee home."

155 Breathe on Me, Breath of God

Edwin Hatch — Robert Jackson

1. Breathe on me, Breath of God, Fill me with life anew,
2. Breathe on me, Breath of God, Until my heart is pure,
3. Breathe on me, Breath of God, Till I am wholly Thine,
4. Breathe on me, Breath of God, So shall I never die,

That I may love what Thou dost love And do what Thou wouldst do.
Un-til with Thee I will one will— To do and to en-dure.
Till all this earth-ly part of me Glows with Thy fire di-vine.
But live with Thee the per-fect life Of Thine e-ter-ni-ty.
Open My Eyes, That I May See
156
Clara H. Scott
Clara H. Scott
1. O-pen my eyes, that I may see Glimpses of truth Thou hast for me;
2. O-pen my ears, that I may hear Voic-es of truth Thou send-est clear;
3. O-pen my mouth, and let me bear Glad-ly the warm truth ev-'ry-where;
Place in my hands the won-der-ful key That shall un-clasp and set me free.
And while the wave-notes fall on my ear, Ev-'ry-thing false will dis-ap-pear.
O-pen my heart and let me pre-pare Love with Thy chil-dren thus to share.
Si-lent-ly now I wait for Thee, Read-y, my God, Thy will to see;
Si-lent-ly now I wait for Thee, Read-y, my God, Thy will to see;
Si-lent-ly now I wait for Thee, Read-y, my God, Thy will to see;
O-pen my eyes— il-lu-mine me, Spir-it di-vine!
O-pen my ears— il-lu-mine me, Spir-it di-vine!
O-pen my heart— il-lu-mine me, Spir-it di-vine!

157 Pentecostal Power

Charles H. Gabriel — Charles H. Gabriel

1. Lord, as of old at Pen - te - cost Thou didst Thy power dis - play,
2. For might - y works for Thee, pre - pare And strength-en ev - ery heart;
3. All self con - sume, all sin de-stroy! With ear - nest zeal en - due
4. Speak, Lord! be - fore Thy throne we wait, Thy prom - ise we be - lieve,

With cleans-ing, pu - ri - fy - ing flame De - scend on us to - day.
Come, take pos - ses - sion of Thine own, And nev - er - more de - part.
Each wait - ing heart to work for Thee; O Lord, our faith re - new!
And will not let Thee go un - til The bless - ing we re - ceive.

REFRAIN

Lord, send the old - time power, The Pen-te-cos - tal power! Thy flood-gates of bless-ing on us throw o - pen wide! Lord, send the old - time power, the Pen - te - cos - tal power, That sinners be con-vert-ed and Thy name glo - ri-fied!

O Holy Spirit

Francis Marion Hickok

Alfred B. Smith

1. O Ho - ly Spir - it, Dove di-vine, Be-stow Thy glo-rious grace;
2. Touch our dull ears with heal-ing power, That we the Lord may hear,
3. Make Thou the path of du - ty plain, Nor from it let us stray;
4. Come, Ho - ly Spir - it, come, O come! Per-form Thy work of grace;

Make clear the truth, that it may shine. Re - veal the Sav-ior's face.
And in this glad, this ho - ly hour, May know His pres-ence near.
And more may we Christ's spir - it gain, In serv - ice, day by day;
Make our poor hearts Thine hon-ored home, Thy cho - sen dwell-ing place.

Dark er - ror's cloud from us re-move, Which in - ter-cepts the light;
With - in us let His im - age grow, His will, our wills con - trol,
That we our mis - sion may ful - fil, Our faith - ful wit - ness give,
And kin - dle there love's heaven - ly fire, A pu - ri - fy - ing flame,

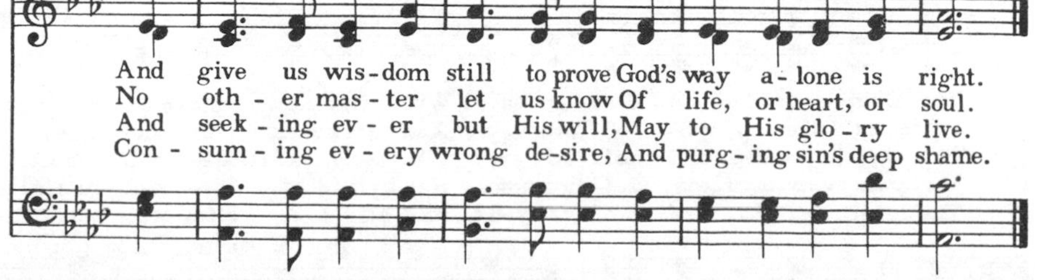

And give us wis - dom still to prove God's way a - lone is right.
No oth - er mas - ter let us know Of life, or heart, or soul.
And seek - ing ev - er but His will, May to His glo - ry live.
Con - sum - ing ev - ery wrong de - sire, And purg - ing sin's deep shame.

159 O Breath of Life

Bessie P. Head
Mary J. Hammond
1. O Breath of Life, come sweeping through us, Re-vive Thy church with life and pow'r;
2. O Wind of God, come bend us, break us, Till hum-bly we con-fess our need;
3. O Breath of Love, come breathe with-in us, Re-new-ing thought and will and heart;
4. O Heart of Christ, once bro-ken for us, 'Tis there we find our strength and rest;
5. Re - vive us, Lord! Is zeal a - ba - ting While harvest fields are vast and white?
O Breath of Life, come, cleanse, renew us, And fit Thy Church to meet this hour.
Then in Thy ten-der-ness re-make us, Re - vive, re - store, for this we plead.
Come, Love of Christ, a-fresh to win us, Re - vive Thy Church in ev - ery part.
Our bro-ken con-trite hearts now solace, And let Thy wait-ing Church be blest.
Re - vive us, Lord, the world is waiting, Equip Thy Church to spread the light. A-MEN.
I Love Thy Kingdom, Lord 160
Timothy Dwight
Aaron Williams
1. I love Thy king - dom, Lord! The house of Thine a - bode—
2. I love Thy Church, O God! Her walls be - fore Thee stand,
3. For her my tears shall fall, For her my prayers as - cend—
4. Be - yond my high - est joy I prize her heav'n - ly ways—
5. Sure as Thy truth shall last, To Zi - on shall be giv'n
The Church our blest Re - deem-er saved With His own pre - cious blood.
Dear as the ap - ple of Thine eye And grav - en on Thy hand.
To her my cares and toils be giv'n Till toils and cares shall end.
Her sweet com-mun - ion, sol - emn vows, Her hymns of love and praise.
The bright - est glo - ries earth can yield, And bright - er bliss of heav'n.

The Church's One Foundation

Samuel J. Stone
Samuel J. Stone
1. The Church's one foun - da - tion Is Je - sus Christ her Lord;
2. E - lect from ev - ery na - tion, Yet one o'er all the earth,
3. Though with a scorn - ful won - der Men see her sore op-pressed,
4. 'Mid toil and trib - u - la - tion, And tu - mult of her war,
5. Yet she on earth hath un - ion With God, the Three in One,
She is His new cre - a - tion, By wa - ter and the word:
Her char - ter of sal - va - tion, One Lord, one faith, one birth;
By schisms rent a - sun - der, By her - e - sies dis-tressed:
She waits the con - sum - ma - tion Of peace for - ev - er - more;
And mvs - tic sweet com - mun - ion With those whose rest is won:
From heav'n He came and sought her To be His ho - ly bride;
One ho - ly name she bless - es, Par - takes one ho - ly food,
Yet saints their watch are keep - ing, Their cry goes up, "How long?"
Till with the vi - sion glo - rious Her long - ing eyes are blest,
O hap - py ones and ho - ly! Lord, give us grace that we,
With His own blood He bought her, And for her life He died.
And to one hope she press - es, With ev - ery grace en - dued.
And soon the night of weep - ing Shall be the morn of song.
And the great Church vic - to - rious Shall be the Church at rest.
Like them, the meek and low - ly, On high may dwell with Thee. A-men.

162 Glorious Things of Thee Are Spoken

John Newton

Franz Joseph Haydn

1. Glo - rious things of thee are spo - ken, Zi - on, cit - y of our God;
2. See, the streams of liv - ing wa - ters, Spring-ing from e - ter - nal love,
3. Round each hab - i - ta - tion hov-'ring, See the cloud and fire ap - pear
He whose word can - not be bro - ken Formed thee for His own a - bode:
Well sup - ply thy sons and daugh-ters And all fear of want re - move:
For a glo - ry and a cov - 'ring, Show - ing that the Lord is near!
On the Rock of A - ges found-ed, What can shake thy sure re - pose?
Who can faint while such a riv - er Ev - er flows their thirst to as-suage?
Glo-rious things of Thee are spo - ken, Zi - on, cit - y of our God;
With sal - va - tion's walls sur-round-ed, Thou mayst smile at all thy foes.
Grace which, like the Lord, the Giv - er, Nev - er fails from age to age.
He whose word can - not be bro - ken Formed thee for His own a - bode.

O Word of God Incarnate 163

William W. How

Arr. by Felix Mendelssohn

1. O Word of God In - car - nate, O Wis - dom from on high,
2. The Church from Thee, her Mas - ter, Re - ceived the gift di - vine,
3. It float - eth like a ban - ner Be - fore God's host un - furled;
4. O make Thy Church, dear Sav - iour, A lamp of pur - est gold,

O Truth un - changed, un - chang - ing, O Light of our dark sky:
And still that light she lift - eth O'er all the earth to shine.
It shin - eth like a bea - con A - bove the dark - ling world.
To bear be - fore the na - tions Thy true light as of old.

We praise Thee for the ra - diance That from the hal - lowed page,
It is the sa - cred cas - ket, Where gems of truth are stored;
It is the chart and com - pass That o'er life's surg - ing sea,
O teach Thy wan-dering pil - grims By this their path to trace,

A lan - tern to our foot - steps, Shines on from age to age.
It is the heaven-drawn pic - ture Of Thee, the liv - ing Word.
Mid mists and rocks and quick-sands, Still guides, O Christ, to Thee.
Till, clouds and dark - ness end - ed, They see Thee face to face. A - MEN.

164 I Am Standing on the Word of God

Earnest M. Wadsworth & A. B. S. | Alfred B. Smith

1. I am stand-ing on the Word of God, Which came to men of old;
2. I am stand-ing on the Word of God, It is ho - ly and 'tis true;
3. I am stand-ing on the Word of God, It is full of life di - vine;
4. I am stand-ing on the Word of God, And thus I am se - cure;

The Book the Ho - ly Fa-thers had, Giv-en by His love un - told.
Through a - ges it has been our Light, With splen-dor ev - er new.
God's Spir - it lives in ev-'ry word And moves in ev - ery line.
Though blows the tem-pest wild and hard, It will ev - er- move en - dure.

Chorus

I am stand - ing, on the might - y Word of God I am trav-'ling in the path the Saints have trod. Tho' the na - tions tum-ble And the earth should crum-ble God's own Word shall nev-er pass a - way.

Thy Word Have I Hid in My Heart

Psalm 119
Adapted by Ernest O. Sellers

Ernest O. Sellers

1. Thy Word is a lamp to my feet, A light to my path al - way,
2. For - ev - er, O Lord, is Thy Word Es - tab-lished and fixed on high;
3. At morn - ing, at noon, and at night I ev - er will give Thee praise;
4. Thro' Him whom Thy Word hath foretold, The Sav-iour and Morn-ing Star,

To guide and to save me from sin, And show me the heav'n-ly way.
Thy faith-ful-ness un - to all men A - bid-eth for - ev - er nigh.
For Thou art my por - tion, O Lord, And shall be thro' all my days!
Sal - va - tion and peace have been bro't To those who have strayed a - far.

REFRAIN

Thy Word have I hid in my heart (in my heart), That I might not sin a-gainst Thee (a - gainst Thee); That I might not sin, that I might not sin, Thy Word have I hid in my heart.

166 Break Thou the Bread of Life

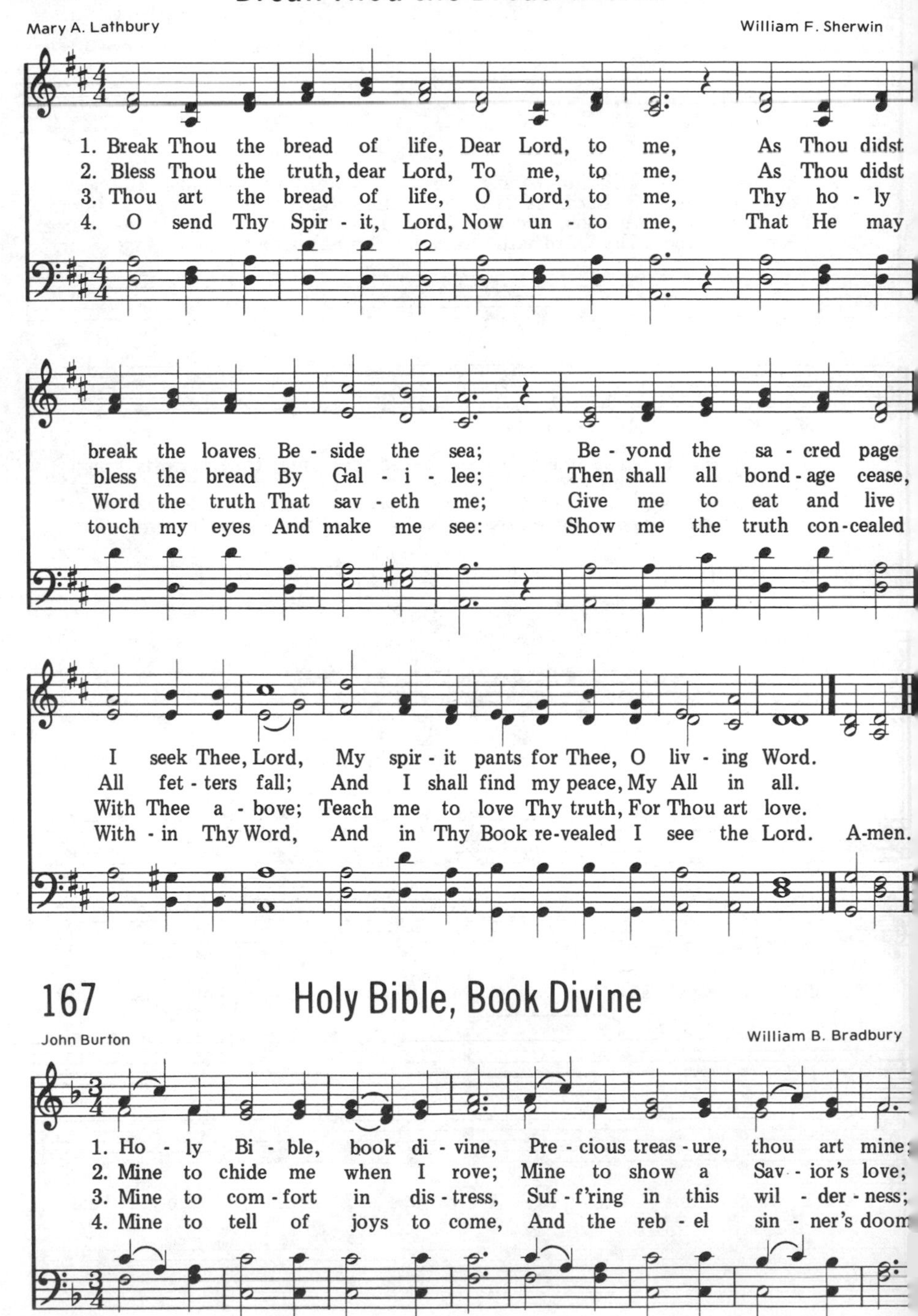
Mary A. Lathbury
William F. Sherwin
1. Break Thou the bread of life, Dear Lord, to me, As Thou didst break the loaves Be - side the sea; Be - yond the sa - cred page I seek Thee, Lord, My spir - it pants for Thee, O liv - ing Word.
2. Bless Thou the truth, dear Lord, To me, to me, As Thou didst bless the bread By Gal - i - lee; Then shall all bond - age cease, All fet - ters fall; And I shall find my peace, My All in all.
3. Thou art the bread of life, O Lord, to me, Thy ho - ly Word the truth That sav - eth me; Give me to eat and live With Thee a - bove; Teach me to love Thy truth, For Thou art love.
4. O send Thy Spir - it, Lord, Now un - to me, That He may touch my eyes And make me see: Show me the truth con-cealed With - in Thy Word, And in Thy Book re-vealed I see the Lord. A-men.
167
Holy Bible, Book Divine
John Burton
William B. Bradbury
1. Ho - ly Bi - ble, book di - vine, Pre - cious treas - ure, thou art mine;
2. Mine to chide me when I rove; Mine to show a Sav - ior's love;
3. Mine to com - fort in dis - tress, Suf - f'ring in this wil - der - ness;
4. Mine to tell of joys to come, And the reb - el sin - ner's doom

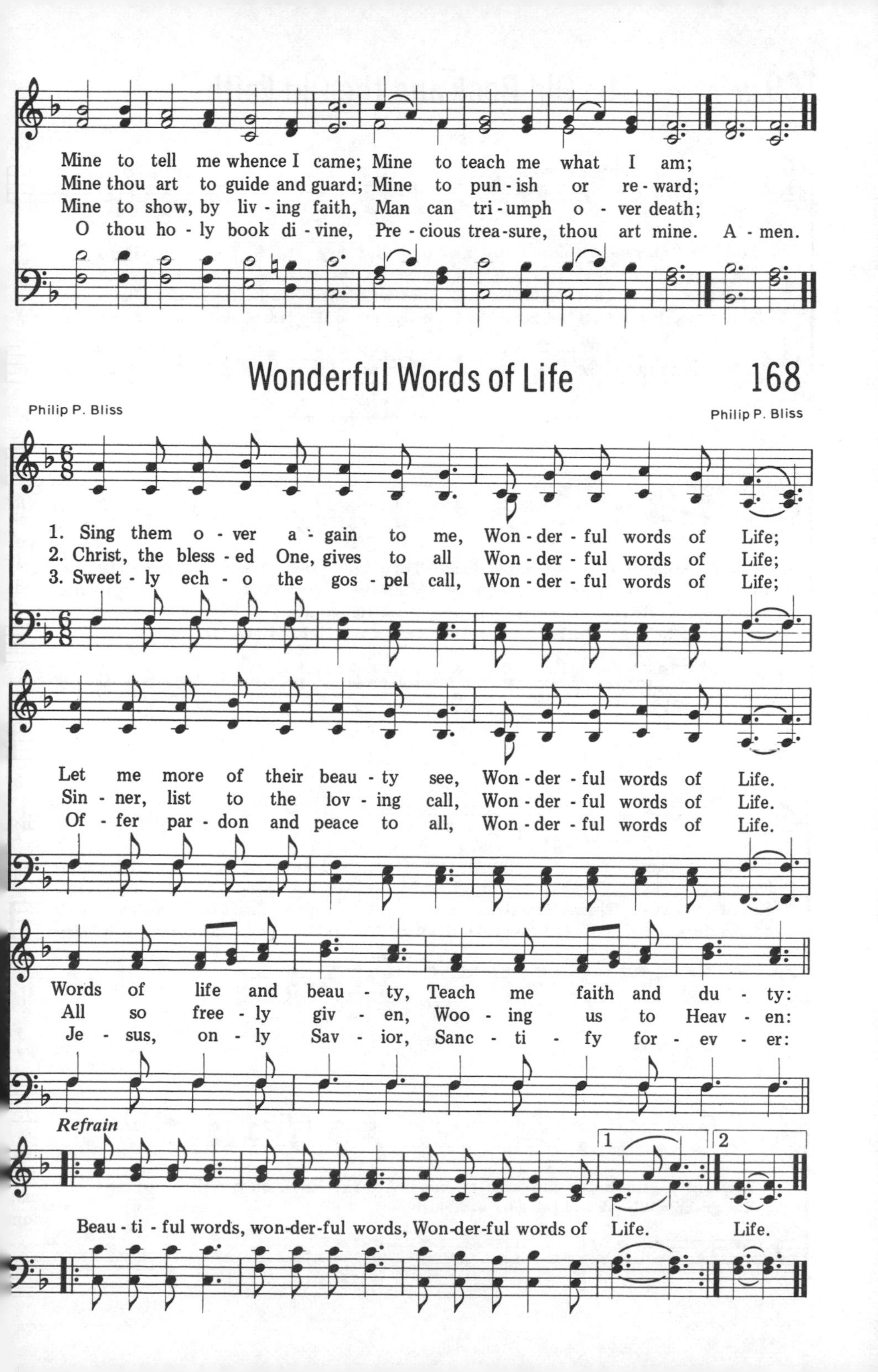
Mine to tell me whence I came; Mine to teach me what I am;
Mine thou art to guide and guard; Mine to pun - ish or re - ward;
Mine to show, by liv - ing faith, Man can tri - umph o - ver death;
O thou ho - ly book di - vine, Pre - cious trea - sure, thou art mine. A - men.
Wonderful Words of Life
168
Philip P. Bliss
Philip P. Bliss
1. Sing them o - ver a - gain to me, Won - der - ful words of Life;
2. Christ, the bless - ed One, gives to all Won - der - ful words of Life;
3. Sweet - ly ech - o the gos - pel call, Won - der - ful words of Life;
Let me more of their beau - ty see, Won - der - ful words of Life.
Sin - ner, list to the lov - ing call, Won - der - ful words of Life.
Of - fer par - don and peace to all, Won - der - ful words of Life.
Words of life and beau - ty, Teach me faith and du - ty:
All so free - ly giv - en, Woo - ing us to Heav - en:
Je - sus, on - ly Sav - ior, Sanc - ti - fy for - ev - er:
Refrain
Beau - ti - ful words, won - der - ful words, Won - der - ful words of Life.
1
2
Life.

169 The Old Book and the Old Faith

George H. Carr George H. Carr

1. 'Mid the storms of doubt and un-be-lief we fear, Stands a Book e-ternal that the world holds dear; Thru the rest-less a-ges it re-mains the same—'Tis the Book of God, and the Bi-ble is its name!
2. 'Tis the Book that tells us of the Fa-ther's love, When He sent His Son to us from heav'n a-bove, Who by rich-est prom-ise cre-ates hope with-in, For 'tis thru His blood we are saved from ev-'ry sin!
3. 'Tis the Book that tells us of the will of God And the Sav-ior's teachings while the earth He trod— How He soothed earth's sor-rows and re-lieved its woe, Thru whom strength is giv-en to con-quer ev-'ry foe!
4. 'Tis the Book that tells us of e-ter-nal life, Aft-er faith-ful serv-ice in a world of strife; And this glo-rious tri-umph o-ver death's dark fears Is the world's best gift in an age of count-less tears!

CHORUS

The old Book and the old Faith Are the Rock on which I stand!
The grand old Book and the dear old Faith on which I stand!

The old Book and the old Faith Are the bul-wark of the land!
The grand old Book and the dear old Faith
Thru storm and stress they stand the test, In ev-'ry clime and na-tion blest;
The old Book and the old Faith Are the hope of ev-'ry land!
The grand old Book and the dear old Faith
GRAND CHORUS AT CLOSE
(May be omitted)
O the grand old Book and the dear old Faith Are the Rock on which I stand!
O the grand old Book and the dear old Faith Are the hope of ev-'ry land!

170 How Firm a Foundation

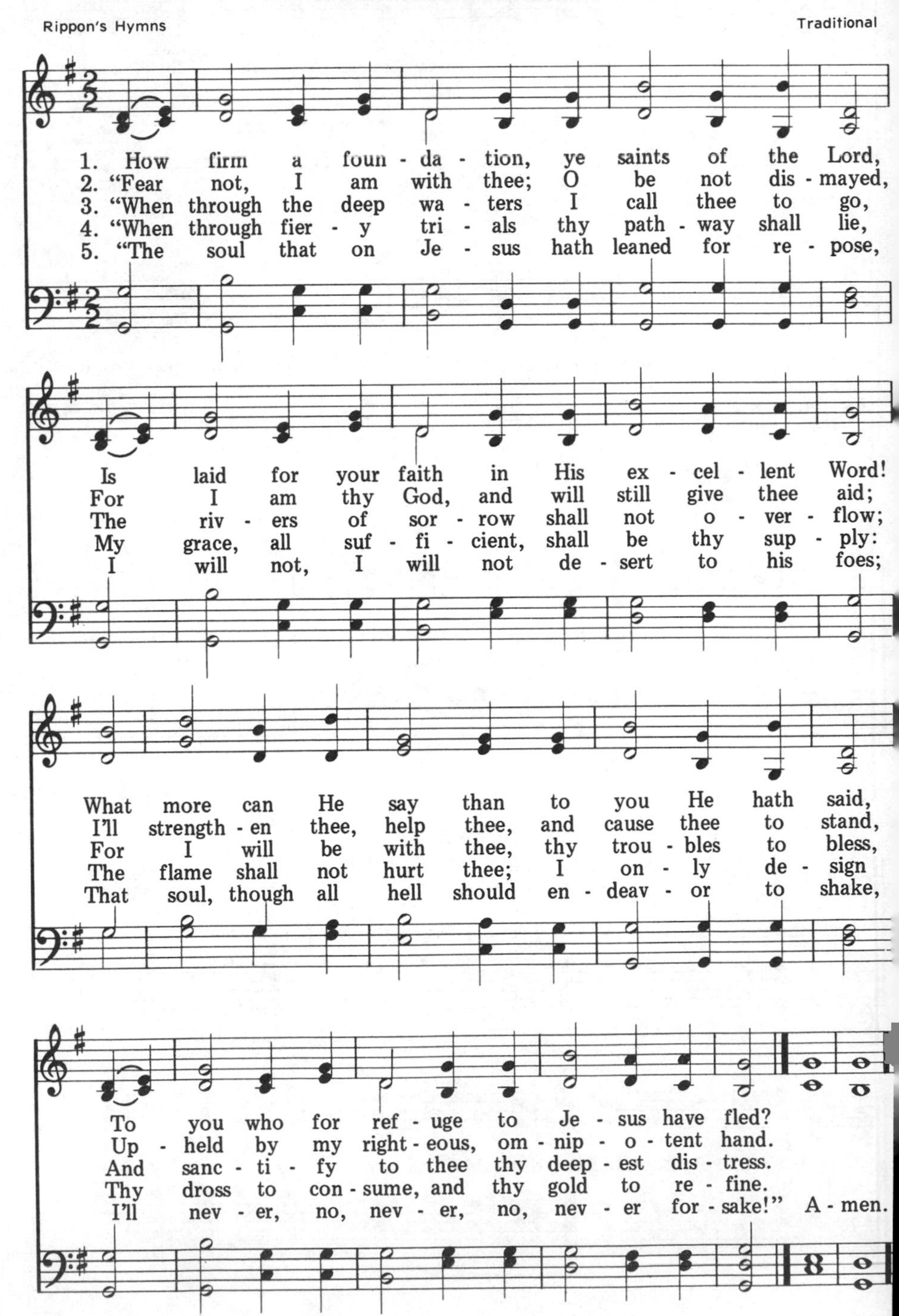

Rippon's Hymns
Traditional
1. How firm a foun - da - tion, ye saints of the Lord,
2. "Fear not, I am with thee; O be not dis - mayed,
3. "When through the deep wa - ters I call thee to go,
4. "When through fier - y tri - als thy path - way shall lie,
5. "The soul that on Je - sus hath leaned for re - pose,
Is laid for your faith in His ex - cel - lent Word!
For I am thy God, and will still give thee aid;
The riv - ers of sor - row shall not o - ver - flow;
My grace, all suf - fi - cient, shall be thy sup - ply:
I will not, I will not de - sert to his foes;
What more can He say than to you He hath said,
I'll strength - en thee, help thee, and cause thee to stand,
For I will be with thee, thy trou - bles to bless,
The flame shall not hurt thee; I on - ly de - sign
That soul, though all hell should en - deav - or to shake,
To you who for ref - uge to Je - sus have fled?
Up - held by my right - eous, om - nip - o - tent hand.
And sanc - ti - fy to thee thy deep - est dis - tress.
Thy dross to con - sume, and thy gold to re - fine.
I'll nev - er, no, nev - er, no, nev - er for - sake!" A - men.

Standing on the Promises

R. Kelso Carter

R. Kelso Carter

1. Stand-ing on the prom-is-es of Christ my King, Through e-ter-nal a-ges let His prais-es ring; Glo-ry in the high-est, I will shout and sing,
2. Stand-ing on the prom-is-es that can-not fail, When the howl-ing storms of doubt and fear as-sail, By the liv-ing word of God I shall pre-vail,
3. Stand-ing on the prom-is-es of Christ the Lord, Bound to Him e-ter-nal-ly by love's strong cord, O-ver-com-ing dai-ly with the Spir-it's sword,
4. Stand-ing on the prom-is-es I can-not fall, Lis-tening ev-ery mo-ment to the Spir-it's call, Rest-ing in my Sav-iour as my all in all,
Stand-ing on the prom-is-es of God.
Refrain
Stand-ing, stand-ing,
Standing on the promises, standing on the promises,
Stand-ing on the prom-is-es of God my Sav-iour; Stand-ing,
Standing on the prom-is-es,
stand-ing, I'm stand-ing on the prom-is-es of God.
stand-ing on the prom-is-es,

172 Behold, What Love!

James McGranahan
Rev. & Arr. by Alfred B. Smith
Robert Boswell
1. Be - hold, what love, what bound - less love, The Fa - ther has be - stowed
2. No lon - ger far from Him, but now By "pre - cious blood" made nigh;
3. What we in glo - ry soon shall be, It does not yet ap - pear;
4. With such a bless - ed hope in view, We would more ho - ly be,
On sin - ners lost, that we should now Be called the sons of God!
Ac - cept - ed in the "Well be - loved," Near to God's heart we lie.
But when our pre - cious Lord we see, We shall His im - age bear.
More like our ris - en, glo - rious Lord, Whose face we soon shall see.
Refrain
Be - hold, what man - ner of love! What man - ner of
(Be - hold)
(what man - ner of love!)
love the Fa - ther hath be - stowed up - on us, That we, that
(that we)
we should be called the sons of God.
(of God.)

Love, Wonderful Love

Miriam E. Arnold
Alt. by A.B.S.
Alfred B. Smith
1. Won - der - ful love that the Fa-ther has giv'n, Send-ing His Son from the
2. Won - der - ful love free - ly of-fered to all! Of-fered to all who on
3. When I be - hold Him, my Sav-iour and King, How heav-en's arch-es with
glo - ries of Heav'n, That I thro' Him might be saved and for - giv'n,
Je - sus will call. He can de - liv - er, tho' sin may en - thrall,
rap - ture will ring! Thro' end-less a - ges His prais - es I'll sing,
O, won-der-ful won-der-ful
Thro' won-der-ful won-der-ful
O, won-der-ful won-der-ful
love. ______
(won-der - ful love.)
Chorus
Love, won - der - ful
love so free, Love flow - ing from Cal - va - ry.
High as the heav-ens and deep as the sea Is God's love for me. (for me.)

174 In the Heart of Jesus

Alice Pugh

C. H. Forrest
Rev. & Arr. by Alfred B. Smith

1. In the heart of Je - sus There is love for you,
2. In the mind of Je - sus There is thought for you,
3. In the field of Je - sus There is work for you,
4. In the home of Je - sus There's a place for you;
Love most pure and ten - der, Love most deep and true.
Warm as sum - mer sun - shine, Sweet as morn - ing dew.
Such as ev - en an - gels Would re - joice to do.
Glori - ous, bright, and joy - ous, Calm and peace - ful too.
Why should you be lone - ly, Why for friend-ship sigh,
Why should you be fear - ful, Why take anx - ious thought,
Why stand id - ly sigh - ing For some life - work grand,
Why then, like a wan - d'rer, Roam with wea - ry pace,
When the heart of Je - sus Has a full sup - ply?
Since the mind of Je - sus Cares for those He bought?
While the field of Je - sus Seeks your reap - ing hand?
If the home of Je - sus Holds for you a place?

Oh, Praise the God of Love

F. J. Crosby & A.B.S.

Alfred B. Smith

1. Oh! praise the God of love! Sing praise to Him a - bove; Take
2. Re-deemed by Him a - lone, Who keeps me day by day; My
3. Oh! love, un-chang-ing love! Not all the hosts a - bove Can
up the song of end - less years, And sing re-deem - ing love! He
life and all its ran-somed powers Could ne'er His love re - pay. His
reach the height, or sound the depth of God's e - ter - nal love. His
did for sin a - tone, When on the cross He died; Re-
mer - cy con - de - scends My hum - ble gift to own; And
love en - folds the world, It fills the realms a - bove; 'Tis
deemed and pur-chased with His blood, Re-deemed and sanc - ti - fied.
thro' the rich - es of His grace, He brings me near His throne.
bound-less as e - ter - ni - ty; Oh, praise the God of love.

176 My Saviour's Love

Charles H. Gabriel	Charles H. Gabriel

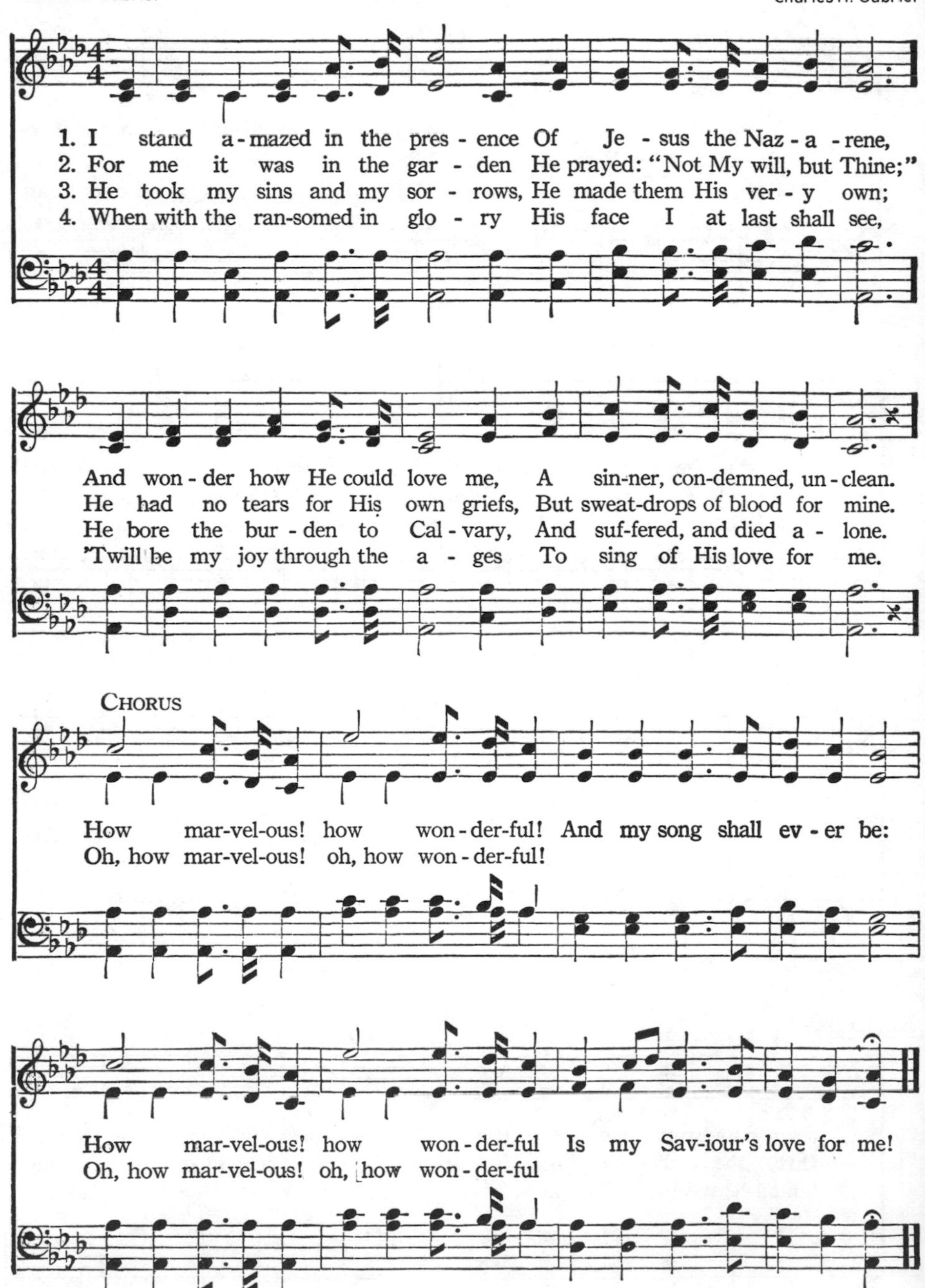
1. I stand a-mazed in the pres - ence Of Je - sus the Naz - a - rene,
2. For me it was in the gar - den He prayed: "Not My will, but Thine;"
3. He took my sins and my sor - rows, He made them His ver - y own;
4. When with the ran-somed in glo - ry His face I at last shall see,
And won - der how He could love me, A sin-ner, con-demned, un - clean.
He had no tears for His own griefs, But sweat-drops of blood for mine.
He bore the bur - den to Cal - vary, And suf-fered, and died a - lone.
'Twill be my joy through the a - ges To sing of His love for me.
CHORUS
How mar-vel-ous! how won-der-ful! And my song shall ev - er be:
Oh, how mar-vel-ous! oh, how won - der-ful!
How mar-vel-ous! how won - der-ful Is my Sav-iour's love for me!
Oh, how mar-vel-ous! oh, how won - der-ful

Love Lifted Me

James Rowe
Howard E. Smith
1. I was sink-ing deep in sin, Far from the peace-ful shore, Ver - y deep - ly stained with-in, Sink-ing to rise no more; But the Mas - ter of the sea Heard my de-spair-ing cry, From the wa-ters lift - ed me, Now safe am I.
2. All my heart to Him I give, Ev - er to Him I'll cling, In His bless-ed pres - ence live, Ev - er His prais-es sing. Love so might - y and so true Mer - its my soul's best songs; Faith-ful, lov-ing serv-ice, too, To Him be - longs.
3. Souls in dan - ger, look a-bove, Je - sus com-plete-ly saves; He will lift you by His love Out of the an - gry waves. He's the Mas - ter of the sea, Bil - lows His will o - bey; He your Sav-iour wants to be—Be saved to - day.
Refrain
Love lift - ed me! e - ven me! Love lift - ed me! e - ven me! When noth - ing else could help, Love lift - ed me. Love lift - ed me.
1
2

Love Found a Way

Avis B. Christiansen

Harry Dixon Loes

1. Won-der-ful love that res-cued me, Sunk deep in sin, Guilt-y and
2. Love bro't my Sav-ior here to die On Cal-va-ry, For such a
3. Love o-pened wide the gates of light To heav'n's do-main, Where in e-
vile as I could be— No hope with-in; When ev-'ry ray of light had fled,
sin-ful wretch as I— How can it be? Love bridged the gulf 'twixt me and heav'n,
ter-nal pow'r and might Je-sus shall reign; Love lift-ed me from depths of woe
O glo-rious day! Rais-ing my soul from out the dead, Love found a way.
Taught me to pray; I am re-deemed, set free, for-giv'n— Love found a way.
To end-less day; There was no help in earth be-low— Love found a way.
CHORUS
Love found a way to re-deem my soul, Love found a
a way, to re-deem my soul,
way that could make me whole; Love sent my Lord to the
a way could make me whole; my Lord

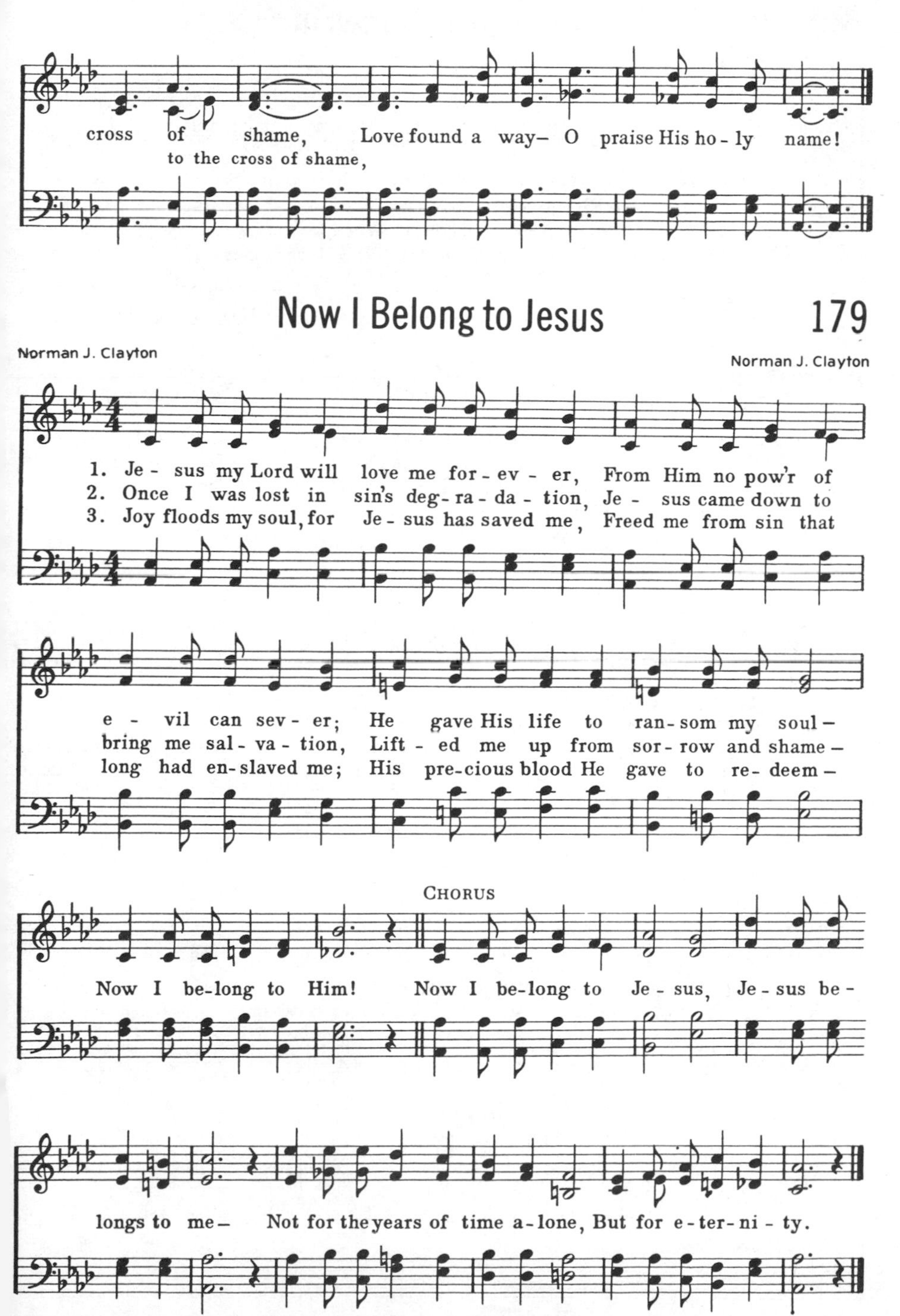
cross of shame, Love found a way— O praise His ho-ly name!
to the cross of shame,
Now I Belong to Jesus
179
Norman J. Clayton
Norman J. Clayton
1. Je-sus my Lord will love me for-ev-er, From Him no pow'r of e-vil can sev-er; He gave His life to ran-som my soul—
2. Once I was lost in sin's deg-ra-da-tion, Je-sus came down to bring me sal-va-tion, Lift-ed me up from sor-row and shame—
3. Joy floods my soul, for Je-sus has saved me, Freed me from sin that long had en-slaved me; His pre-cious blood He gave to re-deem—
Now I be-long to Him!
CHORUS
Now I be-long to Je-sus, Je-sus be-longs to me— Not for the years of time a-lone, But for e-ter-ni-ty.

180 When Love Shines in

Carrie E. Breck | William J. Kirkpatrick

1. Je - sus comes with pow'r to glad-den, When love shines in, Ev - 'ry
2. How the world will grow with beau-ty, When love shines in, And the
3. Dark-est sor - row will grow brighter, When love shines in, And the
4. We may have un - fad-ing splen-dor, When love shines in, And a
life that woe can sad-den, When love shines in. Love will teach us
heart re - joice in du - ty, When love shines in. Tri - als may be
heav- iest bur- den light-er, When love shines in. 'Tis the glo - ry
friend-ship true and ten- der, When love shines in. When earth's vic- t'ries
how to pray, Love will drive the gloom a - way, Turn our dark-ness in - to day -
sanc-ti - fied, And the soul in peace a - bide, Life will all be glo - ri - fied -
that will throw Light to show us where to go; O the heart shall bless-ing know -
shall be won, And our life in heav'n be-gun, There will be no need of sun -
When love shines in.
CHORUS
When love shines in, When love shines
When love, when love shines in, When love shines
in, How the heart is tuned to sing-ing, When love shines

in, When love shines in, When love shines in,
When love, when love shines in, When love shines in,
Joy and peace to oth-ers bring-ing— When love shines in!

O Love That Wilt Not Let Me Go

181

George Matheson

Albert L. Peace

1. O Love that wilt not let me go, I rest my wea-ry soul in Thee; I give Thee back the life I owe, That in Thine o-cean depths its flow May rich-er, full-er be.
2. O Light that fol-l'west all my way, I yield my flick-'ring torch to Thee; My heart re-stores its bor-rowed ray, That in Thy sun-shine's blaze its day May bright-er, fair-er be.
3. O Joy that seek-est me thru pain, I can-not close my heart to Thee; I trace the rain-bow thru the rain, And feel the prom-ise is not vain That morn shall tear-less be.
4. O Cross that lift-est up my head, I dare not ask to fly from Thee; I lay in dust life's glo-ry dead, And from the ground there blos-soms red Life that shall end-less be.

The Greatest Thing Is Love

Lelia N. Morris
Verse 4-A. B. S.

Alfred B. Smith

Solo or Unison
1. O match-less love, how can it be? He took my place and died for me.
2. In ev-'ry land be-neath the sun, It makes us broth-ers, ev-'ry one,
3. It makes all things with joy com-plete, Makes strong the heart, life's cares to meet,
4. It sat-is-fies the long-ing heart, Gives ru-ined lives a brand new start;
I from the bro-ken law go free Through love, won-der-ful love.
Thro' Christ the "well be-lov-ed Son," This love, won-der-ful love.
Turns sor-row's bit-ter in-to sweet, This love, won-der-ful love.
It all be-gins in God's great heart. This love, won-der-ful love.
Chorus - 4 parts
The great-est thing in earth be-low Is love.
(won-der-ful love.)
(piano)
The great-est thing the an-gels know Is love.
(won-der-ful love.)
The great-est grace in God's own heart Is love.
(won-der-ful love.)

In earth and sky, God's rea-son why Is love, won-der-ful love.
My Faith Has Found a Resting Place
183
Norse Air
William J. Kirkpatrick
Lidie H. Edmunds
1. My faith has found a rest-ing-place, Not in de-vice nor creed;
2. E-nough for me that Je-sus saves, This ends my fear and doubt;
3. My heart is lean-ing on the Word, The writ-ten Word of God,
4. My great Phy-si-cian heals the sick, The lost He came to save;
I trust the Ev-er-liv-ing One, His wounds for me shall plead.
A sin-ful soul I come to Him, He'll nev-er cast me out.
Sal-va-tion by my Sav-iour's name, Sal-va-tion thro' His blood.
For me His pre-cious blood He shed, For me His Life He gave.
Chorus
I need no oth-er ar-gu-ment, I need no oth-er plea,
It is e-nough that Je-sus died, And that He died for me.

184 It's Just Like His Great Love

Edna R. Worrell
DeKoven

1. A Friend I have, called Je - sus, Whose love is strong and true, And nev - er
2. Sometimes the clouds of troub-le Be - dim the sky a - bove, I can - not
3. When sorrow's clouds o'ertake me, And break up- on my head, When life seems
4. Oh, I could sing for - ev - er Of Je - sus' love di - vine, Of all His

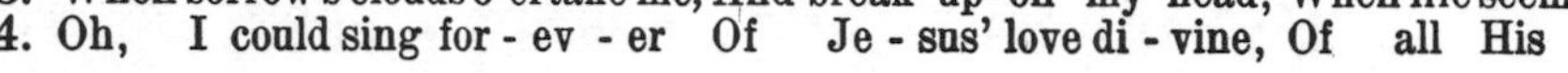

fails how- e'er 'tis tried, No mat - ter what I do; I've sinned a-gainst this
see my Sav - ior's face, I doubt His won-drous love; But He, from Heav-en's
worse than use - less, And I were bet - ter dead; I take my grief to
care and ten - der-ness For this poor life of mine; His love is in and

love of His, But when I knelt to pray, Con - fess - ing all my
mer - cy - seat, Be - hold - ing my de - spair, In pit - y bursts the
Je - sus then, Nor do I go in vain, For heav'n-ly hope He
o - ver all, And wind and waves o - bey When Je - sus whis - pers

CHORUS

guilt to Him, The sin-clouds rolled a - way.
clouds be - tween, And shows me He is there. It's just like Je - sus to
gives that cheers Like sun - shine aft - er rain.
"Peace, be still!" And rolls the clouds a - way.

roll the clouds a-way, It's just like Je - sus to keep me day by day
It's just like Je - sus all a-long the way, It's just like His great love.
Trust Him
185
Will H. Houghton
I would trust Him in the shad - ow, I would trust Him in the light,
I would cast on Him my bur - den, Walk by faith and not by sight.
He in - vites my full sur - ren - der, He my Guide and Strength would be;
I can trust in Him to keep His own Thro' all time and e - ter - ni - ty!
Copyright, 1934, by Will H. Houghton

186 In Tenderness He Sought Me

W. Spencer Walton

Adoniram J. Gordon

1. In ten - der - ness He sought me, Wea - ry and sick with sin, And
2. He washed the bleed-ing sin wounds And poured in oil and wine; He
3. He point - ed to the nail prints, For me His blood was shed; A
4. I'm sit - ting in His pres - ence, The sun-shine of His face, While
5. So while the hours are pass - ing, All now is per - fect rest; I'm
on His shoul - ders brought me Back to His fold a - gain, While
whis - pered to as - sure me, "I've found thee, thou art Mine." I
mock - ing crown so thorn - y Was placed up - on His head: I
with a - dor - ing won - der His bless - ings I re - trace. It
wait - ing for the morn - ing, The bright - est and the best, When
an - gels in His pres-ence sang Un - til the courts of heav - en rang.
nev - er heard a sweet - er voice; It made my ach - ing heart re - joice!
won-dered what He saw in me To suf - fer such deep ag - o - ny.
seems as if e - ter - nal days Are far too short to sound His praise.
He will call us to His side To be with Him, His spot - less bride.
REFRAIN
Oh, the love that sought me! Oh, the blood that bought me! Oh, the grace that
brought me to the fold— Won-drous grace that brought me to the fold!

My Soul Is Filled With Glory
187
J. M. Harris
Alt. A.B.S.
J. M. Harris
Alt. Alfred B. Smith
1. Je - sus found me when a - far I wan-dered; Bro't me par-don from the throne a - bove; Gave me peace that pass-eth un-der-stand-ing, Joy un - speak-a-ble and full of love.
2. Thro' His Word He taught me full sal - va - tion, How His blood could cleanse and sanc - ti - fy; Then by faith I plunged in-to the foun-tain. Now I'm look - ing for that home on high.
3. Tri - als man - y will be - set my path-way, And temp - ta-tions I shall sure - ly meet; But my Sav-iour promised grace to help me Till I lay my tro-phies at His feet.
Refrain
Praise the Lord! my soul is filled with glo-ry! Praise the Lord! I love to tell the sto - ry Of His grace that saves and gives me vic-t'ry, And I'm shout-ing, "Glo-ry!" till I get home.

188 Wonderful Grace of Jesus

Haldor Lillenas — Haldor Lillenas

1. Won - der - ful grace of Je - sus, Great - er than all my sin;
2. Won - der - ful grace of Je - sus, Reach - ing to all the lost,
3. Won - der - ful grace of Je - sus, Reach - ing the most de - filed,

How shall my tongue de - scribe it, Where shall its praise be - gin?
By it I have been par - doned, Saved to the ut - ter - most;
By its trans - form - ing pow - er Mak - ing him God's dear child,

Tak - ing a - way my bur - den, Set - ting my spir - it free,
Chains have been torn a - sun - der, Giv - ing me lib - er - ty,
Pur - chas - ing peace and heav - en For all e - ter - ni - ty—

For the won - der - ful grace of Je - sus reach - es me.
For the won - der - ful grace of Je - sus reach - es me.
And the won - der - ful grace of Je - sus reach - es me.

Refrain

the match-less grace of Je - sus,
Won - der - ful the match-less grace of Je - sus, Deep - er than the

might - y roll - ing sea; the roll - ing sea; Won - der - ful
High - er than the moun - tain,
grace, all suf - fi - cient for
spark - ling like a foun - tain, All suf - fi - cient grace for e - ven
me, for e - ven me; Broad - er than the scope of my trans-
me; trans-
gres - sions, Great - er far than all my sin and shame;
gres - sions, sing it! my sin and shame;
O mag - ni - fy the pre - cious name of Je - sus, Praise His name!
Peace, Perfect Peace
189
Edward H. Bickersteth
Alt. from George T. Caldbeck By Charles J. Vincent
1. Peace, perfect peace, in this dark world of sin? The blood of Jesus whispers peace with - in.
2. Peace, perfect peace, with sorrows surging round? On Je-sus' bos-om naught but calm is found.
3. Peace, perfect peace, our future all unknown? Je - sus we know, and He is on the throne.
4. Peace, perfect peace, death shadowing us and ours? Je-sus has vanquished death and all its powers.
5. It is enough: earth's struggles soon shall cease, And Je-sus call us to heaven's per-fect peace. A - MEN.

190 Grace Greater Than Our Sin

Julia H. Johnston — Daniel B. Towner

1. Mar - vel - ous grace of our lov - ing Lord, Grace that ex - ceeds our
2. Sin and de - spair like the sea waves cold, Threat-en the soul with
3. Dark is the stain that we can - not hide, What can a - vail to
4. Mar - vel - ous, in - fi - nite, match-less grace, Free - ly be-stowed on

sin and our guilt, Yon - der on Cal - va - ry's mount out - poured,
in - fi - nite loss; Grace that is great - er, yes, grace un - told,
wash it a - way? Look! there is flow - ing a crim - son tide;
all who be - lieve; You that are long - ing to see His face,

There where the blood of the Lamb was spilt.
Points to the Ref - uge, the might - y Cross.
Whit - er than snow you may be to - day.
Will you this mo - ment His grace re - ceive?

REFRAIN

Grace, grace,
Mar - vel - ous grace,

God's grace, Grace that will par - don and cleanse with-in; Grace,
in - fi - nite grace, Mar - vel - ous

grace, God's grace, Grace that is great - er than all our sin.
grace, in - fi - nite grace,

Only a Sinner

James M. Gray

Daniel B. Towner

1. Naught have I got - ten but what I re-ceived; Grace hath be-stowed it since
2. Once I was fool - ish, and sin ruled my heart, Caus - ing my foot-steps from
3. Tears un - a - vail - ing, no mer - it had I; Mer - cy had saved me, or
4. Suf - fer a sin - ner whose heart o - ver-flows, Lov - ing his Sav - ior to
I have be - lieved; Boast - ing ex - clud - ed, pride I a - base; I'm
God to de - part; Je - sus hath found me, hap - py my case; I
else I must die; Sin had a - larmed me, fear - ing God's face; But
tell what he knows; Once more to tell it would I em - brace—I'm
on - ly a sin - ner saved by grace!
now am a sin - ner saved by grace!
now I'm a sin - ner saved by grace!
on - ly a sin - ner saved by grace!
Refrain
On - ly a sin - ner saved by grace!
On - ly a sin - ner saved by grace! This is my sto - ry, to
God be the glo - ry— I'm on - ly a sin - ner saved by grace!

192 O Take the Gift of Mercy

James M. Gray
Ed. by A.B.S.
Alfred B. Smith

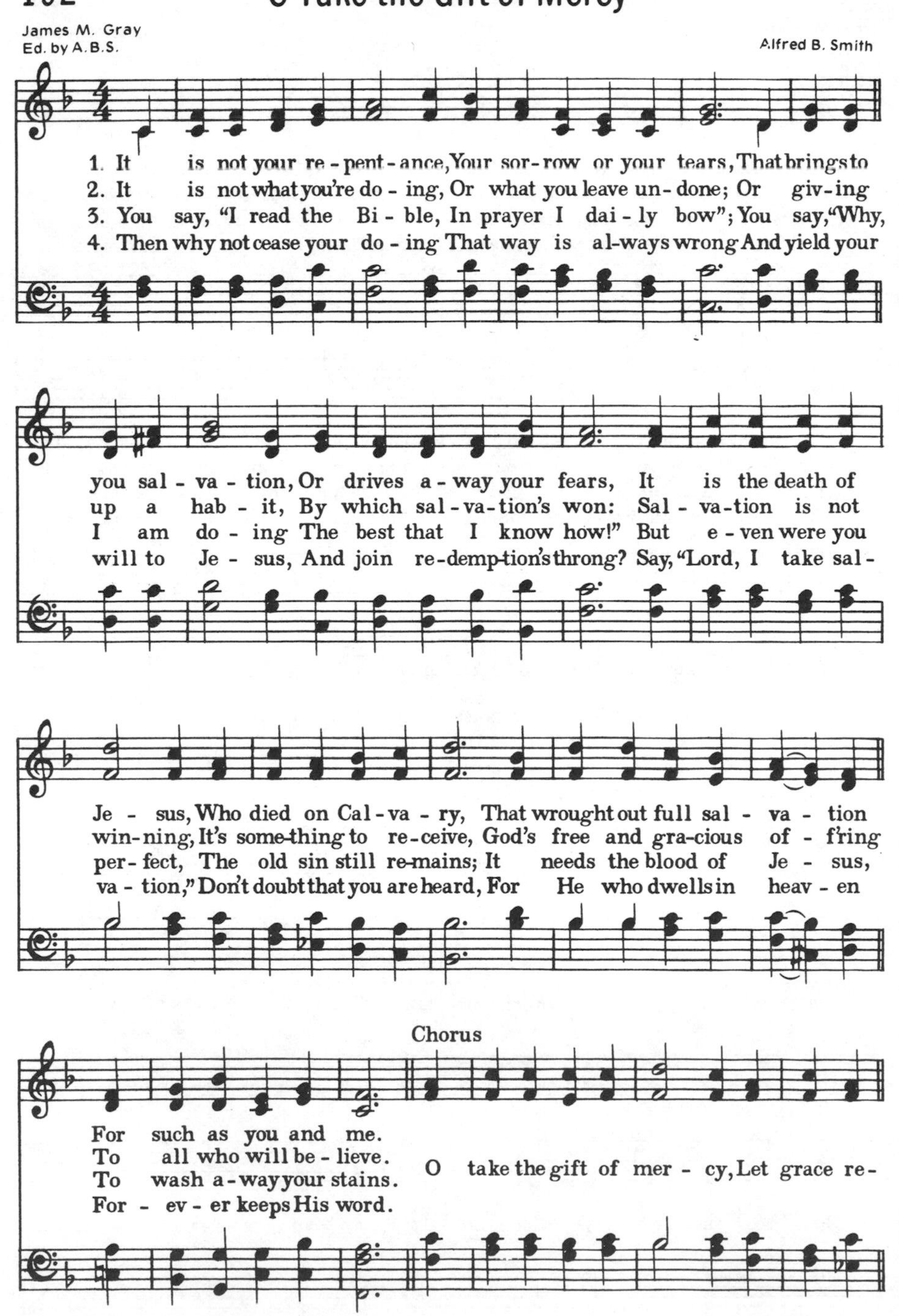
1. It is not your re - pent - ance, Your sor - row or your tears, That brings to
2. It is not what you're do - ing, Or what you leave un - done; Or giv - ing
3. You say, "I read the Bi - ble, In prayer I dai - ly bow"; You say, "Why,
4. Then why not cease your do - ing That way is al-ways wrong And yield your
you sal - va - tion, Or drives a - way your fears, It is the death of
up a hab - it, By which sal - va - tion's won: Sal - va - tion is not
I am do - ing The best that I know how!" But e - ven were you
will to Je - sus, And join re-demp-tion's throng? Say, "Lord, I take sal -
Je - sus, Who died on Cal - va - ry, That wrought out full sal - va - tion
win - ning, It's some-thing to re - ceive, God's free and gra - cious of - f'ring
per - fect, The old sin still re-mains; It needs the blood of Je - sus,
va - tion," Don't doubt that you are heard, For He who dwells in heav - en
For such as you and me.
To all who will be - lieve.
To wash a - way your stains.
For - ev - er keeps His word.
Chorus
O take the gift of mer - cy, Let grace re -

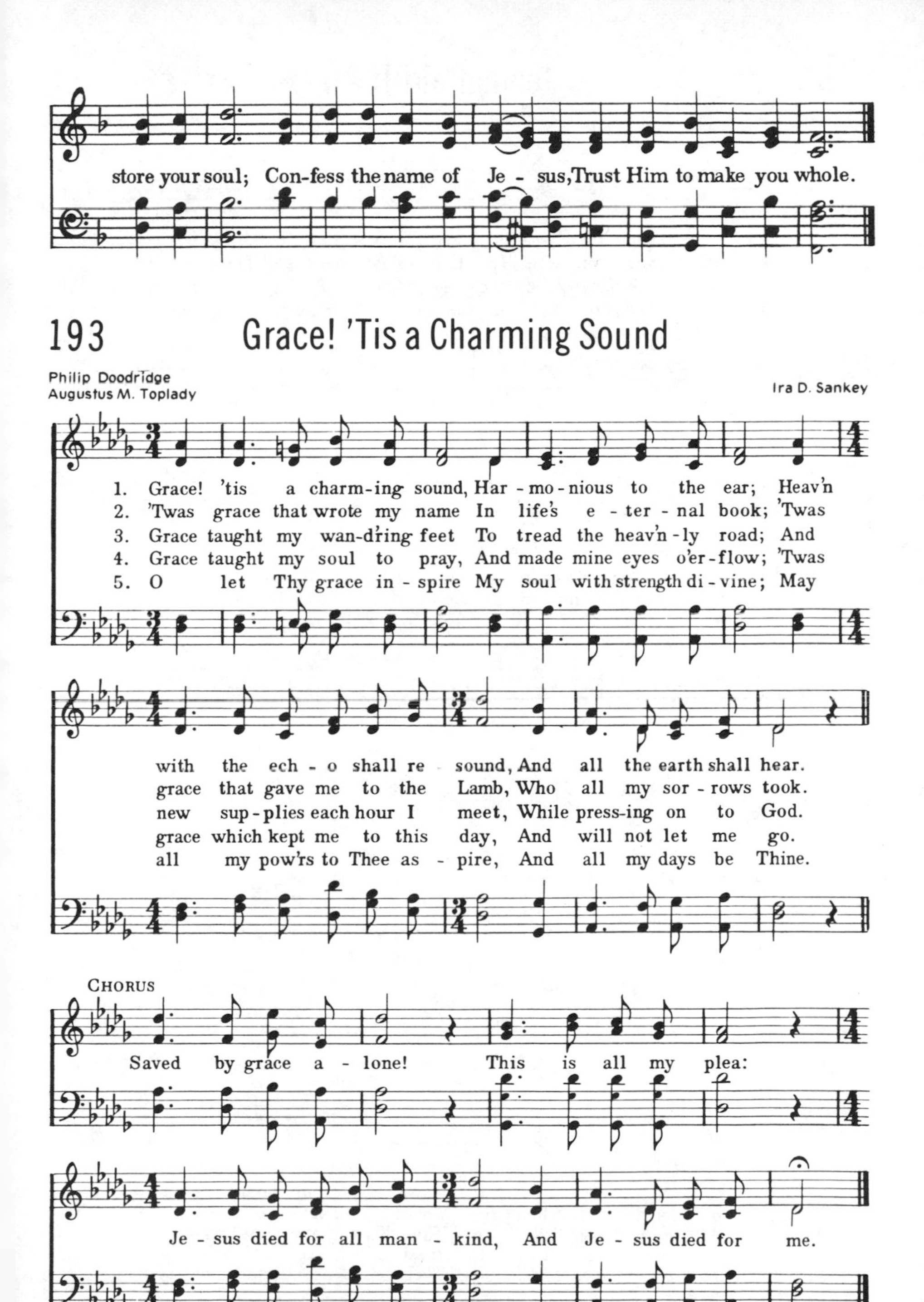
store your soul; Con-fess the name of Je - sus, Trust Him to make you whole.
193 Grace! 'Tis a Charming Sound
Philip Doodridge
Augustus M. Toplady
Ira D. Sankey
1. Grace! 'tis a charm-ing sound, Har - mo - nious to the ear; Heav'n with the ech - o shall re - sound, And all the earth shall hear.
2. 'Twas grace that wrote my name In life's e - ter - nal book; 'Twas grace that gave me to the Lamb, Who all my sor - rows took.
3. Grace taught my wan-d'ring feet To tread the heav'n - ly road; And new sup - plies each hour I meet, While press-ing on to God.
4. Grace taught my soul to pray, And made mine eyes o'er-flow; 'Twas grace which kept me to this day, And will not let me go.
5. O let Thy grace in - spire My soul with strength di - vine; May all my pow'rs to Thee as - pire, And all my days be Thine.
CHORUS
Saved by grace a - lone! This is all my plea:
Je - sus died for all man - kind, And Je - sus died for me.

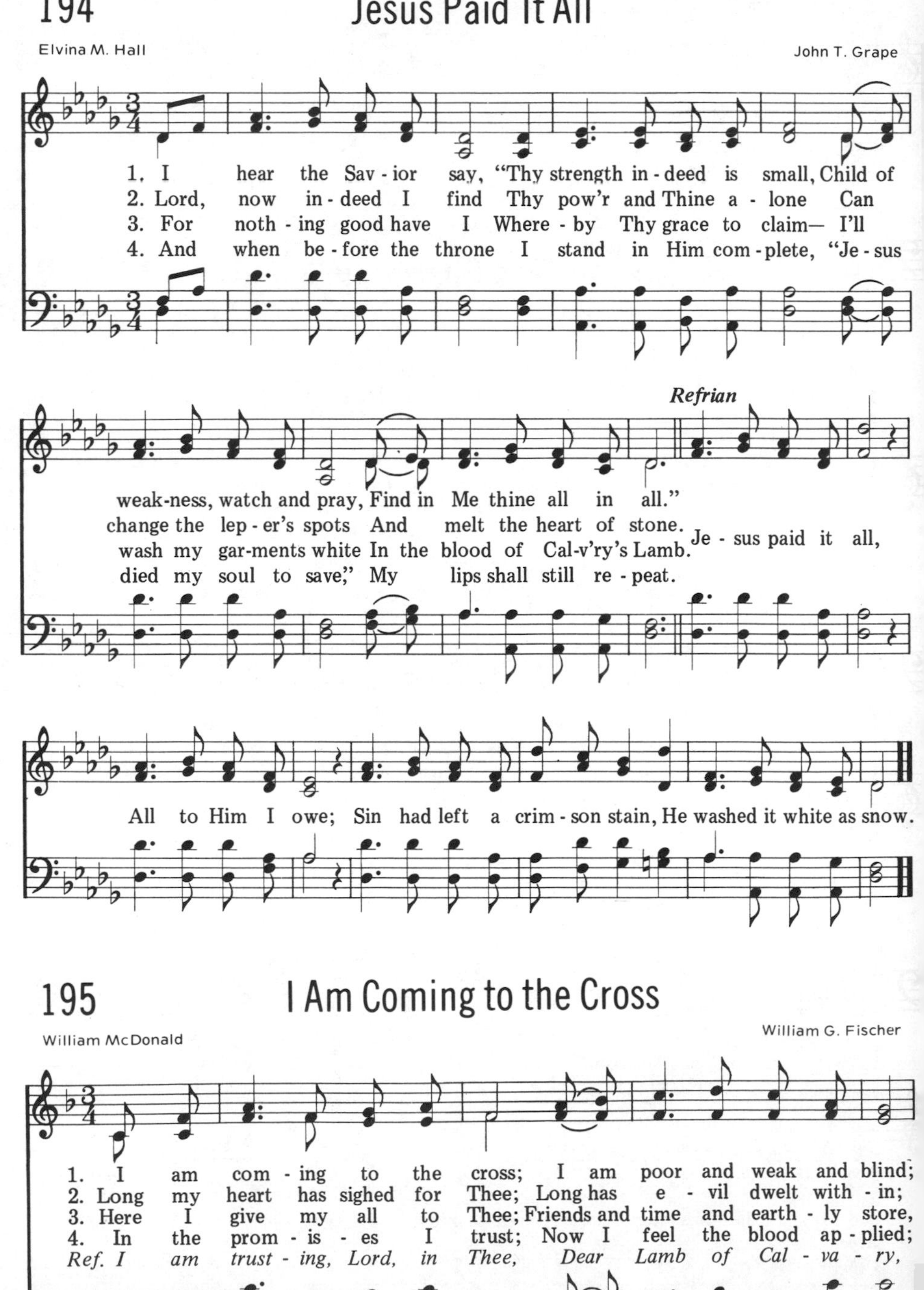
194
Jesus Paid It All
Elvina M. Hall
John T. Grape
1. I hear the Sav - ior say, "Thy strength in - deed is small, Child of
2. Lord, now in - deed I find Thy pow'r and Thine a - lone Can
3. For noth - ing good have I Where - by Thy grace to claim— I'll
4. And when be - fore the throne I stand in Him com - plete, "Je - sus
weak-ness, watch and pray, Find in Me thine all in all."
change the lep - er's spots And melt the heart of stone.
wash my gar-ments white In the blood of Cal-v'ry's Lamb.
died my soul to save," My lips shall still re - peat.
Refrian
Je - sus paid it all,
All to Him I owe; Sin had left a crim - son stain, He washed it white as snow.
195
I Am Coming to the Cross
William McDonald
William G. Fischer
1. I am com - ing to the cross; I am poor and weak and blind;
2. Long my heart has sighed for Thee; Long has e - vil dwelt with - in;
3. Here I give my all to Thee; Friends and time and earth - ly store,
4. In the prom - is - es I trust; Now I feel the blood ap - plied;
Ref. I am trust - ing, Lord, in Thee, Dear Lamb of Cal - va - ry,

D.C. Refrain
I am count - ing all but dross; I shall full sal - va - tion find.
Je - sus sweet - ly speaks to me, "I will cleanse you from all sin."
Soul and bod - y Thine to be, Whol - ly Thine for - ev - er - more.
I am pros - trate in the dust; I with Christ am cru - ci - fied.
Hum - bly at the cross I bow; Save me, Je - sus, save me now.
Majestic Sweetness
196
Samuel Stennett
Thomas Hastings
1. Ma - jes - tic sweet - ness sits en - throned Up - on the Sav - ior's
2. No mor - tal can with Him com - pare, A - mong the sons of
3. He saw me plunged in deep dis - tress, He flew to my re -
4. To Him I owe my life and breath, And all the joys I
5. Since from His boun - ty I re - ceive Such proofs of love di -
brow; His head with ra - diant glo - ries crowned, His
men; Fair - er is He than all the fair That
lief; For me He bore the shame - ful cross And
have; He makes me tri - umph o - ver death, And
vine, Had I a thou - sand hearts to give, Lord,
lips with grace o'er - flow, His lips with grace o'er - flow.
fill the heav'n - ly train, That fill the heav'n - ly train.
car - ried all my grief, And car - ried all my grief.
saves me from the grave, And saves me from the grave.
they should all be Thine, Lord, they should all be Thine. A - men.

197 But as Many as Received Him

Roger M. Hickman
Ed. by A.B.S.

Roger M. Hickman
Rev. by Alfred B. Smith

1. Je - sus came to earth by a low - ly birth, Gave Him-self as an of-f'ring of match - less worth; To His own He came in The Fa - ther's name, But they nailed Him to a tree.
2. Grace and par-don free, all for you and me, Ev - 'ry one who receives Him a son may be; For His blood He spilt to re - move sin's guilt, Made us whit - er than the snow.
3. Not by works we come as the Fa-ther's son, To re - ceive as a wel-come the words "well done". We are saved by Grace— Je - sus took our place When He died on Cal - va - ry.
Refrain (John 1:12)
1. But 2. For 3. For
as man - y as re-ceived Him to them He gave the pow'r, The pow - er to be-come the sons of God; But as man - y as re-ceived Him to them He gave the pow'r to be called the sons of God.

Whosoever Will

Philip P. Bliss

Philip P. Bliss

1. "Who - so - ev - er hear - eth," shout, shout the sound! Spread the bless-ed ti - dings
2. Who - so - ev - er com - eth need not de - lay, Now the door is o - pen,
3. "Who - so - ev - er will," the prom-ise is se - cure; "Who - so - ev - er will," for -

all the world a - round; Tell the joy - ful news wher - ev - er man is found,
en - ter while you may; Je - sus is the true, the on - ly liv - ing Way:
ev - er must en - dure; "Who - so - ev - er will," 'tis life for - ev - er-more;

REFRAIN

"Who - so - ev - er will may come." "Who - so - ev - er will, who - so - ev - er will!"

Send the proc - la - ma - tion o - ver vale and hill; 'Tis a lov - ing

Fa - ther calls the wan-derer home: "Who - so - ev - er will may come."

199 Once for All!

Philip P. Bliss

Philip P. Bliss

1. Free from the law, O hap - py con - di - tion, Je - sus hath bled, and there is re - mis - sion; Cursed by the law and bruised by the fall, Grace hath re-deemed us once for all.
2. Now are we free—there's no con - dem - na - tion, Je - sus pro- vides a per - fect sal - va - tion; "Come un - to Me," O hear His sweet call, Come, and He saves us once for all.
3. Chil - dren of God, O glo - ri - ous call - ing, Sure - ly His grace will keep us from fall - ing; Pass - ing from death to life at His call, Bless-ed sal - va - tion once for all.
CHORUS
Once for all— O sin - ner, re- ceive it; Once for all— O broth - er, be - lieve it; Cling to the cross, the bur - den will fall, Christ hath re-deemed us once for all.

Blessed Assurance

Fanny J. Crosby

Pheobe Palmer Knapp

1. Bless-ed as - sur - ance, Je - sus is mine! Oh, what a fore - taste of
2. Per - fect sub - mis - sion, per-fect de - light, Vi - sions of rap - ture now
3. Per - fect sub - mis - sion, all is at rest; I in my Sav - iour am

glo - ry di - vine! Heir of sal - va - tion, pur-chase of God, Born of His
burst on my sight. An - gels de - scend - ing, bring from a - bove Ech - oes of
hap - py and blest, Watch-ing and wait - ing, look - ing a - bove, Filled with His

Spir - it, washed in His blood.
mer - cy, whis-pers of love.
good-ness, lost in His love.

REFRAIN

This is my sto - ry, this is my song: Prais - ing my Sav - iour all the day long. This is my sto - ry, this is my song: Prais-ing my Sav - iour all the day long.

201
Just When I Need Him Most
William C. Poole
Charles H. Gabriel
1. Just when I need Him, Je-sus is near, Just when I fal-ter, just when I fear; Read-y to help me, read-y to cheer,
2. Just when I need Him, Je-sus is true, Nev-er for-sak-ing all the way thro'; Giv-ing for bur-dens pleas-ures a-new,
3. Just when I need Him, Je-sus is strong, Bear-ing my bur-dens all the day long; For all my sor-row giv-ing a song,
4. Just when I need Him, He is my All, An-swer-ing when up-on Him I call; Ten-der-ly watch-ing lest I should fall,
Just when I need Him most.
REFRAIN
Just when I need Him most, Just when I need Him most; Je-sus is near to com-fort and cheer, Just when I need Him most.
Copyright 1908 by Chas. H. Gabriel. The Rodeheaver Co., owner. © Renewed 1936 (extended), The Rodeheaver Co. Used by permission.

Jesus Never Has Failed Me Yet

W. J. Henry
Edited by Alfred B. Smith

W. J. Henry
Rev. & Arr. by A.B.S.

1. As I trav - el lifes path-way so rug-ged and steep, When I pass thro' the
2. So I walk by His side thro' the heat of the day. Where He leads me I
3. I will dread not the fu-ture, and fear not the foe. For I'm safe in His

val - ley so dark and so deep, When the snares for my soul by my
fol - low; His will I o - bey. And thro' Him I can con-quer the
keep-ing wher - ev - er I go; For no soul that has trust-ed Him

foes have been set, Je - sus nev - er has failed me yet.
foes that be - set, For He nev-er has failed me yet.
will He for-get, For He nev-er has failed me yet.

Refrain

Je-sus nev-er has failed me yet. Je-sus nev-er has failed me yet. I have prov-en Him true; what He says He will do. Je-sus nev-er has failed me yet.

203 Hiding in Thee

William O. Cushing | Ira D. Sankey

1. Oh, safe to the Rock that is high - er than I My
2. In the calm of the noon - tide, in sor - row's lone hour, In
3. How oft in the con - flict, when pressed by the foe, I have
soul in its con - flicts and sor - rows would fly. So sin - ful, so
times when temp - ta - tion casts o'er me its power; In the tem - pests of
fled to my ref - uge and breathed out my woe; How oft - en, when
wea - ry, Thine, Thine would I be! Thou blest Rock of
life, on its wide, heav - ing sea, Thou blest Rock of
tri - als like sea bil - lows roll, Have I hid - den in
Refrain
A - ges, I'm hid - ing in Thee.
A - ges, I'm hid - ing in Thee. Hid - ing in Thee, Hid - ing in
Thee, O Thou Rock of my soul.
Thee, Thou blest Rock of A - ges, I'm hid - ing in Thee.

We Are by Christ Redeemed 204

Mary Bowley Peters

Alfred B. Smith

1. We are by Christ re-deemed; The cost, His pre-cious blood;
2. Our earth-en ves-sels break, The world it-self grows old;
3. Thus far by grace pre-served, Each mo-ment speeds us on;
4. To Him our weak-ness clings, Thro' trib-u-la-tion sore,
Be noth-ing by our souls es-teem'd Like this great good!
But Christ our pre-cious dust will take And fresh-ly mould:
The crown and king-dom are re-served Where Christ is gone.
And seeks the shelt-er of His wings Till all is o'er;
Were the vast world our own, With all its var-ied store,
He'll give these bod-ies vile A fash-ion like His own,
When cloud-less morn-ing shines, We shall His glo-ry share;
And when we've run the race, And fought the faith-ful fight,
And Thou, Lord Je-sus, were un-known, We'd still be poor!
He'll bid the whole cre-a-tion smile, And hush its groan!
In pleas-ant plac-es are the lines! The home, how fair!
We then shall see Him face to face, With saints in light.

205

Faith Is the Victory

Ira D. Sankey

John H. Yates

1. En - camped a - long the hills of light, Ye Chris - tian sol - diers, rise,
2. His ban - ner o - ver us is love, Our sword the Word of God;
3. On ev - ery hand the foe we find Drawn up in dread ar - ray;
4. To him that o - ver - comes the foe White rai - ment shall be given;
And press the bat - tle ere the night Shall veil the glow - ing skies.
We tread the road the saints a - bove With shouts of tri - umph trod.
Let tents of ease be left be - hind, And on - ward to the fray;
Be - fore the an - gels he shall know His name con-fessed in heaven.
A - gainst the foe in vales be - low, Let all our strength be hurled;
By faith they, like a whirl-wind's breath, Swept on o'er ev - ery field;
Sal - va - tion's hel - met on each head, With truth all girt a - bout,
Then on - ward from the hills of light, Our hearts with love a - flame,
Faith is the vic - to - ry, we know, That o - ver-comes the world.
The faith by which they con-quered death Is still our shin - ing shield.
The earth shall trem - ble 'neath our tread And ech - o with our shout.
We'll van - quish all the hosts of night In Je - sus' con-quering name.
Refrain
Faith is the vic - to - ry! Faith is the vic - to - ry!

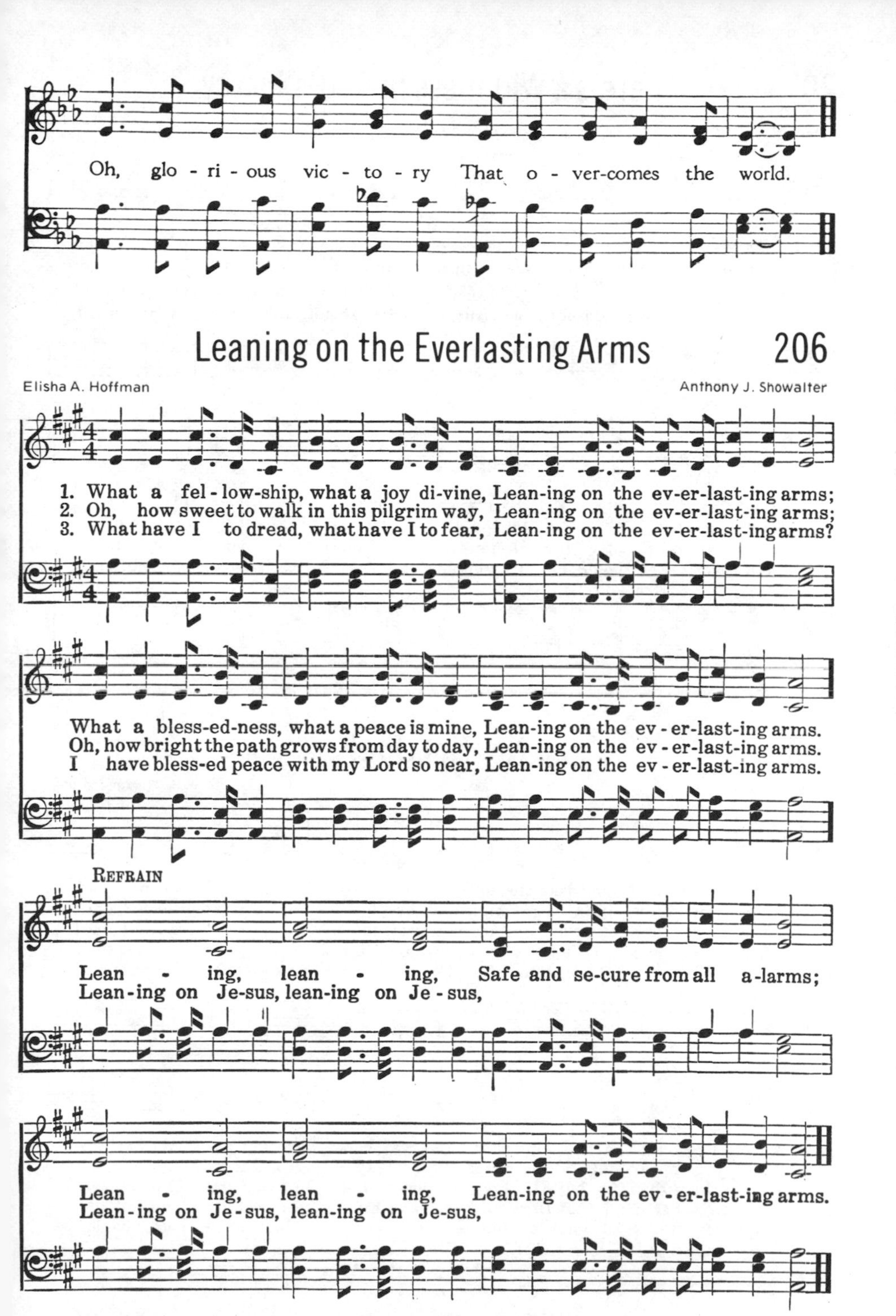
Oh, glo - ri - ous vic - to - ry That o - ver-comes the world.
Leaning on the Everlasting Arms
206
Elisha A. Hoffman
Anthony J. Showalter
1. What a fel - low-ship, what a joy di-vine, Lean-ing on the ev-er-last-ing arms;
2. Oh, how sweet to walk in this pilgrim way, Lean-ing on the ev-er-last-ing arms;
3. What have I to dread, what have I to fear, Lean-ing on the ev-er-last-ing arms?
What a bless-ed-ness, what a peace is mine, Lean-ing on the ev - er-last-ing arms.
Oh, how bright the path grows from day to day, Lean-ing on the ev - er-last-ing arms.
I have bless-ed peace with my Lord so near, Lean-ing on the ev - er-last-ing arms.
Refrain
Lean - ing, lean - ing, Safe and se-cure from all a-larms;
Lean-ing on Je-sus, lean-ing on Je - sus,
Lean - ing, lean - ing, Lean-ing on the ev - er-last-ing arms.
Lean-ing on Je-sus, lean-ing on Je-sus,

207 There's a Wideness in God's Mercy

Frederick W. Faber — Lizzie S. Tourjee

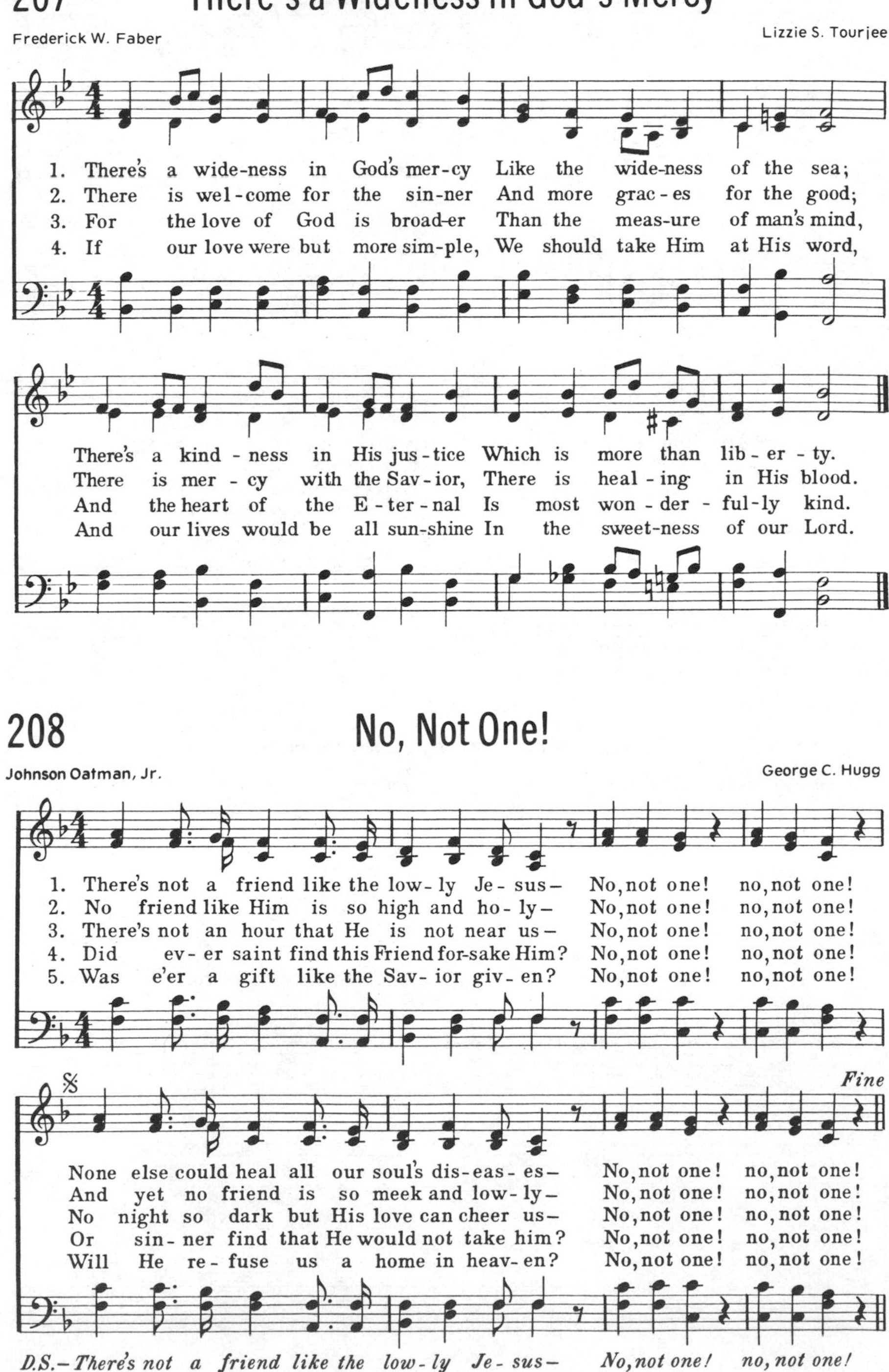
1. There's a wide-ness in God's mer-cy Like the wide-ness of the sea;
2. There is wel-come for the sin-ner And more grac-es for the good;
3. For the love of God is broad-er Than the meas-ure of man's mind,
4. If our love were but more sim-ple, We should take Him at His word,
There's a kind-ness in His jus-tice Which is more than lib-er-ty.
There is mer-cy with the Sav-ior, There is heal-ing in His blood.
And the heart of the E-ter-nal Is most won-der-ful-ly kind.
And our lives would be all sun-shine In the sweet-ness of our Lord.
208
No, Not One!
Johnson Oatman, Jr.
George C. Hugg
1. There's not a friend like the low-ly Je-sus– No, not one! no, not one!
2. No friend like Him is so high and ho-ly– No, not one! no, not one!
3. There's not an hour that He is not near us– No, not one! no, not one!
4. Did ev-er saint find this Friend for-sake Him? No, not one! no, not one!
5. Was e'er a gift like the Sav-ior giv-en? No, not one! no, not one!
Fine
None else could heal all our soul's dis-eas-es– No, not one! no, not one!
And yet no friend is so meek and low-ly– No, not one! no, not one!
No night so dark but His love can cheer us– No, not one! no, not one!
Or sin-ner find that He would not take him? No, not one! no, not one!
Will He re-fuse us a home in heav-en? No, not one! no, not one!
D.S.–There's not a friend like the low-ly Je-sus– No, not one! no, not one!

CHORUS
D.S.
Je-sus knows all a-bout our strug-gles, He will guide till the day is done;
Satisfied
209
Clara Tear Williams
Ralph E. Hudson
1. All my life long I had pant-ed For a draught, from some clear spring,
2. Feed-ing on the husks a-round me, Till my strength was al-most gone,
3. Poor I was, and sought for rich-es, Something that would sat-is-fy,
4. Well of wa-ter, ev-er spring-ing, Bread of life so rich and free,
That I hoped would quench the burn-ing Of the thirst I felt with-in.
Longed my soul for some-thing bet-ter, On-ly still to hun-ger on.
But the dust I gath-ered round me On-ly mocked my soul's sad cry.
Un-told wealth that nev-er fail-eth, My Re-deem-er is to me.
CHORUS
Hal-le-lu-jah! I have found Him Whom my soul so long has craved!
Je-sus sat-is-fies my long-ings—Thru His blood I now am saved.

210 Teach Me to Pray, Lord

Albert S. Reitz | Albert S. Reitz

1. Teach me to pray, Lord, teach me to pray; This is my heart - cry
2. Pow - er in prayer, Lord, pow - er in prayer, Here 'mid earth's sin and
3. My weak - ened will, Lord, Thou canst re - new; My sin - ful na - ture
4. Teach me to pray, Lord, teach me to pray; Thou art my pat - tern,

day un - to day; I long to know Thy will and Thy way; Teach me to
sor - row and care; Men lost and dy - ing, souls in de - spair; O give me
Thou canst sub - due; Fill me just now with pow - er a - new, Pow - er to
day un - to day; Thou art my sure - ty, now and for aye; Teach me to

pray, Lord, teach me to pray.
pow - er, pow - er in prayer!
pray and pow - er to do!
pray, Lord, teach me to pray.

Refrain

Liv - ing in Thee, Lord, and Thou in me; Con - stant a - bid - ing, this is my plea; Grant me Thy pow - er, bound - less and free: Pow - er with men and pow - er with Thee.

I Must Tell Jesus

Elisha A. Hoffman

Elisha A. Hoffman

1. I must tell Jesus all of my trials, I cannot bear these burdens alone;
In my distress He kindly will help me, He ever loves and cares for His own.

2. I must tell Jesus all of my troubles, He is a kind, compassionate Friend;
If I but ask Him, He will deliver, Make of my troubles quickly an end.

3. Tempted and tried, I need a great Savior, One who can help my burdens to bear;
I must tell Jesus, I must tell Jesus, He all my cares and sorrows will share.

4. O how the world to evil allures me! O how my heart is tempted to sin!
I must tell Jesus, and He will help me O-ver the world the vic-t'ry to win.

CHORUS

I must tell Jesus! I must tell Jesus! I cannot bear my burdens alone;
I must tell Jesus! I must tell Jesus! Jesus can help me, Jesus alone.

212 I Am Praying Blessed Saviour

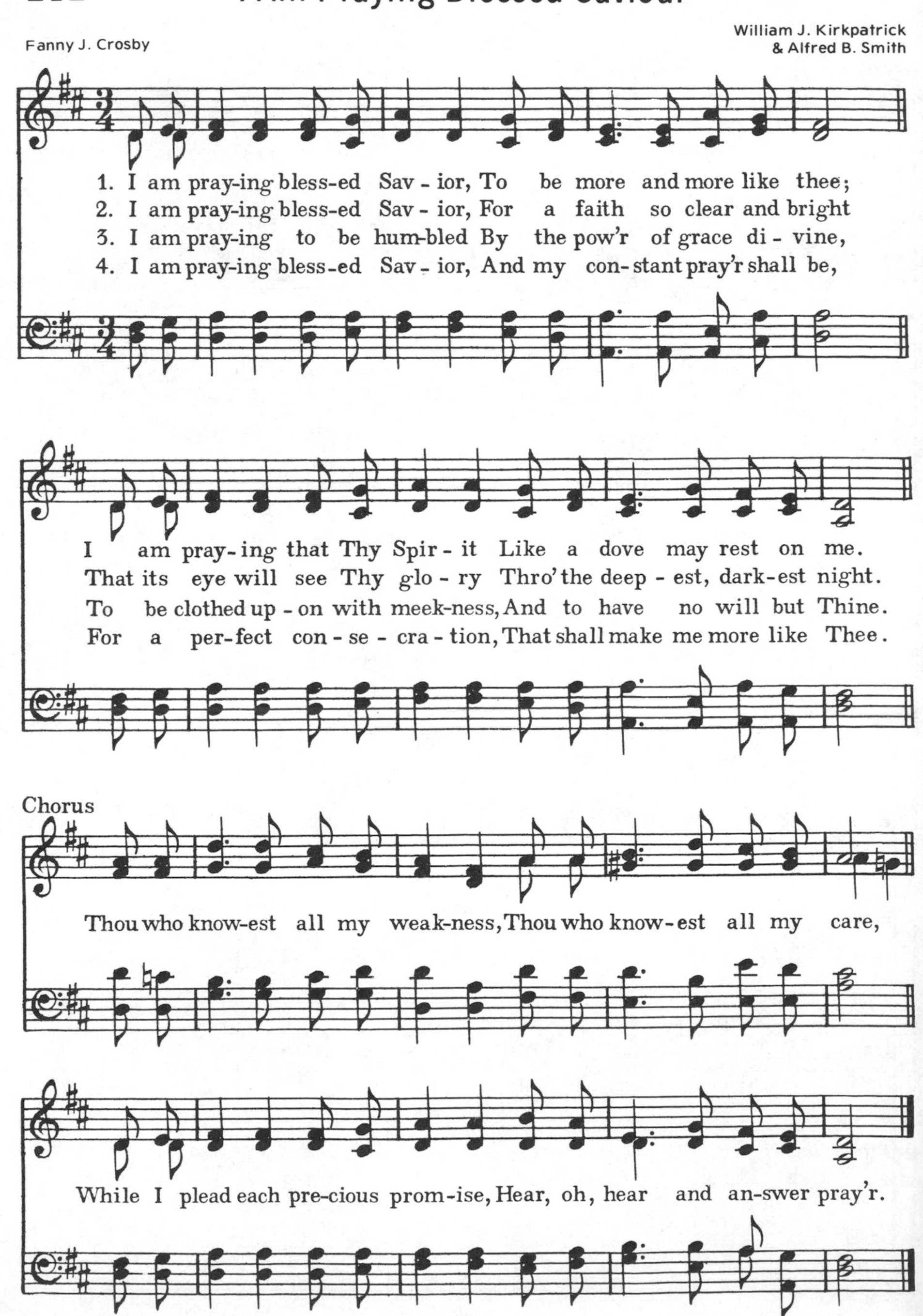
Fanny J. Crosby
William J. Kirkpatrick
& Alfred B. Smith
1. I am pray-ing bless-ed Sav - ior, To be more and more like thee;
2. I am pray-ing bless-ed Sav - ior, For a faith so clear and bright
3. I am pray-ing to be hum-bled By the pow'r of grace di - vine,
4. I am pray-ing bless-ed Sav - ior, And my con-stant pray'r shall be,
I am pray-ing that Thy Spir - it Like a dove may rest on me.
That its eye will see Thy glo - ry Thro' the deep - est, dark-est night.
To be clothed up - on with meek-ness, And to have no will but Thine.
For a per-fect con - se - cra - tion, That shall make me more like Thee.
Chorus
Thou who know-est all my weak-ness, Thou who know-est all my care,
While I plead each pre-cious prom-ise, Hear, oh, hear and an-swer pray'r.

O God, We Want to Thank You

213

James M. Gray
Alfred B. Smith
1. O God, we want to thank You That You have an-swered prayer!
2. Lord, You have nev - er failed us. We ask and we ob - tain,
3. And so we want to thank You, Not one a - lone, but all
We made our sup-pli - ca - tion, Our anx - ious hearts laid bare;
And so with faith made stron-ger Re - turn and ask a - gain;
Who know You as their Fa - ther And on Your boun-ty call;
Lord You have kept Your prom - ise, And from Your throne on high
We knock, and You will o - pen And stand with-in the door,
Re - deemed are we in Je - sus, Your Son You did not spare,
Did bend Your ear to lis - ten And grant Your ser-vants' cry.
And give us gra-cious wel-come To come and ask for more.
And with Him You have giv'n us Your love in Him to share.

214 From Every Stormy Wind

Hugh Stowell

Thomas Hastings

1. From ev - ery storm - y wind that blows, From ev - ery swell - ing tide of woes, There is a calm, a sure re - treat: 'Tis found be - neath the mer - cy seat.
2. There is a place where Je - sus sheds The oil of glad - ness on our heads; A place than all be - side more sweet: It is the blood - bought mer - cy seat.
3. There is a scene where spir - its blend, Where friend holds fel - low- ship with friend; Though sun - dered far, by faith they meet A - round one com - mon mer - cy seat.
4. Ah! whith - er could we flee for aid, When tempt - ed, des - o- late, dis - mayed: Or how the hosts of hell de - feat, Had suf - f'ring saints no mer - cy seat.
5. Ah! there on ea - gle wings we soar, And sin and sense mo- lest no more: And heav'n comes down our souls to greet, While glo - ry crowns the mer - cy seat. A - men.
215
Lord, Speak to Me
Frances R. Havergal
Robert A. Schumann
1. Lord, speak to me, that I may speak In liv - ing ech - oes of Thy tone;
2. O teach me, Lord, that I may teach The pre - cious things Thou dost im-part;
3. O fill me with Thy full - ness, Lord, Un - til my ver - y heart o'er-flow
4. O use me, Lord, use e - ven me, Just as Thou wilt and when and where

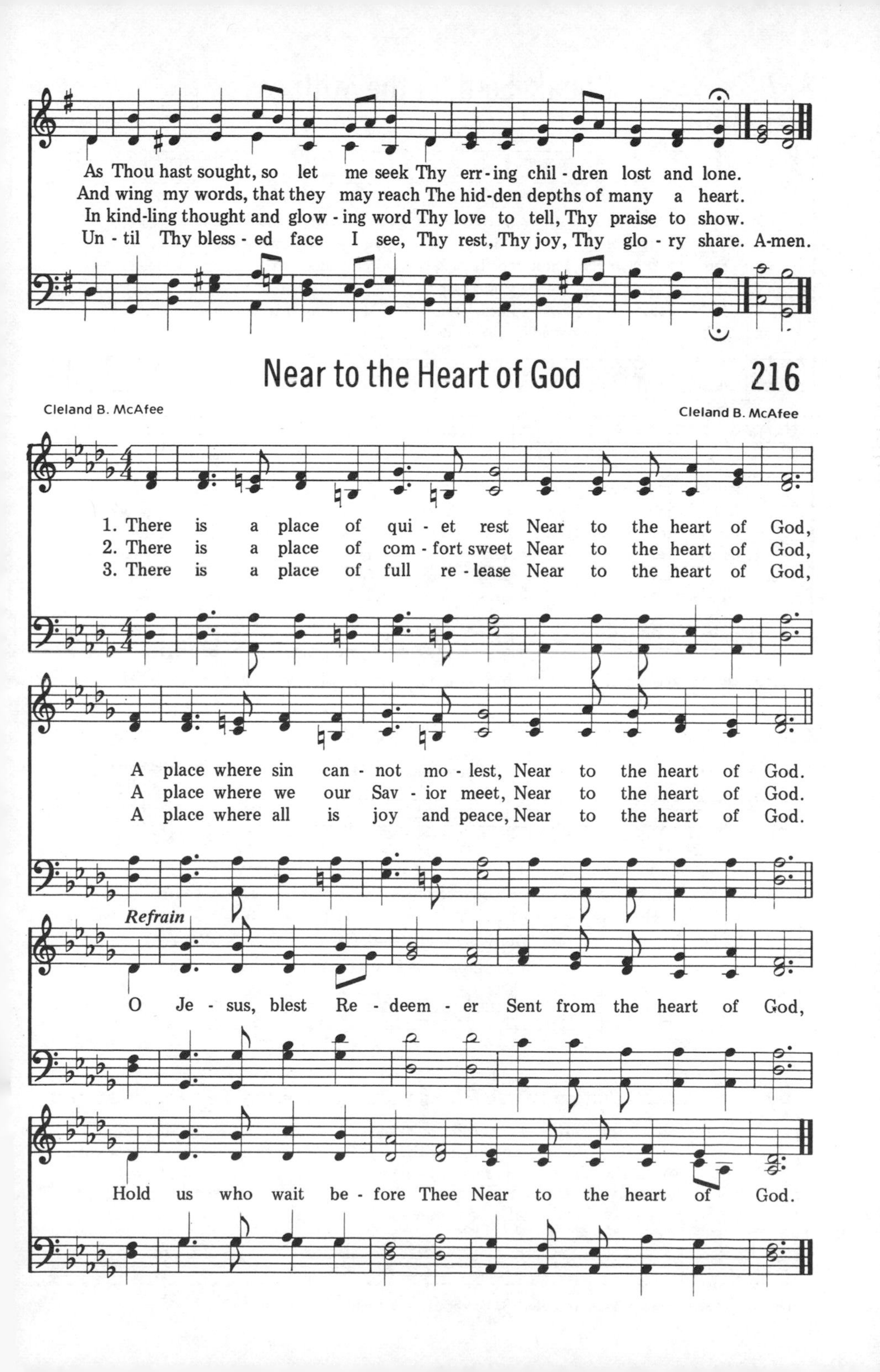
As Thou hast sought, so let me seek Thy err-ing chil-dren lost and lone.
And wing my words, that they may reach The hid-den depths of many a heart.
In kind-ling thought and glow-ing word Thy love to tell, Thy praise to show.
Un-til Thy bless-ed face I see, Thy rest, Thy joy, Thy glo-ry share. A-men.
Near to the Heart of God
216
Cleland B. McAfee
Cleland B. McAfee
1. There is a place of qui-et rest Near to the heart of God,
2. There is a place of com-fort sweet Near to the heart of God,
3. There is a place of full re-lease Near to the heart of God,
A place where sin can-not mo-lest, Near to the heart of God.
A place where we our Sav-ior meet, Near to the heart of God.
A place where all is joy and peace, Near to the heart of God.
Refrain
O Je-sus, blest Re-deem-er Sent from the heart of God,
Hold us who wait be-fore Thee Near to the heart of God.

217 Speak, Lord, in the Stillness

E. May Grimes

Alfred B. Smith

1. Speak, Lord, in the still - ness, While I wait on Thee;
2. Speak, O bless - ed Mas - ter, In this qui - et hour;
3. For the words Thou speak - est, They are life in - deed;
4. All to Thee is yield - ed— I am not my own!
5. Fill me with the knowl - edge Of Thy glo - rious will;
6. Like a wa - tered gar - den Full of fra - grance rare,
Hush'd my heart to lis - ten, In ex - pect - an - cy.
Let me see Thy face, Lord, Feel Thy touch of pow'r.
Liv - ing Bread from heav - en, Now my spir - it feed!
Bliss - ful, glad sur - ren - der— I am Thine a - lone!
All Thine own good plea - sure In Thy child ful - fill.
Lin - g'ring in Thy pres - ence, Let my life ap - pear.

218

Revival Prayer

Richard A. Bennett

2 Chronicles 7: 14.

From Old Hymn Melody
Alfred B. Smith

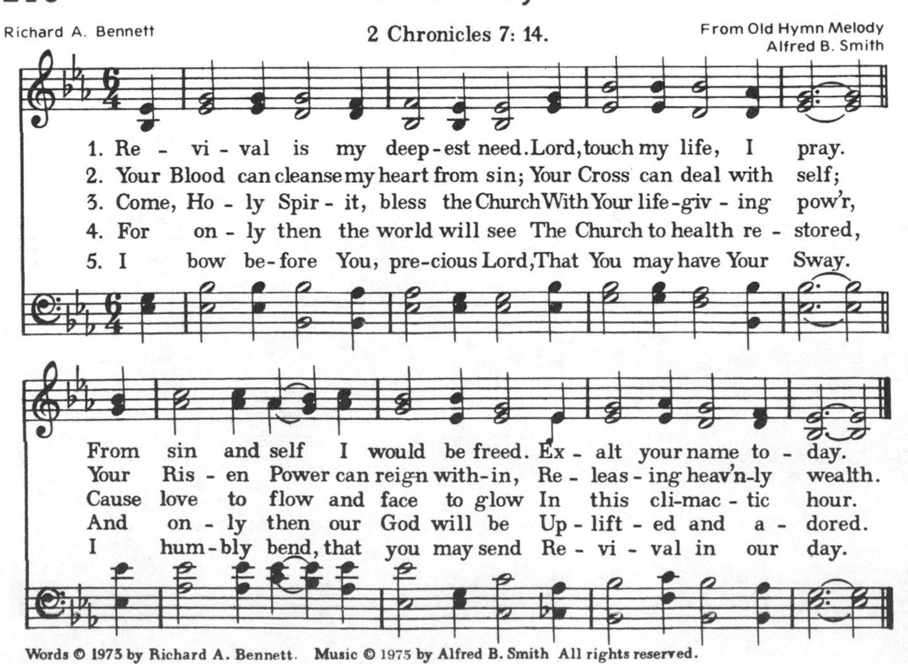
1. Re - vi - val is my deep - est need. Lord, touch my life, I pray.
2. Your Blood can cleanse my heart from sin; Your Cross can deal with self;
3. Come, Ho - ly Spir - it, bless the Church With Your life - giv - ing pow'r,
4. For on - ly then the world will see The Church to health re - stored,
5. I bow be - fore You, pre - cious Lord, That You may have Your Sway.
From sin and self I would be freed. Ex - alt your name to - day.
Your Ris - en Power can reign with - in, Re - leas - ing heav'n - ly wealth.
Cause love to flow and face to glow In this cli - mac - tic hour.
And on - ly then our God will be Up - lift - ed and a - dored.
I hum - bly bend, that you may send Re - vi - val in our day.

For You I Am Praying

S. O. Manney Clough

Ira. D. Sankey

1. I have a Sav - ior, He's plead - ing in glo - ry, A dear, lov - ing
2. I have a Fa - ther; to me He has giv - en A hope for e-
3. I have a peace; it is calm as a riv - er, A peace that the
4. When He has found you, tell oth - ers the sto - ry, That my lov - ing
Sav - ior, tho' earth-friends be few; And now He is watch - ing in
ter - ni - ty, bless - ed and true; And soon He will call me to
friends of this world nev - er knew: My Sav - ior a - lone is its
Sav - ior is your Sav - ior, too; Then pray that your Sav - ior may
ten - der - ness o'er me, But O, that my Sav - ior were your Sav - ior too!
meet Him in heav - en, But O, that He'd let me bring you with me too!
au - thor and giv - er, And O, could I know it was giv - en for you.
bring them to glo - ry, And prayer will be an-swered—'twas an-swered for you!
Refrain
For you I am pray - ing, For you I am pray - ing,
For you I am pray - ing, I'm pray - ing for you.

220 My Heart's Prayer

H. P. Blanchard
Ralph E. Stewart
1. My new life I owe to Thee, Je - sus, Lamb of Cal - va - ry;
2. Hum - bly at Thy cross I'd stay— Je - sus, keep me there, I pray;
3. Grant me wis - dom, grace and pow'r— Lord, I need Thee ev - 'ry hour;
4. Sav - ior, Thou hast heard my plea— Thou art near, so near to me;
Sin was can - celed on the tree— Je - sus, bless - ed Je - sus!
Teach me more of Thee each day, Je - sus, bless - ed Je - sus!
Let my will be lost in Thine, Je - sus, bless - ed Je - sus!
Now I feel Thy strength'ning pow'r, Je - sus, bless - ed Je - sus!
221 Saviour, Breathe an Evening Blessing
James Edmeston
George C. Stebbins
1. Sav - ior, breathe an eve - ning bless - ing Ere re - pose our spir - its seal:
2. Tho de - struc - tion walk a - round us, Tho the ar - rows past us fly,
3. Tho the night be dark and drear - y, Dark - ness can - not hide from Thee;
4. Should swift death this night o'er - take us And our couch be - come our tomb,
Sin and want we come con - fess - ing, Thou canst save, and Thou canst heal.
An - gel - guards from Thee sur - round us— We are safe if Thou art nigh.
Thou art He who, nev - er wea - ry, Watch - est where Thy peo - ple be.
May the morn in heav'n a - wake us, Clad in light and death - less bloom.

I've Found a Friend

222

James G. Small

George C. Stebbins

1. I've found a Friend, O such a Friend! He loved me ere I knew Him;
2. I've found a Friend, O such a Friend! He bled, He died to save me;
3. I've found a Friend, O such a Friend! So kind and true and ten-der,
He drew me with the cords of love, And thus He bound me to Him.
And not a-lone the gift of life, But His own self He gave me.
So wise a Coun-sel-or and Guide, So might-y a De-fend-er!
And round my heart still close-ly twine Those ties which naught can sev-er,
Naught that I have my own I call, I hold it for the Giv-er;
From Him who loves me now so well, What pow'r my soul can sev-er?
For I am His and He is mine, For-ev-er and for-ev-er.
My heart, my strength, my life, my all Are His, and His for-ev-er.
Shall life or death, or earth or hell? No! I am His for-ev-er.

223 Whom Having Not Seen, I Love

Maud Frazer
Chorus A. B. S.
Alfred B. Smith
Not fast
1. A Friend have I who stand-eth near, To com-fort me and still each fear;
2. In vain may fan-cy try to trace My Sav-iour's beau-ty and His grace;
3. This pre-cious hope I have each day Il - lu-mines all my earth-ly way;
4. With that fair man-sion in my view, My pil-grim jour-ney I pur-sue;
It is my Lord and Sav - iour dear, Whom, hav-ing not seen, I love.
More fair than I can dream, His face, Whom, hav-ing not seen, I love.
That He will take me home to stay, Whom, hav-ing not seen, I love.
And strive my Sav-iour's will to, do Whom, hav-ing not seen, I love.
Chorus
This Friend is real, so real to me; He guides my foot-steps con-stant-ly; And
rit.
molto rit.
some glad day not far a-way, I shall see Him, Whom, hav-ing not seen, I love.

My Lord and I

Mrs. I. Shorey

Alfred B. Smith

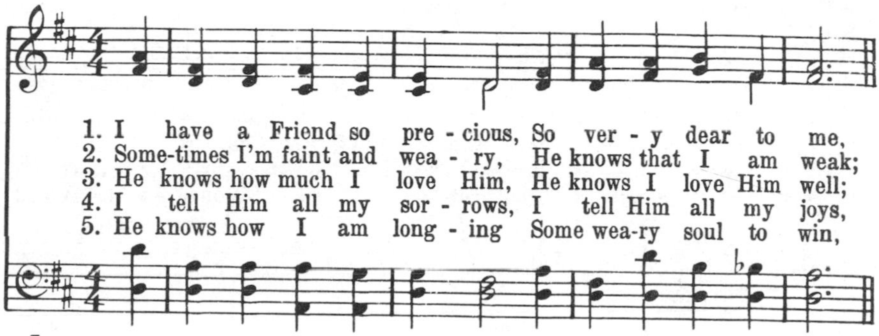

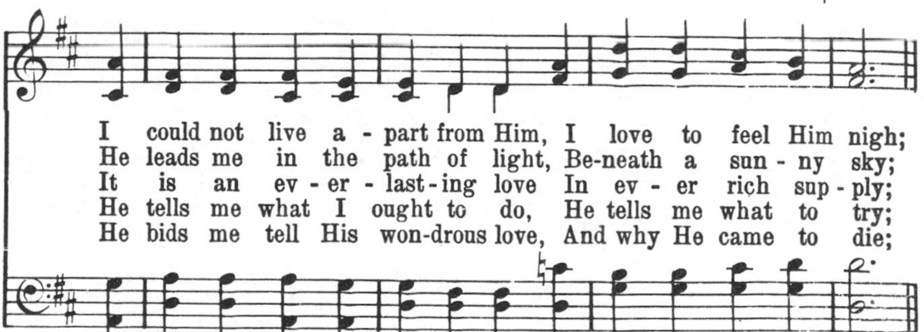

1. I have a Friend so precious, So very dear to me,
He loves me with a tender love, He loves me faithfully;
I could not live apart from Him, I love to feel Him nigh;
And so we dwell together, My Lord and I.

2. Sometimes I'm faint and weary, He knows that I am weak;
And as He bids me lean on Him, His help I'll gladly seek;
He leads me in the path of light, Beneath a sunny sky;
And so we walk together, My Lord and I.

3. He knows how much I love Him, He knows I love Him well;
But with what love He loveth me, My tongue can never tell;
It is an everlasting love In ever rich supply;
And so we love together, My Lord and I.

4. I tell Him all my sorrows, I tell Him all my joys,
I tell Him all that pleases me, I tell Him what annoys;
He tells me what I ought to do, He tells me what to try;
And so we talk together, My Lord and I.

5. He knows how I am longing Some weary soul to win,
And so He bids me go and speak A loving word for Him;
He bids me tell His wondrous love, And why He came to die;
And so we work together, My Lord and I.

225 The Glory of His Presence

Dr. Oswald J. Smith

B. D. Ackley

Solo (or Unison)
1. I have walked a - lone with Je - sus In a fel - low-ship di - vine;
2. On the moun-tain I have seen Him, Christ my Com-fort - er and Friend;
3. In my fail - ure, sin and sor - row, Bro - ken-heart - ed, crushed and torn,
4. In the dark-ness, in the shad - ow, With the Sav - ior I have trod,
Nev - er - more can earth al - lure me, I am His and He is mine.
And the glo - ry of that vi - sion Will be with me to the end.
I have felt His pres-ence near me, He has all my bur-dens borne.
Sweet in - deed have been the les-sons, Since I've walked a - lone with God.
CHORUS (4 parts)
I have seen Him, I have known Him, For He deigns to walk with me; And the glo-ry of His
pres-ence will be mine e - ter - nal - ly. O the glo-ry of His pres-ence, O the
beau-ty of His face; I am His and His for-ev - er, He has won me by His grace.

All the Way Along 226

Ada Blenkhorn — Lewis E. Jones

1. There is One who loves me, One who is my Friend
2. He doth still the tem-pest, bid its tu-mult cease,
3. In my Lord and Sav-iour I will joy-ful be
4. I will sing the prais-es of His won-drous love
All the way a-long, all the way a-long.
He is ev-er near me, read-y to de-fend.
In the time of troub-le keeps in per-fect peace;
Speak-ing words of com-fort sweet and dear to me,
I will sing more sweet-ly in my home a-bove.
REFRAIN
All the way a-long it is Je-sus. All the way a-long it is Je--sus;
All the way a-long, bless-ed Je-sus. He's my joy and song
All the way a-long. All the way a-long it is Je-sus.

227 Only a Touch

Ida L. Reed — B. D. Ackley

1. On - ly a touch of Thy hand, dear Lord, On - ly a word from Thee, Will all my heart's wild an - guish still, Joy - ful my soul shall be....
2. On - ly a touch of Thy hand, dear Lord, On - ly a word from Thee, Calms all my wea - ry, trou - bled soul, Still - eth life's surg - ing sea....
3. On - ly a touch of Thy hand, dear Lord, On - ly a word of love, Will all my wounds and sor - rows heal, Lead me to heav'n a - bove...
CHORUS
On - ly a touch of Thy hand, dear Lord, And o'er my soul shall sweep, Mel - o - dy sweet from life's brok - en chords, A - wak-ened from si - lence deep.

In the Garden

C. Austin Miles

(This song is based upon the meeting of Jesus and Mary on the Resurrection Morning as recorded in St. John xx: 11-18)

C. Austin Miles

1. I come to the gar - den a - lone, While the dew is still on the
2. He speaks, and the sound of His voice Is so sweet the birds hush their
3. I'd stay in the gar - den with Him Though the night a-round me be

ros - es; And the voice I hear, fall -ing on my ear; The
sing - ing, And the mel - o - dy that He gave to me, With-
fall - ing, But He bids me go; through the voice of woe, His

Son of God dis - clos - es.
in my heart is ring - ing.
voice to me is call - ing.

REFRAIN

And He walks with me, and He talks with me, And He tells me I am His own, And the joy we share as we tar - ry there, None oth-er has ev - er known.

229 I Love to Walk With Jesus

Charles F. Weigle

C.F.W. Arr. by Donna Krieger

1. Oh, I love to walk with Je-sus, Like the pub-li-cans of old,
2. Oh, I love to walk with Je-sus, Like the man of long a-go
3. Oh, I love to walk with Je-sus All the way to Cal-v'ry's brow,
4. Oh, some-time I'll walk with Je-sus In the land of end-less day,
When He gath-ered them a-bout Him And the bless-ed tid-ings told:
Who had tar-ried by the way-side Near the gates of Jer-i-cho.
Gaze up-on that scene of suf-f'ring While my tears of sor-row flow.
When our jour-ney here is o-ver And we've reached our home to stay.
How He came to bring de-liv-'rance To the cap-tives in dis-tress,
Je-sus heard his cry for mer-cy, Gave him back his sight that day,
There He tells me how He loves me, Takes my ev-'ry sin a-way;
Then I'll walk with Him for-ev-er, Sing His prais-es o'er and o'er,
Take a-way our ev-'ry bur-den, Giv-ing per-fect peace and rest.
And im-me-diate-ly he fol-lowed Je-sus all a-long the way.
So I fol-low Him so glad-ly, Lead me an-y-where He may.
And with all the saints in glo-ry Love, and wor-ship, and a-dore.

Chorus
I will fol-low where He lead-eth; I will pas-ture where He feed-eth.
I will fol-low all the way, Lord. I will fol-low Je-sus ev-'ry day.
Wonderful Jesus
230
B.A.B.
Not fast
Benjamin A. Baur
Won-der-ful, won-der-ful Je - sus, Who can com-pare with Thee!
Won-der-ful, won-der-ful Je - sus, Fair-er than all art Thou to me!
Won-der-ful, won-der-ful Je - sus, O how my soul loves Thee!
Fair - er than all the fair - est, Je-sus, art Thou to me!

231 Have Faith in God

May Stephens
Ed. by A. B. S.

Alfred B. Smith

1. Do you ev - er feel downheart-ed or dis - cour-aged? Do you
2. It is al-way's dark-est just be - fore the dawn-ing, Sil - ver
3. God is might-y He is a - ble to de - liv - er; Faith can

ev - er think your work is all in vain? Do the bur-dens thrust up-on you make you
lin-ings shine on God's side of the clouds; All your jour-ney He has prom-ised to be
vic - tor be in ev - 'ry try-ing hour; Fear, and care, and sin and sor-row be de -

trem-ble. And you feel that you will not the vic - t'ry gain?
with you, Noth-ing comes to you, but what His love al - lows.
feat - ed By our faith in God's al-might-y conqu'ring power.
Chorus
Have faith in God He can - not fail, Tho' storms of
life your path as - sail. His word is true; He cares for
you. Have faith in God! Have faith in God.

232 The Solid Rock

Edward Mote — William B. Bradbury

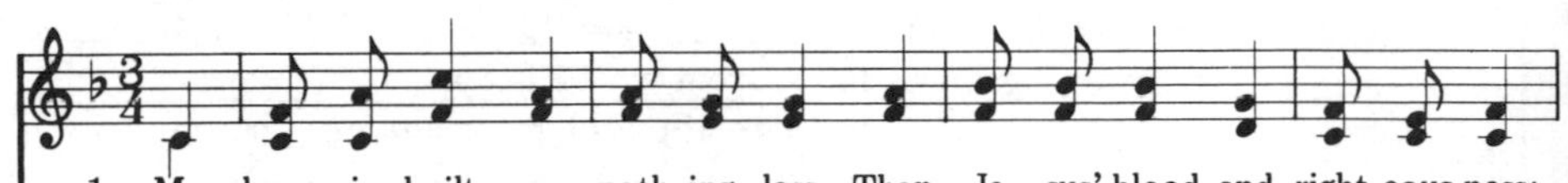

1. My hope is built on noth-ing less Than Je - sus' blood and right-eous-ness;
2. When dark-ness veils His love - ly face, I rest on His un-chang-ing grace;
3. His oath, His cov - e - nant, His blood Sup - port me in the whelm-ing flood;
4. When He shall come with trum - pet sound, O may I then in Him be found;

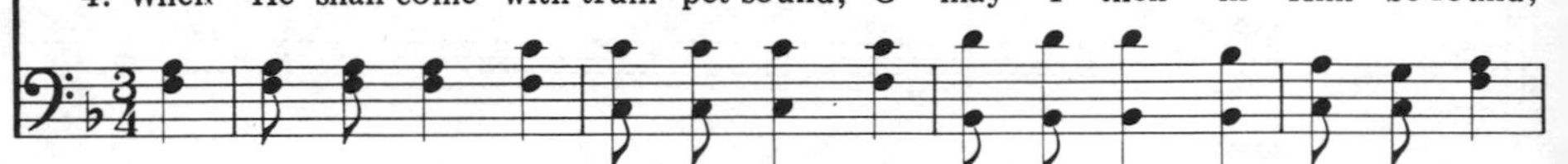

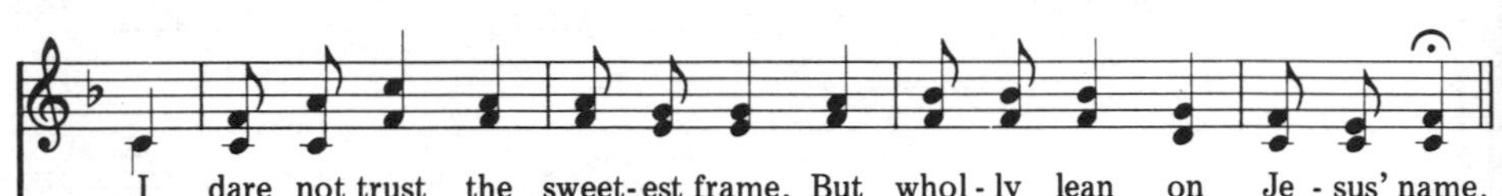

I dare not trust the sweet-est frame, But whol - ly lean on Je - sus' name.
In ev - ery high and storm - y gale, My an - chor holds with - in the veil.
When all a - round my soul gives way He then is all my hope and stay.
Dressed in His right - eous - ness a - lone, Fault - less to stand be - fore the throne.

Chorus

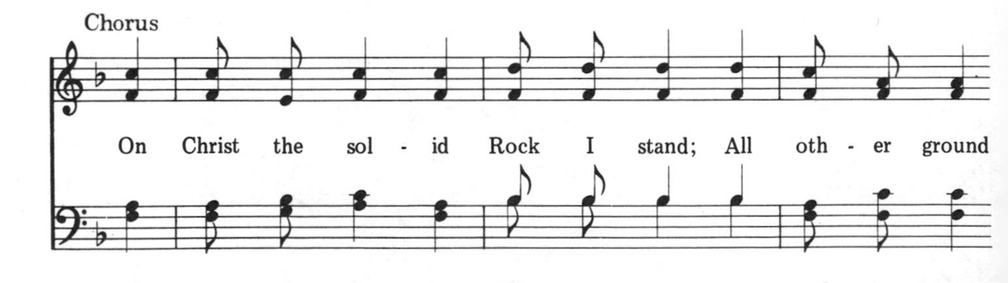
On Christ the sol - id Rock I stand; All oth - er ground

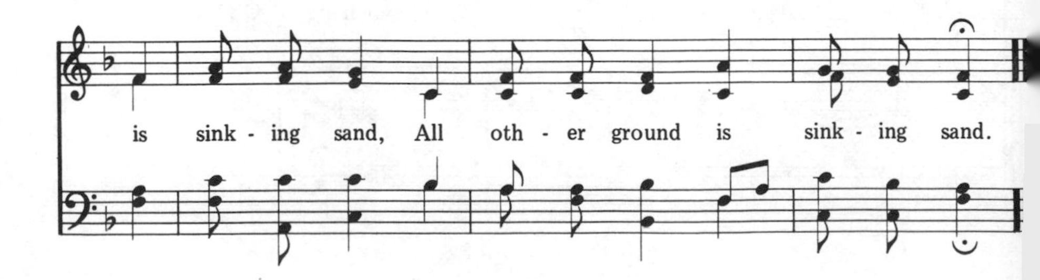
is sink - ing sand, All oth - er ground is sink - ing sand.

Trusting Jesus

Edgar P. Stites
Ira D. Sankey
1. Sim - ply trust - ing ev - ery day, Trust - ing through a storm - y way;
2. Bright - ly doth His Spir - it shine In - to this poor heart of mine;
3. Sing - ing if my way is clear, Pray - ing if the path be drear;
4. Trust - ing Him while life shall last, Trust - ing Him till earth be past;
E - ven when my faith is small, Trust - ing Je - sus—that is all.
While He leads I can - not fall, Trust - ing Je - sus—that is all.
If in dan - ger, for Him call, Trust - ing Je - sus—that is all.
Till with - in the jas - per wall, Trust - ing Je - sus—that is all.
Chorus.
Trust - ing as the mo - ments fly, Trust - ing as the days go by;
Trust - ing Him what - e'er be - fall, Trust - ing Je - sus—that is all.

234 Trust and Obey

John H. Sammis | Daniel B. Towner

1. When we walk with the Lord In the light of His word, What a glo - ry He
2. Not a shad - ow can rise, Not a cloud in the skies, But His smile quick-ly
3. But we nev - er can prove The de - lights of His love Un - til all on the
4. Then in fel - low - ship sweet We will sit at His feet, Or we'll walk by His

sheds on our way! While we do His good will, He a - bides with us still
drives it a - way; Not a doubt nor a fear, Not a sigh nor a tear
al - tar we lay; For the fa - vor He shows And the joy He be-stows
side in the way; What He says we will do, Where He sends we will go—

REFRAIN

And with all who will trust and o - bey.
Can a - bide while we trust and o - bey. Trust and o - bey, for there's no oth - er
Are for them who will trust and o - bey.
Nev - er fear, on - ly trust and o - bey.

way To be hap - py in Je - sus, But to trust and o - bey.

He Is Able to Deliver Thee

William A. Ogden — William A. Ogden

1. 'Tis the grand-est theme thru the a - ges rung, 'Tis the grand-est theme for a
2. 'Tis the grand-est theme in the earth or main, 'Tis the grand-est theme for a
3. 'Tis the grand-est theme, let the ti-dings roll, To the guilt-y heart, to the

mor-tal tongue; 'Tis the grand-est theme that the world e'er sung—"Our God is
mor-tal strain; 'Tis the grand-est theme, tell the world a - gain—"Our God is
sin - ful soul; Look to God in faith, He will make thee whole—"Our God is

a- ble to de - liv-er thee."

CHORUS

He is a - - - ble to de - liv - er thee,
He is a - ble, He is a - ble

He is a - - - ble to de - liv - er thee; Tho by sin op - prest,
He is a - ble, He is a - ble

Go to Him for rest: "Our God is a - ble to de - liv - er thee."

236 Savior, Like a Shepherd Lead Us

Attr. to Dorothy A. Thrupp

William B. Bradbury

1. Sav - ior, like a shep-herd lead us, Much we need Thy ten-der care;
2. We are Thine–do Thou be - friend us, Be the Guard-ian of our way;
3. Thou hast prom-ised to re - ceive us, Poor and sin - ful tho we be;
4. Ear - ly let us seek Thy fa - vor, Ear - ly let us do Thy will;

In Thy pleas-ant pas-tures feed us, For our use Thy folds pre - pare:
Keep Thy flock, from sin de - fend us, Seek us when we go a - stray:
Thou hast mer - cy to re - lieve us, Grace to cleanse and pow'r to free:
Bless-ed Lord and on - ly Sav - ior, With Thy love our bos-oms fill:

Bless - ed Je - sus, Bless-ed Je - sus, Thou hast bought us, Thine we are;
Bless - ed Je - sus, Bless-ed Je - sus, Hear, O hear us when we pray;
Bless - ed Je - sus, Bless-ed Je - sus, Ear - ly let us turn to Thee;
Bless - ed Je - sus, Bless-ed Je - sus, Thou hast loved us, love us still;

Bless - ed Je - sus, Bless-ed Je - sus, Thou hast bought us, Thine we are.
Bless - ed Je - sus, Bless-ed Je - sus, Hear, O hear us when we pray.
Bless - ed Je - sus, Bless-ed Je - sus, Ear - ly let us turn to Thee.
Bless - ed Je - sus, Bless-ed Je - sus, Thou hast loved us, love us still.

All the Way My Savior Leads Me

Fanny J. Crosby
Robert Lowry
1. All the way my Sav-ior leads me— What have I to ask be - side?
2. All the way my Sav-ior leads me— Cheers each wind - ing path I tread,
3. All the way my Sav-ior leads me— O the full - ness of His love!
Can I doubt His ten-der mer - cy, Who thru life has been my Guide?
Gives me grace for ev-'ry tri - al, Feeds me with the liv - ing bread.
Per - fect rest to me is prom-ised In my Fa - ther's house a - bove.
Heav'n - ly peace, di - vin - est com-fort, Here by faith in Him to dwell!
Tho my wea - ry steps may fal - ter And my soul a - thirst may be,
When my spir - it, clothed im - mor - tal, Wings its flight to realms of day,
For I know, what-e'er be - fall me, Je-sus do - eth all things well; well.
Gush-ing from the Rock be - fore me, Lo! a spring of joy I see; see.
This my song thru end-less a - ges: Je-sus led me all the way; way.

238 A Child of the King

Harriett E. Buell | John B. Sumner

1. My Fa - ther is rich in hous - es and lands, He hold - eth the
2. My Fa - ther's own Son, the Sav - ior of men, Once wan - dered on
3. I once was an out - cast stran - ger on earth, A sin - ner by
4. A tent or a cot - tage, why should I care? They're build-ing a
wealth of the world in His hands! Of ru - bies and dia - monds, of
earth as the poor - est of them; But now He is reign - ing for-
choice, and an al - ien by birth; But I've been a - dopt - ed, my
pal - ace for me o - ver there; Though ex - iled from home, yet
sil - ver and gold, His cof - fers are full, He has rich - es un - told.
ev - er on high, And will give me a home in heav'n by and by.
name's writ - ten down, An heir to a man-sion, a robe, and a crown.
still I may sing: All glo - ry to God, I'm a child of the King.
CHORUS
I'm a child of the King, A child of the King:
With Je - sus my Sav - ior, I'm a child of the King.

I Belong to the King

Ida R. Smith
J. Lincoln Hall

1. I be - long to the King, I'm a child of His love, I shall dwell in His
2. I be - long to the King, and He loves me, I know, For His mer - cy and
3. I be - long to the King, and His prom - ise is sure, That we all shall be

pal - ace so fair; For He tells of its bliss in yon heav - en a - bove, And His
kind - ness, so free, Are un - ceas - ing - ly mine where - so - ev - er I go, And my
gath - ered at last In His king - dom a - bove, by life's wa - ters so pure, When this

chil - dren its splen - dors shall share.
ref - uge un - fail - ing is He.
life with its tri - als is past.

CHORUS

I be - long to the King, I'm a

child of His love, And He nev - er for - sak - eth His own; He will call me some

day to His pal - ace a - bove, I shall dwell by His glo - ri - fied throne.

240 The Haven of Rest

Henry L. Gilmore

George Moore
Arr. by Don Peterman

1. My soul in sad ex-ile was out on life's sea, So bur-dened with sin, and dis-trest, Till I heard a sweet voice say-ing, "Make me your choice!" And I en-tered the Ha-ven of Rest.
2. I yield-ed my-self to His ten-der em-brace, And, faith tak-ing hold of the Word, My fet-ters fell off, and I an-chored my soul— The "Ha-ven of Rest" is my Lord.
3. The song of my soul, since the Lord made me whole, Has been the old sto-ry so blest Of Je-sus, who'll save who-so-ev-er will have A home in the Ha-ven of Rest!
4. O come to the Sav-ior— He pa-tient-ly waits To save by His pow-er di-vine; Come, an-chor your soul in the Ha-ven of Rest, And say, "My Be-lov-ed is mine."
CHORUS
I've an-chored my soul in the Ha-ven of Rest, I'll sail the wide seas no more; The tem-pest may sweep o'er the wild, storm-y deep— In Je-sus I'm safe ev-er-more.

Under His Wings

William O. Cushing

Ira D. Sankey

1. Un-der His wings I am safe-ly a-bid-ing, Tho the night deep-ens and tem-pests are wild; Still I can trust Him—I know He will keep me, He has re-deemed me and I am His child.
2. Un-der His wings, what a ref-uge in sor-row! How the heart yearn-ing-ly turns to His rest! Oft-en when earth has no balm for my heal-ing, There I find com-fort and there I am blest.
3. Un-der His wings, O what pre-cious en-joy-ment! There will I hide till life's tri-als are o'er; Shel-tered, pro-tect-ed, no e-vil can harm me, Rest-ing in Je-sus I'm safe ev-er-more.
CHORUS
Un-der His wings, un-der His wings, Who from His love can sev-er?
Un-der His wings my soul shall a-bide, Safe-ly a-bide for-ev-er.

242 All My Sins Have Been Forgiven

Phillip F. Hiller
Trans. by Esther Bergan
Jean J. Rousseau
1. All my sins have been for - giv - en; God is mer - ci - ful to me;
2. My ac - count is closed for - ev - er; Je - sus Christ has paid it all;
3. How my count-less sins de-pressed me, Gave me sor - row, shame and tears,
4. Now my soul shall live for - ev - er; No more can the Foe con-demn;
Faith has claimed the Sav - ior's prom - ise, Grace and par - don, full and free;
Shed His blood my sin to cov - er, Paid the price to save my soul;
How His wrath and an - ger crushed me, Filled my heart with doubts and fears;
Noth - ing from God's love can sev - er, Peace and joy are found in Him.
O my soul, be ev - er prais - ing For the great Re - deem - er's love;
There is now no con - dem - na - tion, I am ful - ly rec - on - ciled;
But my soul cried out in an - guish, Called for mer - cy and for grace,
Thus I jour - ney on to heav - en, Cross death's por - tals joy - ful - ly;
Joy - ous songs to Him be rais - ing, Un - to God in heav'n a - bove.
What a won - der - ful sal - va - tion, For a sin - ner so de - filed!
Je - sus heard my sup - pli - ca - tion, Grant-ed par - don and re - lease.
All my sins have been for - giv - en, God is mer - ci - ful to me.

I Am His, and He Is Mine

George W. Robinson

James Mountain

1. Loved with ev - er - last - ing love, Led by grace that love to know;
2. Heav'n a - bove is soft - er blue, Earth a - round is sweet - er green!
3. Things that once were wild a - larms Can - not now dis - turb my rest;
4. His for - ev - er, on - ly His; Who the Lord and me shall part?

Gra - cious Spir - it from a - bove, Thou hast taught me it is so!
Some-thing lives in ev - ery hue Christ - less eyes have nev - er seen:
Closed in ev - er - last - ing arms, Pil - lowed on the lov - ing breast.
Ah, with what a rest of bliss Christ can fill the lov - ing heart!

O, this full and per - fect peace! O, this trans - port all di - vine!
Birds with glad - der songs o'er - flow, Flow'rs with deep - er beau - ties shine,
O, to lie for - ev - er here, Doubt and care and self re - sign,
Heav'n and earth may fade and flee, First - born light in gloom de - cline;

In a love which can - not cease, I am His, and He is mine. mine.
Since I know, as now I know, I am His, and He is mine. mine.
While He whis - pers in my ear, I am His, and He is mine. mine.
But while God and I shall be, I am His, and He is mine. mine.

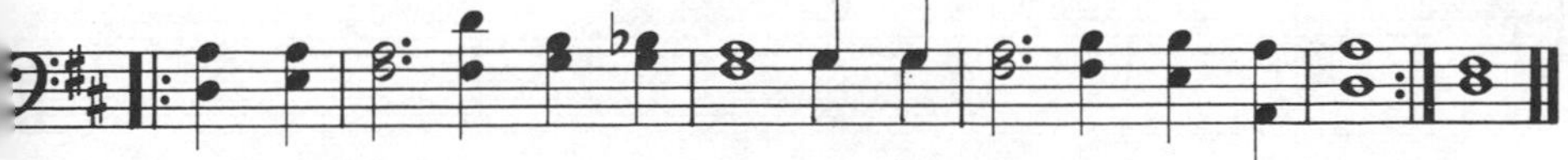

244 Higher Ground

Johnson Oatman, Jr. | Charles H. Gabriel

1. I'm press - ing on the up - ward way, New heights I'm gain - ing ev - ery
2. My heart has no de - sire to stay Where doubts a - rise and fears dis-
3. I want to live a - bove the world, Though Sa-tan's darts at me are
4. I want to scale the ut - most height, And catch a gleam of glo - ry

day; Still pray - ing as I'm on - ward bound, "Lord, plant my
may; Though some may dwell where these a - bound, My prayer, my
hurled; For faith has caught the joy - ful sound, The song of
bright; But still I'll pray till heav'n I've found, "Lord, lead me

feet on high - er ground."
aim is high - er ground.
saints on high - er ground.
on to high - er ground."

Refrain

Lord, lift me up and let me stand

By faith on heav - en's ta - ble - land, A high - er plane

than I have found; Lord, plant my feet on high - er ground.

Only Believe

Paul Rader | Paul Rader

1. Fear not, lit - tle flock, from the cross to the throne, From death in - to
2. Fear not, lit - tle flock, He go - eth a - head, Your Shep - herd se -
3. Fear not, lit - tle flock, what - ev - er your lot; He en - ters all

life He went for His own; All pow - er in earth, all pow-er a-bove,
lect - eth the path you must tread; The wa-ters of Ma-rah He'll sweet-en for thee-
rooms, "the doors be - ing shut." He nev - er for-sakes, He nev-er is gone-

Is giv - en to Him for the flock of His love.
He drank all the bit - ter in Geth-sem - a - ne.
So count on His pres - ence in dark-ness and dawn.

REFRAIN

On - ly be-lieve,

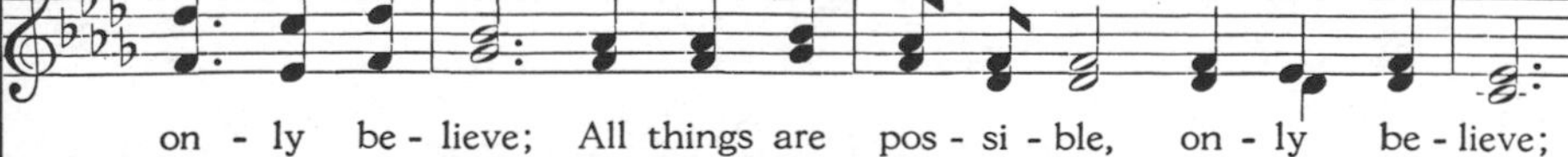

on - ly be - lieve; All things are pos - si - ble, on - ly be - lieve;

On - ly be-lieve, on - ly be - lieve; All things are pos-si-ble, on-ly be-lieve.

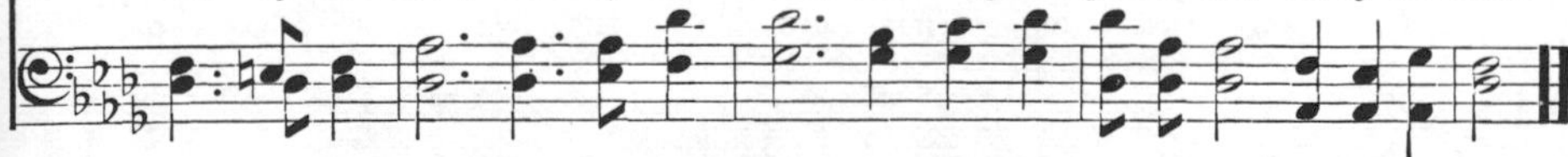

246 Faith of Our Fathers

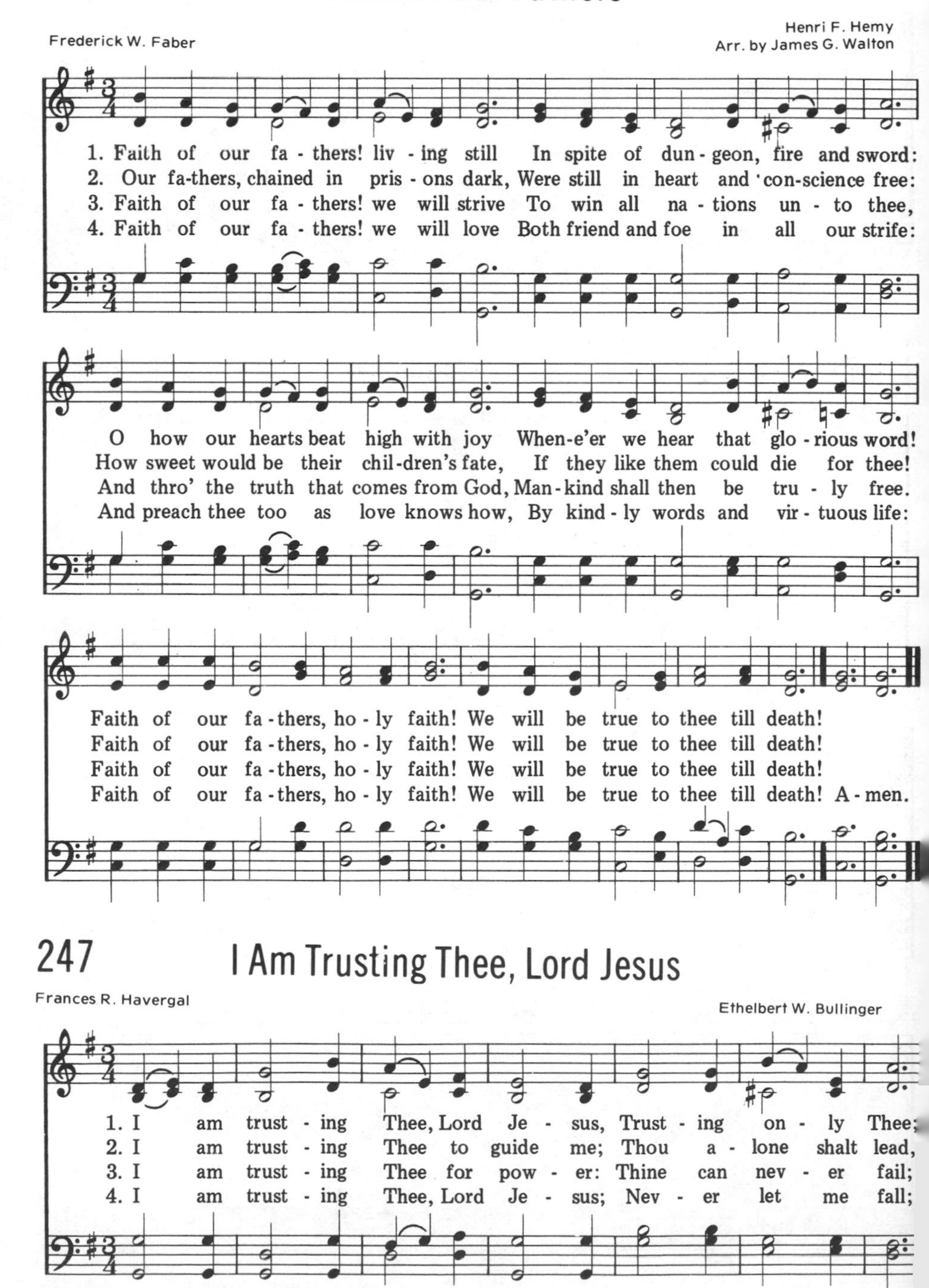
Frederick W. Faber
Henri F. Hemy
Arr. by James G. Walton
1. Faith of our fa - thers! liv - ing still In spite of dun - geon, fire and sword:
2. Our fa-thers, chained in pris - ons dark, Were still in heart and con-science free:
3. Faith of our fa - thers! we will strive To win all na - tions un - to thee,
4. Faith of our fa - thers! we will love Both friend and foe in all our strife:
O how our hearts beat high with joy When-e'er we hear that glo - rious word!
How sweet would be their chil-dren's fate, If they like them could die for thee!
And thro' the truth that comes from God, Man-kind shall then be tru - ly free.
And preach thee too as love knows how, By kind - ly words and vir - tuous life:
Faith of our fa - thers, ho - ly faith! We will be true to thee till death!
Faith of our fa - thers, ho - ly faith! We will be true to thee till death!
Faith of our fa - thers, ho - ly faith! We will be true to thee till death!
Faith of our fa - thers, ho - ly faith! We will be true to thee till death! A - men.
247 I Am Trusting Thee, Lord Jesus
Frances R. Havergal
Ethelbert W. Bullinger
1. I am trust - ing Thee, Lord Je - sus, Trust - ing on - ly Thee;
2. I am trust - ing Thee to guide me; Thou a - lone shalt lead,
3. I am trust - ing Thee for pow - er: Thine can nev - er fail;
4. I am trust - ing Thee, Lord Je - sus; Nev - er let me fall;

Trust - ing Thee for full sal - va - tion, Great and free.
Ev - ery day and hour sup - ply - ing All my need.
Words which Thou Thy - self shalt give me Must pre - vail.
I am trust - ing Thee for - ev - er, And for all. A - men.
My Faith Looks Up to Thee
248
Ray Palmer
Lowell Mason
1. My faith looks up to Thee, Thou Lamb of Cal - va - ry,
2. May Thy rich grace im - part Strength to my faint - ing heart,
3. While life's dark maze I tread, And griefs a - round me spread,
4. When ends life's tran - sient dream, When death's cold, sul - len stream
Sav - ior di - vine! Now hear me while I pray, Take all my
My zeal in - spire; As Thou hast died for me, O may my
Be Thou my guide; Bid dark - ness turn to day, Wipe sor - row's
Shall o'er me roll; Blest Sav - ior, then, in love, Fear and dis -
guilt a - way, O let me from this day Be whol - ly Thine!
love to Thee Pure, warm, and change - less be, A liv - ing fire!
tears a - way, Nor let me ev - er stray From Thee a - side.
trust re - move; O bear me safe a - bove, A ran - somed soul! A - men.

249 Some Time We'll Understand

Maxwell N. Cornelius

James McGranahan

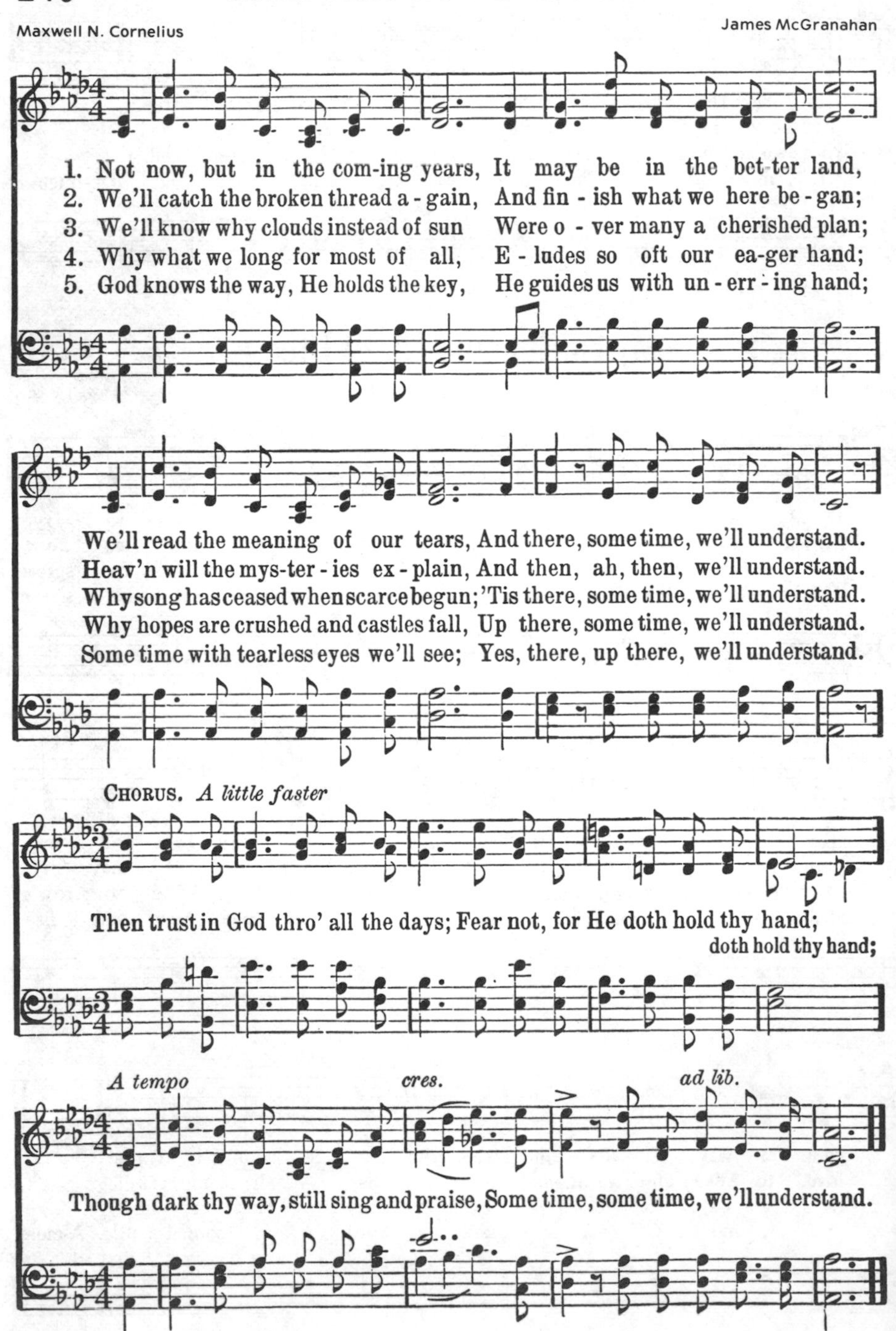
1. Not now, but in the com-ing years, It may be in the bet-ter land,
2. We'll catch the broken thread a - gain, And fin - ish what we here be - gan;
3. We'll know why clouds instead of sun Were o - ver many a cherished plan;
4. Why what we long for most of all, E - ludes so oft our ea-ger hand;
5. God knows the way, He holds the key, He guides us with un - err - ing hand;
We'll read the meaning of our tears, And there, some time, we'll understand.
Heav'n will the mys-ter - ies ex - plain, And then, ah, then, we'll understand.
Why song has ceased when scarce begun; 'Tis there, some time, we'll understand.
Why hopes are crushed and castles fall, Up there, some time, we'll understand.
Some time with tearless eyes we'll see; Yes, there, up there, we'll understand.
CHORUS. A little faster
Then trust in God thro' all the days; Fear not, for He doth hold thy hand;
doth hold thy hand;
A tempo
cres.
ad lib.
Though dark thy way, still sing and praise, Some time, some time, we'll understand.

Jesus Never Fails

Arthur A. Luther

Arthur A. Luther

1. Earth - ly friends may prove un - true, Doubts and fears as - sail;
2. Though the sky be dark and drear, Fierce and strong the gale,
3. In life's dark and bit - ter hour Love will still pre - vail;

One still loves and cares for you: Je - sus nev - er fails.
nev - er fails.
Just re - mem - ber He is near, And He will not fail.
will not fail.
Trust His ev - er - last - ing power, Je - sus will not fail.
will not fail.

REFRAIN

Je - sus nev - er fails, Je - sus nev - er fails;

Heaven and earth may pass a - way, But Je - sus nev - er fails.

251 'Tis So Sweet to Trust in Jesus

Louisa M. R. Stead

William J. Kirkpatrick

1. 'Tis so sweet to trust in Je - sus, Just to take Him at His word; Just to rest up - on His prom - ise; Just to know, "Thus saith the Lord."
2. O how sweet to trust in Je - sus, Just to trust His cleans - ing blood; Just in sim - ple faith to plunge me 'Neath the heal - ing, cleans - ing flood!
3. Yes, 'tis sweet to trust in Je - sus, Just from sin and self to cease; Just from Je - sus sim - ply tak - ing Life and rest, and joy and peace.
4. I'm so glad I learned to trust Thee, Pre - cious Je - sus, Sav - ior, Friend; And I know that Thou art with me, Wilt be with me to the end.

CHORUS

Je - sus, Je - sus, how I trust Him! How I've proved Him o'er and o'er!
Je - sus, Je - sus, pre - cious Je - sus! O for grace to trust Him more!

252 Jesus, Stand Among Us

William Pennefather

Fredrich Filitz

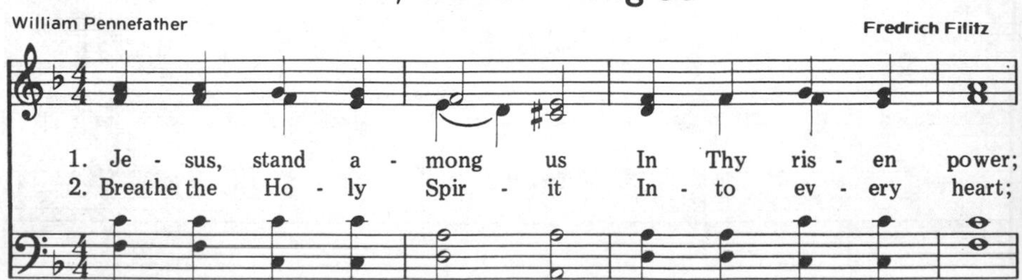
1. Je - sus, stand a - mong us In Thy ris - en power;
2. Breathe the Ho - ly Spir - it In - to ev - ery heart;

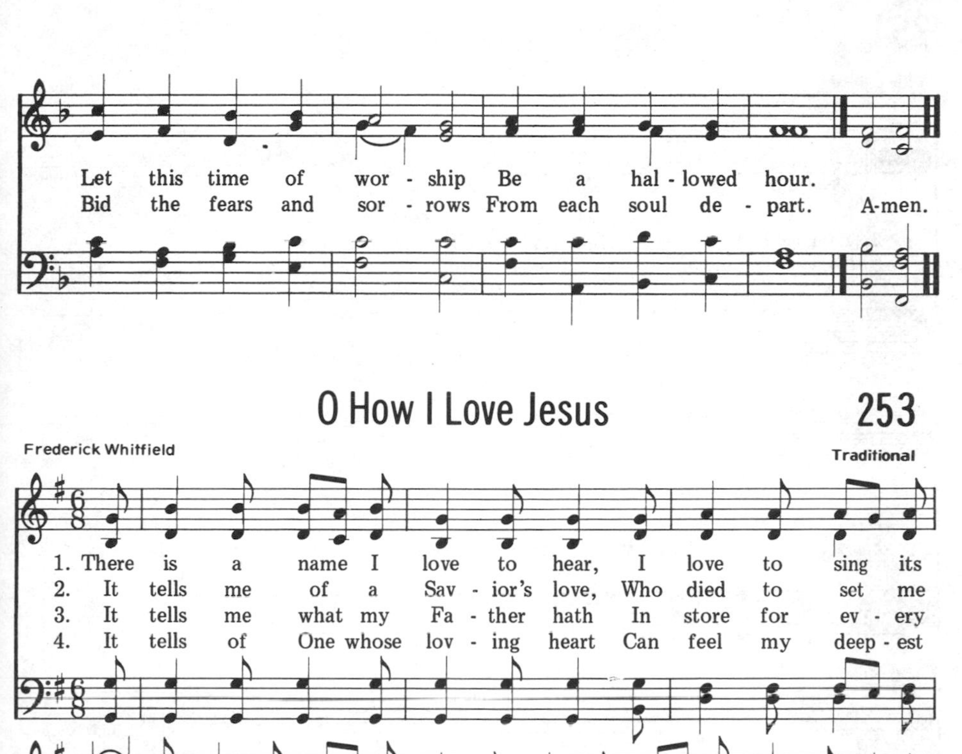
Let this time of wor - ship Be a hal - lowed hour.
Bid the fears and sor - rows From each soul de - part. A-men.

O How I Love Jesus 253

Frederick Whitfield

Traditional

1. There is a name I love to hear, I love to sing its worth; It sounds like mu - sic in my ear, The sweet-est name on earth.
2. It tells me of a Sav - ior's love, Who died to set me free; It tells me of His pre - cious blood, The sin - ner's per - fect plea.
3. It tells me what my Fa - ther hath In store for ev - ery day, And though I tread a dark - some path, Yields sun-shine all the way.
4. It tells of One whose lov - ing heart Can feel my deep - est woe, Who in each sor - row bears a part, That none can bear be - low.
Refrain
O, how I love Je - sus, O, how I love Je - sus,
O, how I love Je - sus, Be - cause He first loved me!

254

Jesus Loves Even Me

Philip P. Bliss

Philip P. Bluss

1. I am so glad that our Fa - ther in heaven Tells of His
2. Though I for - get Him and wan - der a - way, Still He doth
3. Oh, if there's on - ly one song I can sing, When in His

love in the. Book He has given; Won - der - ful things in the
love me wher - ev - er I stray; Back to His dear lov - ing
beau - ty I see the great King, This shall my song in e-

Bi - ble I see— This is the dear - est, that Je - sus loves me.
arms would I flee, When I re - mem - ber that Je - sus loves me.
ter - ni - ty be: "Oh, what a won - der that Je - sus loves me!"

REFRAIN

I am so glad that Je - sus loves me, Je - sus loves me, Je - sus loves me;

I am so glad that Je - sus loves me, Je - sus loves e - ven me.

Jesus Christ Is the Way

Letitia Schuler
Arr. by E. S. Murray

Eleanor S. Murray

Je - sus Christ is the Way, Je - sus Christ is the Truth,
Je - sus Christ is the Life, And He's mine, mine, mine.

Jesus Loves Me

Philip P. Bliss

Philip P. Bliss

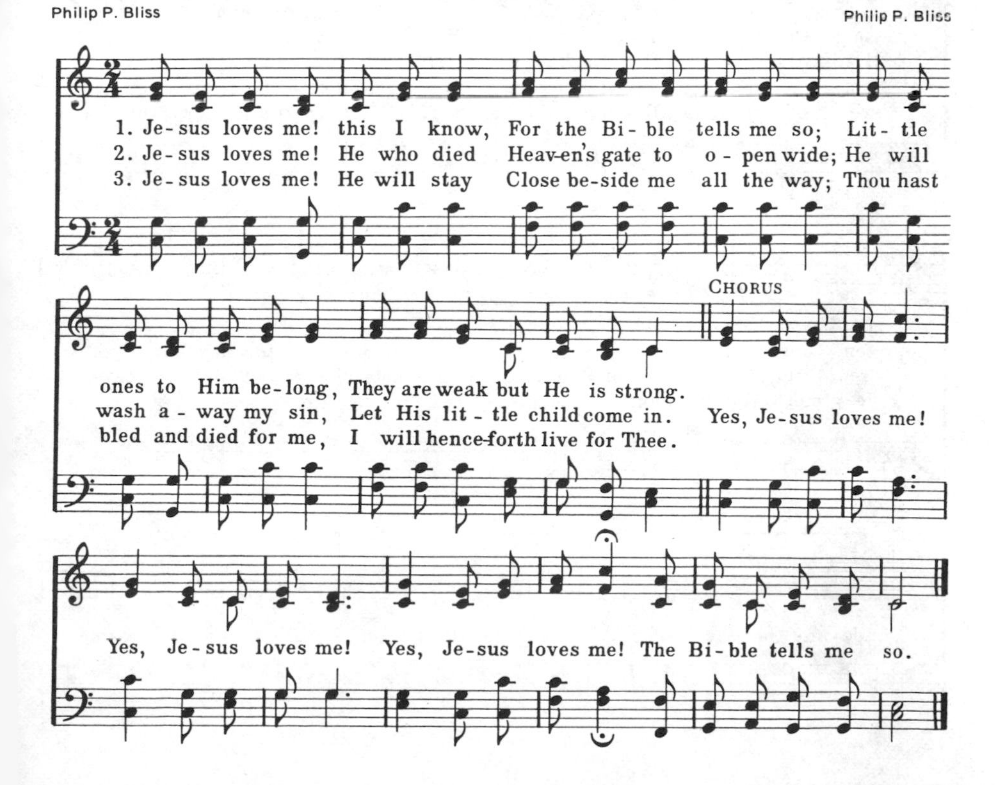
1. Je-sus loves me! this I know, For the Bi-ble tells me so; Lit-tle ones to Him be-long, They are weak but He is strong.
2. Je-sus loves me! He who died Heav-en's gate to o-pen wide; He will wash a-way my sin, Let His lit-tle child come in.
3. Je-sus loves me! He will stay Close be-side me all the way; Thou hast bled and died for me, I will hence-forth live for Thee.
CHORUS
Yes, Je-sus loves me! Yes, Je-sus loves me! Yes, Je-sus loves me! The Bi-ble tells me so.

257 Yesterday, Today, Forever

Albert B. Simpson — James H. Burke

1. O how sweet the glo-rious mes-sage Sim-ple faith may claim: Yes - ter -
2. He who par-doned err - ing Pe - ter Nev-er need'st thou fear, He who
3. He who 'mid the rag - ing bil - lows Walked up-on the sea Still can
4. As of old He walked to Em-ma-us, With them to a - bide, So thru
day, to - day, for - ev - er, Je - sus is the same! Still He loves to
came to faith-less Tho-mas All thy doubt will clear; He who let the
hush our wild-est tem-pest, As on Gal - i - lee; He who wept and
all life's way He walk-eth, Ev - er near our side; Soon a - gain shall
save the sin - ful, Heal the sick and lame, Cheer the mourn-er, calm the
loved dis - ci - ple On His bos-om rest Bids thee still, with love as
prayed in an - guish In Geth-sem - a - ne Drinks with us each cup of
we be-hold Him– Has-ten, Lord, the day! But 'twill still be "this same
CHORUS
tem - pest– Glo - ry to His name!
ten - der, Lean up-on His breast.
trem-bling, In our ag - o - ny.
Je - sus," As He went a - way.
Yes - ter - day, to - day, for - ev - er,
All may change, but Je - sus nev - er–
1
Je - sus is the same;
2
Glo - ry to His name! Glo - ry to His name,

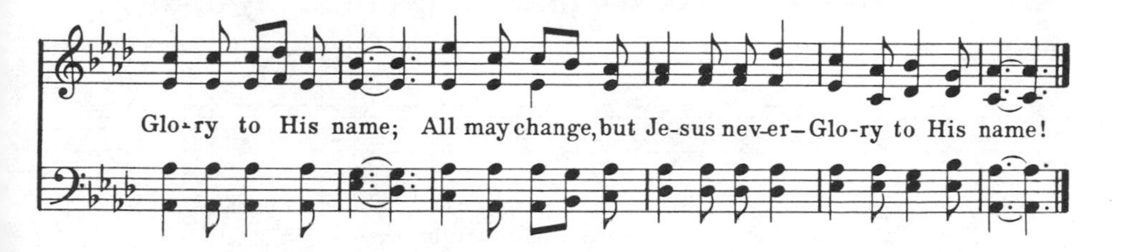
Glo-ry to His name; All may change, but Je-sus nev-er—Glo-ry to His name!

Children of the Heavenly Father 258

Lina Sandell
Tr. Composite-Edit. by A.B.S.

From the Swedish

1. More se - cure is no one ev - er Than the loved ones of the Sav - iour; Not yon star, on high a - bid - ing, Nor the bird in home-nest hid - ing.
2. God His own doth tend and nour - ish, In His ho - ly courts they flour - ish; Like a fa - ther kind He spares them, In His lov - ing arms He bears them.
3. Nei - ther life nor death can ev - er From the Lord His chil - dren sev - er; For His love and deep com - pas - sion Com-forts them in trib - u - la - tion.
4. Lit - tle flock, to joy then yield thee! Ja - cob's God will ev - er shield thee; Rest se - cure with this De - fend - er, At His will all foes sur - ren - der.
5. What He takes or what He gives us Shows the Fa - ther's love so pre - cious; We may trust His pur - pose whol - ly— 'Tis His chil - dren's wel - fare sole - ly.
6. Child - ren of the Heaven - ly Fa - ther Safe - ly in His bos - om gath - er; Free from cares that oft dis - tress us He will love and He will bless us.

259 Heaven Came Down and Glory Filled My Soul

John W. Peterson | John W. Peterson

1. O what a won - der - ful, won - der - ful day— Day I will
2. Born of the Spir - it with life from a - bove In - to God's
3. Now I've a hope that will sure - ly en - dure Aft - er the
nev - er for - get; Aft - er I'd wan - dered in dark - ness a - way,
fam - ily di - vine, Jus - ti - fied ful - ly thro' Cal - va - ry's love,
pass - ing of time; I have a fu - ture in heav - en for sure,
Je - sus my Sav - ior I met. O what a ten - der, com - pas - sion-ate friend—
O what a stand - ing is mine! And the trans - ac - tion so quick - ly was made
There in those man-sions sub - lime. And it's be - cause of that won - der - ful day
He met the need of my heart; Shad - ows dis - pel - ling, With
When as a sin - ner I came, Took of the of - fer Of
When at the cross I be - lieved; Rich - es e - ter - nal And

joy I am tell - ing, He made all the dark - ness de - part!
grace He did prof - fer— He saved me, O praise His dear name!
bless - ings su - per - nal From His pre - cious hand I re - ceived.
CHORUS
Heav - en came down and glo - ry filled my soul,
(filled my soul,)
When at the cross the Sav - ior made me whole;
(made me whole;)
My
sins were washed a - way And my night was turned to day—
Heav - en came down and glo - ry filled my soul!
(filled my soul!)

260 He Keeps Me Singing

Luther B. Bridgers — Luther B. Bridgers

1. There's with-in my heart a mel - o - dy, Je - sus whis-pers sweet and low,
2. All my life was wrecked by sin and strife, Dis-cord filled my heart with pain,
3. Feast-ing on the rich - es of His grace, Rest-ing 'neath His sheltering wing,
4. Tho' some-times He leads thro' wa - ters deep, Tri - als fall a - cross my way,
5. Soon He's com - ing back to wel- come me Far be - yond the star - ry sky;

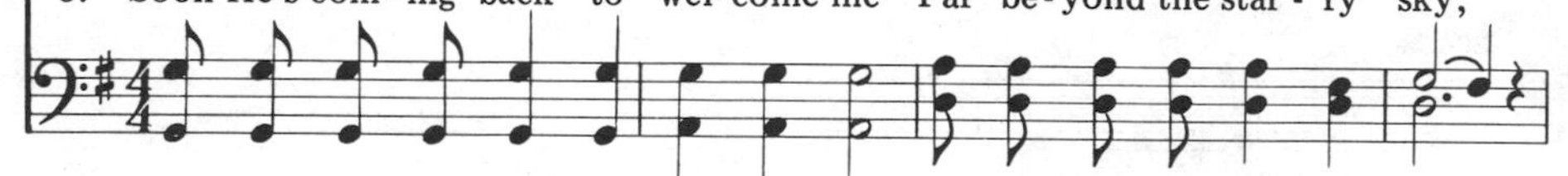

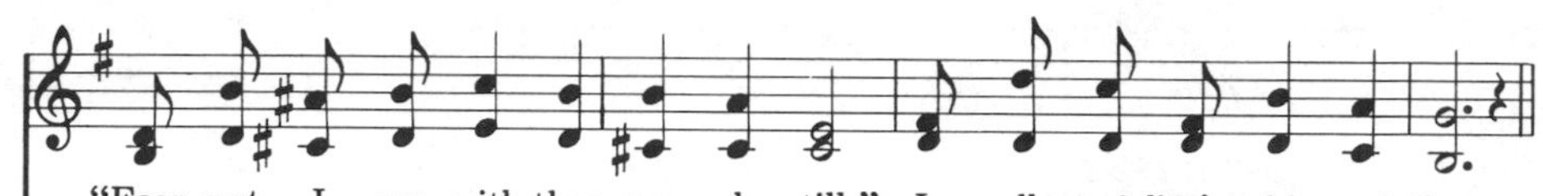

"Fear not, I am with thee, peace, be still," In all of life's ebb and flow.
Je - sus swept a - cross the bro - ken strings, Stirred the slum-b'ring chords a-gain.
Al - ways look-ing on His smil - ing face, That is why I shout and sing.
Tho' some-times the path seems rough and steep, See His foot-prints all the way.
I shall wing my flight to worlds un-known, I shall reign with Him on high.

Refrain

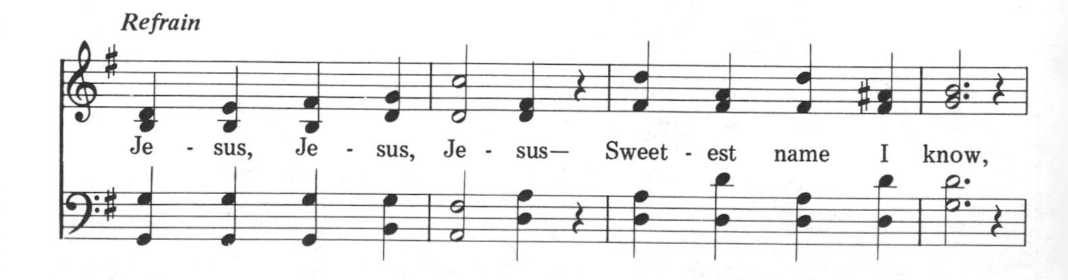
Je - sus, Je - sus, Je - sus— Sweet - est name I know,

Fills my ev - ery long - ing, Keeps me sing - ing as I go.

Happy In Jesus

F. J. Crosby & A.B.S. — Rev. & Arr. by Alfred B. Smith

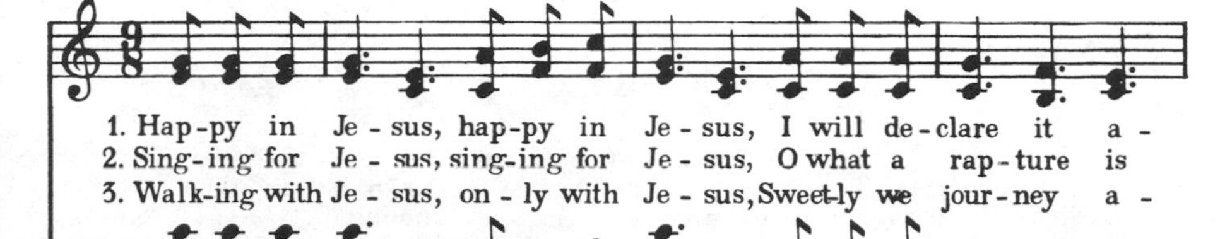
1. Hap-py in Je - sus, hap-py in Je - sus, I will de - clare it a -
2. Sing-ing for Je - sus, sing-ing for Je - sus, O what a rap - ture is
3. Walk-ing with Je - sus, on - ly with Je - sus, Sweet-ly we jour - ney a -

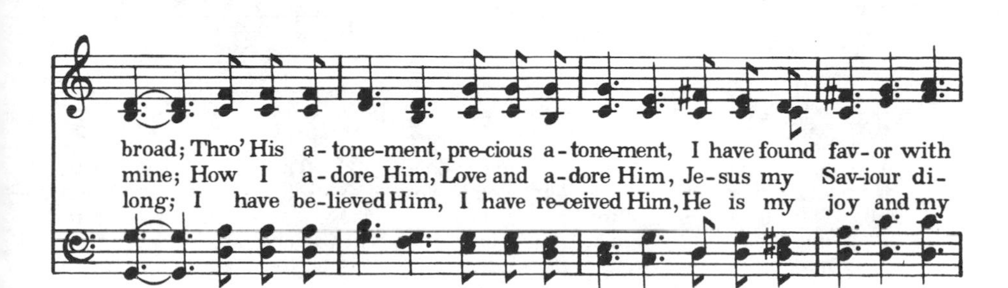
broad; Thro' His a - tone-ment, pre-cious a - tone-ment, I have found fav - or with
mine; How I a - dore Him, Love and a - dore Him, Je - sus my Sav - iour di -
long; I have be - lieved Him, I have re-ceived Him, He is my joy and my

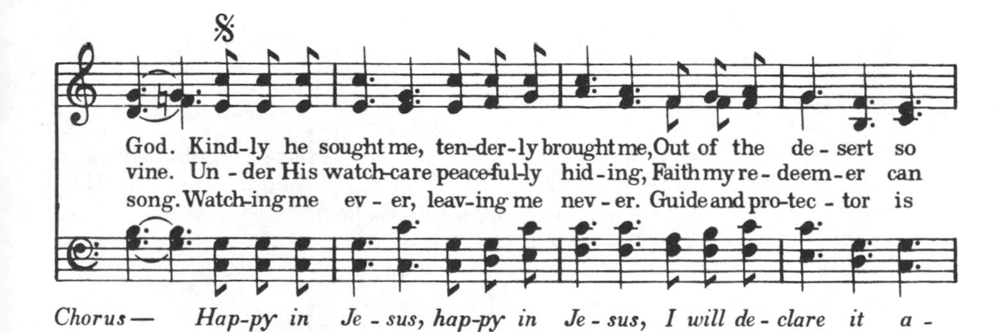
God. Kind-ly he sought me, ten - der - ly brought me, Out of the de - sert so
vine. Un - der His watch-care peace-ful-ly hid - ing, Faith my re - deem - er can
song. Watch-ing me ev - er, leav-ing me nev - er. Guide and pro - tec - tor is
Chorus — Hap-py in Je - sus, hap-py in Je - sus, I will de - clare it a -

D. S. for Chorus

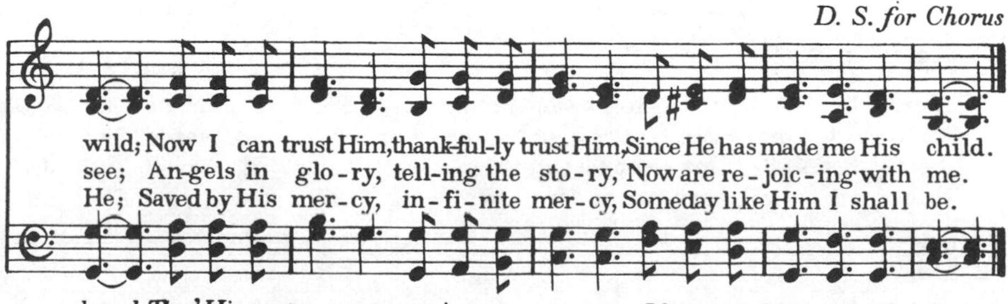
wild; Now I can trust Him, thank-ful-ly trust Him, Since He has made me His child.
see; An-gels in glo - ry, tell-ing the sto - ry, Now are re - joic - ing with me.
He; Saved by His mer - cy, in - fi - nite mer - cy, Someday like Him I shall be.
broad; Thro' His a - tone-ment, pre-cious a - tone-ment, I have found fav - or with God!

262 Jesus, I am Resting, Resting

Jean S. Pigott — James Mountain

1. Je - sus, I am rest - ing, rest - ing In the joy of what Thou art;
2. O, how great Thy lov - ing kind - ness, Vast - er, broad - er than the sea!
3. Sim - ply trust - ing Thee, Lord Je - sus, I be - hold Thee as Thou art,
4. Ev - er lift Thy face up - on me As I work and wait for Thee;
(Ref.) Je - sus, I am rest - ing, rest - ing In the joy of what Thou art;
Fine
I am find - ing out the great - ness Of Thy lov - ing heart.
O, how mar - vel - ous Thy good - ness, Lav - ished all on me!
And Thy love, so pure, so change - less, Sat - is - fies my heart;
Rest - ing 'neath Thy smile, Lord Je - sus, Earth's dark shad - ows flee.
I am find - ing out the great - ness Of Thy lov - ing heart.
Thou hast bid me gaze up - on Thee, And Thy beau - ty fills my soul,
Yes, I rest in Thee, Be - lov - ed, Know what wealth of grace is Thine,
Sat - is - fies its deep - est long - ings, Meets, sup - plies its ev - ery need,
Bright-ness of my Fa - ther's glo - ry, Sun - shine of my Fa - ther's face,
D.C. Refrain
For by Thy trans - form - ing pow - er, Thou hast made me whole.
Know Thy cer - tain - ty of prom - ise, And have made it mine.
Com - pass - eth me round with bless - ings: Thine is love in - deed!
Keep me ev - er trust - ing, rest - ing, Fill me with Thy grace.

Thou Wilt Keep Him in Perfect Peace

263

Stanza 1 V.A.
2, 3 Alfred B. Smith
Vivian K. Amsler
Arr. by Donna J. Krieger
1. Thou wilt keep Him in per-fect peace Whose mind is stayed on Thee;
2. When the lil-ies of the field I see My heart is filled with peace
3. Pre-cious hid-ing place from lifes' a-larms I find O Christ in Thee.
When the shad-ows come and dark-ness falls, He giv-eth in-ward peace;
He who cares for them so faith-ful-ly— He giv-eth sweet re-lease.
Held se-cure-ly in Thy might-y arms No storms can troub-le me.
Chorus
O He is the on-ly per-fect rest-ing place He giv-eth per-fect peace!
Thou wilt keep him in per-fect peace Whose mind is stay'd on Thee.

264

Jesus Understands!

Birdie Bell
Wm. J. Kirkpatrick
Rev. by Alfred B. Smith
1. Bowed be-neath your bur-den, is there none to share? Wea-ry with the
2. Ev - 'ry heav - y bur-den He will glad - ly share. Are you sad and
3. Tho' temp-ta - tion meet you, Je - sus can sus - tain. Life has vex-ing
4. Wea - ry heart, He calls you, "Come to me and rest." Does the path grow
jour-ney, is there none to care? Cour - age, way-worn trav - 'ler;
wea - ry? Je - sus has a care. Well He knows the path - way
prob-lems which He can ex - plain. Serve Him where He sends you,
rug - ged? Yet His way is best. Leave the un-known fu - ture
heed your Lord's commands. There's a tho't to cheer you; Je - sus un - der - stands.
o'er life's burn-ing sands. Cour-age, faint-ing pil-grim; Je - sus un - der - stands.
tho' in dis-tant lands. Do not doubt or ques-tion; Je - sus un - der - stands.
in His might-y hands. He will nev - er fail you, Je - sus un - der - stands.
Chorus
Je - sus un-der-stands All His ways are best Hear Him call-ing you,
"Come to me and rest." Leave the un-known fu - ture

in His might-y hands. He will nev-er fail you Je-sus un-der-stands.
Like a River Glorious
265
Frances R. Havergal
James Mountain
1. Like a riv-er glo-rious Is God's per-fect peace, O-ver all vic-to-rious In its bright in-crease; Per-fect, yet it flow-eth Full-er ev-ery day, Per-fect, yet it grow-eth Deep-er all the way.
2. Hid-den in the hol-low Of His bless-ed hand, Nev-er foe can fol-low, Nev-er trai-tor stand; Not a surge of wor-ry, Not a shade of care, Not a blast of hur-ry Touch the spir-it there.
3. Ev-ery joy or tri-al Fall-eth from a-bove, Traced up-on our di-al By the Sun of Love. We may trust Him ful-ly All for us to do; They who trust Him whol-ly Find Him whol-ly true.
REFRAIN
Stayed up-on Je-ho-vah, Hearts are ful-ly blest; Find-ing, as He prom-ised, Per-fect peace and rest.

266 Day by Day

Carolina Sandell Berg
Trans. by A. L. Skoog

Oscar Ahnfelt

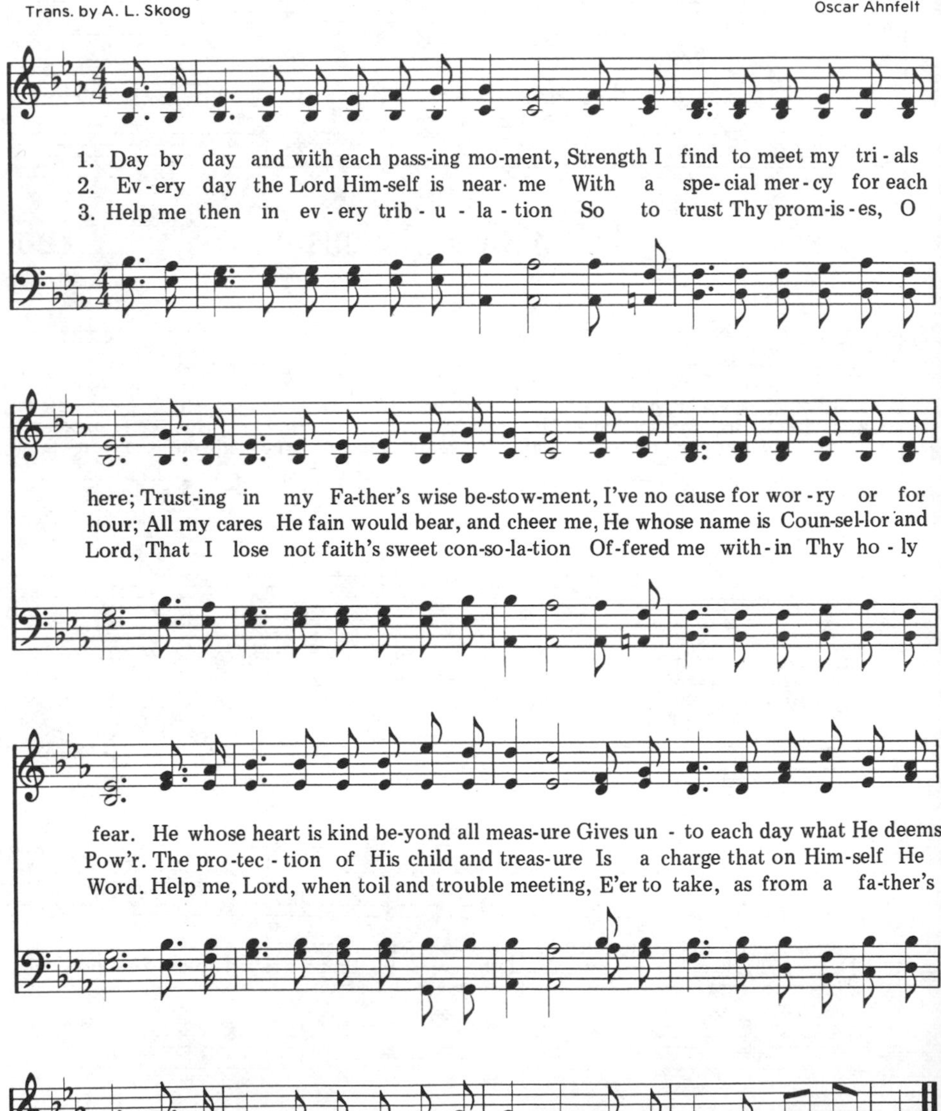

1. Day by day and with each pass-ing mo-ment, Strength I find to meet my tri-als
2. Ev-ery day the Lord Him-self is near me With a spe-cial mer-cy for each
3. Help me then in ev-ery trib-u-la-tion So to trust Thy prom-is-es, O
here; Trust-ing in my Fa-ther's wise be-stow-ment, I've no cause for wor-ry or for
hour; All my cares He fain would bear, and cheer me, He whose name is Coun-sel-lor and
Lord, That I lose not faith's sweet con-so-la-tion Of-fered me with-in Thy ho-ly
fear. He whose heart is kind be-yond all meas-ure Gives un-to each day what He deems
Pow'r. The pro-tec-tion of His child and treas-ure Is a charge that on Him-self He
Word. Help me, Lord, when toil and trouble meeting, E'er to take, as from a fa-ther's

best—Lov-ing-ly, its part of pain and pleas-ure, Min-gling toil with peace and rest.
laid; "As your days, your strength shall be in meas-ure," This the pledge to me He made.
hand, One by one, the days, the mo-ments fleeting, Till I reach the prom-ised land.

Does Jesus Care?

Frank E. Graeff

J. Lincoln Hall

1. Does Je - sus care when my heart is pained Too deep - ly for mirth and song; As the bur - dens press and the cares dis - tress, And the way grows wea - ry and long?
2. Does Je - sus care when my way is dark With a name - less dread and fear? As the day - light fades in - to deep night shades, Does He care e - nough to be near?
3. Does Je - sus care when I've tried and failed To re - sist some temp - ta - tion strong; When for my deep grief I find no re - lief, Though my tears flow all the night long?
4. Does Je - sus care when I've said good - by To the dear - est on earth to me, And my sad heart aches till it near - ly breaks—Is it aught to Him? Does He see?

Refrain

O yes, He cares; I know He cares, His heart is touched with my grief; When the days are wea - ry, the long nights drear - y, I know my Sav - ior cares. (He cares).

268 Sunshine in My Soul

Eliza E. Hewitt

John R. Sweney

1. There is sun-shine in my soul to-day, More glo-ri-ous and bright
2. There is mu-sic in my soul to-day, A car-ol to my King;
3. There is spring-time in my soul to-day, For, when the Lord is near,
4. There is glad-ness in my soul to-day And hope and praise and love
Than glows in an-y earth-ly sky, For Je-sus is my light.
And Je-sus, lis-ten-ing, can hear The songs I can-not sing.
The dove of peace sings in my heart, The flowers of grace ap-pear.
For bless-ings which He gives me now, For joys laid up a-bove.
REFRAIN
Oh, there's sun - shine, bless-ed sun - shine,
Oh, there's sun-shine in my soul, bless-ed sun-shine in my soul,
While the peace-ful, hap-py mo-ments roll; When
hap-py mo-ments roll;
Je-sus shows His smil-ing face, There is sun-shine in my soul.

Heavenly Sunshine

H. J. Zelley, Alt.
H. Cook & Charles Fuller
Arr. by Alfred B. Smith
1. Walk-ing in sun-shine all of my jour-ney, O - ver the moun-tains, thro' the deep vale! Je - sus has said, "I'll nev- er for- sake thee." Prom-ise di - vine that nev- er can fail!
2. Shad-ows a - round me, shad-ows a - bove me Nev-er con-ceal my Sav-iour and Guide. He is the Light; in Him is no dark-ness. And I am walk-ing close to His side.
3. In the bright sun-shine, ev - er re - joic - ing, Press-ing my way to man-sions a - bove, Sing-ing God's prais-es, glad-ly I'm walk-ing— Walk-ing in sun-shine, filled with His love.
Chorus
Heav-en-ly sun-shine Heav-en-ly sun-shine, Flood-ing my soul with glo-ry di - vine: Heav-en-ly sun-shine, Heav-en-ly sun-shine, Hal-le - lu-jah! Je-sus is mine.

270 It Is Well With My Soul

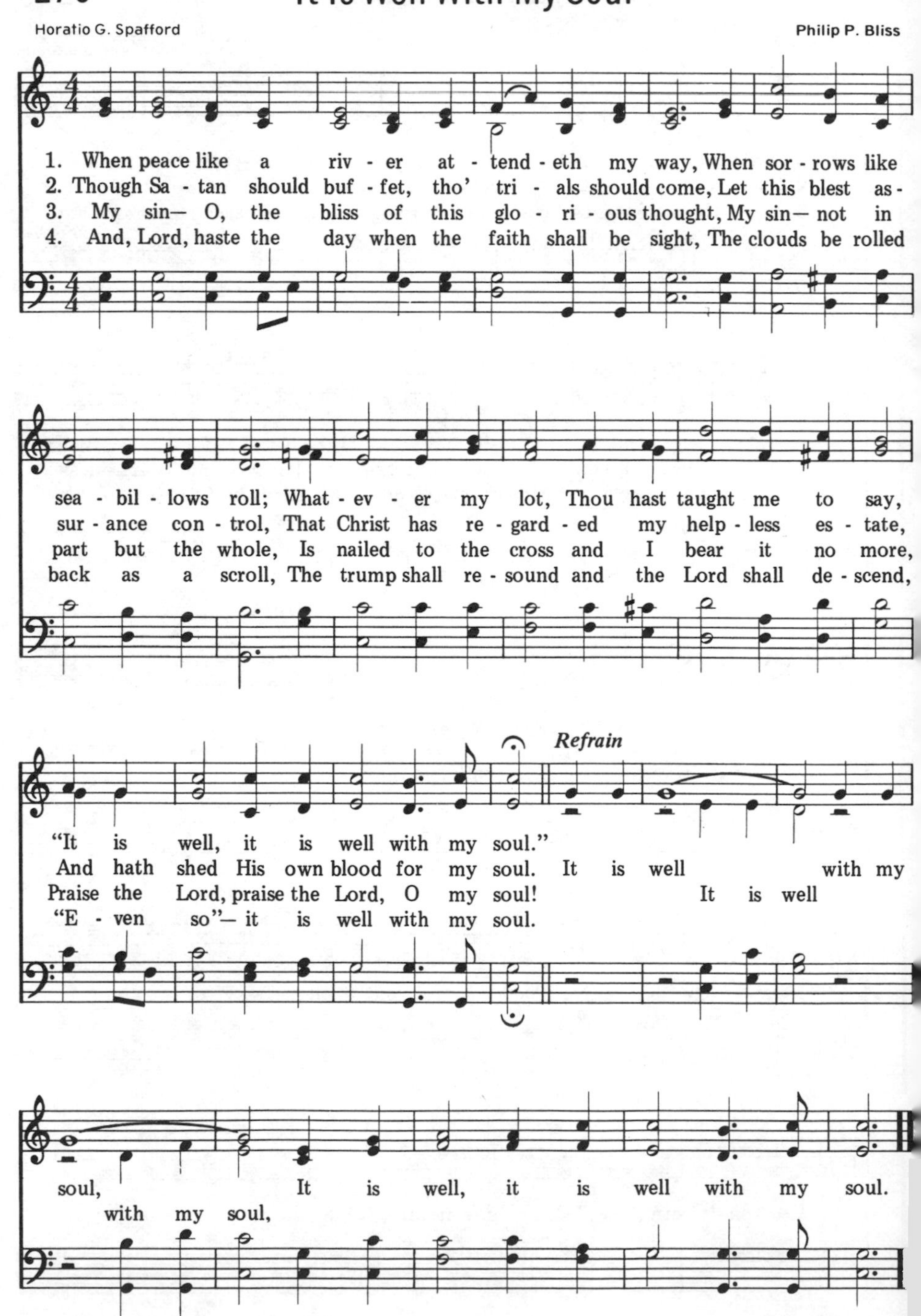
Horatio G. Spafford
Philip P. Bliss
1. When peace like a riv - er at - tend - eth my way, When sor - rows like
2. Though Sa - tan should buf - fet, tho' tri - als should come, Let this blest as -
3. My sin— O, the bliss of this glo - ri - ous thought, My sin— not in
4. And, Lord, haste the day when the faith shall be sight, The clouds be rolled
sea - bil - lows roll; What - ev - er my lot, Thou hast taught me to say,
sur - ance con - trol, That Christ has re - gard - ed my help - less es - tate,
part but the whole, Is nailed to the cross and I bear it no more,
back as a scroll, The trump shall re - sound and the Lord shall de - scend,
"It is well, it is well with my soul."
And hath shed His own blood for my soul.
Praise the Lord, praise the Lord, O my soul!
"E - ven so"— it is well with my soul.
Refrain
It is well with my
It is well
soul, It is well, it is well with my soul.
with my soul,

Wonderful Peace

W. D. Cornell W. G. Cooper

1. Far a - way in the depths of my spir - it to - night Rolls a
2. What a treas - ure I have in this won - der - ful peace Bur - ied
3. I am rest - ing to - night in this won - der - ful peace, Rest - ing
4. And me - thinks when I rise to that cit - y of peace Where the
5. Ah! soul, are you here with - out com - fort and rest, March - ing
mel - o - dy sweet - er than psalm; In ce - les - tial - like strains it un -
deep in the heart of my soul, So se - cure that no pow - er can
sweet - ly in Je - sus' con - trol, For I'm kept from all dan - ger by
Au - thor of peace I shall see, That one strain of the song which the
down the rough path - way of time? Make Je - sus your friend ere the
CHORUS
ceas - ing - ly falls O'er my soul like an in - fi - nite calm.
mine it a - way While the years of e - ter - ni - ty roll.
night and by day, And His glo - ry is flood - ing my soul. Peace! peace!
ran - somed will sing In that heav - en - ly king - dom shall be:
shad - ows grow dark — O ac - cept this sweet peace so sub - lime!
won - der - ful peace, Com - ing down from the Fa - ther a - bove, Sweep o - ver my
spir - it for - ev - er, I pray, In fath - om - less bil - lows of love.

272

He Hideth My Soul

Fanny J. Crosby

William J. Kirkpatrick

1. A wonder-ful Sav-ior is Je-sus my Lord, A won-der-ful
2. A won-der-ful Sav-ior is Je-sus my Lord— He tak-eth my
3. With num-ber-less bless-ings each mo-ment He crowns, And, filled with His
4. When clothed in His brightness trans-port-ed I rise To meet Him in
Sav-ior to me; He hid-eth my soul in the cleft of the rock, Where
bur-den a-way; He hold-eth me up and I shall not be moved, He
full-ness di-vine, I sing in my rap-ture, "O glo-ry to God For
clouds of the sky, His per-fect sal-va-tion, His won-der-ful love, I'll
riv-ers of pleas-ure I see.
giv-eth me strength as my day.
such a Re-deem-er as mine!"
shout with the mil-lions on high.
CHORUS
He hid-eth my soul in the cleft of the rock
That shadows a dry, thirsty land; He hid-eth my life in the depths of His love,
And cov-ers me there with His hand, And cov-ers me there with His hand.

Guide Me, O Thou Great Jehovah 273

William Williams
Trans. by Peter Williams And William Williams

John Hughes

1. Guide me, O Thou great Je - ho - vah, Pil - grim through this bar - ren land;
2. O - pen now the crys - tal foun - tain, Whence the healing stream doth flow;
3. When I tread the verge of Jor - dan, Bid my anx - ious fears sub - side;

I am weak, but Thou art might - y; Hold me with Thy pow'r - ful hand;
Let the fire and cloud - y pil - lar Lead me all my jour - ney through;
Death of death, and hell's de - struc - tion, Land me safe on Ca - naan's side;

Bread of heav - en, Bread of heav - en, Feed me till I want no
Strong De - liv - erer, strong De - liv - erer, Be Thou still my strength and
Songs of prais - es, songs of prais - es I will ev - er give to

more, (want no more,) Feed me till I want no more.
shield, (strength and shield,) Be Thou still my strength and shield.
Thee, (give to Thee,) I will ev - er give to Thee. A - men.

274 Jesus, Lover of My Soul

Charles Wesley

Joseph Parry

1. Je - sus, Lov - er of my soul, Let me to Thy bos - om fly,
2. Oth - er ref - uge have I none; Hangs my help - less soul on Thee;
3. Thou, O Christ, art all I want; More than all in Thee I find;
4. Plen-teous grace with Thee is found, Grace to cov - er all my sin;
While the near - er wa - ters roll, While the tem - pest still is high:
Leave, ah, leave me not a - lone, Still sup - port and com - fort me.
Raise the fall - en, cheer the faint, Heal the sick, and lead the blind.
Let the heal - ing streams a - bound; Make and keep me pure with - in.
Hide me, O my Sav - iour, hide, Till the storm of life is past;
All my trust on Thee is stayed, All my help from Thee I bring;
Just and ho - ly is Thy name, I am all un - right - eous - ness;
Thou of life the Foun - tain art, Free - ly let me take of Thee;
Safe in - to the ha - ven guide; O re - ceive my soul at last!
Cov - er my de - fense - less head With the shad - ow of Thy wing.
False and full of sin I am, Thou art full of truth and grace.
Spring Thou up with - in my heart, Rise to all e - ter - ni - ty.
A-MEN.

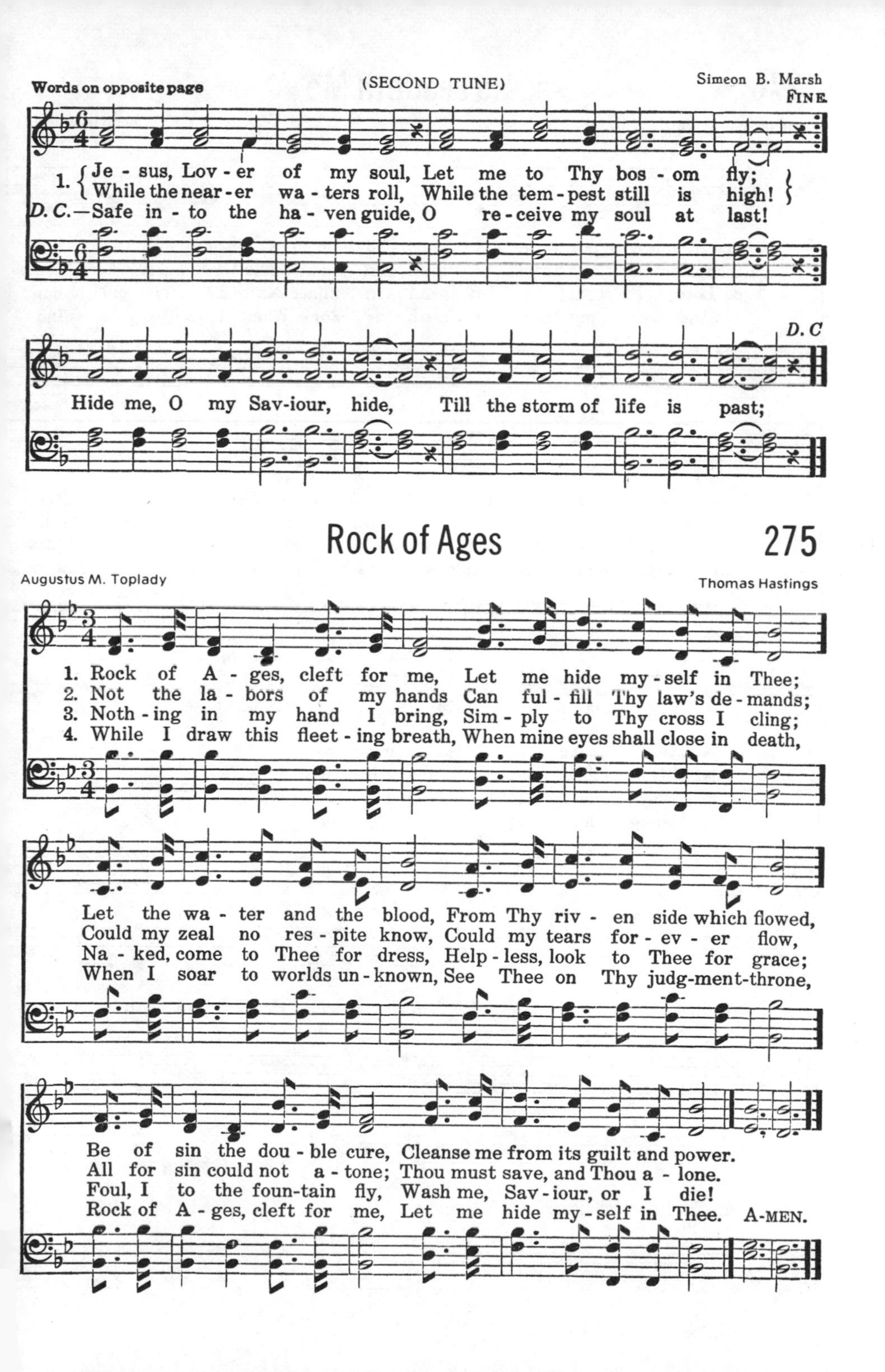
Words on opposite page
(SECOND TUNE)
Simeon B. Marsh
FINE
1. { Je - sus, Lov - er of my soul, Let me to Thy bos - om fly;
While the near - er wa - ters roll, While the tem - pest still is high! }
D. C.—Safe in - to the ha - ven guide, O re - ceive my soul at last!
D. C
Hide me, O my Sav - iour, hide, Till the storm of life is past;
Rock of Ages
275
Augustus M. Toplady
Thomas Hastings
1. Rock of A - ges, cleft for me, Let me hide my - self in Thee;
2. Not the la - bors of my hands Can ful - fill Thy law's de - mands;
3. Noth - ing in my hand I bring, Sim - ply to Thy cross I cling;
4. While I draw this fleet - ing breath, When mine eyes shall close in death,
Let the wa - ter and the blood, From Thy riv - en side which flowed,
Could my zeal no res - pite know, Could my tears for - ev - er flow,
Na - ked, come to Thee for dress, Help - less, look to Thee for grace;
When I soar to worlds un - known, See Thee on Thy judg - ment - throne,
Be of sin the dou - ble cure, Cleanse me from its guilt and power.
All for sin could not a - tone; Thou must save, and Thou a - lone.
Foul, I to the foun - tain fly, Wash me, Sav - iour, or I die!
Rock of A - ges, cleft for me, Let me hide my - self in Thee. A - MEN.

276

He Leadeth Me

Joseph H. Gilmore

William B. Bradbury

1. He lead - eth me, O bless - ed thought! O words with heav'n - ly
2. Some-times 'mid scenes of deep - est gloom, Some-times where E - den's
3. Lord, I would clasp Thy hand in mine, Nor ev - er mur - mur
4. And when my task on earth is done, When by Thy grace the
com - fort fraught! What - e'er I do, wher - e'er I be, Still
bow - ers bloom, By wa - ters still, o'er trou - bled sea, Still
nor re - pine; Con - tent, what - ev - er lot I see, Since
vic - t'ry's won, E'en death's cold wave I will not flee, Since
'tis God's hand that lead - eth me.
'tis His hand that lead - eth me.
'tis my God that lead - eth me.
God through Jor - dan lead - eth me.
Refrain
He lead - eth me, He
lead - eth me! By His own hand He lead - eth me! His
faith - ful fol - l'wer I would be, For by His hand He lead-eth me.

God Leads Us Along

G. A. Young G. A. Young

1. In shad-y, green pas-tures, so rich and so sweet, God leads His dear
2. Some-times on the mount where the sun shines so bright, God leads His dear
3. Tho sor-rows be-fall us and Sa-tan op-pose, God leads His dear
4. A - way from the mire and a - way from the clay, God leads His dear
chil-dren a - long; Where the wa-ter's cool flow bathes the wea-ry one's feet,
chil-dren a - long; Some - times in the val-ley, in dark-est of night,
chil-dren a - long; Thru grace we can con-quer, de-feat all our foes,
chil-dren a - long; A - way up in glo-ry, e - ter-ni-ty's day,
God leads His dear chil-dren a - long.
CHORUS
Some thru the wa-ters, some thru the flood,
Some thru the fire, but all thru the blood; Some thru great sor-row, but
God gives a song, In the night sea-son and all the day long.

278 A Shelter in the Time of Storm

Vernon J. Charlesworth
Adapt. by Ira D. Sankey
Ira D. Sankey
1. The Lord's our rock, in Him we hide, A shel - ter in the time of storm;
2. A shade by day, de-fense by night, A shel - ter in the time of storm;
3. The rag - ing storms may round us beat, A shel - ter in the time of storm;
4. O Rock di - vine, O Ref - uge dear, A shel - ter in the time of storm;
Se - cure what-ev - er ill be - tide, A shel - ter in the time of storm.
No fears a - larm, no foes af - fright, A shel - ter in the time of storm.
We'll nev - er leave our safe re - treat, A shel - ter in the time of storm.
Be Thou our help - er ev - er near, A shel - ter in the time of storm.
Refrain
O, Je - sus is a rock in a wea-ry land, A wea-ry land, a wea-ry land;
O, Je - sus is a rock in a wea-ry land, A shel-ter in the time of storm.

We Have an Anchor

Priscilla J. Owens

William J. Kirkpatrick

1. Will your an - chor hold in the storms of life, When the clouds un - fold
2. It is safe - ly moored, 'twill the storm with-stand, For 'tis well se - cured
3. It will firm - ly hold in the straits of fear, When the break-ers have told
4. When our eyes be - hold through the gath - ering night The cit - y of gold,
their wings of strife? When the strong tides lift and the ca - bles strain,
by the Sav - iour's hand; And the ca - bles, passed from His heart to mine,
the reef is near; Though the tem - pest rave and the wild winds blow,
our har - bor bright, We shall an - chor fast by the heaven-ly shore,
Will your an - chor drift or firm re - main?
Can de - fy that blast through strength di - vine.
Not an an - gry wave shall our bark o'er - flow.
With the storms all past for - ev - er - more.
Refrain
We have an an - chor that
keeps the soul Stead - fast and sure while the bil - lows roll, Fas-tened to the
Rock which can - not move, Ground-ed firm and deep in the Sav-iour's love.

280 He Will Hold Me Fast

Ada R. Habershon — Robert Harkness

1. When I fear my faith will fail, Christ will hold me fast;
When the tempt-er would pre-vail, He can hold me fast. . .

2. I could nev-er keep my hold, He will hold me fast;
For my love is oft-en cold, He must hold me fast. . .

3. I am pre-cious in His sight, He will hold me fast;
Those He saves are His de-light, He will hold me fast. . .

4. He'll not let my soul be lost, Christ will hold me fast;
Bought by Him at such a cost, He will hold me fast. . .

rall.

REFRAIN *a tempo*

He will hold me fast, hold me fast,
He will hold me fast; hold me fast;
rall.
For my Sav-ior loves me so, He will hold me fast.

God Will Take Care of You 281

Civilla D. Martin — W. Stillman Martin

1. Be not dis - mayed what-e'er be - tide, God will take care of you;
2. Through days of toil when heart doth fail, God will take care of you;
3. All you may need He will pro - vide, God will take care of you;
4. No mat - ter what may be the test, God will take care of you;

Be - neath His wings of love a - bide, God will take care of you.
When dan-gers fierce your path as - sail, God will take care of you.
Noth - ing you ask will be de - nied, God will take care of you.
Lean, wea - ry one, up - on His breast, God will take care of you.

Refrain

God will take care of you, Through ev-ery day, O'er all the way;

He will take care of you, God will take care of you..........
take care of you.

282 Loving Care

Avis B. Christiansen

Alfred B. Smith

1. As I tread life's tan-gled path-way, Hid-den dan-gers ev - 'ry-where,
2. In the dark-est hour of mid-night He is watch-ing from a-bove,
3. When the last long mile is end - ed, On my jour-ney here be - low,
Oh how pre-cious the as - sur - ance Of my Heav'n-ly Fa-ther's care!
O - ver - rul - ing in His mer - cy, O - ver - shad - ow - ing in love.
And I en - ter Heav-en's Glo - ry, Ev - er - last - ing joy to know,--
With His arms of love a - bout me, Naught of e - vil need I fear,
O how bless-ed is the know-ledge That my Lord is ev - er there,
Through - out e - ter - nal a - ges I shall praise Him o - ver there
For where ev - er He may call me He has prom-ised to be near.
And though shad-ows round me gath - er, I am safe with-in His care!
For His nev - er - fail - ing mer - cy And His ten - der lov - ing care!
Chorus
Lov-ing care! Lov-ing care! Pre-cious is God's ten-der lov-ing
(Lov - ing care!) (Lov - ing care!) ten - der

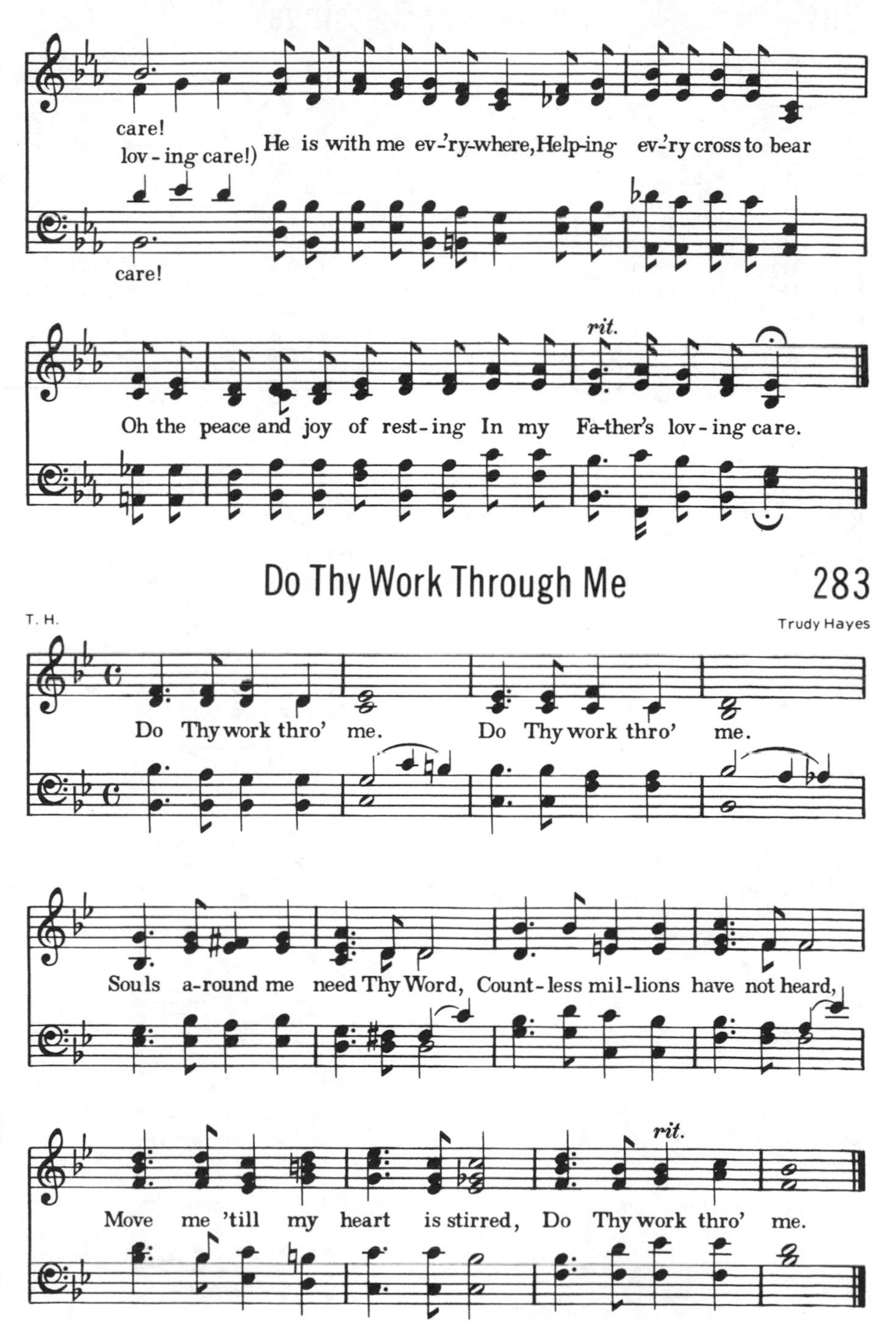
care!
lov - ing care!)
He is with me ev-'ry-where, Help-ing ev-'ry cross to bear
care!
rit.
Oh the peace and joy of rest-ing In my Fa-ther's lov-ing care.
Do Thy Work Through Me
283
T. H.
Trudy Hayes
Do Thy work thro' me. Do Thy work thro' me.
Souls a-round me need Thy Word, Count-less mil-lions have not heard,
rit.
Move me 'till my heart is stirred, Do Thy work thro' me.

284 Showers of Blessings

Daniel W. Whittle | James McGranahan

1. There shall be show - ers of bless - ing— This is the prom-ise of love;
2. There shall be show - ers of bless - ing— Pre - cious, re - viv - ing a - gain;
3. There shall be show - ers of bless - ing— Send them up - on us, O Lord!
4. There shall be show - ers of bless - ing— Oh, that to - day they might fall,
5. There shall be show - ers of bless - ing, If we but trust and o - bey;

There shall be sea - sons re - fresh - ing Sent from the Sav-iour a - bove.
O - ver the hills and the val - leys Sound of a - bun-dance of rain.
Grant to us now a re - fresh - ing; Come, and now hon - or Thy Word.
Now as to God we're con - fess - ing, Now as on Je - sus we call!
There shall be sea - sons re - fresh - ing, If we let God have His way.

REFRAIN

Show - - ers of bless - ing,
Show - ers, show - ers of bless - ing, Show - ers of bless - ing we need;
Mer - cy drops round us are fall - ing, But for the show - ers we plead.

Moment by Moment

Daniel W. Whittle | May Whittle Moody

1. Dy - ing with Je - sus, by death reck-oned mine; Liv - ing with Je - sus, a
2. Nev - er a tri - al that He is not there, Nev - er a bur - den that
3. Nev - er a heart-ache and nev - er a groan, Nev - er a tear-drop and
4. Nev - er a weak-ness that He doth not feel, Nev - er a sick-ness that
new life di - vine; Look-ing to Je - sus till glo - ry doth shine, Mo-ment by
He doth not bear, Nev - er a sor - row that He doth not share, Mo-ment by
nev - er a moan; Nev - er a dan - ger, but there on the throne, Mo-ment by
He can - not heal; Mo - ment by mo-ment, in woe or in weal, Je - sus, my
Refrain
mo-ment, O Lord, I am Thine.
mo-ment I'm un - der His care; Mo-ment by mo-ment I'm kept in His love;
mo-ment, He thinks of His own.
Sav-iour, a-bides with me still.
Mo-ment by mo-ment I've life from a - bove; Look - ing to Je - sus till
glo - ry doth shine; Mo - ment by mo - ment, O Lord, I am Thine.

286 Surely Goodness and Mercy

John W. Peterson
& Alfred B. Smith

Alfred B. Smith &
John W. Peterson

1. A pil-grim was I, and a - wan - d'ring, In the cold night of sin I did roam, When Je-sus the kind Shep-herd found me, And now I am on my way home.
2. He re-stor-eth my soul when I'm wea - ry, He giv - eth me strength day by day; He leads me be-side the still wa - ters, He guards me each step of the way.
3. When I walk thru the dark lone-some val - ley, My Sav - ior will walk with me there; And safe-ly His great hand will lead me To the man - sions He's gone to pre - pare.

CHORUS

Sure-ly good-ness and mer - cy shall fol - low me All the days, all the days of my life; Sure-ly good-ness and mer - cy shall fol - low me All the days, all the days of my life.

May be omitted until final chorus:
And I shall dwell in the house of the Lord for-ev-er, And I shall feast at the
ta-ble spread for me; Sure-ly good-ness and mer-cy shall fol - low me
All the days, all the days of my life, All the days, all the days of my life.
May the Mind of Christ, My Saviour
287
Kate B. Wilkinson
A. Cyril Barham-Gould
1. May the mind of Christ, my Sav-ior, Live in me from day to day,
2. May the Word of God dwell rich-ly In my heart from hour to hour,
3. May the peace of God, my Fa-ther, Rule my life in ev-'ry-thing,
4. May the love of Je-sus fill me, As the wa-ters fill the sea;
5. May I run the race be-fore me, Strong and brave to face the foe,
6. May His beau-ty rest up-on me As I seek the lost to win,
By His love and pow'r con-trol-ling All I do and say.
So that all may see I tri-umph On-ly thru His pow'r.
That I may be calm to com-fort Sick and sor-row-ing.
Him ex-alt-ing, self a-bas-ing– This is vic-to-ry.
Look-ing on-ly un-to Je-sus As I on-ward go.
And may they for-get the chan-nel, See-ing on-ly Him.
by permission of Miss E.W.M. Gould.

288 My Father Planned It All

H. H. Pierson — Alfred B. Smith

1. What tho' the way be lone-ly And dark the shad-ows fall; I know wher-e'er it lead-eth, My Fa-ther planned it all.
2. There may be sunshine tomorrow, Shadows may break and flee; 'Twill be the way He choos-es, The Fa-ther's plan for me.
3. He guides my falt'ring foot-steps A - long the wea-ry way, For well He knows the path-way Will lead to end-less day.
4. A day of light and glad-ness On which no shade will fall: 'Tis this at last a-waits me— My Fa-ther planned it all.
CHORUS
I sing thro' the shade and the sun-shine, I'll trust Him what-ev-er be-fall; be-fall;
I sing for I can-not be si-lent— My Fa-ther planned it all. (it all.)

The Great Physician

William Hunter

John H. Stockton

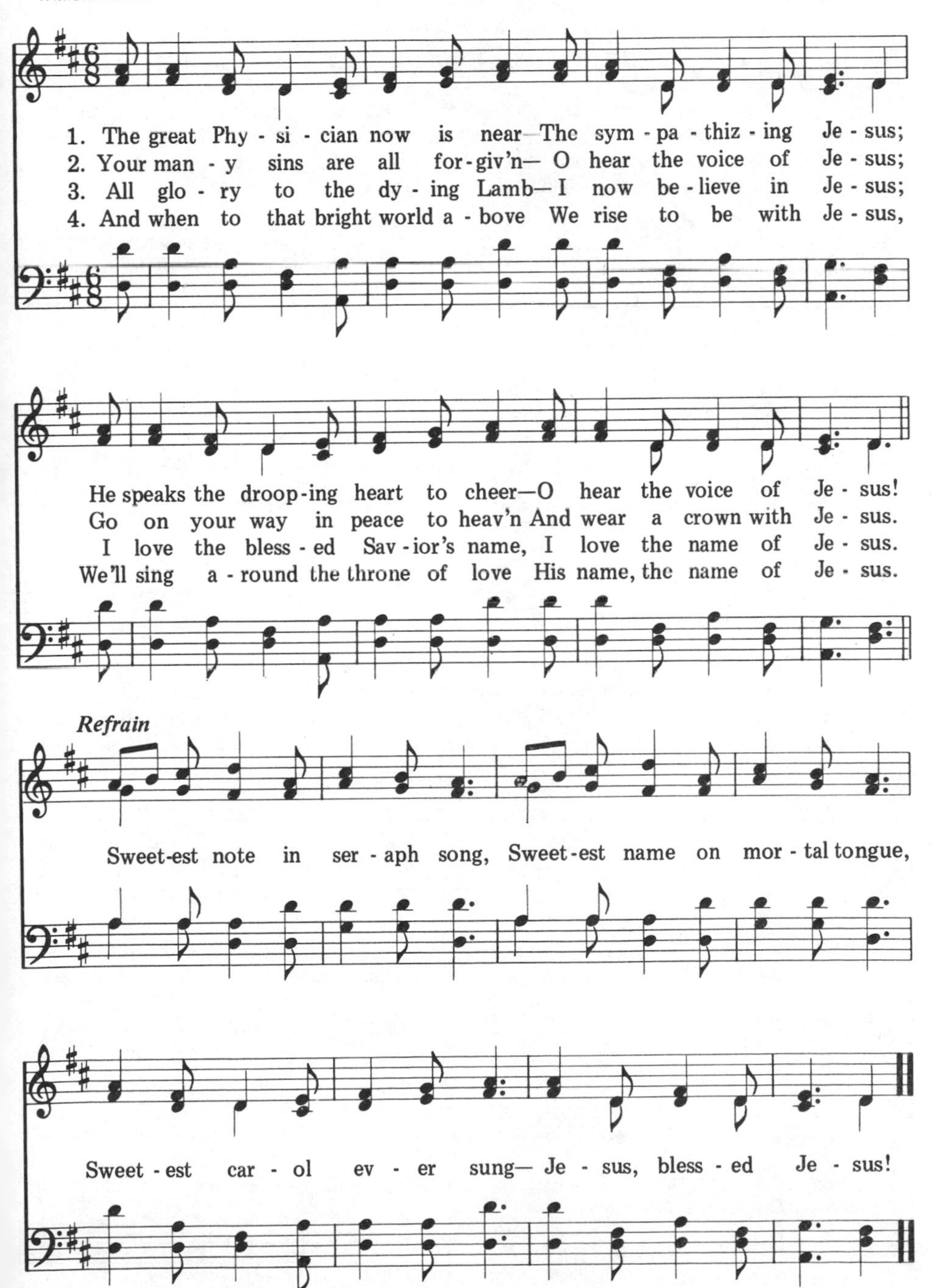
1. The great Phy - si - cian now is near—The sym - pa - thiz - ing Je - sus;
2. Your man - y sins are all for - giv'n— O hear the voice of Je - sus;
3. All glo - ry to the dy - ing Lamb—I now be - lieve in Je - sus;
4. And when to that bright world a - bove We rise to be with Je - sus,
He speaks the droop - ing heart to cheer—O hear the voice of Je - sus!
Go on your way in peace to heav'n And wear a crown with Je - sus.
I love the bless - ed Sav - ior's name, I love the name of Je - sus.
We'll sing a - round the throne of love His name, the name of Je - sus.
Refrain
Sweet - est note in ser - aph song, Sweet - est name on mor - tal tongue,
Sweet - est car - ol ev - er sung— Je - sus, bless - ed Je - sus!

290 My Anchor Holds

W. C. Martin

Daniel B. Towner

1. Though the an - gry surg - es roll On my tem - pest - driv - en soul,
2. Might - y tides a - bout me sweep, Per - ils lurk with - in the deep,
3. I can feel the an - chor fast As I meet each sud - den blast,
4. Trou - bles al - most 'whelm the soul; Griefs like bil - lows o'er me roll;
I am peace - ful, for I know, Wild - ly though the winds may blow,
An - gry clouds o'er - shade the sky, And the tem - pest ris - es high;
And the ca - ble, though un - seen, Bears the heav - y strain be - tween;
Tempt - ers seek to lure a - stray; Storms ob - scure the light of day:
I've an an - chor safe and sure That can ev - er - more en - dure.
Still I stand the tem - pest's shock, For my an - chor grips the Rock.
Thro' the storm I safe - ly ride, Till the turn - ing of the tide.
But in Christ I can be bold, I've an an - chor that shall hold.
Refrain
And it holds, my an - chor holds; Blow your wild - est, then, O
And it holds, my an - chor holds; Blow your wild - est,
gale, On my bark so small and frail; By His grace I shall not
then, O gale,

fail, For my an - chor holds, my an - chor holds.
For my an - chor holds, it firm - ly holds,
Jesus, Saviour, Pilot Me
291
Edward Hopper
John E. Gould
1. Je - sus, Sav - iour, pi - lot me O - ver life's tem - pes - tuous sea;
2. As a moth - er stills her child, Thou canst hush the o - cean wild;
3. When at last I near the shore, And the fear - ful break - ers roar
Un-known waves be - fore me roll, Hid - ing rock and treacherous shoal;
Bois-terous waves o - bey Thy will When Thou say'st to them, "Be still!"
'Twixt me and the peace-ful rest, Then, while lean - ing on Thy breast,
Fine
Chart and com-pass came from Thee: Je - sus, Sav - iour, pi - lot me.
Won-drous Sovereign of the sea, Je - sus, Sav - iour, pi - lot me.
May I hear Thee say to me, "Fear not, I will pi - lot thee.

292 I Need Thee Every Hour

Annie S. Hawks

Robert Lowry

1. I need Thee ev - ery hour, Most gra - cious Lord; No ten - der voice like Thine Can peace af - ford.
2. I need Thee ev - ery hour, Stay Thou near by; Temp - ta - tions lose their pow'r When Thou art nigh.
3. I need Thee ev - ery hour In joy or pain; Come quick - ly and a- bide Or life is vain.
4. I need Thee ev - ery hour, Most Ho - ly One; O make me Thine in- deed, Thou bless - ed Son!

Refrain

I need Thee, O I need Thee; Ev - ery hour I need Thee; O bless me now, my Sav - ior, I come to Thee!

293 The Lord's My Shepherd

Scottish Psalter
William Whittingham and others

Arr. by David Grant

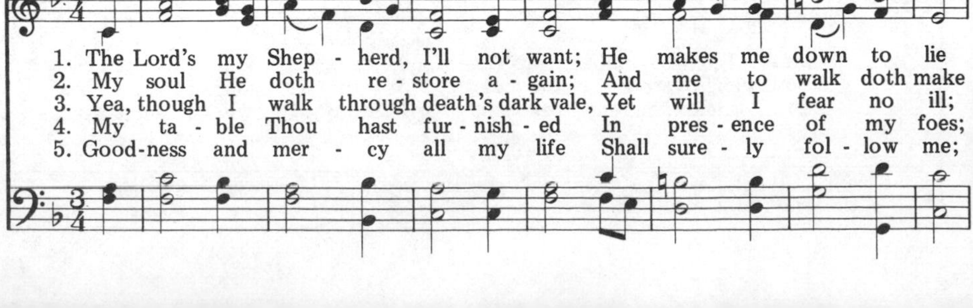

1. The Lord's my Shep - herd, I'll not want; He makes me down to lie
2. My soul He doth re - store a - gain; And me to walk doth make
3. Yea, though I walk through death's dark vale, Yet will I fear no ill;
4. My ta - ble Thou hast fur - nish - ed In pres - ence of my foes;
5. Good-ness and mer - cy all my life Shall sure - ly fol - low me;

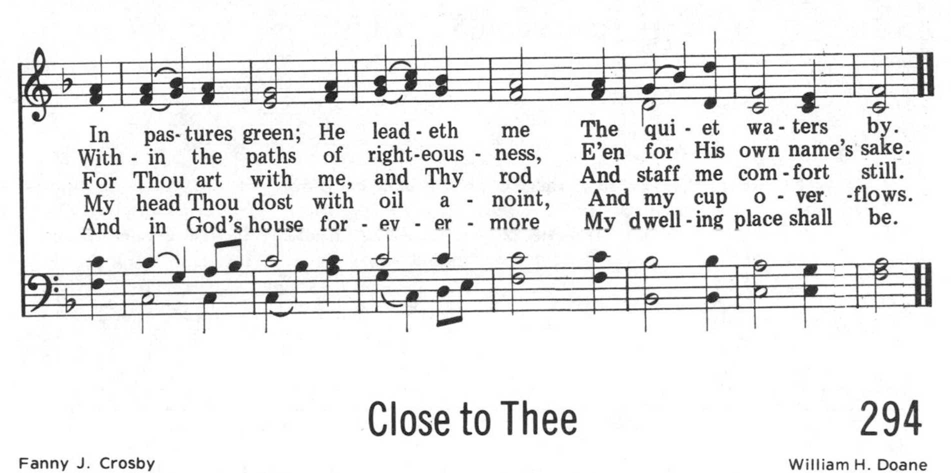
In pas-tures green; He lead-eth me The qui-et wa-ters by.
With-in the paths of right-eous-ness, E'en for His own name's sake.
For Thou art with me, and Thy rod And staff me com-fort still.
My head Thou dost with oil a-noint, And my cup o-ver-flows.
And in God's house for-ev-er-more My dwell-ing place shall be.

Close to Thee

294

Fanny J. Crosby

William H. Doane

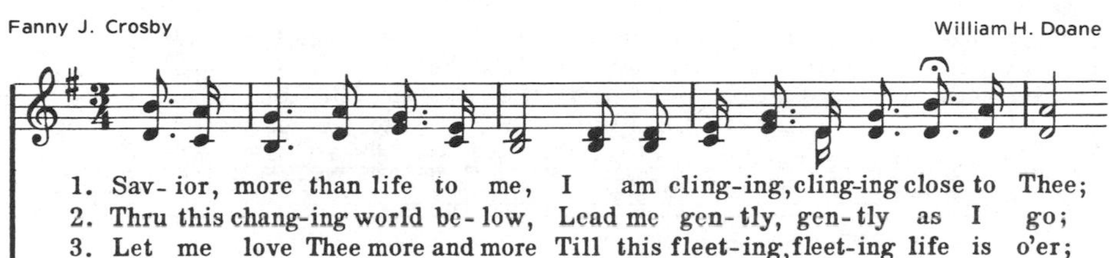
1. Sav-ior, more than life to me, I am cling-ing, cling-ing close to Thee;
2. Thru this chang-ing world be-low, Lead me gen-tly, gen-tly as I go;
3. Let me love Thee more and more Till this fleet-ing, fleet-ing life is o'er;

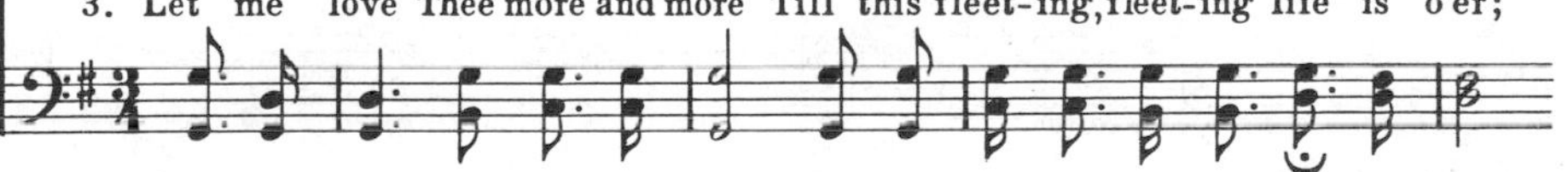

Fine
Let Thy pre-cious blood, ap-plied, Keep me ev-er, ev-er near Thy side.
Trust-ing Thee, I can-not stray– I can nev-er, nev-er lose my way.
Till my soul is lost in love In a bright-er, bright-er world a-bove.
D.S.– May Thy ten-der love to me Bind me clos-er, clos-er, Lord, to Thee.

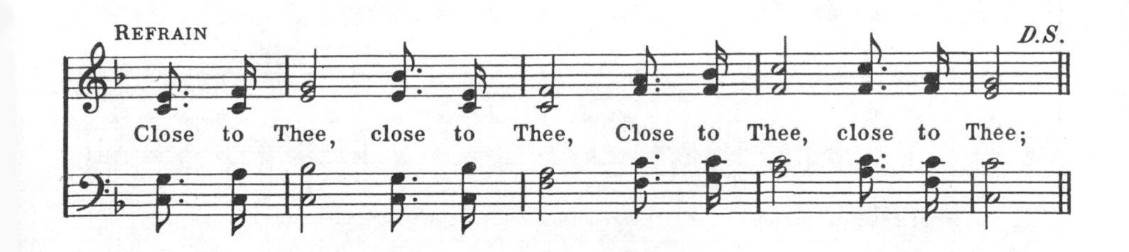
Refrain
D.S.
Close to Thee, close to Thee, Close to Thee, close to Thee;

295 If Jesus Goes With Me

C. Austin Miles
C. Austin Miles
1. It may be in the val-ley, where countless dan-gers hide; It may be in the sun-shine that I, in peace, a-bide. But this one thing I know— if it be dark or fair, If Je-sus is with me, I'll go an-y-where!
2. It may be I must car-ry the bless-ed word of life A-cross the burning des-erts to those in sin-ful strife; And tho' it be my lot to bear my col-ors there, If Je-sus goes with me, I'll go an-y-where!
3. But if it be my por-tion to bear my cross at home, While oth-ers bear their bur-dens be-yond the bil-lows' foam, I'll prove my faith in Him, con-fess His judg-ments fair; And if He stays with me, I'll stay an-y-where!
4. It is not mine to ques-tion the judg-ments of my Lord; It is but mine to fol-low the lead-ings of His Word. But if to go or stay, or wheth-er here or there, I'll be, with my Sav-iour, Con-tent an-y-where!
REFRAIN
If Je-sus goes with me, I'll go ___ I'll go An-y-where! 'Tis heav-en to me, Wher-e'er I may be, If He is there! I count it a priv-i-lege here ___ His His cross, His

cross to bear. If Je - sus goes with me, I'll go An - y - where!
cross, His cross to bear.

Hold Thou My Hand

296

Fanny J. Crosby
Alt. A.B.S.

Alfred B. Smith

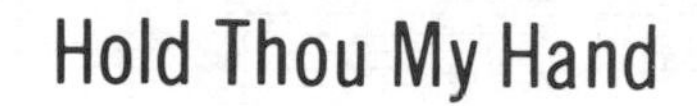

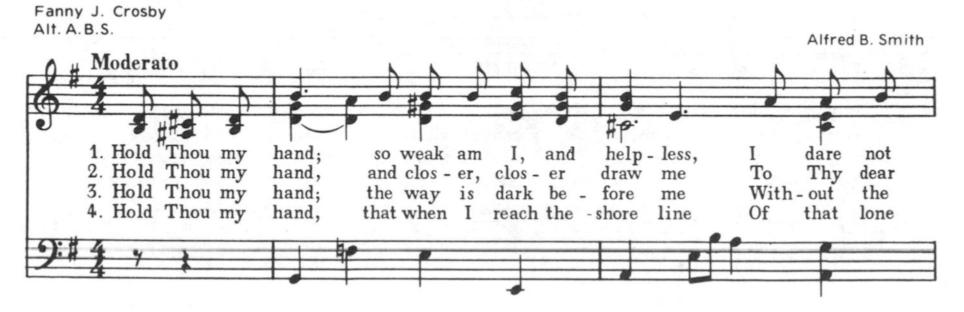
Moderato
1. Hold Thou my hand; so weak am I, and help - less, I dare not
2. Hold Thou my hand, and clos - er, clos - er draw me To Thy dear
3. Hold Thou my hand; the way is dark be - fore me With - out the
4. Hold Thou my hand, that when I reach the - shore line Of that lone

take one step with - out Thine aid; Hold Thou my hand; for then, O lov - ing
self my hope, my joy, my all; Hold Thou my hand, lest care - less I should
sun - light of Thy face di - vine; But when by faith I catch its ra - diant
riv - er Thou didst cross for me, A heav'n - ly light may shine a - long its

Sav - iour, No dread or fear shall make my soul a - fraid.
wan - der, And, miss - ing Thee, my trem - bling feet should fall.
glo - ry, What heights of joy, what rap - ture songs are mine!
wa - ters, And ev - 'ry wave like crys - tal bright shall be.

297 Count Your Blessings

Johnson Oatman, Jr. | Edwin O. Excell

1. When up-on life's bil-lows you are tem-pest-tossed, When you are dis-
2. Are you ev-er bur-dened with a load of care? Does the cross seem
3. When you look at oth-ers with their lands and gold, Think that Christ has
4. So a-mid the con-flict, wheth-er great or small, Do not be dis-
cour-aged, think-ing all is lost, Count your man-y bless-ings—name them
heav-y you are called to bear? Count your man-y bless-ings— ev-'ry
prom-ised you His wealth un-told; Count your man-y bless-ings— mon-ey
cour-aged—God is o-ver all; Count your man-y bless-ings— an-gels
one by one, And it will sur-prise you what the Lord hath done.
doubt will fly, And you will be sing-ing as the days go by.
can-not buy Your re-ward in heav-en nor your home on high.
will at-tend, Help and com-fort give you to your jour-ney's end.
CHORUS
Count your bless-ings—name them one by one; Count your
Count your man-y bless-ings— name them one by one; Count your man-y
bless-ings— see what God hath done; Count your bless-ings—
bless-ings— see what God hath done; Count your man-y bless-ings—

name them one by one; Count your man-y bless-ings—see what God hath done.
Let the Lower Lights Be Burning
298
Philip P. Bliss
Philip P. Bliss
1. Bright-ly beams our Fa-ther's mer-cy From His light-house ev-er-more,
2. Dark the night of sin has set-tled, Loud the an-gry bil-lows roar;
3. Trim your fee-ble lamp, my broth-er! Some poor sail-or tem-pest-tossed,
But to us He gives the keep-ing Of the lights a-long the shore.
Ea-ger eyes are watch-ing, long-ing, For the lights a-long the shore.
Try-ing now to make the har-bor, In the dark-ness may be lost.
CHORUS
Let the low-er lights be burn-ing! Send a gleam a-cross the wave!
Some poor faint-ing, strug-gling sea-man You may res-cue, you may save.

299 Undergirded

Walt Huntley

Alfred B. Smith

Smoothly
1. I have a Sav - iour who lift - ed my bur - den,
2. I'm un - der - gird - ed and noth - ing can harm me,
3. Long af - ter moun - tains have shift - ed and tum - bled,
When I was help - less in sin and dis - pair.
I'm just as safe as in Hea - ven a - bove.
Af - ter the foun - tains on earth have run dry,
Kneel - ing be - fore Him I found grace and fav - or,
My faith in Je - sus for - ev - er a - bid - ing,
Je - sus will love me I know He will keep me
Now I'm sup - por - ted by His lov - ing care.
I'm un - der - gird - ed by His match - less love.
Safe while e - ter - nal a - ges roll on by.
Chorus
Un - der - gird - ed, Un - der - gird - ed,

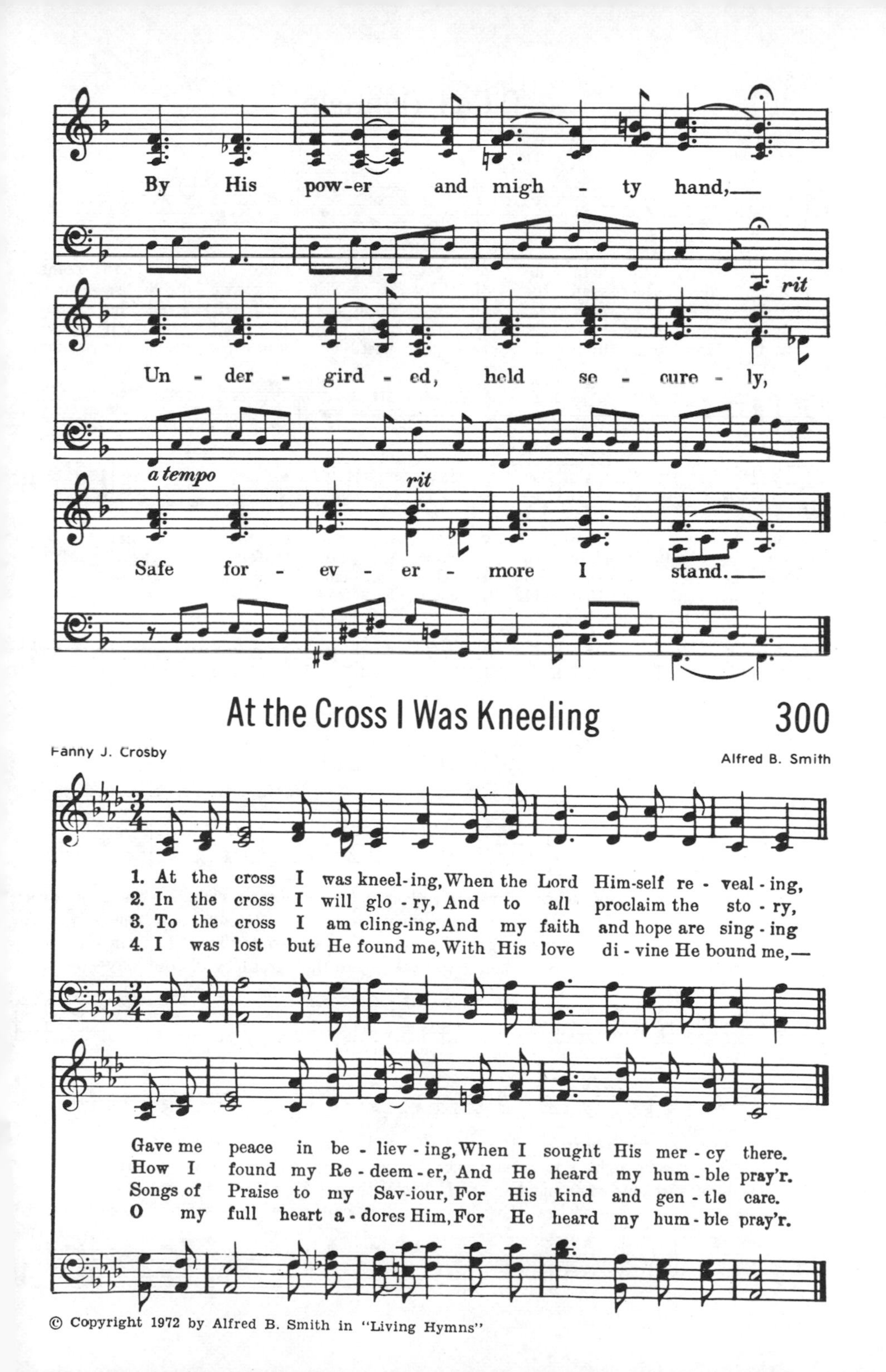
By His pow-er and migh - ty hand,
Un - der - gird - ed, held se - cure - ly,
rit
a tempo
rit
Safe for - ev - er - more I stand.
At the Cross I Was Kneeling
300
Fanny J. Crosby
Alfred B. Smith
1. At the cross I was kneel-ing, When the Lord Him-self re - veal - ing,
2. In the cross I will glo - ry, And to all proclaim the sto - ry,
3. To the cross I am cling-ing, And my faith and hope are sing - ing
4. I was lost but He found me, With His love di - vine He bound me,—
Gave me peace in be - liev - ing, When I sought His mer - cy there.
How I found my Re - deem - er, And He heard my hum - ble pray'r.
Songs of Praise to my Sav-iour, For His kind and gen - tle care.
O my full heart a - dores Him, For He heard my hum - ble pray'r.
© Copyright 1972 by Alfred B. Smith in "Living Hymns"

301
O God, Our Help
Psalm 90
Isaac Watts
William Croft
1. O God, our help in a - ges past, Our hope for years to come,
2. Un - der the shad - ow of Thy throne Still may we dwell se - cure;
3. Be - fore the hills in or - der stood, Or earth re - ceived her frame,
4. A thou - sand a - ges in Thy sight Are like an eve - ning gone;
5. O God, our help in a - ges past, Our hope for years to come,
Our shel - ter from the storm - y blast, And our e - ter - nal home!
Suf - fi - cient is Thine arm a - lone, And our de - fense is sure.
From ev - er - last - ing Thou art God, To end - less years the same.
Short as the watch that ends the night, Be - fore the ris - ing sun.
Be Thou our guide while life shall last, And our e - ter - nal home! A-men.

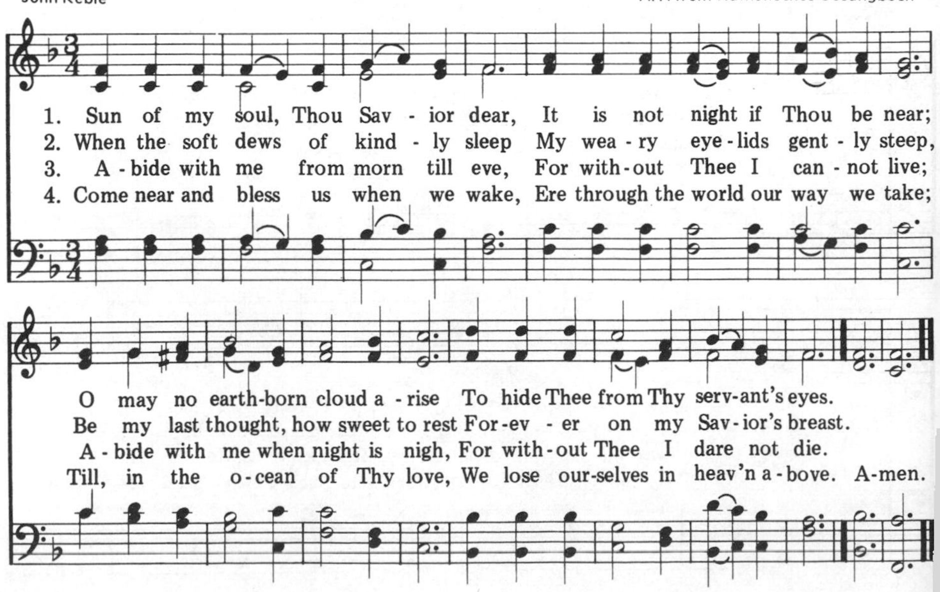
302
Sun of My Soul
John Keble
Arr. from Katholisches Gesangbuch
1. Sun of my soul, Thou Sav - ior dear, It is not night if Thou be near;
2. When the soft dews of kind - ly sleep My wea - ry eye - lids gent - ly steep,
3. A - bide with me from morn till eve, For with - out Thee I can - not live;
4. Come near and bless us when we wake, Ere through the world our way we take;
O may no earth-born cloud a - rise To hide Thee from Thy serv-ant's eyes.
Be my last thought, how sweet to rest For - ev - er on my Sav - ior's breast.
A - bide with me when night is nigh, For with - out Thee I dare not die.
Till, in the o - cean of Thy love, We lose our - selves in heav'n a - bove. A-men.

I Would Be Like Jesus

James Rowe

Bentley D. Ackley

1. Earth-ly pleas-ures vain-ly call me, I would be like Je - sus;
Noth-ing world-ly shall en-thrall me, I would be like Je - sus.

2. He has bro-ken ev-ery fet-ter, I would be like Je - sus;
That my soul may serve Him bet-ter, I would be like Je - sus.

3. All the way from earth to glo-ry, I would be like Je - sus;
Tell-ing o'er and o'er the sto-ry, I would be like Je - sus.

4. That in heav-en He may meet me, I would be like Je - sus;
That His words "Well done" may greet me, I would be like Je - sus.

would be like Je-sus;
would be like Je-sus.

Refrain

Be like Je-sus, this my song, In the home and in the throng;
Be like Je-sus, all day long! I would be like Je-sus.

304 Once It Was the Blessing

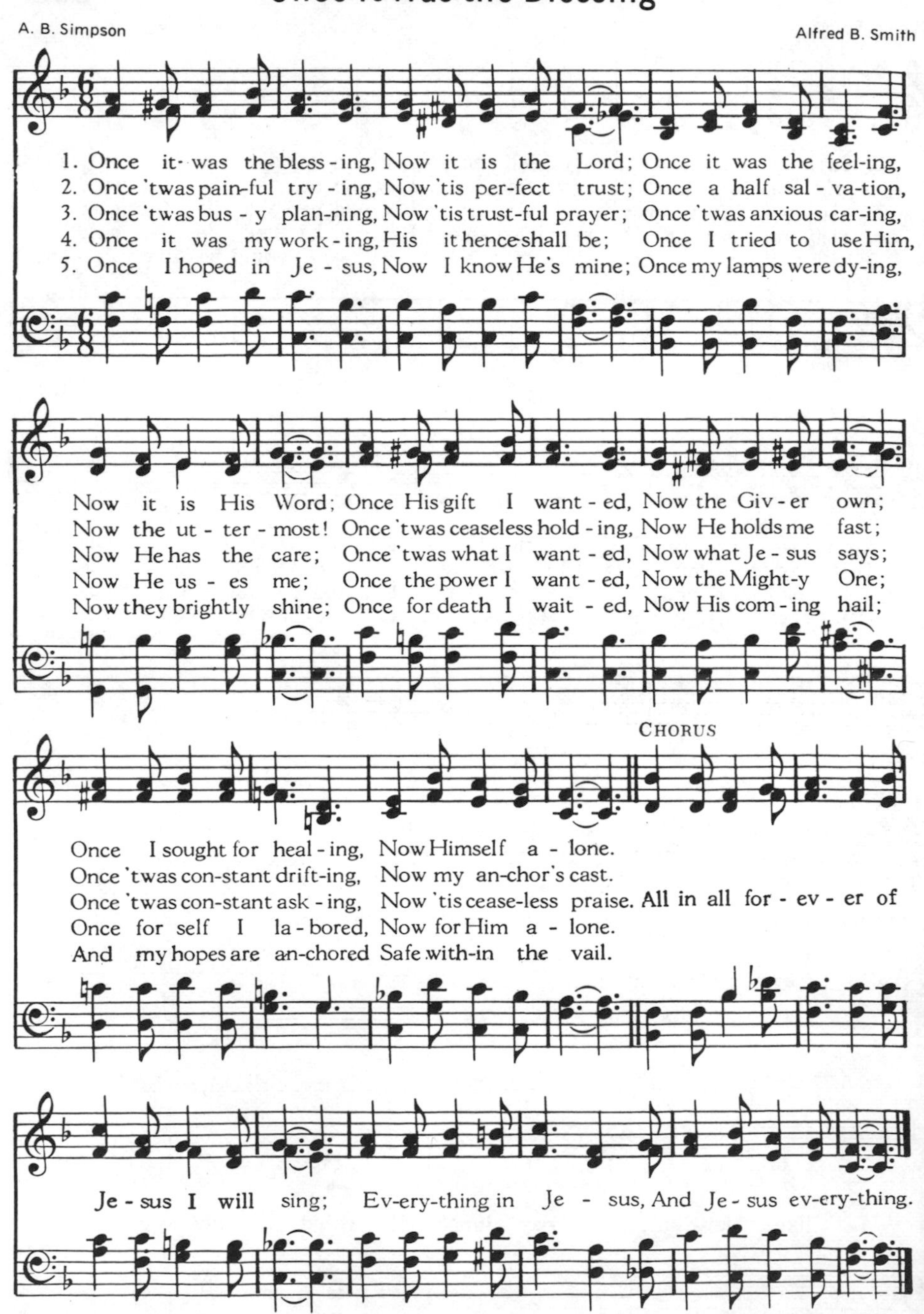
A. B. Simpson
Alfred B. Smith
1. Once it-was the bless-ing, Now it is the Lord; Once it was the feel-ing,
2. Once 'twas pain-ful try-ing, Now 'tis per-fect trust; Once a half sal-va-tion,
3. Once 'twas bus-y plan-ning, Now 'tis trust-ful prayer; Once 'twas anxious car-ing,
4. Once it was my work-ing, His it hence-shall be; Once I tried to use Him,
5. Once I hoped in Je-sus, Now I know He's mine; Once my lamps were dy-ing,
Now it is His Word; Once His gift I want-ed, Now the Giv-er own;
Now the ut-ter-most! Once 'twas ceaseless hold-ing, Now He holds me fast;
Now He has the care; Once 'twas what I want-ed, Now what Je-sus says;
Now He us-es me; Once the power I want-ed, Now the Might-y One;
Now they brightly shine; Once for death I wait-ed, Now His com-ing hail;
CHORUS
Once I sought for heal-ing, Now Himself a-lone.
Once 'twas con-stant drift-ing, Now my an-chor's cast.
Once 'twas con-stant ask-ing, Now 'tis cease-less praise. All in all for-ev-er of
Once for self I la-bored, Now for Him a-lone.
And my hopes are an-chored Safe with-in the vail.
Je-sus I will sing; Ev-ery-thing in Je-sus, And Je-sus ev-ery-thing.

I Surrender All

Judson W. VanDeVenter — Winfield S. Weeden

1. All to Je - sus I sur-ren - der, All to Him I free - ly give;
2. All to Je - sus I sur-ren - der, Hum-bly at His feet I bow,
3. All to Je - sus I sur-ren - der, Make me, Sav - ior, whol - ly Thine;
4. All to Je - sus I sur-ren - der, Lord, I give my-self to Thee;
I will ev - er love and trust Him, In His pres-ence dai - ly live.
World - ly pleas-ures all for - sak - en, Take me, Je - sus, take me now.
May Thy Ho - ly Spir - it fill me, May I know Thy pow'r di - vine.
Fill me with Thy love and pow - er, Let Thy bless-ing fall on me.
Refrain
I sur-ren-der all, I sur-ren-der all.
I sur-ren-der all, I sur-ren-der all.
All to Thee, my bless - ed Sav - ior, I sur - ren - der all.

306 More Like My Saviour

Charles H. Gabriel Alt.
Charles H. Gabriel
1. More like my Sav - iour I would ev - er be, More of His meek-ness,
2. More like my Sav - iour is my dai - ly prayer; More strength to car-ry
3. More like my Sav - iour I would live and grow; More of His love to
more hu - mil - i - ty; More zeal to la - bor, more cour-age to be true,
cross - es I must bear; More ear-nest ef - fort to lead some soul to Him;
oth - ers I would show; More self - de - ni - al, like His in Gal - i - lee,
More con - se - cra - tion for work He bids me do.
More of His Spir - it, the wan - der - er to win.
More like my Sav - iour I long to ev - er be.
REFRAIN
Take Thou my
Take my heart, O
heart, I would be Thine a - lone; Take Thou my life and
take my heart, I would be Thine a-lone; Take my life, O take my life and
make it all Thine own; Purge me from sin, O Lord, I now im-
make it all Thine own; Purge Thou me from ev - 'ry sin, O Lord, I

plore, Wash me and keep me Thine for - ev - er - more.
now im-plore, Wash and keep, O wash and keep me Thine for - ev - er - more.

Nearer, Still Nearer

307

Mrs. C. H. Morris — Mrs. C. H. Morris

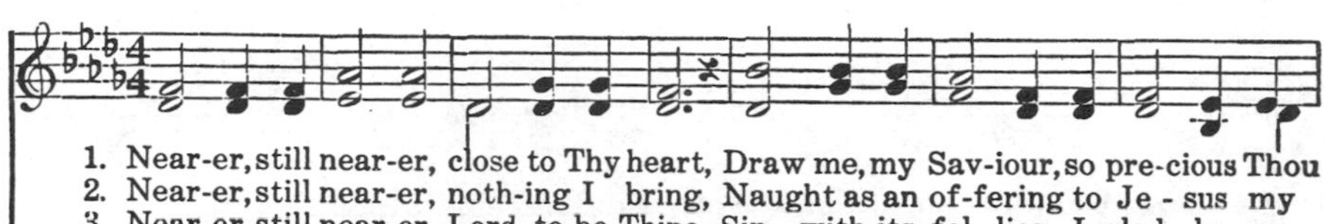

1. Near-er, still near-er, close to Thy heart, Draw me, my Sav-iour, so pre-cious Thou
2. Near-er, still near-er, noth-ing I bring, Naught as an of-fering to Je - sus my
3. Near-er, still near-er, Lord, to be Thine, Sin, with its fol - lies, I glad - ly re-
4. Near-er, still near-er, while life shall last, Till safe in glo - ry my an - chor is

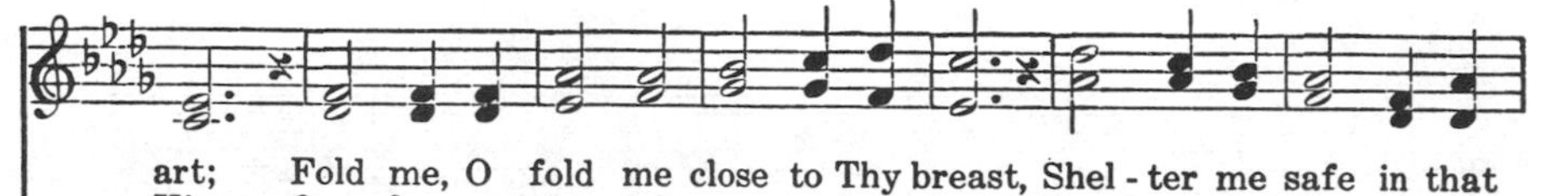

art; Fold me, O fold me close to Thy breast, Shel - ter me safe in that
King; On - ly my sin - ful, now con-trite heart, Grant me the cleansing Thy
sign; All of its pleas-ures, pomp and its pride, Give me but Je - sus, my
cast; Through endless a - ges, ev - er to be, Near - er, my Sav-iour, still

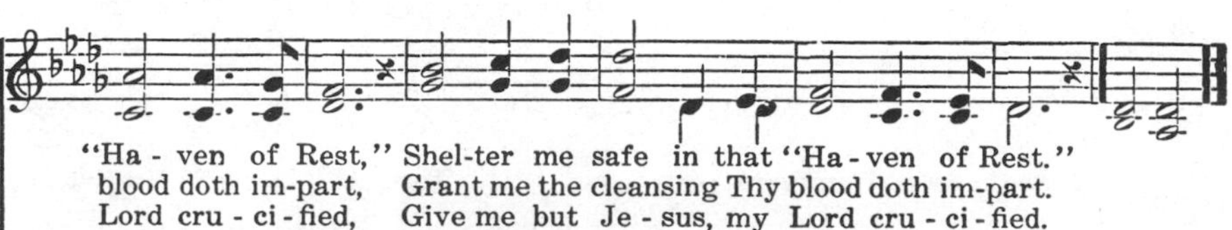

"Ha - ven of Rest," Shel-ter me safe in that "Ha - ven of Rest."
blood doth im-part, Grant me the cleansing Thy blood doth im-part.
Lord cru - ci - fied, Give me but Je - sus, my Lord cru - ci - fied.
near - er to Thee, Near-er, my Saviour, still near - er to Thee. A-MEN.

308 O to Be Kept for Jesus

Edith G. Cherry
Edit. by A.B.S.

Alfred B. Smith

1. Oh, to be "Kept for Je - sus!" Kept by the pow'r of God;
Kept, from the world un - spot - ted, Tread-ing where Je - sus trod.

2. Oh, to be "Kept' for Je - sus!" Serv - ing as He shall choose;
"Kept" for the Mas - ter's pleas - ure; "Kept" for the Mas - ter's use.

3. Oh, to be "Kept for Je - sus!" Kept from the world a - part;
Low - ly in mind and spir - it, Gen - tle and pure in heart.

4. Oh, to be "Kept for Je - sus!" Oh, to be all His own;
Kept, to be His for - ev - er, Kept to be His a - lone!

Chorus

Oh, to be "Kept for Je - sus!" Lord at Thy feet I fall;
I would be noth-ing– my heart en-thral! Thou shalt be all in all!

rit.

Channels Only

Mary E. Maxwell

Ada Rose Gibbs

1. How I praise Thee, pre-cious Sav - iour, That Thy love laid hold of me;
2. Emp-tied that Thou should-est fill me, A clean ves - sel in Thy hand;
3. Wit - ness - ing Thy power to save me, Set - ting free from self and sin,
4. Je - sus, fill now with Thy Spir - it Hearts that full sur - ren - der know;

Thou hast saved and cleansed and filled me That I might Thy chan-nel be.
With no power but as Thou giv - est Gra-cious - ly with each com-mand.
Thou who bought-est to pos - sess me, In Thy full - ness, Lord, come in.
That the streams of liv - ing wa - ter From our in - ner man may flow.

REFRAIN
Chan-nels on - ly, bless - ed Mas - ter, But with all Thy won-drous power

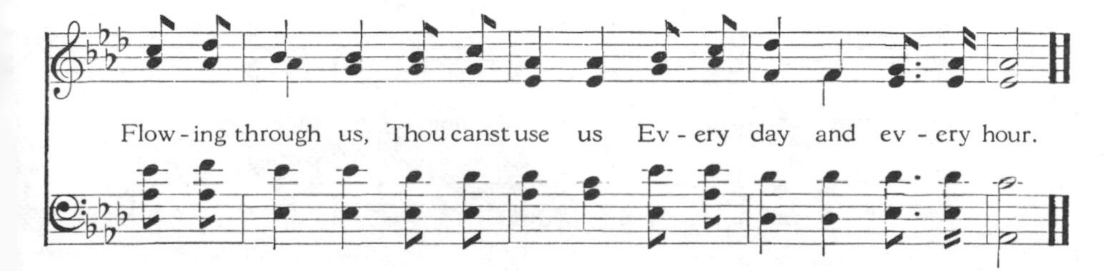
Flow - ing through us, Thou canst use us Ev - ery day and ev - ery hour.

310

Lord, Search My Life

Stephen F. Olford — Paul F. Liljestrand

1. Lord, search my life in ev'-ry part, Re-veal the sins that make me fail, Till with a brok-en, con-trite heart— I kneel to con-quer and pre-vail.
2. Lord, cleanse my life from ev'-ry stain, As I con-fess my sins to Thee; Let no un-ho-ly thought re-main, For Thy Name's sake, oh, set me free!
3. Lord, take my life, whate'-er the price— My self, my gifts, my bo-dy, too; And through this "liv-ing sac-ri-fice," "U-nite my heart" Thy will to do.
4. Lord, fill my life with heav'-nly grace, That I may wit-ness to Thy love; I ask in faith and seek Thy face— For Thy Free Spir-it from a-bove.
5. Lord, use my life to reach the lost, On friend-ly shore or for-eign soil; And may I nev-er count the cost— To win Thy smile for faith-ful toil.
CODA - sing after last stanza
Lord, hear my pray'r, I hum-bly plead, And in Thy mer-cy meet my need.

Jesus, I My Cross Have Taken

Henry F. Lyte

Attr. to Wolfgand A. Mozart
Arr. by Hubert P. Main

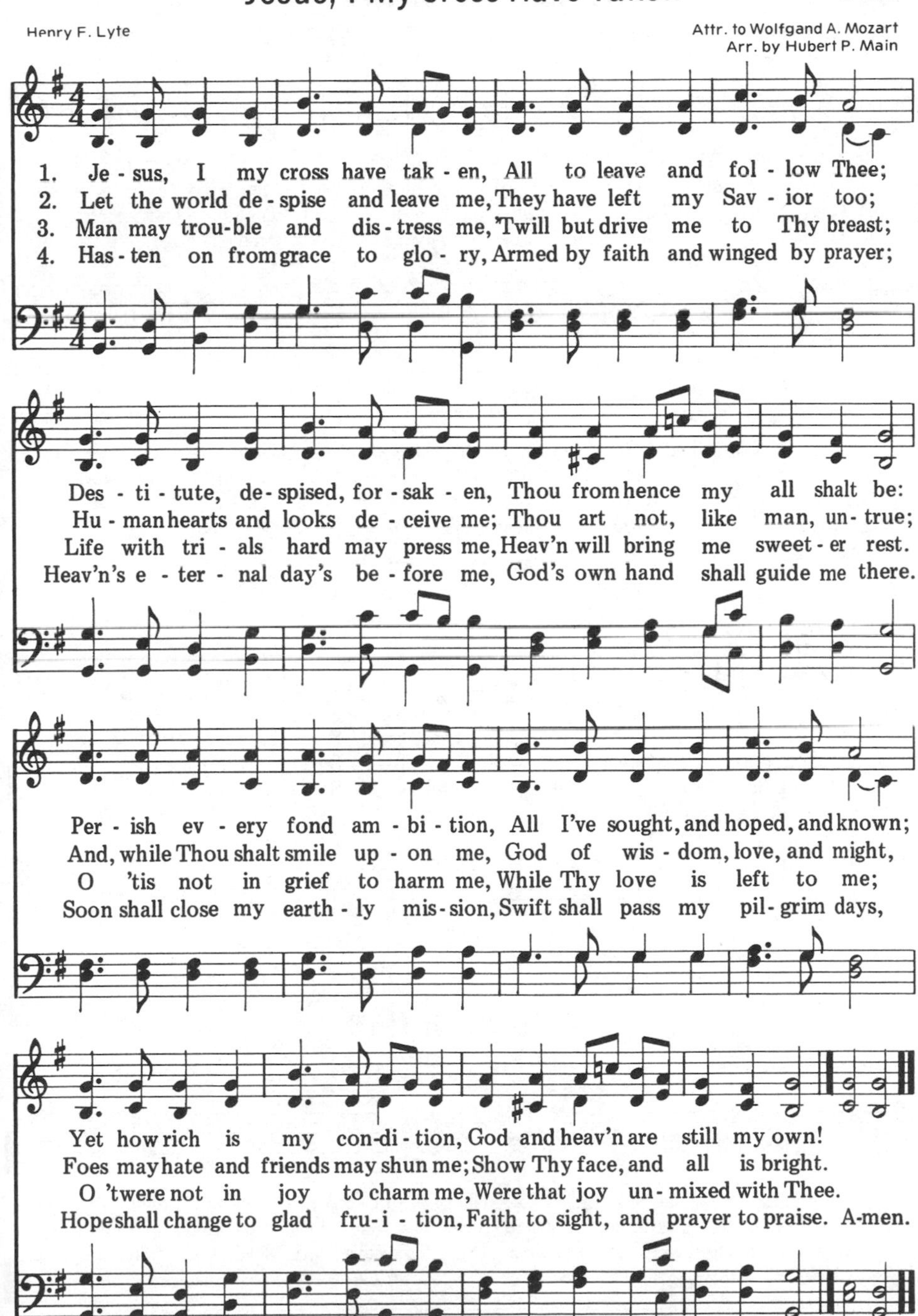
1. Je - sus, I my cross have tak - en, All to leave and fol - low Thee;
2. Let the world de - spise and leave me, They have left my Sav - ior too;
3. Man may trou-ble and dis - tress me, 'Twill but drive me to Thy breast;
4. Has - ten on from grace to glo - ry, Armed by faith and winged by prayer;
Des - ti - tute, de - spised, for - sak - en, Thou from hence my all shalt be:
Hu - man hearts and looks de - ceive me; Thou art not, like man, un - true;
Life with tri - als hard may press me, Heav'n will bring me sweet - er rest.
Heav'n's e - ter - nal day's be - fore me, God's own hand shall guide me there.
Per - ish ev - ery fond am - bi - tion, All I've sought, and hoped, and known;
And, while Thou shalt smile up - on me, God of wis - dom, love, and might,
O 'tis not in grief to harm me, While Thy love is left to me;
Soon shall close my earth - ly mis - sion, Swift shall pass my pil - grim days,
Yet how rich is my con - di - tion, God and heav'n are still my own!
Foes may hate and friends may shun me; Show Thy face, and all is bright.
O 'twere not in joy to charm me, Were that joy un - mixed with Thee.
Hope shall change to glad fru - i - tion, Faith to sight, and prayer to praise. A-men.

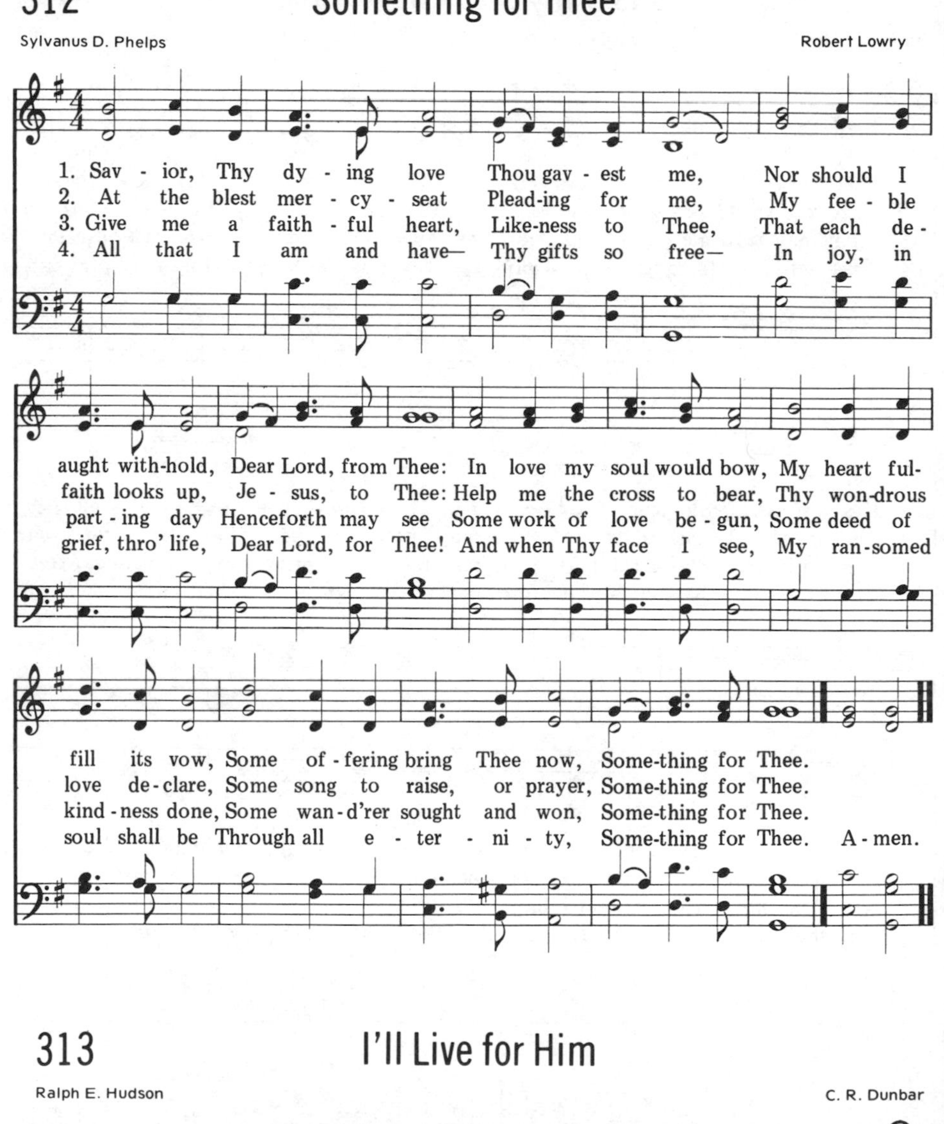
312
Something for Thee
Sylvanus D. Phelps
Robert Lowry
1. Sav - ior, Thy dy - ing love Thou gav - est me, Nor should I
2. At the blest mer - cy - seat Plead-ing for me, My fee - ble
3. Give me a faith - ful heart, Like-ness to Thee, That each de -
4. All that I am and have— Thy gifts so free— In joy, in
aught with-hold, Dear Lord, from Thee: In love my soul would bow, My heart ful-
faith looks up, Je - sus, to Thee: Help me the cross to bear, Thy won-drous
part - ing day Henceforth may see Some work of love be - gun, Some deed of
grief, thro' life, Dear Lord, for Thee! And when Thy face I see, My ran-somed
fill its vow, Some of - fering bring Thee now, Some-thing for Thee.
love de-clare, Some song to raise, or prayer, Some-thing for Thee.
kind - ness done, Some wan - d'rer sought and won, Some-thing for Thee.
soul shall be Through all e - ter - ni - ty, Some-thing for Thee. A - men.

313 I'll Live for Him

Ralph E. Hudson

C. R. Dunbar

1. My life, my love I give to Thee, Thou Lamb of God who died for me;
2. I now be-lieve Thou dost re - ceive, For Thou hast died that I might live;
3. O Thou who died on Cal - va - ry, To save my soul and make me free,
Ref. – *I'll live for Him who died for me, How hap - py then my life shall be!*

D.C. Refrain
O may I ev - er faith - ful be, My Sav - ior and my God!
And now hence - forth I'll trust in Thee, My Sav - ior and my God!
I'll con - se - crate my life to Thee, My Sav - ior and my God!
I'll live for Him who died for me, My Sav - ior and my God!

Take My Life, and Let It Be 314

Frances R. Havergal | Henri A. Cesar Malan

1. Take my life, and let it be Con - se - crat - ed, Lord, to Thee. Take my hands, and let them move At the im - pulse of Thy love, At the im - pulse of Thy love.
2. Take my feet, and let them be Swift and beau - ti - ful for Thee. Take my voice, and let me sing Al - ways, on - ly, for my King; Al - ways, on - ly, for my King.
3. Take my lips, and let them be Filled with mes - sag - es for Thee. Take my sil - ver and my gold; Not a mite would I with - hold, Not a mite would I with - hold.
4. Take my will and make it Thine; It shall be no lon - ger mine. Take my heart; it is Thine own! It shall be Thy roy - al throne. It shall be Thy roy - al throne.
5. Take my love; my God, I pour At Thy feet its treas - ure store. Take my - self and I will be Ev - er, on - ly, all for Thee; Ev - er, on - ly, all for Thee.

315 True-Hearted, Whole-Hearted

Frances R. Havergal

George C. Stebbins

1. True-heart-ed, whole-heart-ed, faith-ful and loy-al, King of our lives, by Thy grace we will be; Un-der the stan-dard ex-alt-ed and roy-al, Strong in Thy strength we will bat-tle for Thee.
2. True-heart-ed, whole-heart-ed, full-est al-le-giance Yield-ing hence-forth to our glo-ri-ous King; Val-iant en-deav-or and lov-ing o-be-dience, Free-ly and joy-ous-ly now would we bring.
3. True-heart-ed, whole-heart-ed, Sav-ior all-glo-rious! Take Thy great pow-er and reign there a-lone, O-ver our wills and af-fec-tions vic-to-rious, Free-ly sur-ren-dered and whol-ly Thine own.

CHORUS

Peal out the watch-word! si-lence it nev-er! Song of our spir-its, re-joic-ing and free; Peal out the watch-word!

Peal out the watch-word! si-lence it nev-er! Song of our spir-its, re-joic-ing and free; Peal out the watch-word!

loy - al for - ev - er, King of our lives, by Thy grace we will be.
loy - al for - ev - er, King of our lives, by Thy grace we will be.
Cleanse Me
316
J. Edwin Orr
Traditional Maori Melody
1. Search me, O God, and know my heart to - day; Try me, O Sav - ior, know my thoughts, I pray. See if there be some wick - ed way in me; Cleanse me from ev - ery sin and set me free.
2. I praise Thee, Lord, for cleans - ing me from sin; Ful - fill Thy Word and make me pure with - in. Fill me with fire where once I burned with shame; Grant my de - sire to mag - ni - fy Thy name.
3. Lord, take my life and make it whol - ly Thine; Fill my poor heart with Thy great love di - vine. Take all my will, my pas - sion, self and pride; I now sur - ren - der, Lord— in me a - bide.
4. O Ho - ly Spir - it, re - viv - al comes from Thee; Send a re - viv - al— start the work in me. Thy Word de - clares Thou wilt sup - ply our need; For bless - ings now, O Lord, I hum - bly plead.

317 Living for Jesus

Thomas O. Chisholm
C. Harold Lowden
1. Liv - ing for Je - sus a life that is true, Striv - ing to please Him in all that I do; Yield - ing al - le - giance, glad - heart - ed and free, This is the path - way of bless - ing for me.
2. Liv - ing for Je - sus who died in my place, Bear - ing on Cal - v'ry my sin and dis - grace; Such love con - strains me to an - swer His call, Fol - low His lead - ing and give Him my all.
3. Liv - ing for Je - sus wher - ev - er I am, Do - ing each du - ty in His ho - ly name; Will - ing to suf - fer af - flic - tion and loss, Deem - ing each tri - al a part of my cross.
4. Liv - ing for Je - sus through earth's lit - tle while, My dear - est treas - ure, the light of His smile; Seek - ing the lost ones He died to re - deem, Bring - ing the wea - ry to find rest in Him.
Refrain
O Je - sus, Lord and Sav - ior, I give my - self to Thee, For Thou, in Thy a - tone - ment, Didst give Thy - self for me; I own no oth - er Mas - ter, My heart shall be Thy

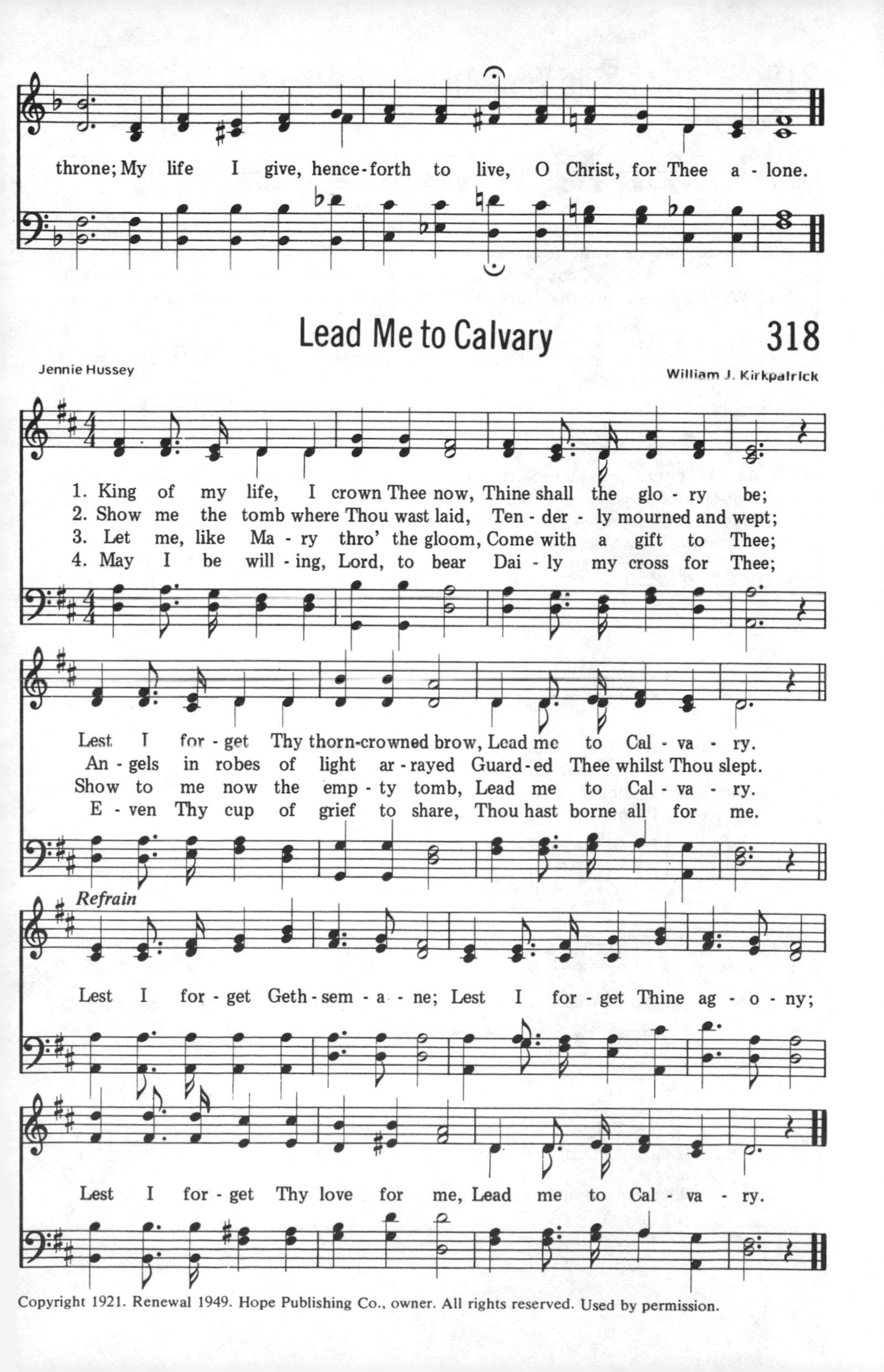
throne; My life I give, hence-forth to live, O Christ, for Thee a - lone.
Lead Me to Calvary
318
Jennie Hussey
William J. Kirkpatrick
1. King of my life, I crown Thee now, Thine shall the glo - ry be;
2. Show me the tomb where Thou wast laid, Ten - der - ly mourned and wept;
3. Let me, like Ma - ry thro' the gloom, Come with a gift to Thee;
4. May I be will - ing, Lord, to bear Dai - ly my cross for Thee;
Lest I for - get Thy thorn-crowned brow, Lead me to Cal - va - ry.
An - gels in robes of light ar - rayed Guard - ed Thee whilst Thou slept.
Show to me now the emp - ty tomb, Lead me to Cal - va - ry.
E - ven Thy cup of grief to share, Thou hast borne all for me.
Refrain
Lest I for - get Geth - sem - a - ne; Lest I for - get Thine ag - o - ny;
Lest I for - get Thy love for me, Lead me to Cal - va - ry.
Copyright 1921. Renewal 1949. Hope Publishing Co., owner. All rights reserved. Used by permission.

319 Is Your All on the Altar?

Elisha A. Hoffman — Elisha A. Hoffman

1. You have longed for sweet peace and for faith to in-crease, And have earn-est-ly,
2. Would you walk with the Lord in the light of His Word, And have peace and con-
3. O we nev-er can know what the Lord will be-stow Of the bless-ings for
4. Who can tell all the love He will send from a-bove, And how hap-py our
fer-vent-ly prayed; But you can-not have rest or be per-fect-ly blest
tent-ment al-way? You must do His sweet will to be free from all ill—
which we have prayed, Till our bod-y and soul He doth ful-ly con-trol,
hearts will be made, Of the fel-low-ship sweet we shall share at His feet
Un-til all on the al-tar is laid.
On the al-tar your all you must lay.
And our all on the al-tar is laid.
When our all on the al-tar is laid!
CHORUS
Is your all on the al-tar of
sac-ri-fice laid? Your heart does the Spir-it con-trol? You can on-ly be
blest and have peace and sweet rest As you yield Him your bod-y and soul.

Give Me Jesus

Fanny J. Crosby

John R. Sweeney

1. Take the world, but give me Je - sus. All its joys are but a name;
2. Take the world, but give me Je - sus, Sweet-est com - fort of my soul;
3. Take the world, but give me Je - sus. Let me view His constant smile;
4. Take the world, but give me Je - sus. In His cross my trust shall be,
But His love a - bid - eth ev - er, Thro' e - ter - nal years the same.
With my Sav - iour watch-ing o'er me, I can sing though bil-lows roll.
Then thro'- out my pil - grim jour - ney Light will cheer me all the while.
Till, with clear - er, bright-er vi - sion, Face - to - face my Lord I see.
REFRAIN
Oh, the height and depth of mer - cy! Oh, the length and breadth of love!
Oh, the full - ness of re - demp - tion, Pledge of end - less life a - bove!

321 True to the End

Avis B. Christiansen

Alfred B. Smith

1. Temp - ted and tried on my path-way be - low, Bur - dened by trials and sor - row and woe, Let me not fal - ter though e - vils at - tend; Keep me, Lord Je - sus, true to the end.
2. Storms may as - sail me, and dan-gers be - fall, Lord, grant me grace to keep trust - ing through all. Fierce though the temp-ests that on me de - scend, Keep me, I pray Thee, true to the end.
3. Lord, hold me fast in Thy ten-der em - brace! Shel - ter my soul with Thy mer - cy and grace Strength-en my heart as life's path-way I wend. Keep me, I pray Thee, true to the end.
Chorus
True to the end, Lord true to the end! Keep me, I pray Thee, true to the end.
Though cares and tri-als my path-way at-tend, Keep me, Lord Je-sus true to the end.

Give of Your Best to the Master

Howard B. Grose — Charlotte A. Barnard

1. Give of your best to the Mas-ter, Give of the strength of your youth;
2. Give of your best to the Mas-ter, Give Him first place in your heart;
3. Give of your best to the Mas-ter, Naught else is wor-thy His love;
Ref. Give of your best to the Mas-ter, Give of the strength of your youth;
Fine
Throw your soul's fresh, glow-ing ar-dor In-to the bat-tle for truth.
Give Him first place in your serv-ice, Con-se-crate ev-ery part.
He gave Him-self for your ran-som, Gave up His glo-ry a-bove;
Clad in sal-va-tion's full ar-mor, Join in the bat-tle for truth.
Je-sus has set the ex-am-ple—Daunt-less was He, young and brave;
Give, and to you shall be giv-en—God His be-lov-ed Son gave;
Laid down His life with-out mur-mur, You from sin's ru-in to save;
D.C. Refrain
Give Him your loy-al de-vo-tion, Give Him the best that you have.
Grate-ful-ly seek-ing to serve Him, Give Him the best that you have.
Give Him your heart's ad-o-ra-tion, Give Him the best that you have.

323 Thy Will Be Done

Adelaide A. Procter

Alfred B. Smith

1. Thy will, O Lord, be done, ful-ly in me; Je-sus, Thou ho-ly One, make me like Thee; Cleanse me, O Son of God, In Thy re-deem-ing blood; Je-sus, in pur-i-ty___ make me like Thee!
2. Thy will, O Lord, be done, ful-ly in me; Je-sus, Thou low-ly One, make me like Thee; Meek-ly for Thy dear name Bear-ing re-proach and shame; In deep hu-mil-i-ty___ make me like Thee!
3. Thy will, O Lord, be done, ful-ly in me; Je-sus, Thou lov-ing One, make me like Thee; Sweet Spir-it from a-bove, Fill all my heart with love; Je-sus, Thy will for me___ make me like Thee!

324 The Future Is Exciting

D.J.K.

Donna J. Krieger

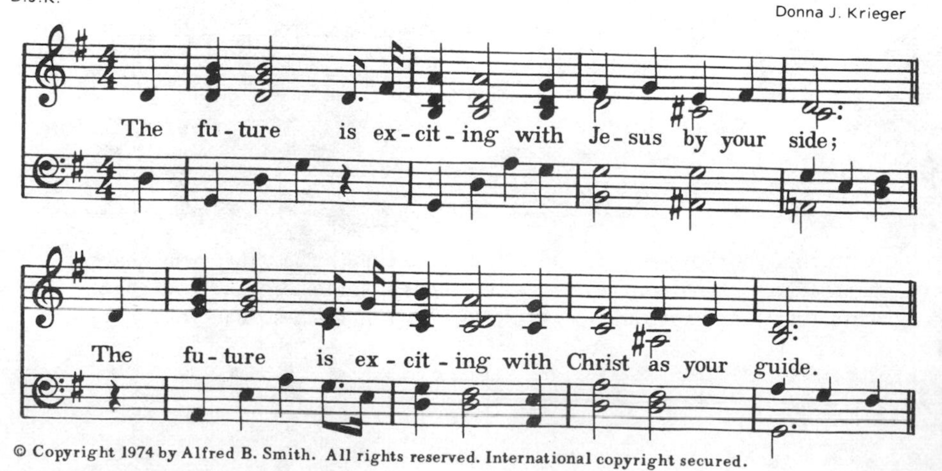
The fu-ture is ex-cit-ing with Je-sus by your side;
The fu-ture is ex-cit-ing with Christ as your guide.

So trust Him to-day and to-mor-row, Serve Him with all that you have.
The fu-ture is ex-cit-ing with God in con-trol.
O What a Saviour
325
Albert Midlane
Alt. A.B.S.
Alfred B. Smith
1. O what a Sav-iour is Je-sus the Lord! Well may His name
2. Now from the glo-ry He waits to im-part Peace to the con-
3. Thou-sands have fled to His spear-pierc-ed side, All have been wel-
by His saints be a-dored! He has re-deemed them from death by His
science, and joy to the heart— Waits to be gra-cious, to par-don and
come— not one was de-nied Wea-ry and lad-en, they all have been
blood, Saved them for-ev-er, and brought them to God.
heal All who their sins and un-wor-thi-ness feel.
blest; Joy-ful-ly now in the Sav-iour they rest.

326 Full Surrender

Rebecca S. Pollard

Daniel B. Towner

1. Sav - iour, 'tis a full sur - ren - der, All I leave to fol - low Thee;
Thou my lead - er and de - fend - er From this hour shalt ev - er be.

2. As I come in deep con - tri - tion, At this con - se - cra - ted hour,
Hear, O Christ, my heart's pe - ti - tion Let me feel the Spir - it's power.

3. No with-hold - ing— full con - fes - sion; Pleas - ures, rich - es, all must flee;
Ho - ly Spir - it, take pos - ses - sion, I no more, but Thou in me.

4. Be this theme my song and sto - ry Now and un - til life is o'er;
This my rap - ture, this my glo - ry Till I reach the shin - ing shore.

5. Oh, the joy of full sal - va - tion! Oh, the peace of love di - vine!
Oh, the bliss of con - se - cra - tion—I am His, and He is mine!

REFRAIN

I sur - ren - der all! I sur - ren - der all!
All I have I bring to Je - sus; I sur - ren - der all!

Full Consecration

E. S. Elliott

Alfred B. Smith

1. Full con - se - cra - tion! heart and spir - it yield - ed
2. Full con - se - cra - tion! whith - er, Lord, Thou go - est,
3. Full con - se - cra - tion! let us go forth brave - ly,
4. Thine, Lord, for - ev - er! keep us, we im - plore Thee,

In the calm rest of res - ur - rec - tion life;
We, too, would fol - low, list'n-ing for Thy call;
Bear - ing His cross who lived for us and died;
Yield - ed to Thee as ris - en from the dead;

With - in the se - cret of God's pres - ence shield - ed
The true, glad watch - word of our hearts Thou know - est,
Tak - ing grief calm - ly, mak - ing con - quest grave - ly,
Each in his priest - ly white to walk be - fore Thee,

From care in serv - ice, and from harm of strife.
All, all for Christ, and Christ our all in all.
With the sweet qui - et of the sat - is - fied.
Thy con - se - cra - tion ev - er on his head.

328 Have Thine Own Way, Lord

Adelaide A. Pollard

George C. Stebbins

1. Have Thine own way, Lord! Have Thine own way! Thou art the Pot - ter; I am the clay. Mould me and make me After Thy will, While I am wait - ing, Yield-ed and still.
2. Have Thine own way, Lord! Have Thine own way! Search me and try me, Mas-ter, to - day! Whit - er than snow, Lord, Wash me just now, As in Thy pres - ence Hum-bly I bow.
3. Have Thine own way, Lord! Have Thine own way! Wound-ed and wea - ry, Help me, I pray! Pow - er— all pow - er— Sure-ly is Thine! Touch me and heal me, Sav - iour di - vine!
4. Have Thine own way, Lord! Have Thine own way! Hold o'er my be - ing Ab - so - lute sway! Fill with Thy Spir - it Till all shall see Christ on - ly, al - ways, Liv - ing in me!
A - MEN.

329 We May Not Climb the Heavenly Steeps

John G. Whittier

William V. Wallace

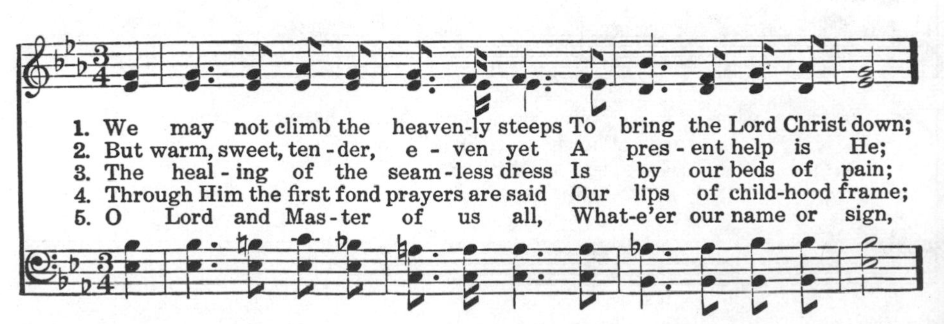
1. We may not climb the heaven-ly steeps To bring the Lord Christ down;
2. But warm, sweet, ten - der, e - ven yet A pres - ent help is He;
3. The heal - ing of the seam - less dress Is by our beds of pain;
4. Through Him the first fond prayers are said Our lips of child-hood frame;
5. O Lord and Mas - ter of us all, What-e'er our name or sign,

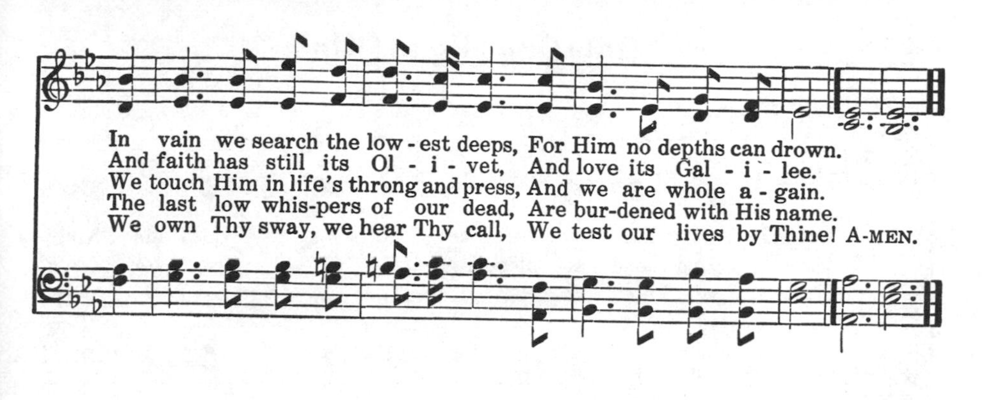
In vain we search the low-est deeps, For Him no depths can drown.
And faith has still its Ol - i - vet, And love its Gal - i - lee.
We touch Him in life's throng and press, And we are whole a - gain.
The last low whis-pers of our dead, Are bur-dened with His name.
We own Thy sway, we hear Thy call, We test our lives by Thine! A-MEN.

Jesus Only, Let Me See 330

Oswald J. Smith

Daniel B. Towner

1. For sal - va - tion full and free, Pur - chased once on Cal - va - ry,
2. He my guide from day to day As I jour - ney on life's way;
3. May my mod - el ev - er be Christ the Lord, and none save He,
4. He shall reign from shore to shore; His the glo - ry ev - er - more.
Christ a - lone shall be my plea— Je - sus! Je - sus on - ly!
Close be - side Him let me stay— Je - sus! Je - sus on - ly!
That the world may see in me— Je - sus! Je - sus on - ly!
Heaven and earth shall bow be - fore— Je - sus! Je - sus on - ly!
REFRAIN
Je - sus on - ly, let me see, Je - sus on - ly, none save He;
Then my song shall ev - er be— Je - sus! Je - sus on - ly!

331 Only One Life to Offer

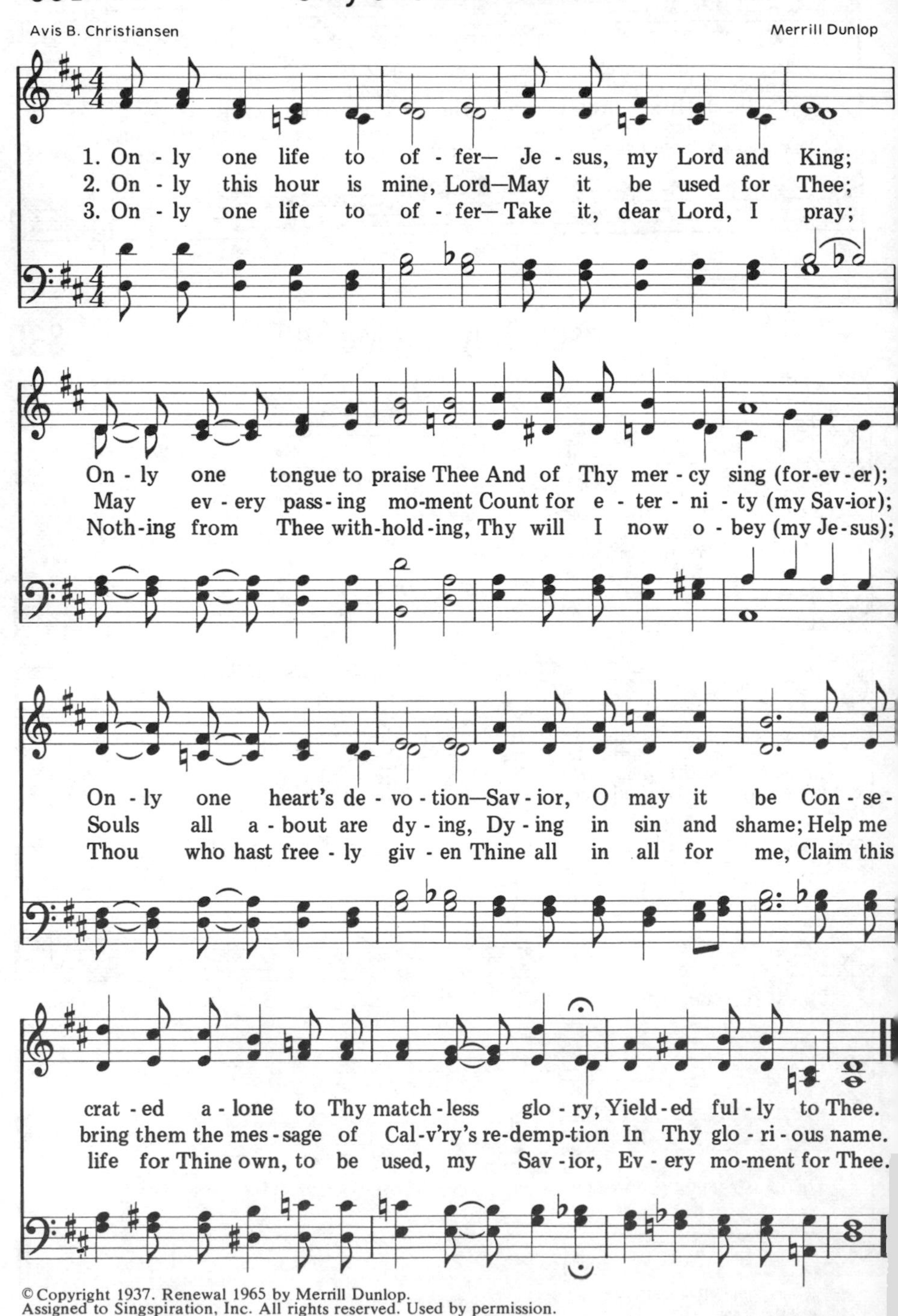
Avis B. Christiansen
Merrill Dunlop
1. On - ly one life to of - fer— Je - sus, my Lord and King;
2. On - ly this hour is mine, Lord—May it be used for Thee;
3. On - ly one life to of - fer—Take it, dear Lord, I pray;
On - ly one tongue to praise Thee And of Thy mer - cy sing (for-ev - er);
May ev - ery pass - ing mo-ment Count for e - ter - ni - ty (my Sav-ior);
Noth-ing from Thee with-hold-ing, Thy will I now o - bey (my Je-sus);
On - ly one heart's de - vo - tion—Sav - ior, O may it be Con - se -
Souls all a - bout are dy - ing, Dy - ing in sin and shame; Help me
Thou who hast free - ly giv - en Thine all in all for me, Claim this
crat - ed a - lone to Thy match - less glo - ry, Yield - ed ful - ly to Thee.
bring them the mes - sage of Cal - v'ry's re - demp - tion In Thy glo - ri - ous name.
life for Thine own, to be used, my Sav - ior, Ev - ery mo-ment for Thee.

Make Me a Captive Lord

George Matheson

Alfred B. Smith

1. Make me a cap - tive, Lord, And then I shall be free;
2. My heart is weak and poor Un - til it mas - ter find;
3. My pow'r is faint and low Till I have learned to serve:
4. My will is not my own Till Thou hast made it Thine;

Force me to ren - der up my sword, And I shall con-queror be;
It has no spring of ac - tion sure— It va - ries with the wind;
It wants the need - ed fire to glow, It wants the breeze to nerve;
If it would reach the monarch's throne It must its crown re - sign:

I sink in life's a - larms When by my - self I stand;
It can - not free - ly move Till Thou has wrought its chain;
It can - not drive the world Un - til it - self be driv'n;
It on - ly stands un - bent, A - mid the clash - ing strife,

Im - pris - on me with - in Thine arms, And strong shall be my hand.
En-slave it with Thy match-less love, And death-less it shall reign.
Its flag can on - ly be un-furled When Thou shalt breathe from heav'n.
When on Thy bos - om it has leaned, And found in Thee its life.

333 O the Bitter Pain and Sorrow

Theodor Monod
Mrs. L. S. C.

Mrs. Lewis S. Chafer
& Alfred B. Smith

Duet
1. O the bit - ter pain and sor - row, That a time could ev - er be,
2. Yet He found me, I be - held Him, Bleed-ing on th'ac-curs-ed tree,
3. Day by day His ten-der mer-cies, Heal-ing, help - ing, full, and free,
4. High - er than the high-est heav-ens, Deep-er than the deep-est sea,
When I proud - ly said to Je - sus, All of self and none of Thee.
And my self - ish heart said faint - ly, Some of self and some of Thee.
Brought me low - er, while I whis-pered, Less of self and more of Thee.
Lord, Thy love at last has conquered, None of self and all of Thee.
8va
All of self and none of Thee, All of self and none of Thee;
Some of self and some of Thee, Some of self and some of Thee;
Less of self and more of Thee, Less of self and more of Thee;
None of self and all of Thee, None of self and all of Thee;
When I proud - ly said to Je - sus, All of self and none of Thee.
And my self - ish heart said faint - ly, Some of self and some of Thee.
Brought me low - er, while I whis-pered, Less of self and more of Thee.
Lord, Thy love at last has con-quered, None of self and all of Thee.

Deeper and Deeper

Oswald J. Smith

Oswald J. Smith

1. In-to the heart of Je - sus Deep-er and deep - er I go,
2. In-to the will of Je - sus Deep-er and deep - er I go,
3. In-to the cross of Je - sus Deep-er and deep - er I go,
4. In-to the joy of Je - sus Deep-er and deep - er I go,
5. In-to the love of Je - sus Deep-er and deep - er I go,
Seek-ing to know the rea - son Why He should love me so—
Pray - ing for grace to fol - low, Seek-ing His way to know;
Fol - low-ing thru the gar - den, Fac - ing the dread - ed foe;
Ris - ing, with soul en - rap - tured, Far from the world be - low;
Prais-ing the One who brought me Out of my sin and woe;
Why He should stoop to lift me Up from the mir - y clay,
Bow- ing in full sur - ren - der Low at His bless - ed feet,
Drink-ing the cup of sor - row— Sob-bing with bro - ken heart,
Joy in the place of sor - row, Peace in the midst of pain,
And thru e - ter - nal a - ges Grate-ful - ly I shall sing,
Sav - ing my soul, mak-ing me whole, Tho I had wan-dered a - way.
Bid-ding Him take, break me and make, Till I am mold-ed and meet.
"O Sav- ior, help! dear Sav-ior, help! Grace for my weak-ness im - part."
Je - sus will give, Je - sus will give— He will up-hold and sus - tain.
"O how He loved! O how He loved! Je - sus, my Lord and my King!"

335 I Heard the Voice of Jesus Say

Horatius Bonar

John Bacchus Dykes

1. I heard the voice of Je - sus say, "Come un - to Me and rest;
2. I heard the voice of Je - sus say, "Be - hold, I free - ly give
3. I heard the voice of Je - sus say, "I am this dark world's light;

Lay down, thou wea - ry one, lay down Thy head up - on My breast."
The liv - ing wa - ter; thirst - y one, Stoop down, and drink, and live."
Look un - to Me, thy morn shall rise, And all thy day be bright."

I came to Je - sus as I was, Wea - ry, and worn, and sad;
I came to Je - sus, and I drank Of that life - giv - ing stream;
I looked to Je - sus, and I found In Him my star, my sun;

I found in Him a rest - ing-place, And He has made me glad.
My thirst was quenched, my soul re-vived, And now I live in Him.
And in that light of life I'll walk Till travel-ing days are done. A-MEN.

I Have Learned the Wondrous Secret

336

A. B. Simpson

Suggested by tune "Rifted Rock"
Alfred B. Smith

1. I have learned the won-drous se - cret Of a - bid - ing in the Lord;
2. I am cru - ci - fied with Je - sus, And He lives and dwells with me;
3. All my sick-ness - es I bring Him, And He bears them all a - way;
4. For my words I take His wis - dom, For my works His Spir - it's power;
I have tast - ed life's pure foun-tain, I am drink - ing of His word;
I have ceased from all my strug-gling, 'Tis no long - er I, but He.
All my fears and griefs I tell Him, All my cares from day to day,
For my ways His cease-less pres - ence Guards and guides me ev - ery hour.
3
I have found the strength and sweet-ness Of a - bid - ing 'neath the blood;
All my will is yield - ing to Him, And His Spir - it reigns with - in;
All my strength I draw from Je - sus, By His breath I live and move;
Of my heart, He is the por - tion, Of my joy the bound-less spring;
3
I have lost my - self in Je - sus, I am sink - ing in - to God.
And His pre-cious blood each mo-ment Keeps me cleansed and free from sin.
E'en His ver - y mind He gives me, And His faith, and life, and love.
Bless-ed Sav-iour, my Re - deem - er, Glo - rious Lord, and com - ing King.

337 One Day

J. Wilbur Chapman

Charles H. Marsh

1. One day when heaven was filled with His praises, One day when sin was as black as could be, Jesus came forth to be born of a virgin, Dwelt among men, my example is He!

2. One day they led Him up Calvary's mountain, One day they nailed Him to die on the tree; Suffering anguish, despised and rejected, Bearing our sins, my Redeemer is He!

3. One day they left Him alone in the garden, One day He rested, from suffering free; Angels came down o'er His tomb to keep vigil; Hope of the hopeless, my Savior is He!

4. One day the grave could conceal Him no longer, One day the stone rolled away from the door; Then He arose, over death He has conquered; Now is ascended, my Lord evermore!

5. One day the trumpet will sound for His coming, One day the skies with His glory will shine; Wonderful day, my beloved ones bringing; Glorious Savior, this Jesus is mine!

Refrain

Living, He loved me; dying, He saved me; Buried, He carried my sins far away; Rising, He justified

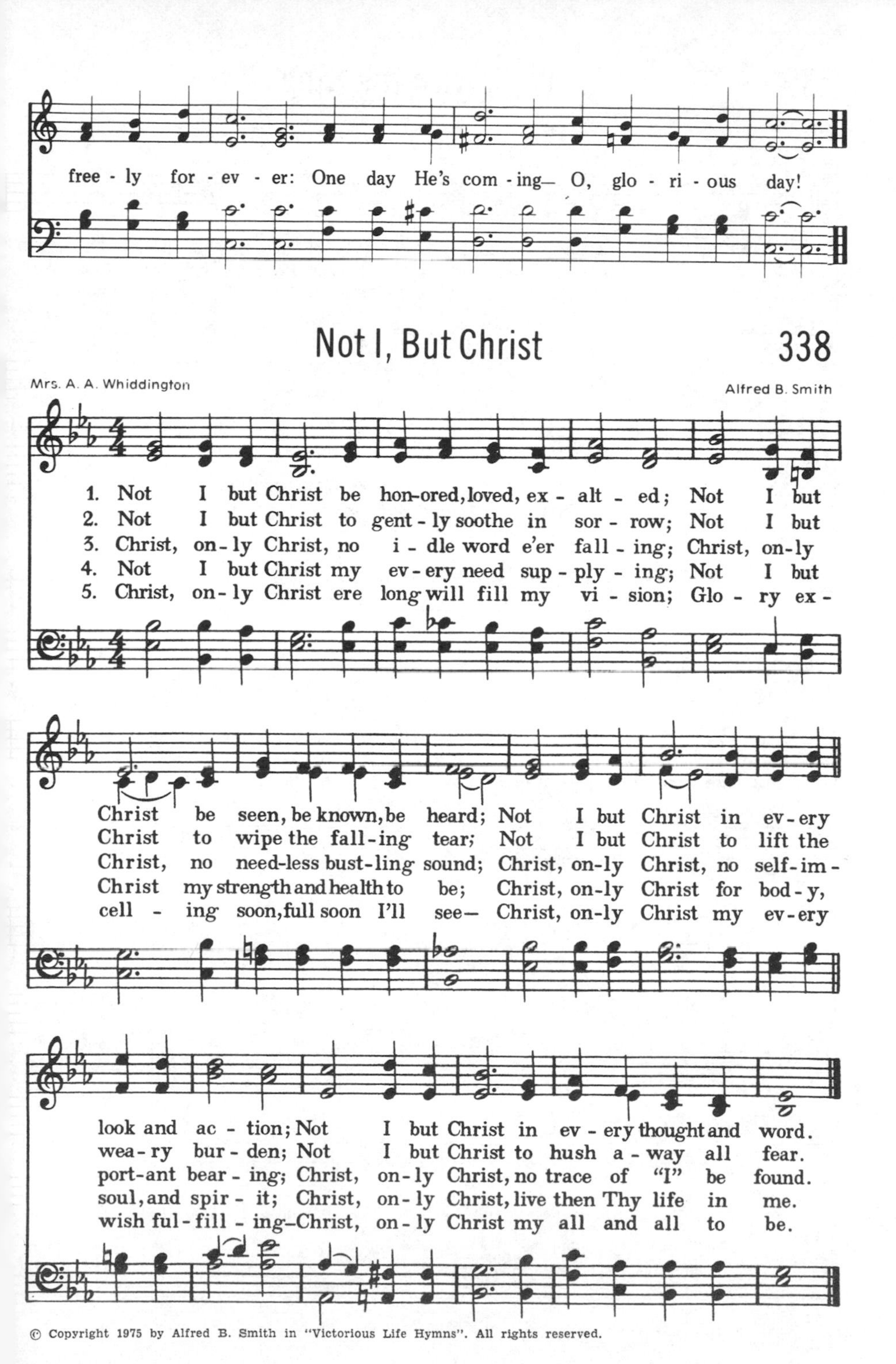
free - ly for - ev - er: One day He's com - ing— O, glo - ri - ous day!
Not I, But Christ
338
Mrs. A. A. Whiddington
Alfred B. Smith
1. Not I but Christ be hon-ored, loved, ex - alt - ed; Not I but
2. Not I but Christ to gent - ly soothe in sor - row; Not I but
3. Christ, on - ly Christ, no i - dle word e'er fall - ing; Christ, on - ly
4. Not I but Christ my ev - ery need sup - ply - ing; Not I but
5. Christ, on - ly Christ ere long will fill my vi - sion; Glo - ry ex -
Christ be seen, be known, be heard; Not I but Christ in ev - ery
Christ to wipe the fall - ing tear; Not I but Christ to lift the
Christ, no need-less bust - ling sound; Christ, on - ly Christ, no self - im -
Christ my strength and health to be; Christ, on - ly Christ for bod - y,
cell - ing soon, full soon I'll see— Christ, on - ly Christ my ev - ery
look and ac - tion; Not I but Christ in ev - ery thought and word.
wea - ry bur - den; Not I but Christ to hush a - way all fear.
port - ant bear - ing; Christ, on - ly Christ, no trace of "I" be found.
soul, and spir - it; Christ, on - ly Christ, live then Thy life in me.
wish ful - fill - ing—Christ, on - ly Christ my all and all to be.
© Copyright 1975 by Alfred B. Smith in "Victorious Life Hymns". All rights reserved.

339 I Walk With the King

James Rowe
Bentley D. Ackley
1. In sor-row I wan-dered, my spir-it op-prest, But now I am hap-py— se-cure-ly I rest; From morn-ing till eve-ning glad car-ols I sing, And this is the rea-son—I walk with the King.
2. For years in the fet-ters of sin I was bound, The world could not help me—no com-fort I found; But now like the birds and the sun-beams of spring, I'm free and re-joic-ing—I walk with the King.
3. O soul near de-spair in the low-lands of strife, Look up and let Je-sus come in-to your life; The joy of sal-va-tion to you He would bring—Come in-to the sun-light and walk with the King.
CHORUS
I walk with the King, hal-le-lu-jah! I walk with the King, praise His name! No lon-ger I roam, my soul fac-es home, I walk and I talk with the King.

I Need Jesus

George O. Webster

Charles H. Gabriel

1. I need Je-sus, my need I now con-fess; No friend like Him in times of
2. I need Je-sus, I need a friend like Him, A friend to guide when paths of
3. I need Jesus, I need Him to the end; No one like Him, He is the

deep dis-tress; I need Je-sus, the need I glad-ly own; Though some may bear their
life are dim; I need Je-sus, when foes my soul as-sail; A - lone I know I
sin-ner's Friend; I need Je-sus, no oth-er friend will do; So con-stant, kind, so

load a-lone, Yet, I need Je-sus.
can but fail, So I need Je-sus.
strong and true, Yes, I need Je-sus.

REFRAIN

I need Je-sus, I need Je-sus,
I need Je-sus with me, I need Je-sus al-ways,

I need Je-sus ev-ery day;
ev-ery day;
Need Him in the sun-shine hour,

Need Him when the storm-clouds lower; Every day along my way, Yes, I need Je-sus.

341 I Know Whom I Have Believed

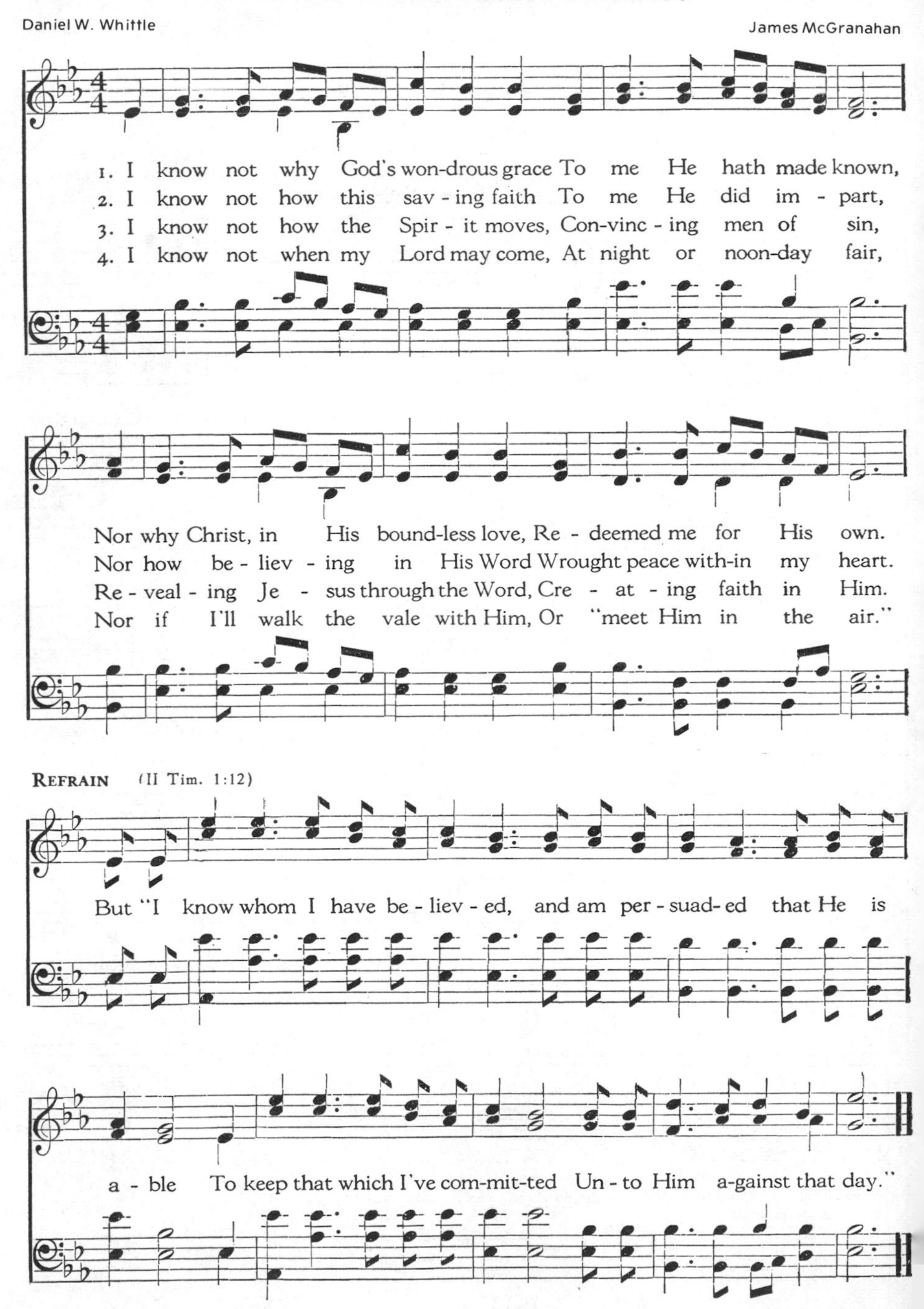
Daniel W. Whittle
James McGranahan
1. I know not why God's won-drous grace To me He hath made known,
2. I know not how this sav - ing faith To me He did im - part,
3. I know not how the Spir - it moves, Con-vinc - ing men of sin,
4. I know not when my Lord may come, At night or noon-day fair,
Nor why Christ, in His bound-less love, Re - deemed me for His own.
Nor how be - liev - ing in His Word Wrought peace with-in my heart.
Re - veal - ing Je - sus through the Word, Cre - at - ing faith in Him.
Nor if I'll walk the vale with Him, Or "meet Him in the air."
REFRAIN (II Tim. 1:12)
But "I know whom I have be - liev - ed, and am per - suad- ed that He is
a - ble To keep that which I've com-mit-ted Un - to Him a-gainst that day."

How Tedious and Tasteless the Hours 342

John Newton

Lewis Edson
Revised by Alfred B. Smith

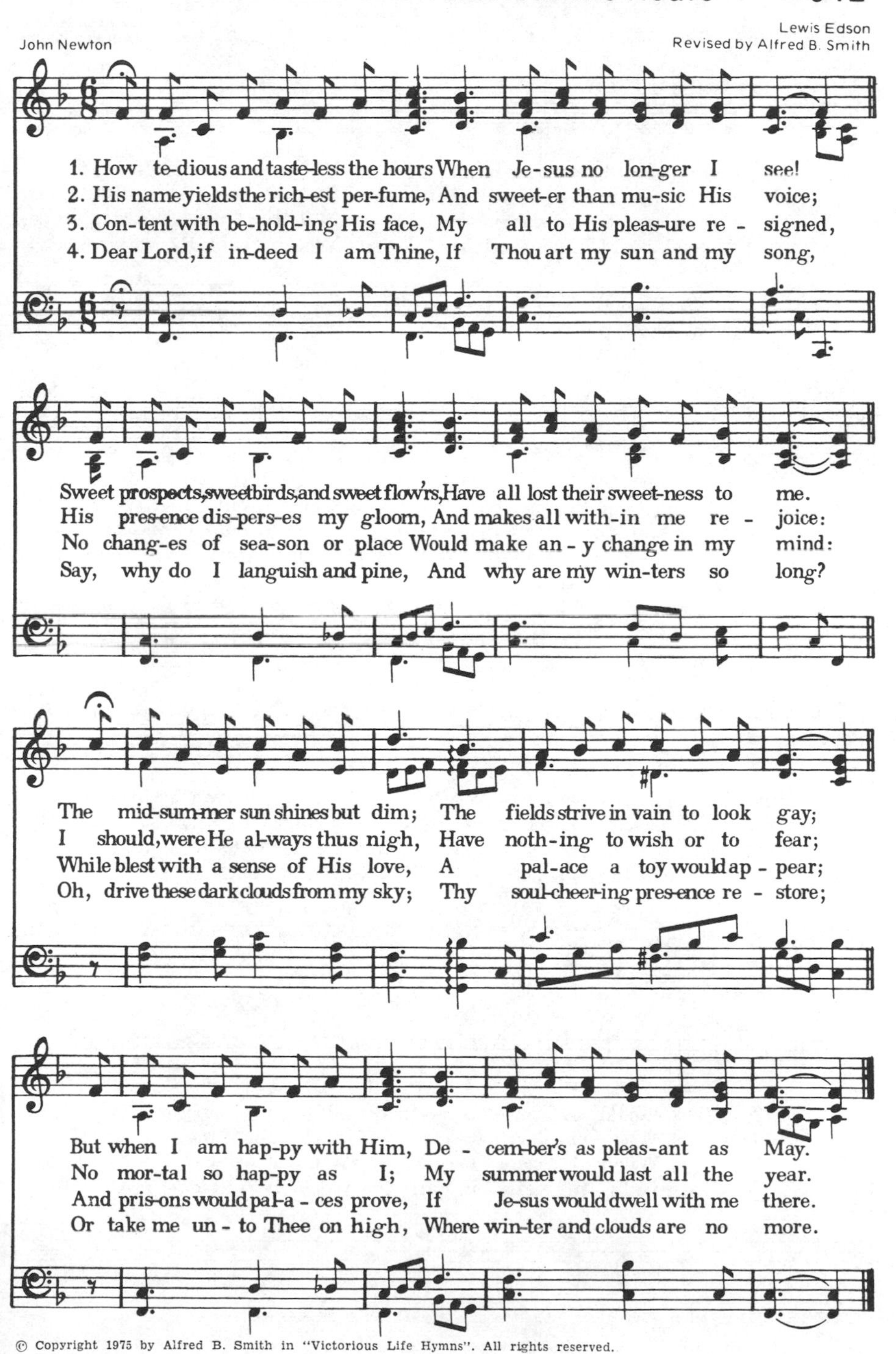
1. How te-dious and taste-less the hours When Je-sus no lon-ger I see!
2. His name yields the rich-est per-fume, And sweet-er than mu-sic His voice;
3. Con-tent with be-hold-ing His face, My all to His pleas-ure re - signed,
4. Dear Lord, if in-deed I am Thine, If Thou art my sun and my song,
Sweet prospects, sweet birds, and sweet flow'rs, Have all lost their sweet-ness to me.
His pres-ence dis-pers-es my gloom, And makes all with-in me re - joice:
No chang-es of sea-son or place Would make an - y change in my mind:
Say, why do I languish and pine, And why are my win-ters so long?
The mid-sum-mer sun shines but dim; The fields strive in vain to look gay;
I should, were He al-ways thus nigh, Have noth-ing to wish or to fear;
While blest with a sense of His love, A pal-ace a toy would ap - pear;
Oh, drive these dark clouds from my sky; Thy soul-cheer-ing pres-ence re - store;
But when I am hap-py with Him, De - cem-ber's as pleas-ant as May.
No mor-tal so hap-py as I; My summer would last all the year.
And pris-ons would pal-a - ces prove, If Je-sus would dwell with me there.
Or take me un - to Thee on high, Where win-ter and clouds are no more.

343 If I Gained the World

Anna Olander
Alt. A.B.S.
Swedish Melody
Arr. by Alfred B. Smith
1. If I gained the world, but had not Je - sus, Were my life worth liv-ing for a
2. Had I wealth and love in full-est meas-ure, And a name re-vered both far and
3. O what emp-ti-ness—without the Sav-ior 'Mid the sins and sor-rows here be-
4. O the joy of hav-ing all in Je - sus! What a balm the bro-ken heart to
day? Could my yearn-ing heart find rest and com - fort In the
near, Yet no hope be-yond, no har-bor wait - ing, Where my
low! And e - ter - ni - ty, how dark with-out Him!—On - ly
heal! Ne'er a sin so great, but He'll for - give it, Nor a
things that soon must pass a - way? If I gained the world, but had not
storm-tossed ves-sel I could steer; If I gained the world, but had not
night and tears and end-less woe! What, tho' I might live with-out the
sor - row that He does not feel! If I have but Je - sus, on - ly
Je - sus, Would my gain be worth the life-long strife? Are all
Je - sus, Who en-dured the cross and died for me, Could then
Sav - ior, When I come to die, how would it be? O to
Je - sus;—Noth - ing else in all the world be - side— O then

earth-ly pleas-ures worth com-par - ing For a mo-ment with a Christ-filled life?
all the world af-ford a ref - uge, Whither, in my an-guish, I might flee?
face the val-ley's gloom with-out Him! And with-out Him all e - ter-ni - ty!
ev - 'ry-thing is mine in Je - sus; For my needs and more He will pro-vide.
Name of Jesus! Highest Name!
344
Gerhard Tersteegan
Alfred B. Smith
1. Name of Je - sus! high - est Name! Name that
2. Name of Je - sus! liv - ing tide! Days of
3. Name of Je - sus! dear - est Name! Bread of
4. Je - sus gives for - give - ness free, Je - sus
5. On - ly Je - sus! fair - est Name! Life, and
earth and Heav'n a - dore! From the heart of
thirst for me are past; How much more than
Heav'n and balm of love, Oil of glad - ness,
cleans - es all my stains, Je - sus gives His
rest, and peace, and bliss; Je - sus ev - er -
God it came, Leads me to God's heart once more.
sat - is - fied Are my thirst - y lips at last!
sur - est claim To the treas-ures stored a - bove.
life to me, Je - sus al - ways He re - mains.
more the same, He is mine and I am His.
© Copyright 1975 by Alfred B. Smith in "Victorious Life Hymns". All rights reserved.

345 Jesus My All

R. Kelso Carter
Edit. by A.B.S.

Alfred B. Smith

1. Je - sus my pro - phet stands, Je - sus my all, Bear - ing in wound - ed hands God's lov - ing call. Con - qu'ring sins rag - ing strife, He made the way of life, pro - phet with bless - ing rife, Je - sus my all.
2. Je - sus my Priest for me, Je - sus my all, He drained on Cal - va - ry worm - wood and gall. Sin - less tho' much in - ticed, Lamb that was sac - ri - ficed, Je - sus my Priest, the Christ, Je - sus my all.
3. Je - sus my King as - cends, Je - sus my all, Mer - cy with jus - tice blends, o - ver the fall. Je - sus sal - va - tion brings, Je - sus, the e - cho rings, Je - sus the King of kings, Je - sus my all.
© Copyright 1974 by Alfred B. Smith. All rights reserved. International copyright secured.
346
One God and One Mediator
I Timothy 2:5,6
Arr. by Donna Krieger
For there is one God and one med - i - a - tor be - tween God and men,
D.C.
For there is one God and one med - i - a - tor, the Man, Christ Je - sus.

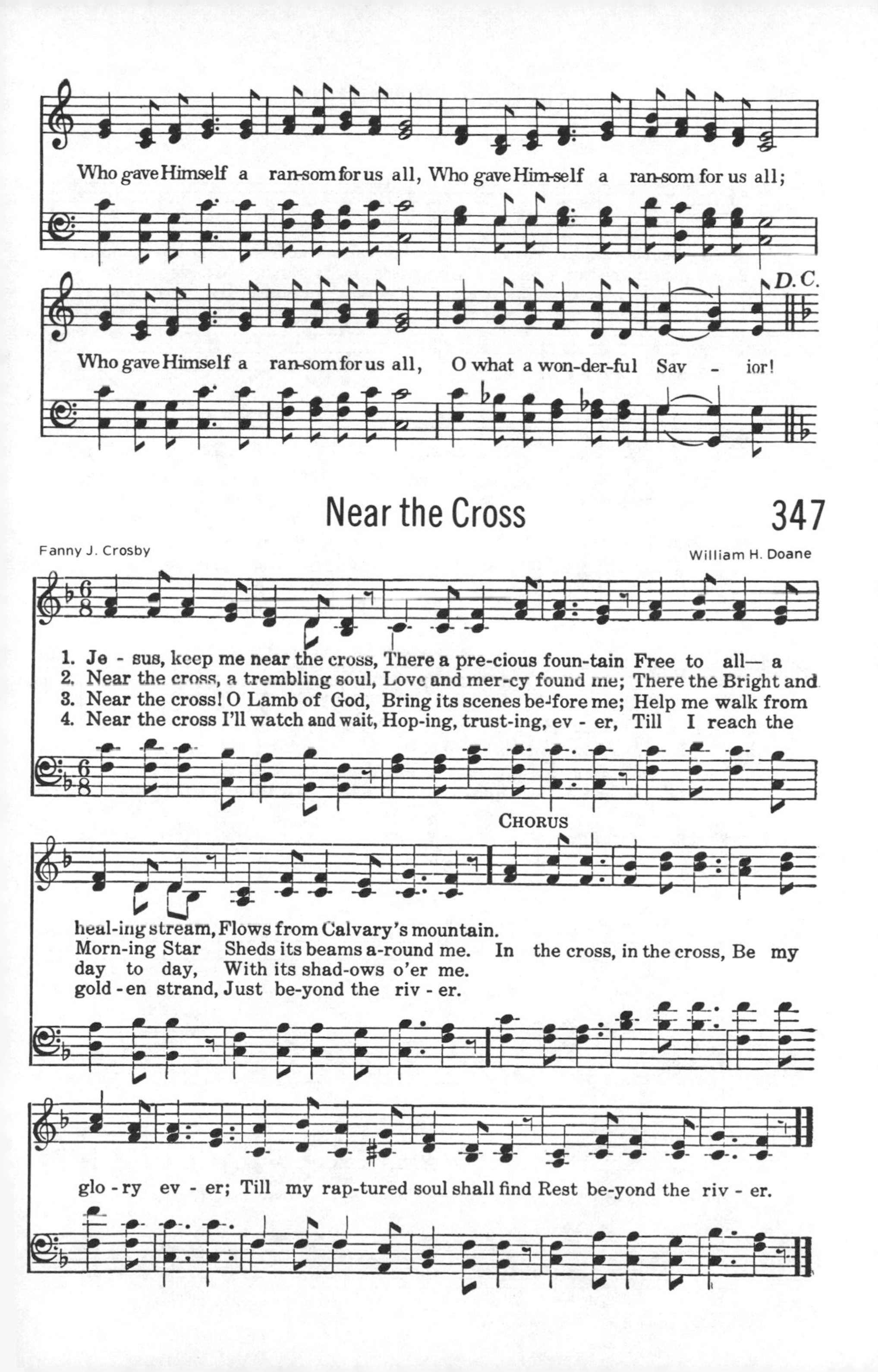
Who gave Himself a ran-som for us all, Who gave Him-self a ran-som for us all;
Who gave Himself a ran-som for us all, O what a won-der-ful Sav - ior!
D. C.
Near the Cross
347
Fanny J. Crosby
William H. Doane
1. Je - sus, keep me near the cross, There a pre-cious foun-tain Free to all— a heal-ing stream, Flows from Calvary's mountain.
2. Near the cross, a trembling soul, Love and mer-cy found me; There the Bright and Morn-ing Star Sheds its beams a-round me.
3. Near the cross! O Lamb of God, Bring its scenes be-fore me; Help me walk from day to day, With its shad-ows o'er me.
4. Near the cross I'll watch and wait, Hop-ing, trust-ing, ev - er, Till I reach the gold - en strand, Just be-yond the riv - er.
CHORUS
In the cross, in the cross, Be my glo - ry ev - er; Till my rap-tured soul shall find Rest be-yond the riv - er.

348 He Brought Me Out

Psalm 40
Henry J. Zelley & A.B.S.
Henry L. Gilmour
Rev. Alfred B. Smith
1. My heart was in fear 'neath Je-ho-vah's dread frown, And low from the pit where my sins dragged me down. I cried to the Lord from the deep, mir-y clay. He ten-der-ly brought me in to gold-en day.
2. He placed me up-on the strong rock by His side. My steps were es-ta-blished, and here I'll a-bide. No dan-ger of fall-ing while here I re-main, But stand by His grace un-til the crown I gain.
3. He gave me a song; 'twas a new song of praise. By day and by night its sweet notes I will raise. My heart's o-ver-flow-ing; I'm hap-py and free. I'll praise my Re-deem-er, who has res-cued me.
4. I'll sing of His won-der-ful mer-cy to me; I'll praise Him till all men His good-ness shall see; I'll sing of sal-va-tion at home and a-broad, Till man-y shall hear the truth and trust in God.
Chorus— A.B.S.
He brought me out of the mir-y clay; mir-y clay, mir-y clay. He set my feet on the rock to stay, And put a new song in my heart!

Victory All the Time

L. N. Morris | Lelia N. Norris & Alfred B. Smith

1. They who know the Sav - iour shall in Him be strong, Might-y in the
2. In the midst of bat - tle do not be dis-mayed, Tho' the pow'rs of
3. Brave to bear life's test - ing, strong the foe to meet, Walk-ing like a
con-flict of the right 'gainst wrong. This the bless-ed prom-ise giv - en in God's Word,
dark-ness 'gainst thee are ar-rayed. God, thy strength, is with thee, He will help thee stand;
he - ro midst the fur-nace heat, Do - ing wondrous ex-ploits with the Spir-it's Sword,
Do - ing won-drous ex-ploits, they who know the Lord
Heav-en's might-y ar-mies wait at thy com-mand.
Win-ning souls for Je - sus, praise, oh, praise the Lord!
Chorus
Vic-to-ry! vic-to-ry!
bless-ed, Blood-bo't vic-to - ry! Vic-to-ry! vic-to-ry! vic-t'ry all the time! As Je-ho-vah
liv-eth, strength di-vine He giv-eth Un-to those who know Him, vic-t'ry all the time.

350 Dwelling in Beulah Land

C. A. Miles C. A. Miles

1. Far a-way the noise of strife up-on my ear is fall-ing, Then I know the
2. Far be-low the storm of doubt up-on the world is beat-ing, Sons of men in
3. Let the storm-y breez-es blow, their cry can-not a-larm me; I am safe-ly
4. Viewing here the works of God, I sink in con-tem-pla-tion, Hearing now His
sins of earth be-set on ev-'ry hand: Doubt and fear and things of earth in
bat-tle long the en-e-my with-stand: Safe am I with-in the cas-tle
sheltered here, pro-tect-ed by God's hand: Here the sun is al-ways shin-ing,
bless-ed voice, I see the way He planned: Dwell-ing in the Spir-it, here I
vain to me are call-ing, None of these shall move me from Beu-lah Land.
of God's word re-treat-ing, Nothing then can reach me—'tis Beu-lah Land.
here there's naught can harm me, I am safe for-ev-er in Beu-lah Land.
learn of full sal-va-tion, Glad-ly will I tar-ry in Beu-lah Land.
CHORUS
I'm liv-ing on the moun-tain, un-der-neath a cloud-less sky, I'm
Praise God!
drink-ing at the foun-tain that never shall run dry; O yes! I'm feasting on the

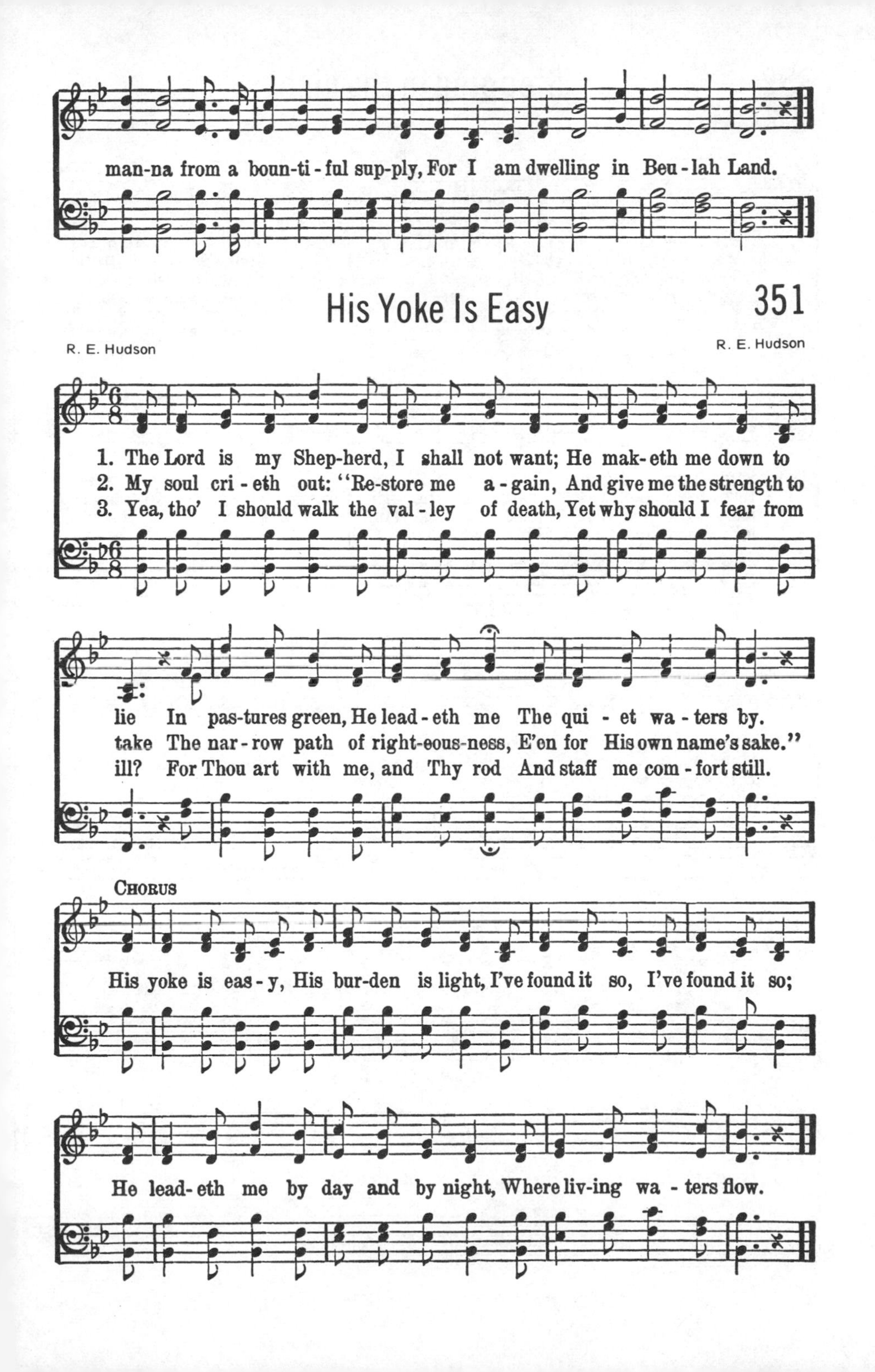
man-na from a boun-ti-ful sup-ply, For I am dwelling in Beu-lah Land.
His Yoke Is Easy
351
R. E. Hudson
R. E. Hudson
1. The Lord is my Shep-herd, I shall not want; He mak-eth me down to
2. My soul cri-eth out: "Re-store me a-gain, And give me the strength to
3. Yea, tho' I should walk the val-ley of death, Yet why should I fear from
lie In pas-tures green, He lead-eth me The qui-et wa-ters by.
take The nar-row path of right-eous-ness, E'en for His own name's sake."
ill? For Thou art with me, and Thy rod And staff me com-fort still.
Chorus
His yoke is eas-y, His bur-den is light, I've found it so, I've found it so;
He lead-eth me by day and by night, Where liv-ing wa-ters flow.

352 Stepping in the Light

Eliza E. Hewitt

William J. Kirkpatrick

1. Try - ing to walk in the steps of the Sav-iour, Try - ing to fol - low our
2. Press-ing more close - ly to Him who is lead-ing, When we are tempt-ed to
3. Walk-ing in foot - steps of gen - tle for-bear-ance, Foot-steps of faith-ful-ness,
4. Try - ing to walk in the steps of the Sav-iour, Up-ward, still up-ward we'll
Sav - iour and King; Shap - ing our lives by His bless - ed ex - am - ple,
turn from the way; Trust - ing the arm that is strong to de - fend us,
mer - cy and love; Look - ing to Him for the grace free - ly prom - ised,
fol - low our Guide; When we shall see Him, "the King in His beau - ty,"
Hap - py, how hap-py, the songs that we bring.
Hap - py, how hap-py, our prais - es each day.
Hap - py, how hap-py, our jour - ney a - bove!
Hap - py, how hap-py, our place at His side!
Refrain
How beau - ti - ful to walk in the
steps of the Sav - iour, Step-ping in the light, Step-ping in the light; How
beau - ti - ful to walk in the steps of the Sav-iour, Led in paths of light!

Fill All My Vision

353

Avis B. Christiansen

Homer Hammontree

1. Fill all my vi - sion, Sav - iour, I pray, Let me see on - ly
2. Fill all my vi - sion, ev - ery de - sire Keep for Thy glo - ry;
3. Fill all my vi - sion, let naught of sin Shad - ow the bright - ness
Je - sus to - day; Though thro' the val - ley Thou lead - est me,
my soul in - spire With Thy per - fec - tion, Thy ho - ly love
shin - ing with - in. Let me see on - ly Thy bless - ed face,
Thy fade - less glo - ry en - com - pass - eth me.
Flood - ing my path - way with light from a - bove.
Feast - ing my soul on Thy in - fi - nite grace.
REFRAIN
Fill all my vi - sion,
Sav - iour di - vine, Till with Thy glo - ry my spir - it shall shine. Fill all my
vi - sion, that all may see Thy ho - ly Im - age re - flect - ed in me.

354 Take Time to be Holy

William D. Longstaff — George C. Stebbins

1. Take time to be ho - ly, Speak oft with thy Lord; A - bide in Him
2. Take time to be ho - ly, The world rush - es on; Much time spend in
3. Take time to be ho - ly, Let Him be thy guide, And run not be-
4. Take time to be ho - ly, Be calm in thy soul; Each thought and each

al - ways, And feed on His Word. Make friends of God's chil - dren; Help
se - cret With Je - sus a - lone; By look - ing to Je - sus, Like
fore Him What - ev - er be - tide; In joy or in sor - row Still
mo - tive Be - neath His con - trol; Thus led by His Spir - it To

those who are weak; For - get - ting in noth - ing His bless - ing to seek.
Him thou shalt be; Thy friends in thy con - duct His like - ness shall see.
fol - low thy Lord, And, look - ing to Je - sus, Still trust in His Word.
foun-tains of love, Thou soon shalt be fit - ted For ser - vice a - bove.

355 We Give Thee But Thine Own

William W. How — Mason and Webb's Cantica Laudis

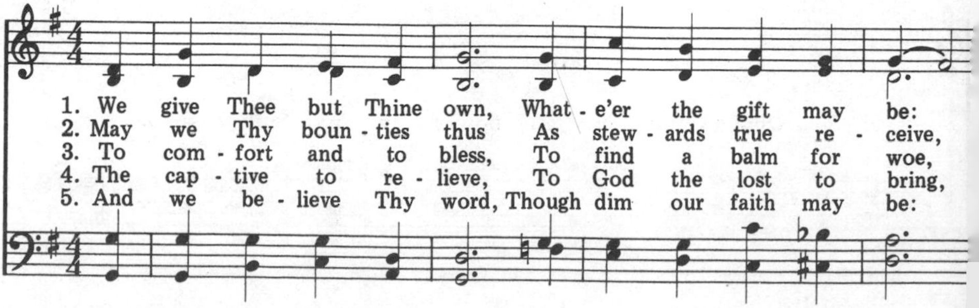

1. We give Thee but Thine own, What - e'er the gift may be:
2. May we Thy boun - ties thus As stew - ards true re - ceive,
3. To com - fort and to bless, To find a balm for woe,
4. The cap - tive to re - lieve, To God the lost to bring,
5. And we be - lieve Thy word, Though dim our faith may be:

All that we have is Thine a - lone, A trust, O Lord, from Thee.
And glad - ly, as Thou bless - est us, To Thee our first-fruits give.
To tend the lone and fa - ther - less, Is an - gels' work be - low.
To teach the way of life and peace— It is a Christ-like thing.
What - e'er for Thine we do, O Lord, We do it un - to Thee. A-men.

More Holiness Give Me

356

Philip P. Bliss | Philip P. Bliss

1. More ho - li - ness give me, More striv - ing with - in; More pa-tience in
2. More grat - i - tude give me, More trust in the Lord; More pride in His
3. More pu - ri - ty give me, More strength to o'er - come; More free-dom from

suf - f'ring, More sor - row for sin; More faith in my Sav - ior,
glo - ry, More hope in His word; More tears for His sor - rows,
earth-stains, More long - ings for home; More fit for the king - dom,

More sense of His care; More joy in His ser - vice, More pur - pose in prayer.
More pain at His grief; More meek-ness in tri - al, More praise for re - lief.
More used would I be; More bless-ed and ho - ly, More, Sav - ior, like Thee.

357 Draw Me Nearer

Fanny J. Crosby

William H. Doane

1. I am Thine, O Lord– I have heard Thy voice, And it told Thy
2. Con - se - crate me now to Thy serv - ice, Lord, By the pow'r of
3. O the pure de - light of a sin - gle hour That be - fore Thy
4. There are depths of love that I can - not know Till I cross the
love to me; But I long to rise in the arms of faith
grace di - vine; Let my soul look up with a stead - fast hope
throne I spend, When I kneel in pray'r and with Thee, my God,
nar - row sea; There are heights of joy that I may not reach
CHORUS
And be clos - er drawn to Thee.
And my will be lost in Thine. Draw me near - er, near - er,
I com - mune as friend with friend. near - er, near - er,
Till I rest in peace with Thee.
bless - ed Lord, To the cross where Thou hast died; Draw me near - er,
near - er, near - er, bless - ed Lord, To Thy pre - cious, bleed - ing side.

O to Be Like Thee

Thomas O. Chisholm

William J. Kirkpatrick

1. O to be like Thee! bless - ed Re - deem - er, This is my con - stant
2. O to be like Thee! full of com - pas - sion, Lov - ing, for - giv - ing,
3. O to be like Thee! low - ly in spir - it, Ho - ly and harm - less,
4. O to be like Thee! while I am plead - ing, Pour out Thy Spir - it,

long - ing and prayer. Glad - ly I'll for - feit all of earth's treas - ures,
ten - der and kind, Help - ing the help - less, cheer - ing the faint - ing,
pa - tient and brave; Meek - ly en - dur - ing cru - el re - proach - es,
fill with Thy love; Make me a tem - ple meet for Thy dwell - ing,

Je - sus, Thy per - fect like - ness to wear.
Seek - ing the wan - d'ring sin - ner to find.
Will - ing to suf - fer oth - ers to save.
Fit me for life and heav - en a - bove.

CHORUS

O to be like Thee!

O to be like Thee, Bless-ed Re - deem - er, pure as Thou art! Come in Thy

sweet - ness, come in Thy full - ness; Stamp Thine own im - age deep on my heart.

359 He Lifted Me

Charles H. Gabriel — Charles H. Gabriel

1. In lov-ing-kind-ness Je-sus came My soul in mer-cy to re-claim,
2. He called me long be-fore I heard, Be-fore my sin-ful heart was stirred,
3. His brow was pierced with man-y a thorn, His hands by cru-el nails were torn,
4. Now on a high-er plane I dwell, And with my soul I know 'tis well;

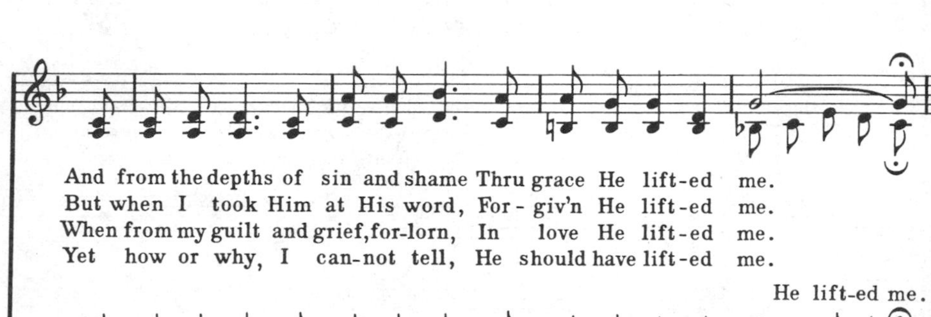
And from the depths of sin and shame Thru grace He lift-ed me.
But when I took Him at His word, For-giv'n He lift-ed me.
When from my guilt and grief, for-lorn, In love He lift-ed me.
Yet how or why, I can-not tell, He should have lift-ed me.
He lift-ed me.

CHORUS

From sink-ing sand He lift-ed me, With ten-der hand He lift-ed me;

From shades of night to plains of light, O praise His name, He lift-ed me!

Christ Liveth in Me

Daniel W. Whittle

James McGranahan

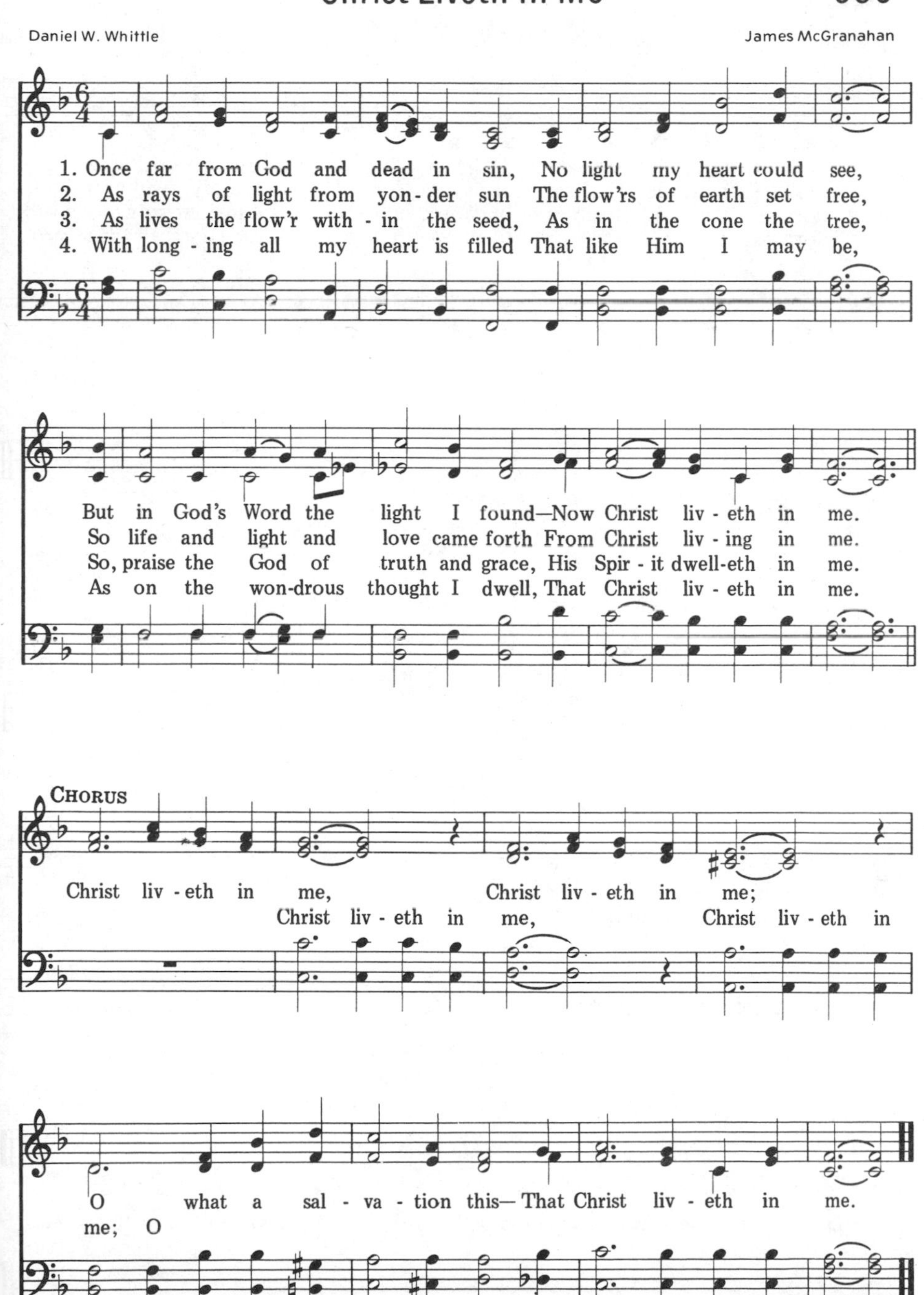
1. Once far from God and dead in sin, No light my heart could see,
2. As rays of light from yon-der sun The flow'rs of earth set free,
3. As lives the flow'r with-in the seed, As in the cone the tree,
4. With long-ing all my heart is filled That like Him I may be,
But in God's Word the light I found—Now Christ liv-eth in me.
So life and light and love came forth From Christ liv-ing in me.
So, praise the God of truth and grace, His Spir-it dwell-eth in me.
As on the won-drous thought I dwell, That Christ liv-eth in me.
Chorus
Christ liv-eth in me, Christ liv-eth in me;
Christ liv-eth in me, Christ liv-eth in me; O
O what a sal-va-tion this—That Christ liv-eth in me.

361 More About Jesus

Eliza E. Hewitt

John R. Sweney

1. More a - bout Je - sus would I know, More of His grace to oth - ers show;
2. More a - bout Je - sus let me learn, More of His ho - ly will dis - cern;
3. More a - bout Je - sus; in His Word, Hold-ing com-mun- ion with my Lord;
4. More a - bout Je - sus on His throne, Rich-es in glo - ry all His own;
More of His sav - ing ful - ness see, More of His love who died for me.
Spir - it of God, my teach - er be, Show-ing the things of Christ to me.
Hear - ing His voice in ev - ery line, Mak - ing each faith - ful say - ing mine.
More of His king-dom's sure in-crease; More of His com - ing, Prince of Peace.
Chorus
More, more a - bout Je - sus, More, more a - bout Je - sus;
More of His sav - ing ful - ness see, More of His love who died for me.

Ivory Palaces

Henry Barraclough — Henry Barraclough

1. My Lord has gar-ments so won-drous fine, And myrrh their tex-ture fills;
2. His life had al - so its sor-rows sore, For al - oes had a part;
3. His gar-ments too were in cas - sia dipped, With heal-ing in a touch;
4. In gar-ments glo - ri - ous He will come, To o - pen wide the door;
Its fra-grance reached to this heart of mine, With joy my be - ing thrills.
And when I think of the cross He bore, My eyes with tear-drops start.
Each time my feet in some sin have slipped, He took me from its clutch.
And I shall en - ter my heav'n-ly home, To dwell for - ev - er - more.
Refrain
Out of the i - vo - ry pal - a - ces, In - to a world of woe,
On - ly His great, e - ter - nal love Made my Sav - ior go.

363 Beneath the Cross of Jesus

Elizabeth C. Clephane
Frederick C. Maker
1. Be - neath the cross of Je - sus I fain would take my stand—
2. Up - on that cross of Je - sus Mine eye at times can see
3. I take, O cross, thy shad - ow For my a - bid - ing place;
The shad - ow of a might - y Rock With - in a wea - ry land;
The ver - y dy - ing form of One Who suf - fered there for me;
I ask no oth - er sun - shine than The sun - shine of His face;
A home with - in the wil - der - ness, A rest up - on the way,
And from my smit - ten heart with tears Two won - ders I con - fess—
Con - tent to let the world go by, To know no gain nor loss,
From the burn-ing of the noon-tide heat, And the bur-den of the day.
The won-ders of re-deem-ing love And my un-wor-thi-ness.
My sin - ful self my on - ly shame, My glo - ry all the cross. A-men.

Whiter Than Snow 364

James L. Nicholson
William G. Fischer
1. Lord Je - sus, I long to be per - fect - ly whole; I want You for - ev - er to live in my soul, Break down ev - ery i - dol, cast out ev - ery foe;
2. Lord Je - sus, look down from Your throne in the skies, And help me to make a com - plete sac - ri - fice; I give up my - self, and what - ev - er I know,
3. Lord Je - sus, for this I most hum - bly en - treat, I wait, bless - ed Lord, at Your cru - ci - fied feet; By faith, for my cleans - ing I see Your blood flow,
4. Lord Je - sus, You see that I pa - tient - ly wait, Come now, and with - in me a new heart cre - ate; To those who have sought You, You nev - er said "No,"
Now wash me and I shall be whit - er than snow.
Refrain
Whit - er than snow, yes, whit - er than snow; Now wash me, and I shall be whit - er than snow.

365 I Was a Wandering Sheep

Horatius Bonar

J. Zundel

1. I was a wan-d'ring sheep, I did not love the fold;
2. The Shep-herd sought his sheep, The Fa-ther sought his child;
3. Je-sus my Shep-herd is; 'Twas he that loved my soul,
4. No more a wan-d'ring sheep, I love to be con-trolled;
I did not love my Shep-herd's voice, I would not be con-trolled:
He fol-lowed me o'er vale and hill, O'er des-erts waste and wild:
'Twas he that washed me in his blood, 'Twas he that made me whole;
I love my ten-der Shep-herd's voice, I love the peace-ful fold:
I was a way-ward child, I did not love my home;
He found me nigh to death, Fam-ished and faint and lone;
'Twas he that sought the lost, That found the wan-d'ring sheep;
No more a way-ward child, I seek no more to roam;
I did not love my Fa-ther's voice, I loved a-far to roam.
He bound me with the bands of love, He saved the wan-d'ring one.
'Twas he that brought me to the fold, 'Tis he that still doth keep.
I love my heav'n-ly Fa-ther's voice, I love, I love his home! A-men

I Would Be True

Howard A. Walter

Joseph Y. Peck

1. I would be true, for there are those who trust me; I would be
2. I would be friend of all— the foe, the friend - less; I would be
3. I would be learn - ing day by day the les - sons My heav'n-ly
4. I would be prayer - ful through each bus - y mo - ment; I would be

pure, for there are those who care: I would be strong, for there is
giv - ing, and for - get the gift; I would be hum - ble, for I
Fa - ther gives me in His Word; I would be quick to hear His
con - stant - ly in touch with God; I would be tuned to hear His

much to suf - fer; I would be brave, for there is much to
know my weak - ness; I would look up, and laugh, and love, and
light - est whis - per, And prompt and glad to do the things I've
slight - est whis - per, I would have faith to keep the path Christ

dare; I would be brave, for there is much to dare.
lift; I would look up, and laugh, and love, and lift.
heard; And prompt and glad to do the things I've heard.
trod; I would have faith to keep the path Christ trod. A-men.

367 Jesus Is the Joy of Living

Alfred H. Ackley | Alfred H. Ackley

1. I have found a won-drous Sav - iour, Je - sus Christ, the Soul's De-light;
2. Life is grow-ing rich with beau - ty; Toil has lost its wea - ry strain;
3. Heav'nly wis-dom He pro - vides me, Grace to keep my spir - it free;
4. Oh, what Splen-dor, oh, what Glo - ry, Oh, what matchless Pow'r di - vine
Ev - 'ry bless-ing of His fa - vor Fills my heart with hope so bright.
Now a ha - lo crowns each du - ty, And I sing a glad re - frain.
In His own sweet way He guides me When the path I can - not see.
Is the Christ of gos - pel sto - ry! Christ, the Sav-iour, who is mine!
REFRAIN
Je - sus is the Joy of Liv - ing; He's the King of Life to me.
of Life to me.
Un - to Him my all I'm giv - ing, His for - ev - er-more to be (to be).
I will do what He com-mands me; An - y-where He leads I'll go (I'll go).

rit.
Je - sus is the Joy of Liv - ing; He's the dear-est Friend I know.
Stand Up for Jesus
368
George Duffield
George J. Webb
1. Stand up, stand up for Je - sus, Ye sol - diers of the cross!
2. Stand up, stand up for Je - sus, The trum - pet call o - bey;
3. Stand up, stand up for Je - sus, Stand in His strength a - lone;
4. Stand up, stand up for Je - sus, The strife will not be long;
Lift high His roy - al ban - ner– It must not suf - fer loss.
Forth to the might - y con - flict In this His glo - rious day.
The arm of flesh will fail you– Ye dare not trust your own.
This day the noise of bat - tle– The next, the vic - tor's song.
From vic - t'ry un - to vic - t'ry His ar - my shall He lead,
Ye that are men now serve Him A - gainst un - num - bered foes;
Put on the gos - pel ar - mor, Each piece put on with prayer;
To Him that o - ver - com - eth A crown of life shall be:
Till ev - 'ry foe is van - quished And Christ is Lord in - deed.
Let cour - age rise with dan - ger And strength to strength op - pose.
Where du - ty calls or dan - ger, Be nev - er want - ing there.
He with the King of glo - ry Shall reign e - ter - nal - ly.

369 O Happy Day!

Philip Doddridge

Edward F. Rimbault

1. O hap-py day that fixed my choice On Thee, my Sav-ior and my God!
2. O hap-py bond that seals my vows To Him who mer-its all my love!
3. 'Tis done, the great trans-ac-tion's done— I am my Lord's and He is mine;
4. Now rest, my long-di-vid-ed heart, Fixed on this bliss-ful cen-ter, rest;
Well may this glow-ing heart re-joice And tell its rap-tures all a-broad.
Let cheer-ful an-thems fill His house, While to that sa-cred shrine I move.
He drew me, and I fol-lowed on, Charmed to con-fess the voice di-vine.
Nor ev-er from my Lord de-part, With Him of ev-'ry good pos-sessed.
CHORUS
Hap-py day, hap-py day, When Je-sus washed my sins a-way!
He taught me how to watch and pray And live re-joic-ing ev-'ry day;
Hap-py day, hap-py day, When Je-sus washed my sins a-way!

Yield Not to Temptation

Horatio R. Palmer
Horatio R. Palmer
Arr. by Norman Johnson
1. Yield not to temp-ta-tion For yield-ing is sin, Each vic-t'ry will
2. Shun e-vil com-pan-ions, Bad lan-guage dis-dain, God's name hold in
3. To him that o'er-com-eth God giv-eth a crown, Thru faith we will
help you Some oth-er to win; Fight man-ful-ly on-ward, Dark
rev-'rence, Nor take it in vain; Be thought-ful and ear-nest, Kind-
con-quer Tho oft-en cast down; He who is our Sav-ior Our
pas-sions sub-due, Look ev-er to Je-sus— He'll car-ry you through.
heart-ed and true, Look ev-er to Je-sus— He'll car-ry you through.
strength will re-new, Look ev-er to Je-sus— He'll car-ry you through.
CHORUS
Ask the Sav-ior to help you, Com-fort, strength-en and keep you;
He is will-ing to aid you— He will car-ry you through.

371 Rise With Thy Risen Lord

Albert B. Simpson

Alfred B. Smith

1. Rise with thy ris - en Lord, As - cend with Christ a - bove,
2. Walk as a heaven - ly race, Prin - ces of roy - al blood;
3. Your full re - demp - tion rights With ho - ly bold - ness claim,

And in the heaven-lies walk with Him Whom, see - ing not, you love.
Walk as the chil - dren of the light, The sons and heirs of God.
And to its ut - most full - ness prove The power of Je - sus' name.

Look on your tri - als here As He be - holds them now;
Fear not to take your place With Je - sus on the throne,
Your life is hid - den now, Your glo - ry none can see,

Look on this world as it will seem When glo - ry crowns your brow.
And bid the powers of hell and earth His sov-ereign scep - tor own.
But when He comes His bride will shine All glo - ri - ous as He.

My Goal Is God Himself

F. Brook
Alt. A.B.S.
Alfred B. Smith
1. My goal is God Him - self— not joy, nor peace,
2. So faith bounds for - ward to its goal in God,
3. No mat - ter if the way be some - times dark,
4. One thing I know, I can - not say Him nay;
Nor e - ven bless - ing, but Him - self, my God.
And love can trust her Lord to lead her there;
No mat - ter though the cost be oft - times great,
One thing I do, I press on to my Lord;
'Tis His to lead me there, not mine, but His—
Up - held by Him, my soul is fol - lowing hard,
He know - eth how I best shall reach the mark—
My God my glo - ry here from day to day,
"At an - y cost, dear Lord, by an - y road!"
Till God has an - swered full my deep - est prayer.
The way that leads to Him must needs be strait.
And in the glo - ry there my Great Re - ward.

373 Complete in Thee

Aaron R. Wolfe
Refrain, James M. Gray

Talmadge J. Bittikofer

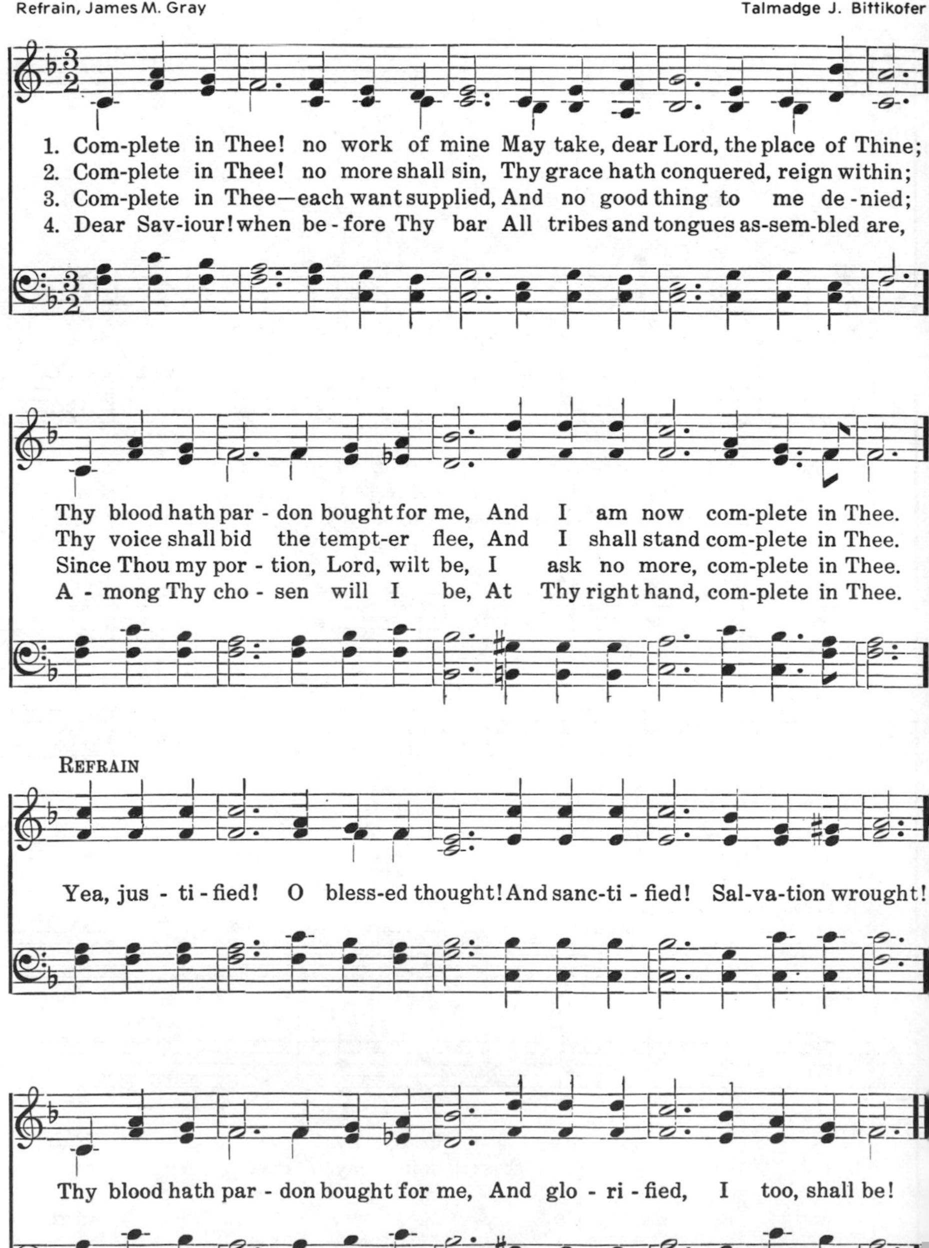
1. Com-plete in Thee! no work of mine May take, dear Lord, the place of Thine;
2. Com-plete in Thee! no more shall sin, Thy grace hath conquered, reign within;
3. Com-plete in Thee—each want supplied, And no good thing to me de-nied;
4. Dear Sav-iour! when be-fore Thy bar All tribes and tongues as-sem-bled are,
Thy blood hath par - don bought for me, And I am now com-plete in Thee.
Thy voice shall bid the tempt-er flee, And I shall stand com-plete in Thee.
Since Thou my por - tion, Lord, wilt be, I ask no more, com-plete in Thee.
A - mong Thy cho - sen will I be, At Thy right hand, com-plete in Thee.
Refrain
Yea, jus - ti - fied! O bless-ed thought! And sanc-ti - fied! Sal-va-tion wrought!
Thy blood hath par - don bought for me, And glo - ri - fied, I too, shall be!

Go to the Deeps of God's Promise

Mrs. Frank A. Breck — Charles H. Gabriel

1. Go to the deeps of God's prom - ise; Ask free - ly of
2. Go to the deeps of God's prom - ise, And know of His
3. Go to the deeps of God's prom - ise; The bless - ing is
4. Go to the deeps of God's prom - ise, And claim what - so-
Him, and re - ceive; All good may be had for the ask - ing,
won - der - ful might; What - ev - er would be a true bless - ing,
nev - er de - nied; He loves, and re - mem - bers His chil - dren,
ev - er ye will; The bless - ing of God will not fail thee,
CHORUS
If, seek - ing, ye tru - ly be - lieve.
For Je - sus' sake, comes as thy right. Go to the deeps of God's
And ev - 'ry good thing is sup - plied.
His word He will sure - ly ful - fill.
prom - ise; There's wideness of mean-ing un - told In the prom - is - es
giv - en His peo - ple, And the treasures they ev - er un - fold.

375 Accepted in the Beloved

Civilla D. Martin — Wendell P. Loveless

1. "In the Be-lov-ed" ac-cept-ed am I, Ris-en, as-cend-ed, and seat-ed on high; Saved from all sin thro' His in-fi-nite grace, With the re-deemed ones ac-cord-ed a place.
2. "In the Be-lov-ed"–how safe my re-treat, In the Be-lov-ed ac-count-ed com-plete; "Who can con-demn me?" In Him I am free, Sav-ior and Keep-er for-ev-er is He.
3. "In the Be-lov-ed" I went to the tree, There, in His Per-son, by faith I may see In-fi-nite wrath roll-ing o-ver His head, In-fi-nite grace, for He died in my stead.

CHORUS

"In the Be-lov-ed," God's mar-vel-ous grace Calls me to dwell in this won-der-ful place; God sees my Sav-ior and then He sees me "In the Be-lov-ed," ac-cept-ed and free.

Yielded to God

Alfred B. Smith
George C. Stebbins
F. J. Crosby
1. Yield - ed to God, my bod - y, soul and spir - it,
2. Yield - ed to God, re - pos - ing 'neath His shad - ow,
3. Yield - ed to God, my life and its de - vo - tion
4. Yield - ed to God, and in His ho - ly keep - ing,
O what re - joic - ing fills my peace-ful breast;
Sun - shine and glad - ness round my path-way fall;
Yield - ed the serv - ice of my days and years;
My heart His tem - ple ev - er - more shall be;
All, all is well, no doubt nor fear dis - turbs me,
Yield - ed to God, whose love dis - pels all sor - row,
O what a peace per - vades my ev - 'ry feel - ing,
Yield - ed to God, in will - ing con - se - cra - tion,
While on His prom - ise now a - lone I rest.
He is my Ref - uge, and my All in All.
O what sweet vis - ions on my sight ap - pears.
Bless - ed Re - deem - er, I am lost in Thee.

377 To the Work!

Fanny J. Crosby — William H. Doane

1. To the work! to the work! we are serv-ants of God, Let us fol-low the
2. To the work! to the work! let the hun-gry be fed, To the foun-tain of
3. To the work! to the work! there is la-bor for all, For the king-dom of
4. To the work! to the work! in the strength of the Lord, And a robe and a
path that our Mas-ter has trod; With the balm of His coun-sel our
life let the wea-ry be led; In the cross and its ban-ner our
dark-ness and er-ror shall fall; And the name of Je-ho-vah ex-
crown shall our la-bor re-ward When the home of the faith-ful our
strength to re-new, Let us do with our might what our hands find to do.
glo-ry shall be, While we her-ald the ti-dings, "Sal-va-tion is free!"
alt-ed shall be In the loud swell-ing cho-rus, "Sal-va-tion is free!"
dwell-ing shall be And we shout with the ran-somed, "Sal-va-tion is free!"
CHORUS
Toil-ing on, toil-ing on, Toil-ing
Toil-ing on, toil-ing on,
on, toil-ing on; Let us hope,
Toil-ing on, toil-ing on; and trust,

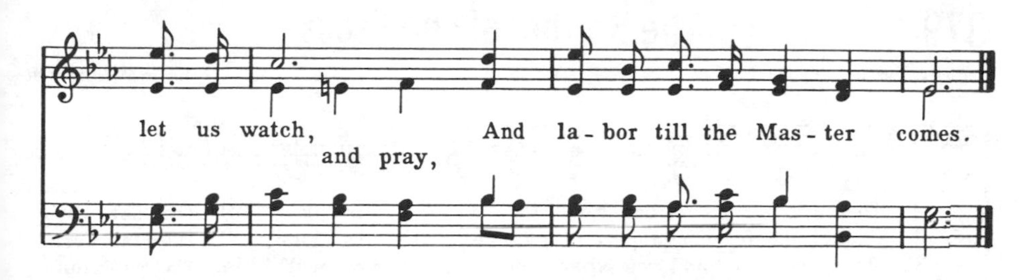
let us watch, and pray, And la-bor till the Mas-ter comes.

Shall I Empty-Handed Be? 378

Rev. Neal A. McAuley

John P. Hillis
Alfred B. Smith

1. Shall I emp-ty-hand-ed be When be-side the crys-tal sea
2. When the har-vest day's are past, Shall I hear Him say at last,
3. When the books are o-pened wide, And the deeds of all are tried,
I shall stand be-fore the ev-er-last-ing throne?
"Wel-come pil-grim, I've pre-pared for thee a place?"
May I have a rec-ord whit-er than the snow;
Must I have a heart of shame As I an-swer to my name,
Shall I bring Him gold-en sheaves, Rip-ened fruit, not fad-ed leaves,
When my race on earth is run, May I hear Him say, "Well done,"
With no works that my Re-deem-er there can own?
When I see the bless-ed Sav-ior face to face?
Take the crown that Love im-mor-tal doth be-stow."

379

The Banner of the Cross

Daniel W. Whittle

James McGranahan

1. There's a roy- al ban- ner giv- en for dis- play To the sol- diers
2. Though the foe may rage and gath- er as the flood, Let the stan- dard
3. O - ver land and sea, wher - ev - er men may dwell, Make the glo- rious
4. When the glo- ry dawns—'tis draw- ing ver- y near— It is has- t'ning

of the King; As an en- sign fair we lift it up to- day,
be dis- played; And be- neath its folds, as sol- diers of the Lord,
ti - dings known; Of the crim- son ban- ner now the sto- ry tell,
day by day— Then be- fore our King the foe shall dis- ap- pear,

While as ran- somed ones we sing.
For the truth be not dis- mayed.
While the Lord shall claim His own.
And the cross the world shall sway.

CHORUS

March- ing on, march- ing
on, on,

on, For Christ count ev-'ry-thing but loss! And to
on, on, ev-'ry-thing, ev - 'ry-thing but loss!

crown Him King, toil and sing 'Neath the ban- ner of the cross!
we'll Be - neath

I'll Go Where You Want Me to Go

Mary Brown &
Charles E. Prior
Carrie E. Rounsefell
1. It may not be on the moun-tain's height Or o-ver the storm-y sea,
2. Per-haps to-day there are lov-ing words Which Je-sus would have me speak,
3. There's sure-ly some-where a low-ly place In earth's har-vest fields so wide,
It may not be at the bat-tle's front My Lord will have need of me;
There may be now, in the paths of sin, Some wan-d'rer whom I should seek;
Where I may la-bor thru life's short day For Je-sus the Cru-ci-fied;
But if by a still, small voice He calls To paths I do not know,
O Sav-ior, if Thou wilt be my Guide, Tho dark and rug-ged the way,
So, trust-ing my all un-to Thy care— I know Thou lov-est me—
Fine
I'll an-swer, dear Lord, with my hand in Thine, I'll go where You want me to go.
My voice shall ech-o the mes-sage sweet, I'll say what You want me to say.
I'll do Thy will with a heart sin-cere, I'll be what You want me to be.
D.S.- I'll say what You want me to say, dear Lord, I'll be what You want me to be.
CHORUS
D.S.
I'll go where You want me to go, dear Lord, O'er moun-tain or plain or sea;

381 We've a Story to Tell to the Nations

H. Ernest Nichol H. Ernest Nichol

1. We've a sto - ry to tell to the na - tions That shall
2. We've a song to be sung to the na - tions That shall
3. We've a mes - sage to give to the na - tions That the
4. We've a Sav - ior to show to the na - tions Who the
turn their hearts to the right, A sto - ry of truth and mer - cy,
lift their hearts to the Lord, A song that shall con - quer e - vil
Lord who reign - eth a - bove Hath sent us His Son to save us,
path of sor - row hath trod, That all of the world's great peo - ples
A sto - ry of peace and light, A sto - ry of peace and light.
And shat - ter the spear and sword, And shat - ter the spear and sword.
And show us that God is love, And show us that God is love.
Might come to the truth of God, Might come to the truth of God.
CHORUS
For the dark-ness shall turn to dawn-ing, And the dawn-ing to noon-day bright,
And Christ's great king-dom shall come to earth, The king - dom of love and light.

Make Me a Blessing

Ira B. Wilson

George S. Schuler

1. Out in the high-ways and by-ways of life, Man-y are wea-ry and sad;
are wea-ry and sad;
2. Tell the sweet sto-ry of Christ and His love, Tell of His pow'r to for-give;
His pow'r to for-give;
3. Give as 'twas giv-en to you in your need, Love as the Mas-ter loved you;
the Mas-ter loved you;

Car-ry the sun-shine where dark-ness is rife, Mak-ing the sor-row-ing glad.
Oth-ers will trust Him if on-ly you prove True, ev-ery mo-ment you live.
Be to the help-less a help-er in-deed, Un-to your mis-sion be true.

CHORUS

Make me a bless-ing, make me a bless-ing, Out of my life
out of my life
may Je-sus shine; Make me a bless-ing, O Sav-ior, I pray,
I pray Thee, my Sav-ior, Make me a bless-ing to some-one to-day.

383

Who Is on the Lord's Side?

C. Luise Reichardt
Frances R. Havergal
Arr. John Goss
1. Who is on the Lord's side? Who will serve the King? Who will be His
2. Not for weight of glo - ry, Not for crown and palm, En - ter we the
3. Je - sus, Thou hast bought us, Not with gold or gem, But with Thine own
4. Fierce may be the con - flict, Strong may be the foe, But the King's own
help - ers, Oth - er lives to bring? Who will leave the world's side?
ar - my, Raise the war - rior psalm; But for love that claim - eth
life - blood, For Thy di - a - dem. With Thy bless - ing fill - ing
ar - my None can o - ver - throw. Round His stand - ard rang - ing
Who will face the foe? Who is on the Lord's side? Who for
Lives for whom He died; He whom Je - sus nam - eth Must be
Each who comes to Thee, Thou hast made us will - ing, Thou hast
Vic - t'ry is se - cure; For His truth un - chang - ing Makes the
Him will go? By Thy call of mer - cy, By Thy grace di - vine,
on His side. By Thy love con - strain - ing, By Thy grace di - vine,
made us free. By Thy grand re - demp - tion, By Thy grace di - vine,
tri - umph sure. Joy - ful - ly en - list - ing By Thy grace di - vine,
We are on the Lord's side, Sav - ior, we are Thine. A - men.

Onward, Christian Soldiers

Sabine Baring-Gould

Arthur S. Sullivan

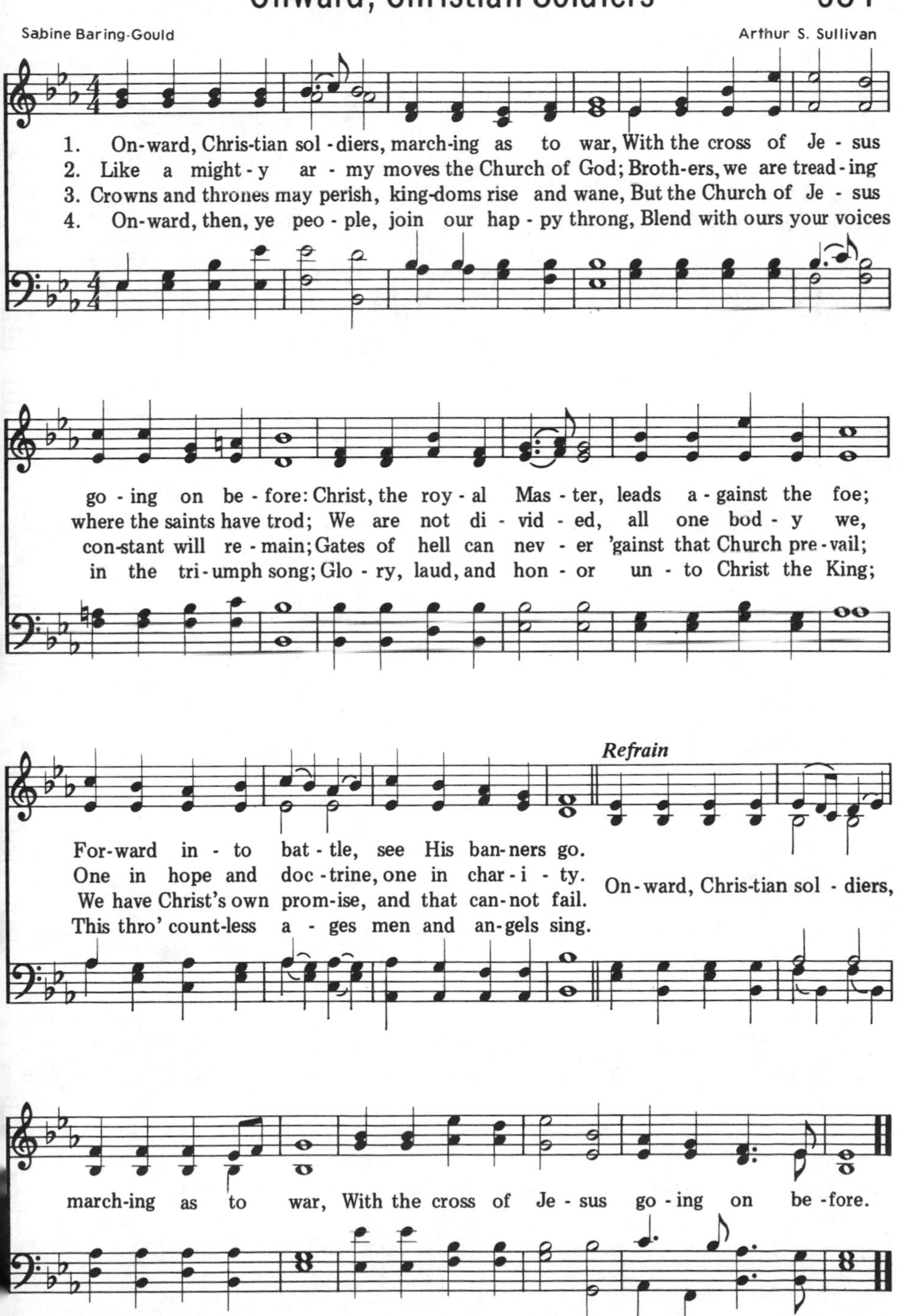
1. On-ward, Chris-tian sol - diers, march-ing as to war, With the cross of Je - sus
2. Like a might - y ar - my moves the Church of God; Broth-ers, we are tread - ing
3. Crowns and thrones may perish, king-doms rise and wane, But the Church of Je - sus
4. On-ward, then, ye peo - ple, join our hap - py throng, Blend with ours your voices
go - ing on be - fore: Christ, the roy - al Mas - ter, leads a - gainst the foe;
where the saints have trod; We are not di - vid - ed, all one bod - y we,
con-stant will re - main; Gates of hell can nev - er 'gainst that Church pre - vail;
in the tri - umph song; Glo - ry, laud, and hon - or un - to Christ the King;
Refrain
For-ward in - to bat - tle, see His ban-ners go.
One in hope and doc - trine, one in char - i - ty.
We have Christ's own prom-ise, and that can-not fail.
This thro' count-less a - ges men and an-gels sing.
On - ward, Chris-tian sol - diers,
march-ing as to war, With the cross of Je - sus go - ing on be - fore.

385 The Master Has Come, and He Calls Us

Sarah Doudney

Traditional Welsh Melody

1. The Mas-ter has come, and He calls us to fol - low The track of the foot-prints He leaves on our way; Far o - ver the moun-tain and through the deep hol - low, The path leads us on to the man-sions of day: The Mas - ter has called us, the chil - dren who fear Him, Who march 'neath Christ's
2. The Mas-ter has called us; the road may be drear - y, And dan-gers and sor - rows are strewn on the track; But God's Ho - ly Spir - it shall com - fort the wea - ry; We fol - low the Sav - ior and can - not turn back; The Mas - ter has called us: tho' doubt and temp-ta - tion May com - pass our
3. The Mas-ter has called us in life's ear - ly morn-ing, With spir - its as fresh as the dew on the sod; We turn from the world with its smiles and its scorn-ing, To cast in our lot with the peo - ple of God: The Mas - ter has called us, His sons and His daugh-ters, We plead for His

ban - ner, His own lit - tle band; We love Him and seek Him, we
jour - ney, we cheer - ful - ly sing: "Press on - ward, look up - ward," thro'
bless - ing and trust in His love; And through the green pas - tures, be -
long to be near Him, And rest in the light of His beau - ti - ful land.
much trib - u - la - tion; The chil-dren of Zi - on must fol - low their King.
side the still wa - ters, He'll lead us at last to His king-dom a - bove.
Jesus Calls Us
386
Cecil F. Alexander
William H. Jude
1. Je - sus calls us o'er the tu - mult Of our life's wild, rest - less sea;
2. Je - sus calls us from the wor - ship Of the vain world's gold - en store,
3. In our joys and in our sor - rows, Days of toil and hours of ease,
4. Je - sus calls us— by Thy mer - cies, Sav- iour, may we hear Thy call,
Day by day His sweet voice sound-eth, Say-ing, "Chris-tian, fol - low Me."
From each i - dol that would keep us, Say-ing, "Chris-tian, love Me more."
Still He calls, in cares and pleas-ures, "Chris-tian, love Me more than these."
Give our hearts to Thine o - be-dience, Serve and love Thee best of all. A-MEN.

387 Joy in Serving Jesus

Rev. Oswald J. Smith — B. D. Ackley

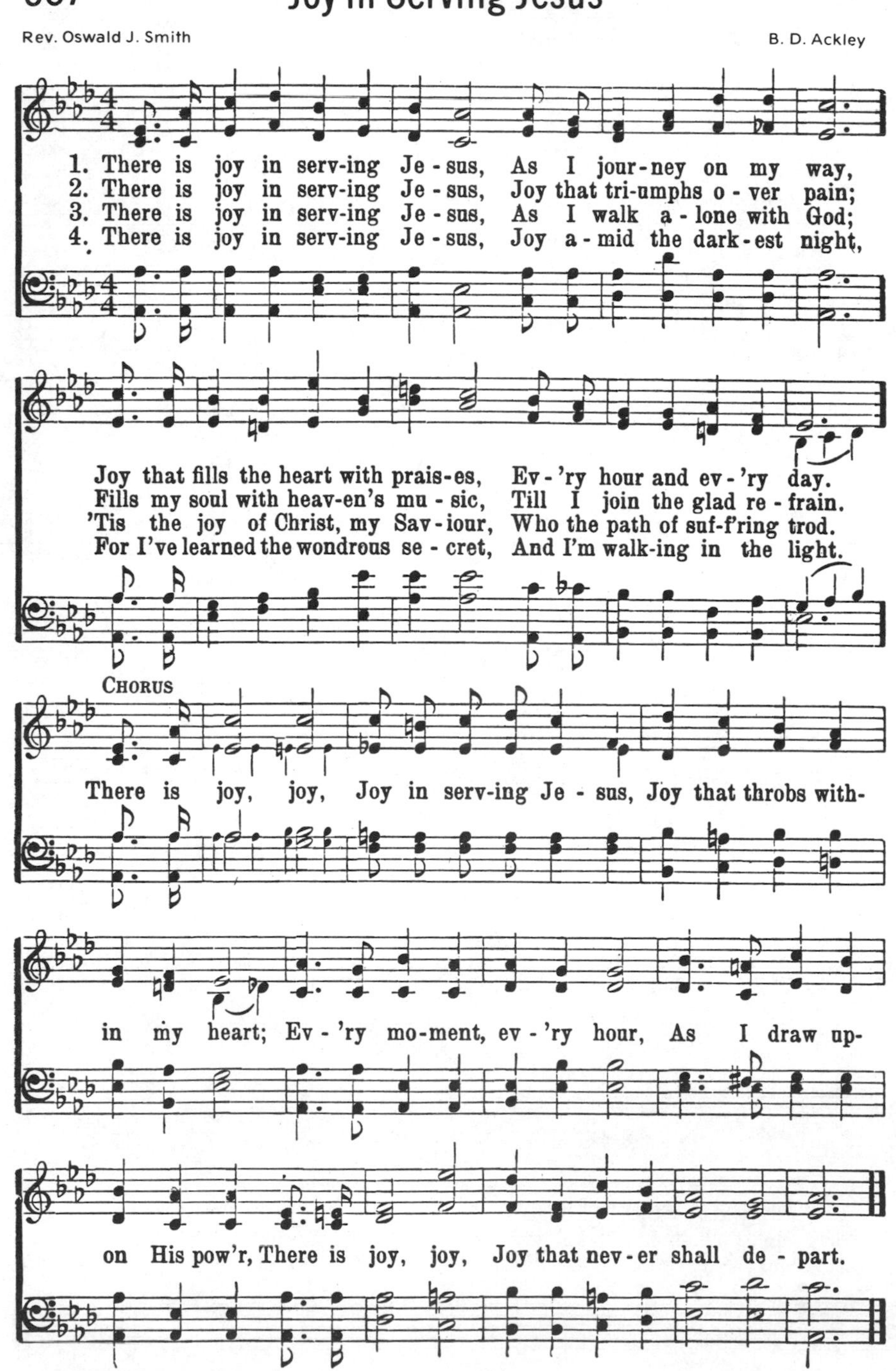
1. There is joy in serv-ing Je - sus, As I jour-ney on my way,
2. There is joy in serv-ing Je - sus, Joy that tri-umphs o - ver pain;
3. There is joy in serv-ing Je - sus, As I walk a - lone with God;
4. There is joy in serv-ing Je - sus, Joy a - mid the dark - est night,
Joy that fills the heart with prais-es, Ev - 'ry hour and ev - 'ry day.
Fills my soul with heav-en's mu - sic, Till I join the glad re - frain.
'Tis the joy of Christ, my Sav - iour, Who the path of suf-f'ring trod.
For I've learned the wondrous se - cret, And I'm walk-ing in the light.
CHORUS
There is joy, joy, Joy in serv-ing Je - sus, Joy that throbs with-
in my heart; Ev - 'ry mo-ment, ev - 'ry hour, As I draw up-
on His pow'r, There is joy, joy, Joy that nev - er shall de - part.

Jesus Saves

Priscilla J. Owens
William J. Kirkpatrick
1. We have heard the joy - ful sound: Je - sus saves! Je - sus saves!
2. Waft it on the roll - ing tide: Je - sus saves! Je - sus saves!
3. Sing a - bove the bat - tle strife: Je - sus saves! Je - sus saves!
4. Give the winds a might - y voice: Je - sus saves! Je - sus saves!
Spread the ti - dings all a - round: Je - sus saves! Je - sus saves!
Tell to sin - ners far and wide: Je - sus saves! Je - sus saves!
By His death and end - less life, Je - sus saves! Je - sus saves!
Let the na - tions now re - joice, Je - sus saves! Je - sus saves!
Bear the news to ev - ery land, Climb the steeps and cross the waves;
Sing, ye is - lands of the sea; Ech - o back, ye o - cean caves;
Sing it soft - ly through the gloom, When the heart for mer - cy craves;
Shout sal - va - tion full and free; High - est hills and deep - est caves;
On - ward! 'tis our Lord's com - mand; Je - sus saves! Je - sus saves!
Earth shall keep her ju - bi - lee: Je - sus saves! Je - sus saves!
Sing in tri - umph o'er the tomb, Je - sus saves! Je - sus saves!
This our song of vic - to - ry: Je - sus saves! Je - sus saves!

389 Stir Me, Oh, Stir Me Lord

Mrs. A. Head

Alfred B. Smith

Ad lib.-With deep feeling
1. Stir me, oh, stir me, Lord, I care not how,
2. Stir me, oh, stir me, Lord, till all my heart
3. Stir me, oh, stir me, Lord, till prayer is pain,
4. Stir me, oh, stir me, Lord, Thy heart was stirred
5. Stir me, oh, stir me, Lord, for I can see
But stir my heart in pas-sion for the world, Stir
Is filled with strong com-pass-ion for these souls; Till
Till prayer is joy, till prayer turns in - to praise; Stir
By love's in - ten - sest fire, till Thou didst give Thine
Thy glor - ious tri - umph-day be - gin to break; The
me to give, to go, but most to pray; Stir, till the
Thy com-pell - ing word drives me to pray; Till Thy con -
me, till heart and will and mind, yea, all Is whol - ly
on - ly Son, Thy best be - lov - ed One, E'en to the
dawn al - read - y gilds the east - ern sky: Oh, Church of
4 parts
blood red ban-ner be un-furled. O'er lands that still in
strain-ing love reach to the poles Far north and south, in
Thine to use thro' all the days. Stir, till I learn to
dread-ful cross, that I might live. Stir me to give my -
Christ, a - rise, a - wake, a - wake; Oh! stir us, Lord, as

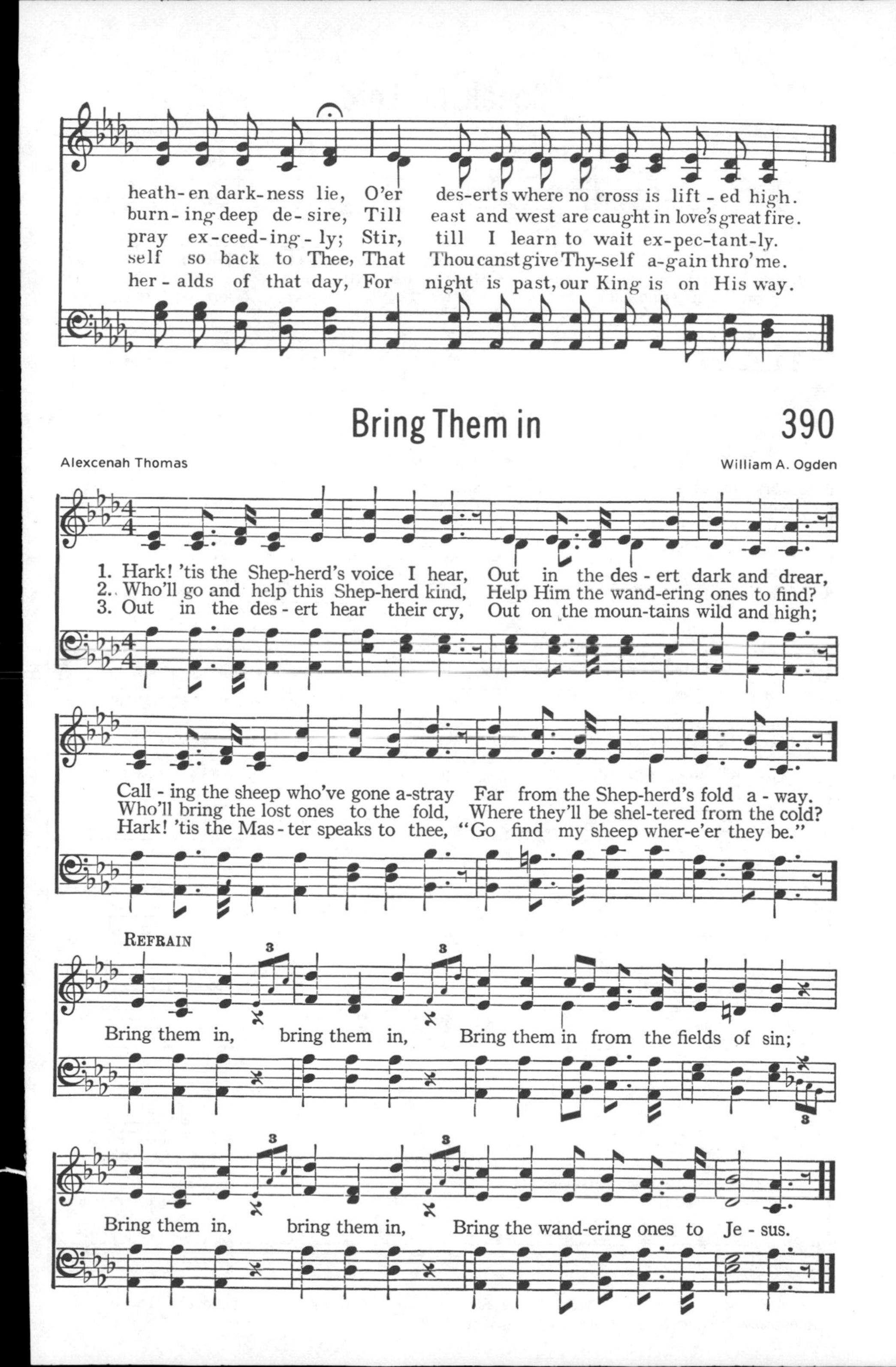
heath-en dark-ness lie, O'er des-erts where no cross is lift-ed high.
burn-ing deep de-sire, Till east and west are caught in love's great fire.
pray ex-ceed-ing-ly; Stir, till I learn to wait ex-pec-tant-ly.
self so back to Thee, That Thou canst give Thy-self a-gain thro' me.
her-alds of that day, For night is past, our King is on His way.
Bring Them in
390
Alexcenah Thomas
William A. Ogden
1. Hark! 'tis the Shep-herd's voice I hear, Out in the des-ert dark and drear,
2. Who'll go and help this Shep-herd kind, Help Him the wand-ering ones to find?
3. Out in the des-ert hear their cry, Out on the moun-tains wild and high;
Call-ing the sheep who've gone a-stray Far from the Shep-herd's fold a-way.
Who'll bring the lost ones to the fold, Where they'll be shel-tered from the cold?
Hark! 'tis the Mas-ter speaks to thee, "Go find my sheep wher-e'er they be."
REFRAIN
Bring them in, bring them in, Bring them in from the fields of sin;
Bring them in, bring them in, Bring the wand-ering ones to Je-sus.

391 Speak, My Lord

George Bennard — George Bennard

1. Hear the Lord of har - vest sweet - ly call - ing, "Who will go and work for Me to - day? Who will bring to Me the lost and dy - ing? Who will point them to the nar - row way?"
2. When the coal of fire touched the proph - et, Mak - ing him as pure, as pure can be, When the voice of God said, "Who'll go for us?" Then he an-swered, "Here I am, send me."
3. Mil - lions now in sin and shame are dy - ing, Lis - ten to their sad and bit - ter cry; Has - ten, broth - er, has - ten to the res - cue; Quick - ly an-swer, "Mas - ter, here am I."
4. Soon the time for reap - ing will be o - ver; Soon we'll gath - er for the har - vest home; May the Lord of har - vest smile up - on us, May we hear His bless-ed, "Child, well done."
REFRAIN
Speak, my Lord, speak, my Lord, Speak, and I'll be quick to an - swer Thee;
Speak, my Lord, Speak, my Lord, to an-swer Thee;
Speak, my Lord, speak, my Lord, Speak, and I will an-swer, "Lord, send me."
Speak, my Lord, "Lord, send me."

So Send I You

E. Margaret Clarkson

John W. Peterson

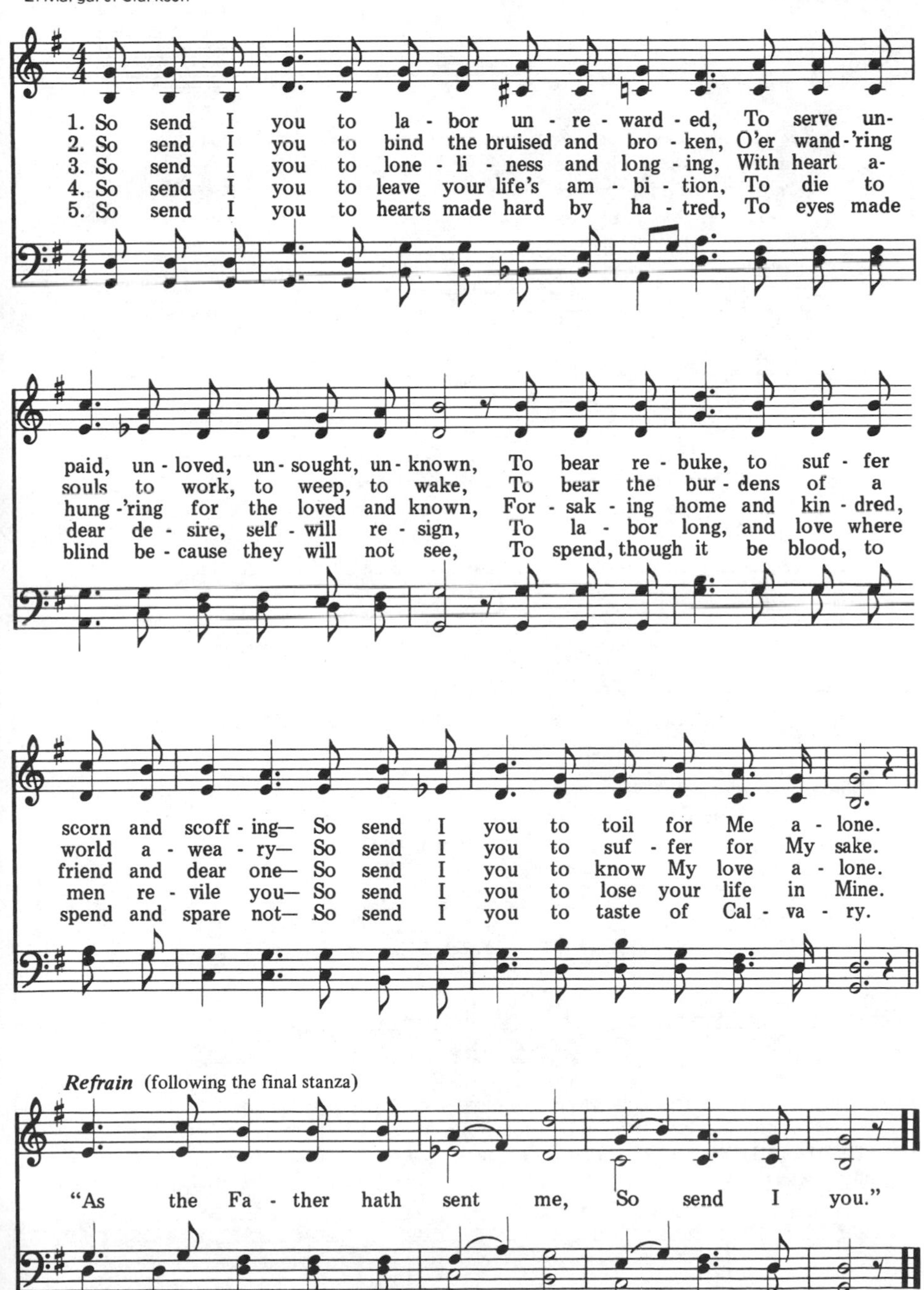
1. So send I you to la - bor un - re - ward - ed, To serve un-
2. So send I you to bind the bruised and bro - ken, O'er wand-'ring
3. So send I you to lone - li - ness and long - ing, With heart a-
4. So send I you to leave your life's am - bi - tion, To die to
5. So send I you to hearts made hard by ha - tred, To eyes made
paid, un - loved, un - sought, un - known, To bear re - buke, to suf - fer
souls to work, to weep, to wake, To bear the bur - dens of a
hung -'ring for the loved and known, For - sak - ing home and kin - dred,
dear de - sire, self - will re - sign, To la - bor long, and love where
blind be - cause they will not see, To spend, though it be blood, to
scorn and scoff - ing— So send I you to toil for Me a - lone.
world a - wea - ry— So send I you to suf - fer for My sake.
friend and dear one— So send I you to know My love a - lone.
men re - vile you— So send I you to lose your life in Mine.
spend and spare not— So send I you to taste of Cal - va - ry.
Refrain (following the final stanza)
"As the Fa - ther hath sent me, So send I you."

393 The Son of God Goes Forth

Reginald Heber
Henry S. Cutler
1. The Son of God goes forth to war, A king - ly crown to gain;
2. The mar - tyr first, whose ea - gle eye Could pierce be - yond the grave,
3. A glo - rious band, the cho - sen few On whom the Spir - it came,
4. A no - ble ar - my, men and boys, The ma - tron and the maid,
His blood - red ban - ner streams a - far: Who fol - lows in His train?
Who saw his Mas - ter in the sky And called on Him to save—
Twelve val - iant saints, their hope they knew And mocked the cross and flame.
A - round the Sav-iour's throne re - joice In robes of light ar-rayed.
Who best can drink his cup of woe, Tri - umph - ant o - ver pain;
Like Him, with par - don on his tongue, In midst of mor - tal pain,
They met the ty - rant's brand-ished steel, The li - on's go - ry mane;
They climbed the steep as - cent of heaven Through per - il, toil, and pain.
Who pa - tient bears his cross be - low—He fol - lows in His train.
He prayed for them that did the wrong—Who fol - lows in his train?
They bowed their necks the death to feel. Who fol - lows in their train?
O God, to us may grace be given To fol - low in their train! A-MEN.

Lead on, O King Eternal

Ernest W. Shurtleff

Henry T. Smart

1. Lead on, O King E - ter - nal, The day of march has come;
2. Lead on, O King E - ter - nal, Till sin's fierce war shall cease,
3. Lead on, O King E - ter - nal, We fol - low, not with fears;
Hence-forth in fields of con - quest Your tents shall be our home.
And ho - li - ness shall whis - per The sweet A - men of peace;
For glad - ness breaks like morn - ing Wher - e'er Your face ap - pears;
Through days of prep - a - ra - tion Your grace has made us strong,
For not with swords loud clash - ing, Nor roll of stir - ring drums,
Your cross is lift - ed o'er us; We jour - ney in its light:
And now, O King E - ter - nal, We lift our bat - tle song.
With deeds of love and mer - cy The heav'n - ly king - dom comes.
The crown a - waits the con - quest; Lead on, O God of might. A-men.

395 Till the Whole World Knows

Alfred H. Ackley
Bentley D. Ackley

1. I'll tell to all that God is love; For the world has nev - er known
The great com - pas - sion of His heart For the way - ward and the lone.

2. I'll tell of mer - cy's bound-less tide, Like the wa - ters of the sea,
That cov - ers ev - ery sin of man; 'Tis sal - va - tion full and free.

3. I'll tell of grace that keeps the soul, Of a - bid - ing peace with - in,
Of faith that o - ver - comes the world, With its tu - mult and its din.

4. E - ter - nal glo - ry is the goal That a - waits the sons of light;
E - ter - nal dark - ness, black as death, For the chil - dren of the night.

Refrain
Till the whole world knows, Till the whole world
Till the world, till the whole world knows, Till the world, till the whole world,
Till the world, the whole world knows,

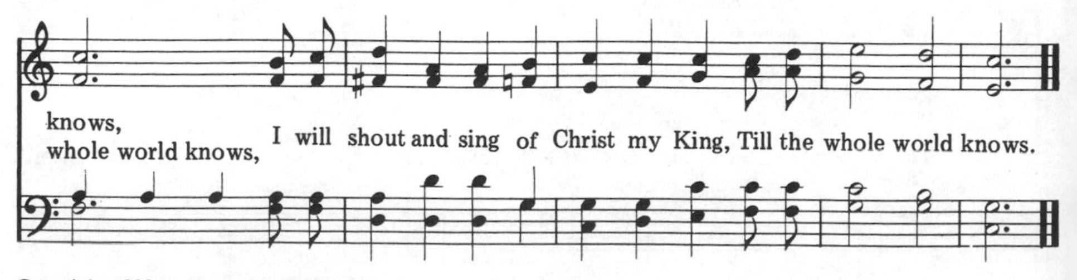
knows,
whole world knows,
I will shout and sing of Christ my King, Till the whole world knows.

Speak Just a Word for Jesus

Katherine O. Barker

D. B. Towner & A.B.S.

1. Speak just a word for Je - sus, Tell how He died for you;
Of - ten re-peat the sto - ry, Won - der - ful, glad and true!

2. Speak just a word for Je - sus, Tell how He helps you live;
Tell of the strength and com - fort Which He will free - ly give!

3. Speak just a word for Je - sus, Do not for oth - ers wait;
Glad - ly pro-claim the mes - sage Soon it will be too late!

4. Speak just a word for Je - sus, Why should you doubt or fear?
Sure - ly His love will bless it; Some one will glad - ly hear.

5. Speak just a word for Je - sus, Tell of His love for men!
Some one dis-tressed may lis - ten, Will - ing to trust Him then.

Chorus

Speak just a word, Ev - er to Him be true;
Speak just a word, just a word for Je-sus,

Speak just a word, Tell what He's do-ing for you!
Speak just a word, just a word for Je-sus,

397 The King's Business

E. Taylor Cassel

Flora H. Cassel

1. I am a stran - ger here with - in a for - eign land, My home is
2. This is the King's com-mand, that all men ev - ery-where Re - pent and
3. My home is bright - er far than Shar-on's ros - y plain, E - ter - nal
far a - way up - on a gold - en strand; Am - bas - sa - dor to be of
turn a - way from sin's se - duc - tive snare; That all who will o - bey with
life and joy through-out its vast do-main; My Sov-ereign bids me tell how
realms be - yond the sea, I'm here on busi-ness for my King.
Him shall reign for aye, And that's my busi-ness for my King.
mor - tals there may dwell, And that's my busi-ness for my King.
Refrain
This is the
mes - sage that I bring, A mes-sage an - gels fain would sing; "Oh, be ye
rec - on-ciled," Thus saith my Lord and King, "Oh, be ye rec - on - ciled to God."

Anywhere With Jesus

Jessie B. Pounds

Daniel B. Towner

1. An - y-where with Je - sus I can safe - ly go; An - y-where He leads me in this world be - low; An - y-where with-out Him dear - est joys would fade; An - y-where with Je - sus I am not a - fraid.
2. An - y-where with Je - sus I am not a - lone; Oth - er friends may fail me, He is still my own; Though His hand may lead me o - ver drear - y ways, An - y-where with Je - sus is a house of praise.
3. An - y-where with Je - sus I can go to sleep, When the darkening shad-ows round a - bout me creep; Know-ing I shall wak - en nev - er more to roam, An - y-where with Je - sus will be home, sweet home.
Refrain
An - y - where! an - y - where! Fear I can - not know;
An - y - where with Je - sus I can safe - ly go.

399 O Zion,* Haste

Mary A. Thomson — James Walch

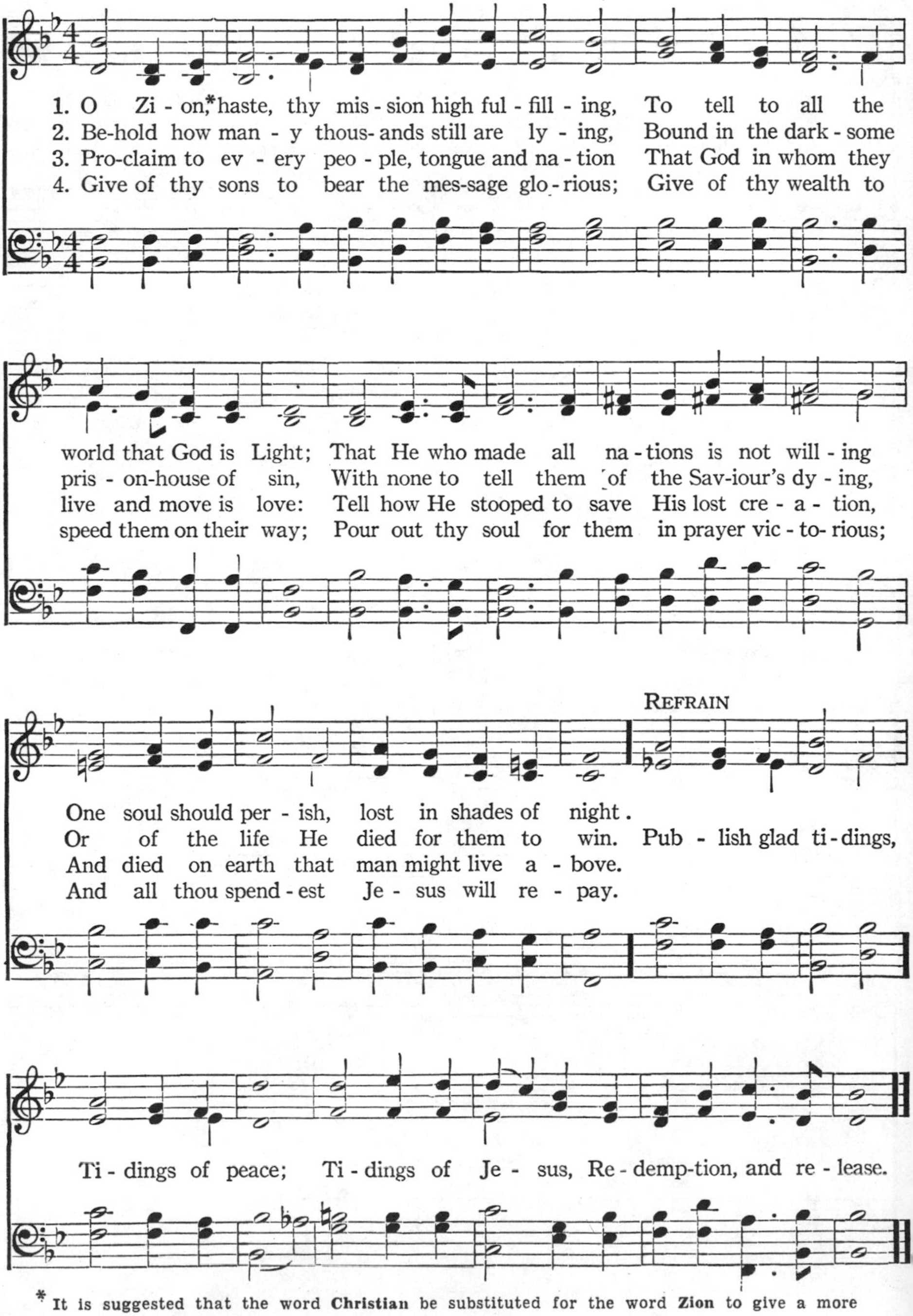

1. O Zi-on,* haste, thy mis-sion high ful-fill-ing, To tell to all the world that God is Light; That He who made all na-tions is not will-ing One soul should per-ish, lost in shades of night.
2. Be-hold how man-y thous-ands still are ly-ing, Bound in the dark-some pris-on-house of sin, With none to tell them of the Sav-iour's dy-ing, Or of the life He died for them to win.
3. Pro-claim to ev-ery peo-ple, tongue and na-tion That God in whom they live and move is love: Tell how He stooped to save His lost cre-a-tion, And died on earth that man might live a-bove.
4. Give of thy sons to bear the mes-sage glo-rious; Give of thy wealth to speed them on their way; Pour out thy soul for them in prayer vic-to-rious; And all thou spend-est Je-sus will re-pay.

REFRAIN

Pub-lish glad ti-dings, Ti-dings of peace; Ti-dings of Je-sus, Re-demp-tion, and re-lease.

* It is suggested that the word **Christian** be substituted for the word **Zion** to give a more personal application to this great missionary hymn.

The Battle Is the Lord's

E. Margaret Clarkson

Hebrew Melody
Adapted by Meyer Lyon

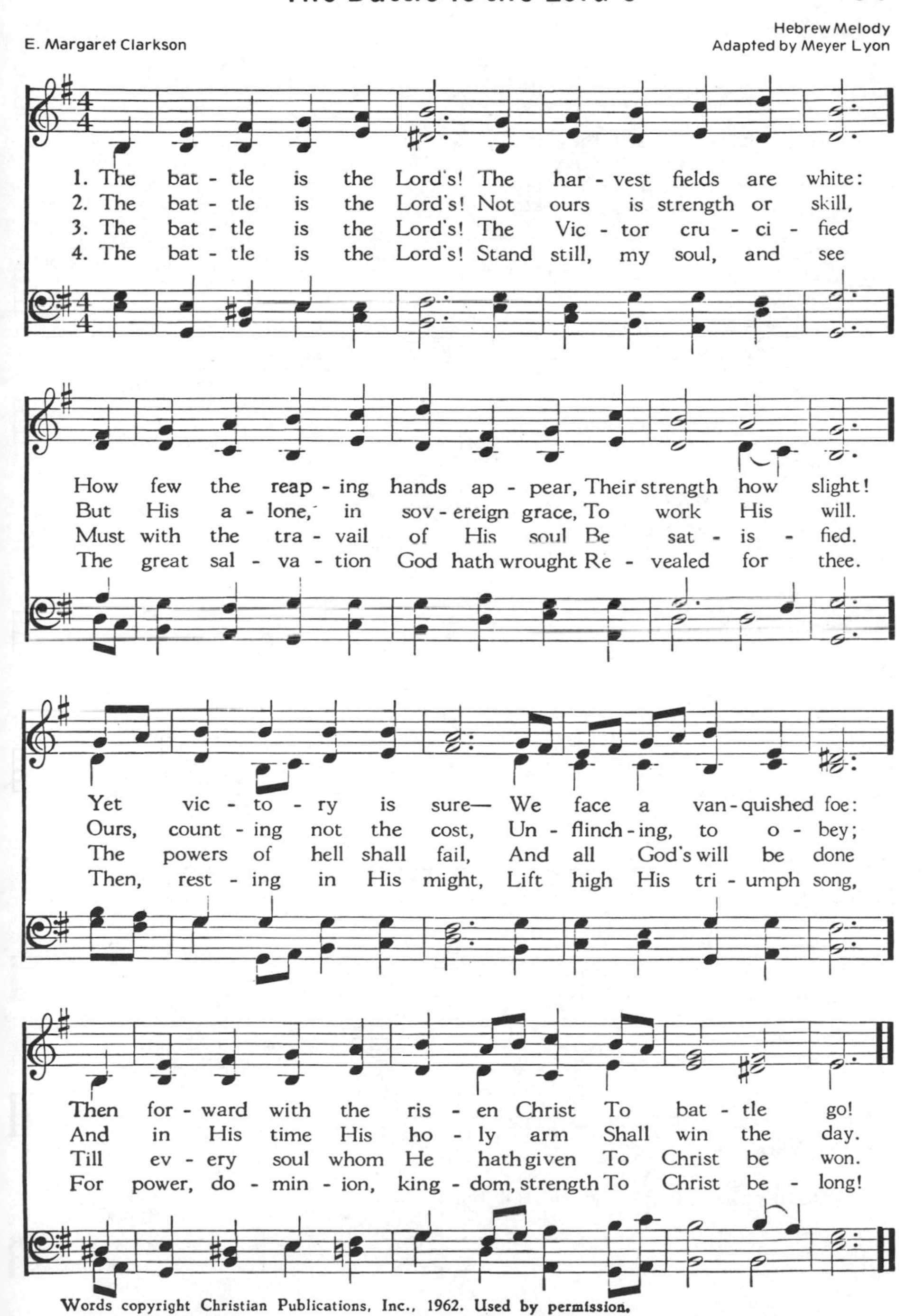
1. The bat - tle is the Lord's! The har - vest fields are white:
2. The bat - tle is the Lord's! Not ours is strength or skill,
3. The bat - tle is the Lord's! The Vic - tor cru - ci - fied
4. The bat - tle is the Lord's! Stand still, my soul, and see
How few the reap - ing hands ap - pear, Their strength how slight!
But His a - lone, in sov - ereign grace, To work His will.
Must with the tra - vail of His soul Be sat - is - fied.
The great sal - va - tion God hath wrought Re - vealed for thee.
Yet vic - to - ry is sure— We face a van - quished foe:
Ours, count - ing not the cost, Un - flinch - ing, to o - bey;
The powers of hell shall fail, And all God's will be done
Then, rest - ing in His might, Lift high His tri - umph song,
Then for - ward with the ris - en Christ To bat - tle go!
And in His time His ho - ly arm Shall win the day.
Till ev - ery soul whom He hath given To Christ be won.
For power, do - min - ion, king - dom, strength To Christ be - long!

401 I Love to Tell the Story

A. Catherine Hankey

William G. Fischer

1. I love to tell the sto - ry Of un - seen things a - bove, Of Je - sus and His glo - ry, Of Je - sus and His love. I love to tell the sto - ry, Be - cause I know 'tis true; It sat - is - fies my long-ings As noth-ing else can do.
2. I love to tell the sto - ry, More won-der - ful it seems Than all the gold - en fan - cies Of all our gold - en dreams. I love to tell the sto - ry, It did so much for me; And that is just the rea - son I tell it now to thee.
3. I love to tell the sto - ry, 'Tis pleas - ant to re - peat What seems, each time I tell it, More won - der - ful - ly sweet. I love to tell the sto - ry, For some have nev - er heard The mes - sage of sal - va - tion From God's own Ho - ly Word.
4. I love to tell the sto - ry, For those who know it best Seem hun - ger - ing and thirst - ing To hear it like the rest. And when, in scenes of glo - ry, I sing the new, new song, 'Twill be the old, old sto - ry That I have loved so long.
REFRAIN
I love to tell the sto - ry, 'Twill be my theme in glo - ry To tell the old, old sto - ry Of Je - sus and His love.

Go Ye Into All the World

James McGranahan — James McGranahan

1. Far, far a-way, in hea-then dark-ness dwell-ing, Mil-lions of souls for ev-er may be lost; Who, who will go, sal-va-tion's sto-ry tell-ing, Look-ing to Je-sus, count-ing not the cost?
2. See o'er the world wide-o-pen doors in-vit-ing; Sol-diers of Christ, a-rise and en-ter in! Chris-tians, a-wake! Your forc-es all u-nit-ing, Send forth the gos-pel, break the chains of sin.
3. "Why will ye die?" the voice of God is call-ing, "Why will ye die?" re-ech-o in His name; Je-sus hath died to save from death ap-pall-ing, Life and sal-va-tion there-fore go pro-claim.
4. God speed the day when those of ev-ery na-tion "Glo-ry to God!" tri-umphant-ly shall sing; Ran-somed, re-deemed, re-joic-ing in sal-va-tion, Shout "Hal-le-lu-jah, for the Lord is King."

REFRAIN

"All power is giv-en un-to me, All power is giv-en un-to me, Go ye in-to all the world and preach the gos-pel, And lo, I am with you al-way."

403 O Master, Let Me Walk With Thee

Washington Gladden
H. Percy Smith
1. O Mas-ter, let me walk with Thee In low-ly paths of ser-vice free;
2. Help me the slow of heart to move By some clear, win-ning word of love;
3. Teach me Thy pa-tience! still with Thee In clos-er, dear-er com-pa-ny,
4. In hope that sends a shin-ing ray Far down the fu-ture's broad'ning way,
Tell me Thy se-cret; help me bear The strain of toil, the fret of care.
Teach me the way-ward feet to stay, And guide them in the homeward way.
In work that keeps faith sweet and strong, In trust that tri-umphs o-ver wrong;
In peace that on-ly Thou canst give, With Thee, O Mas-ter, let me live. A-men.
404 Must I Go, and Empty-Handed?
Charles C. Luther
George C. Stebbins
1. Must I go, and emp-ty-hand-ed, Thus my dear Re-deem-er meet?
2. Not at death I shrink nor fal-ter, For my Sav-ior saves me now;
3. O the years in sin-ning wast-ed! Could I but re-call them now,
4. O ye saints, a-rouse, be ear-nest, Up and work while yet 'tis day;
Not one day of serv-ice give Him, Lay no tro-phy at His feet?
But to meet Him emp-ty-hand-ed, Thought of that now clouds my brow.
I would give them to my Sav-ior—To His will I'd glad-ly bow.
Ere the night of death o'er-take thee, Strive for souls while still you may.

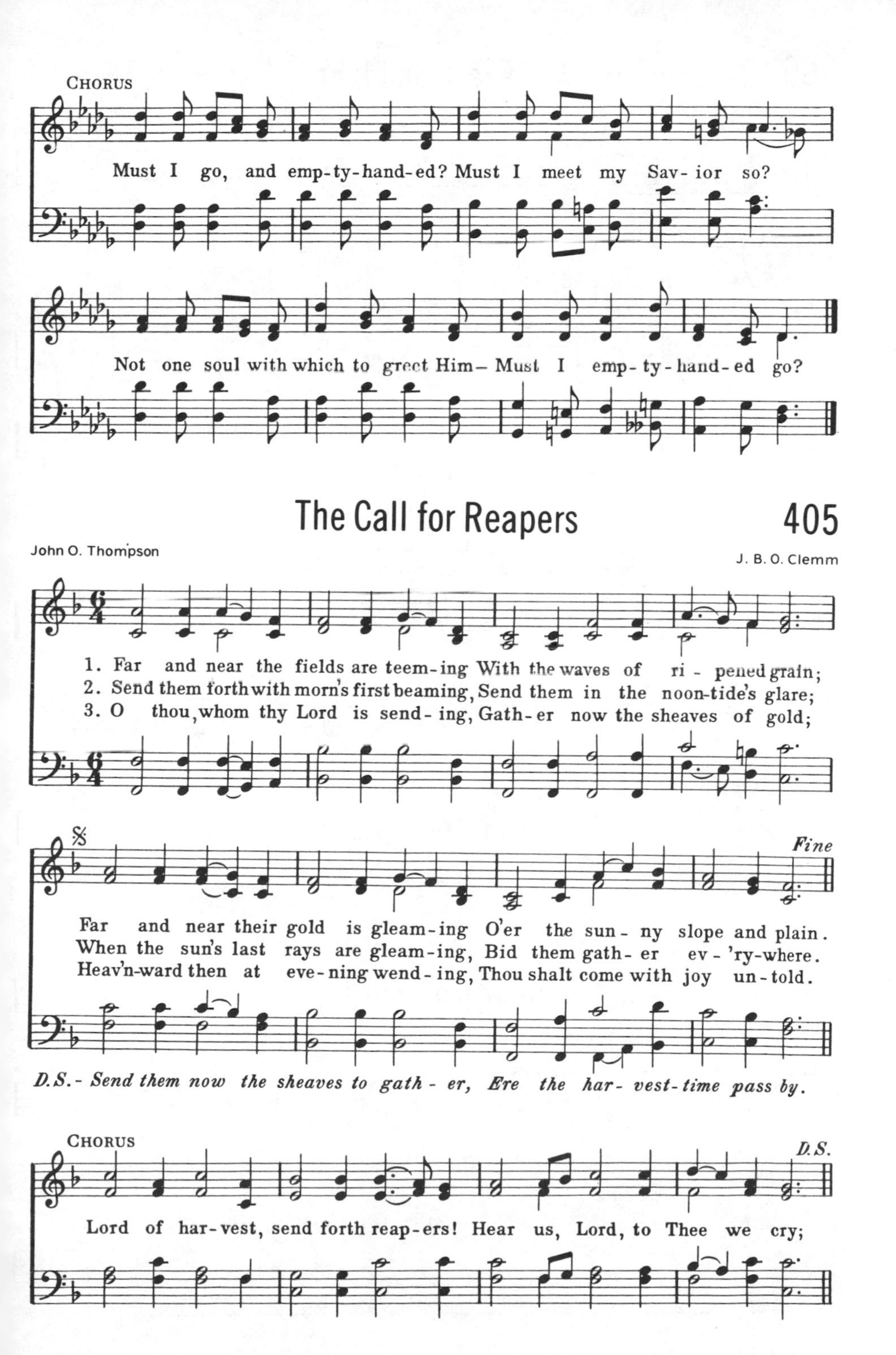

CHORUS
Must I go, and emp-ty-hand-ed? Must I meet my Sav-ior so?
Not one soul with which to greet Him– Must I emp-ty-hand-ed go?
The Call for Reapers
405
John O. Thompson
J. B. O. Clemm
1. Far and near the fields are teem-ing With the waves of ri - pened grain;
2. Send them forth with morn's first beaming, Send them in the noon-tide's glare;
3. O thou, whom thy Lord is send-ing, Gath-er now the sheaves of gold;
Fine
Far and near their gold is gleam-ing O'er the sun - ny slope and plain.
When the sun's last rays are gleam-ing, Bid them gath - er ev - 'ry-where.
Heav'n-ward then at eve-ning wend-ing, Thou shalt come with joy un-told.
D.S.- Send them now the sheaves to gath - er, Ere the har- vest-time pass by.
CHORUS
D.S.
Lord of har-vest, send forth reap-ers! Hear us, Lord, to Thee we cry;

406 Let There Be Light

John Marriott,
Edit. by A. B. S.
Alfred B. Smith
1. Thou whose al might - y word Cha - os and dark-ness heard And took their flight, Hear us, we hum-bly pray, And, where the gos-pel-day Sheds not its rad-iant, glo-rious ray, Let there be light.
2. Thou who didst come to bring On Thy re-deem-ing wing Heal - ing and sight, Health to the sick in mind, Sight to the in - ly blind, O now to all of earths' man-kind, Let there be light.
3. Spir - it of truth and love, Life - giv - er from a - bove, Speed forth Thy flight: Move on the wa-ters' face, Bear - ing the lamp of grace, And in earth's dark-est sin cursed place Let there be light.
4. Ho - ly and bless - ed Three, Glo - ri - ous Trin - i - ty, Wis - dom, Love, Might, Bound-less as o-cean tide, Roll - ing in full-est pride, Through-out the world both far and wide, Let there be light.

407 My Soul, Be on Thy Guard

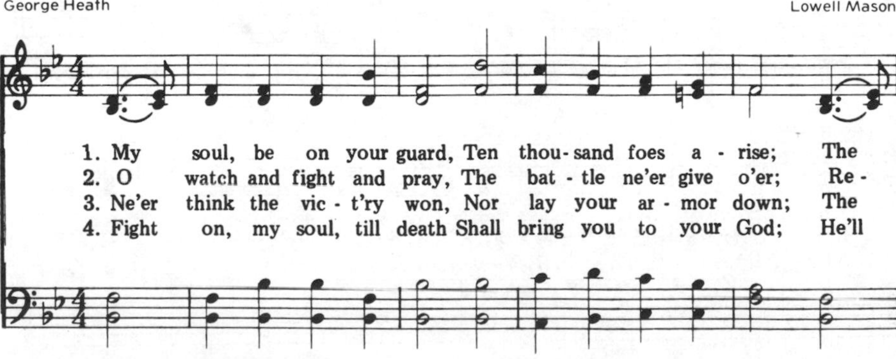
George Heath
Lowell Mason
1. My soul, be on your guard, Ten thou - sand foes a - rise; The
2. O watch and fight and pray, The bat - tle ne'er give o'er; Re -
3. Ne'er think the vic - t'ry won, Nor lay your ar - mor down; The
4. Fight on, my soul, till death Shall bring you to your God; He'll

hosts of sin are press - ing hard To draw you from the skies.
new it bold - ly ev - ery day, And help di - vine im - plore.
work of faith will not be done Till you ob - tain the crown.
take you at your part - ing breath, To His di - vine a - bode. A-men.
Lord of the Living Harvest
408
John S. B. Monsell
Alfred B. Smith
1. Lord of the liv - ing har - vest That whit-ens o'er the plain,
2. As la-borers in Thy vine - yard, Send them out, Christ, to be,
3. Be with them, God the Fa - ther; Be with them, God the Son;
Where Saints of Thine are gath - 'ring Their sheaves of gold - en grain,
Con - tent to bear the bur - den Of bus - y days for Thee,
Be with them, God the Spir - it, E - ter - nal Three in One!
Ac - cept fresh hands to la - bor, Fresh hearts to trust and love,
Con - tent to ask no wag - es When Thou shalt call them home,
Make them a roy - al priest-hood, Thee right - ly to a - dore,
And deign with them to has - ten Thy king-dom from a - bove.
But to have shared the trav - ail That makes Thy king - dom come.
And fill them with Thy full - ness Now and for ev - er - more.

409 The Fight Is on

Lelia N. Morris | Lelia N. Morris

1. The fight is on— the trum-pet sound is ring-ing out, The cry "To
2. The fight is on— a - rouse, ye sol-diers brave and true! Je - ho - vah
3. The Lord is lead - ing on to cer-tain vic - to - ry, The bow of
arms!" is heard a - far and near; The Lord of hosts is march - ing
leads, and vic - t'ry will as - sure; Go buck - le on the ar - mor
prom - ise spans the east - ern sky; His glo - rious name in ev - 'ry
on to vic - to - ry, The tri - umph of the Christ will soon ap - pear.
God has giv - en you, And in His strength un - to the end en - dure.
land shall hon-ored be, The morn will break— the dawn of peace is nigh.
CHORUS
The fight is on, O Chris-tian sol-dier, And face to face in stern ar - ray,
With ar-mor gleam-ing and col-ors streaming, The right and wrong engage to-day!

The fight is on, but be not wea-ry, Be strong and in His might hold fast;
If God be for us, His ban-ner o'er us, We'll sing the vic-tor's song at last!
for us, o'er us,
Where He Leads Me
410
E. W. Blandy
John S. Norris
1. I can hear my Sav - ior call - ing, I can hear my Sav - ior call - ing,
2. I'll go with Him thro' the gar - den, I'll go with Him thro' the gar - den,
3. I'll go with Him thro' the judg - ment, I'll go with Him thro' the judg-ment,
4. He will give me grace and glo - ry, He will give me grace and glo - ry,
Ref. – Where He leads me I will fol - low, Where He leads me I will fol - low,
D.C. Refrain
I can hear my Sav - ior call - ing, "Take thy cross and fol - low, fol - low Me."
I'll go with Him thro' the gar - den, I'll go with Him, with Him all the way.
I'll go with Him thro' the judg-ment, I'll go with Him, with Him all the way.
He will give me grace and glo - ry, And go with me, with me all the way.
Where He leads me I will fol - low, I'll go with Him, with Him all the way.

411 A Passion for Souls

Herbert G. Tovey

Foss L. Fellers

1. Give me a pas-sion for souls, dear Lord, A pas-sion to save the lost;
2. Though there are dan-gers un-told and stern Con-front-ing me in the way,
3. How shall this pas-sion for souls be mine? Lord, make Thou the an-swer clear;
O that Thy love were by all a-dored, And wel-comed at an-y cost.
Will-ing-ly still would I go, nor turn, But trust Thee for grace each day.
Help me to throw out the old life-line To those who are strug-gling near.
Refrain
Je-sus, I long, I long to be win-ning Men who are lost, and con-stant-ly sin-ning; O may this hour be one of be-gin-ning The sto-ry of par-don to tell.

Rescue the Perishing

Fanny J. Crosby

William H. Doane

1. Res-cue the per-ish-ing, care for the dy-ing, Snatch them in pit-y from
2. Though they are slight-ing Him, still He is wait-ing, Wait-ing the pen-i-tent
3. Down in the hu-man heart, crushed by the tempt-er, Feel-ings lie bur-ied that
4. Res-cue the per-ish-ing, du-ty de-mands it; Strength for thy la-bor the

sin and the grave; Weep o'er the err-ing one, lift up the fall-en,
child to re-ceive; Plead with them ear-nest-ly, plead with them gen-tly,
grace can re-store; Touched by a lov-ing heart, wak-ened by kind-ness,
Lord will pro-vide; Back to the nar-row way pa-tient-ly win them;

Refrain

Tell them of Je-sus the might-y to save.
He will for-give if they on-ly be-lieve.
Cords that are bro-ken will vi-brate once more.
Tell the poor wan-d'rer a Sav-ior has died.

Res-cue the per-ish-ing,

care for the dy-ing; Je-sus is mer-ci-ful, Je-sus will save.

Ring the Bells of Heaven

William O. Cushing | George F. Root

1. Ring the bells of heav - en! There is joy to - day For a soul re -
2. Ring the bells of heav - en! There is joy to - day For the wan-derer
3. Ring the bells of heav - en! Spread the feast to - day! An - gels, swell the

turn-ing from the wild! See, the Fa - ther meets him out up - on the way,
now is rec - on - ciled: Yes, a soul is res - cued from his sin - ful way
glad, tri-umph-ant strain! Tell the joy - ful ti - dings, bear it far a - way,

Wel - com-ing His wea - ry, wan-dering child.
And is born a - new a ran-somed child.
For a pre-cious soul is born a - gain.

REFRAIN

Glo - ry! Glo - ry! How the an - gels sing; Glo - ry! Glo - ry! How the loud harps ring! 'Tis the ran-somed ar - my, like a might - y sea, Peal - ing forth the an - them of the free.

Look and Live

William A. Ogden

William A. Ogden

1. I've a mes-sage from the Lord, Hal-le - lu - jah! The mes-sage un - to you I'll
2. I've a mes-sage full of love, Hal-le - lu - jah! A mes-sage, O my friend, for
3. Life is of-fered un - to you, Hal-le - lu - jah! E - ter - nal life your soul shall
give; 'Tis re - cord - ed in His word, Hal - le - lu - jah! It is
you; 'Tis a mes - sage from a - bove, Hal - le - lu - jah! Je - sus
have, If you'll on - ly look to Him, Hal - le - lu - jah! Look to
Refrain
on - ly that you "look and live."
said it and I know 'tis true. Look and live, O sin - ner,
Je - sus, who a - lone can save. Look and live, O sin - ner,
live, Look to Je - sus now and live; 'Tis re-
live, Look and live,
cord - ed in His word, Hal-le - lu - jah! It is on - ly that you look and live.

415 The Light of the World Is Jesus

Philip P. Bliss
Philip P. Bliss
1. The whole world was lost in the dark-ness of sin; The Light of the world is Je - sus; Like sun-shine at noon-day His glo - ry shone in,
2. No dark-ness have we who in Je - sus a - bide, The Light of the world is Je - sus; We walk in the Light when we fol - low our Guide,
3. Ye dwell - ers in dark-ness with sin-blind - ed eyes, The Light of the world is Je - sus; Go, wash at His bid - ding, and light will a - rise,
4. No need of the sun - light in heav - en, we're told, The Light of the world is Je - sus; The Lamb is the Light in the Cit - y of Gold,
The Light of the world is Je - sus.
Refrain
Come to the Light, 'tis shin - ing for thee; Sweet - ly the Light has dawned up - on me;
Once I was blind, but now I can see; The Light of the world is Je - sus.

Ye Must Be Born Again

William T. Sleeper.

George C. Stebbins

1. A ruler once came to Jesus by night To ask Him the way of salvation and light; The Master made answer in words true and plain, "Ye must be born again."
2. Ye children of men, attend to the word So solemnly uttered by Jesus, the Lord; And let not this message to you be in vain, "Ye must be born again."
3. Oh, ye who would enter that glorious rest And sing with the ransomed the song of the blest, The life everlasting if ye would obtain, "Ye must be born again."
4. A dear one in heaven thy heart yearns to see At the beautiful gate may be watching for thee; Then list to the note of this solemn refrain, "Ye must be born again."

REFRAIN

"Ye must be born again, Ye must be born again, I verily, verily say unto you, Ye must be born again."

417 Choose Now

Harriet Fithian
Alfred B. Smith
1. "Some day," you say, "I will seek the Lord; Some day I will make my choice; Some-day, some-day, I will heed His Word, And an-swer the Spir - it's voice."
2. God's time is now, for the days fly fast, And swift - ly the sea - sons roll; To - day is yours, it may be your last; Choose life for your price - less soul!
3. Choose now, just now! for your soul's at stake! O what will your an - swer be? 'Tis life or death; and the choice you make Is made for e - ter - ni - ty.
Refrain
Choose now, just now, for the Lord is here, And an-gels your an-swer wait;
Choose now, just now, while the call is clear: To-mor-row may be too late!

Turn Your Eyes Upon Jesus

Helen H. Lemmel   Helen H. Lemmel

1. O soul, are you wea-ry and troub-led? No light in the dark-ness you see? There's light for a look at the Sav-ior, And life more a-bun-dant and free!

2. Through death in-to life ev-er-last-ing He passed, and we fol-low Him there; O-ver us sin no more hath do-min-ion— For more than con-qu'rors we are!

3. His word shall not fail you—He prom-ised; Be-lieve Him and all will be well: Then go to a world that is dy-ing, His per-fect sal-va-tion to tell!

Refrain:
Turn your eyes up-on Je-sus, Look full in His won-der-ful face; And the things of earth will grow strange-ly dim In the light of His glo-ry and grace.

419 Calling Today

Fanny J. Crosby

George C. Stebbins

1. Je - sus is ten - der - ly call - ing you home, Call - ing to - day,
2. Je - sus is call - ing the wea - ry to rest, Call - ing to - day,
3. Je - sus is wait - ing, O come to Him now, Wait - ing to - day,
4. Je - sus is plead - ing, O list to His voice: Hear Him to - day,
call - ing to - day, Why from the sun - shine of love will you roam
call - ing to - day, Bring Him your bur - den and you shall be blest;
wait - ing to - day, Come with your sins, at His feet low - ly bow;
hear Him to - day, They who be - lieve on His name shall re - joice;
Far - ther and far - ther a - way?
He will not turn you a - way.
Come, and no long - er de - lay.
Quick - ly a - rise and a - way.
Refrain
Call - ing to - day,
Call - ing, call - ing to - day, to - day,
Call - ing to - day,
Call - ing, call - ing to - day, to - day,
Je - sus is
Je - sus is ten - der - ly
call - ing, Is ten - der - ly call - ing to - day.
call - ing to - day,

Softly and Tenderly 420

Will L. Thompson
Will L. Thompson
1. Soft-ly and ten-der-ly Je-sus is call-ing, Call-ing for you and for me; See, on the por-tals He's wait-ing and watch-ing, Watch-ing for you and for me.
2. Why should we tar-ry when Je-sus is plead-ing, Plead-ing for you and for me? Why should we lin-ger and heed not His mer-cies, Mer-cies for you and for me?
3. Time is now fleet-ing, the mo-ments are pass-ing, Pass-ing from you and from me; Shad-ows are gath-er-ing, death-beds are com-ing, Com-ing for you and for me.
4. O for the won-der-ful love He has prom-ised, Prom-ised for you and for me; Tho we have sinned He has mer-cy and par-don, Par-don for you and for me.
CHORUS
Come home, come home, Come home, come home,
Ye who are wea-ry, come home; Ear-nest-ly, ten-der-ly, Je-sus is call-ing– Call-ing, "O sin-ner, come home!"

421 I Gave My Life for Thee

Frances R. Havergal

Philip P. Bliss

1. I gave My life for thee, My pre - cious blood I shed,
2. My Fa - ther's house of light, My glo - ry - cir - cled throne
3. I suf - fered much for thee, More than thy tongue can tell,
4. And I have brought to thee, Down from My home a - bove,
That thou might'st ran-somed be, And quick - ened from the dead;
I left for earth - ly night, For wan - derings sad and lone;
Of bit - terest ag - o - ny, To res - cue thee from hell;
Sal - va - tion full and free, My par - don and My love;
I gave, I gave My life for thee, What hast thou giv'n for Me?
I left, I left it all for thee, Hast thou left aught for Me?
I've borne, I've borne it all for thee, What hast thou borne for Me?
I bring, I bring rich gifts to thee, What hast thou brought to Me?

422 Just as I Am

Charlotte Elliott

William B. Bradbury

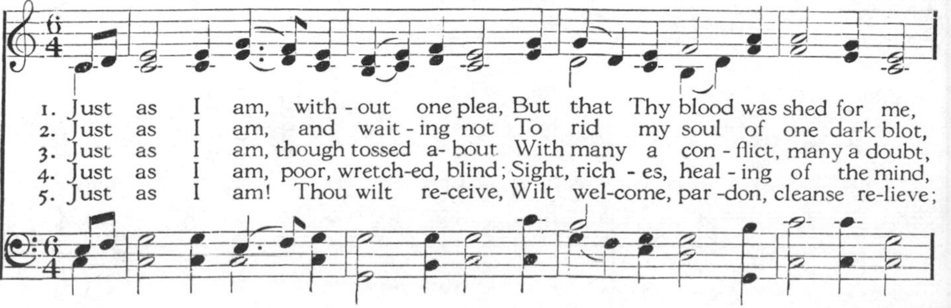
1. Just as I am, with - out one plea, But that Thy blood was shed for me,
2. Just as I am, and wait - ing not To rid my soul of one dark blot,
3. Just as I am, though tossed a - bout With many a con - flict, many a doubt,
4. Just as I am, poor, wretch-ed, blind; Sight, rich - es, heal - ing of the mind,
5. Just as I am! Thou wilt re-ceive, Wilt wel-come, par -don, cleanse re-lieve;

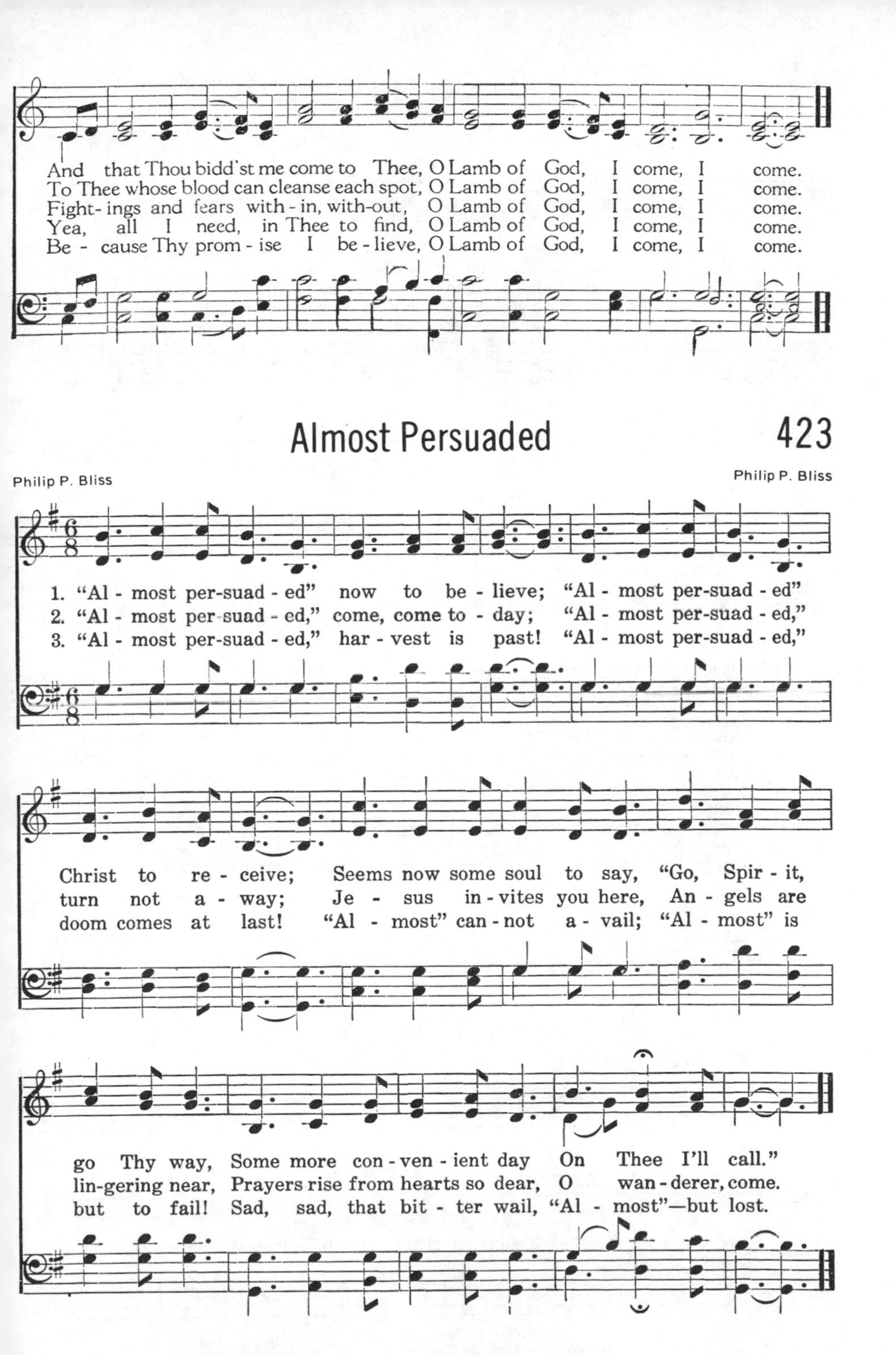
And that Thou bidd'st me come to Thee, O Lamb of God, I come, I come.
To Thee whose blood can cleanse each spot, O Lamb of God, I come, I come.
Fight- ings and fears with - in, with-out, O Lamb of God, I come, I come.
Yea, all I need, in Thee to find, O Lamb of God, I come, I come.
Be - cause Thy prom - ise I be - lieve, O Lamb of God, I come, I come.
Almost Persuaded
423
Philip P. Bliss
Philip P. Bliss
1. "Al - most per-suad - ed" now to be - lieve; "Al - most per-suad - ed"
2. "Al - most per-suad - ed," come, come to - day; "Al - most per-suad - ed,"
3. "Al - most per-suad - ed," har - vest is past! "Al - most per-suad - ed,"
Christ to re - ceive; Seems now some soul to say, "Go, Spir - it,
turn not a - way; Je - sus in - vites you here, An - gels are
doom comes at last! "Al - most" can - not a - vail; "Al - most" is
go Thy way, Some more con - ven - ient day On Thee I'll call."
lin-gering near, Prayers rise from hearts so dear, O wan - derer, come.
but to fail! Sad, sad, that bit - ter wail, "Al - most"—but lost.

424 Oh, Believe It

John Ferguson
James R. Murray
Revised by Alfred B. Smith
1. There's a sto-ry ev-er new, It is won-der-ful and true, And the best thing you can do, Is be lieve it: It will calm your trou-bled breast, And will give you peace and rest, It's of all the news the best, Oh, be-lieve it!
2. I was serv-ing Sa-tan well, And in sin did far ex-cel, And would soon have been in hell; I be lieve it: But the Sav-iour, He drew near, And He stopped my mad ca-reer, And He told me nev-er fear, Just be-lieve it!
3. Then I lis-tened and He said, It was just for you I bled, And with me He sweet-ly pled, To be lieve it: This is now sal-va-tion's day, Sin has all been put a-way, This is what I heard Him say, Oh, be-lieve it!
4. I could then with-stand no more, For I saw my sins, He bore, So I en-tered by the door, And be lieved it: Now I'm hap-py all the day, I can sing as well as pray, For my sins are washed a-way, I be-lieve it!
Refrain
Oh, be-lieve it! Oh, be-lieve it! Christ has died up-on the tree, That from sin you might be free; Oh, be-lieve it!

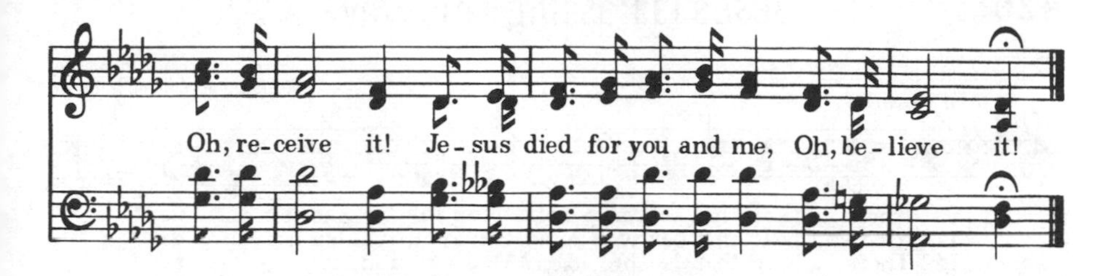

Oh, re-ceive it! Je-sus died for you and me, Oh, be-lieve it!

Whosoever Will Believe 425

Arther T. Pierson

James McGranahan
Arr. by A. B. S.

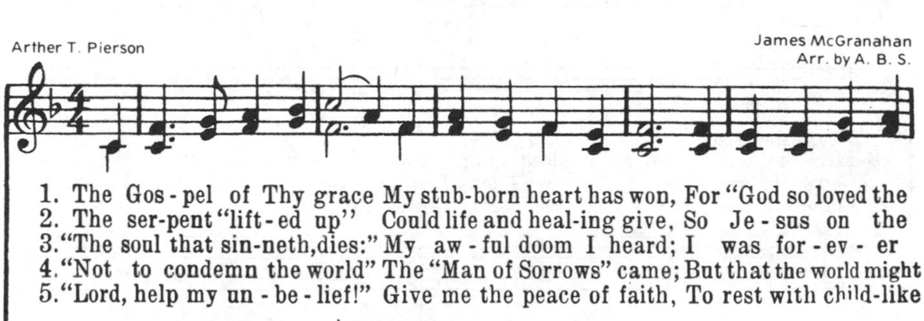

1. The Gos-pel of Thy grace My stub-born heart has won, For "God so loved the
2. The ser-pent "lift-ed up" Could life and heal-ing give, So Je-sus on the
3. "The soul that sin-neth, dies:" My aw-ful doom I heard; I was for-ev-er
4. "Not to condemn the world" The "Man of Sorrows" came; But that the world might
5. "Lord, help my un-be-lief!" Give me the peace of faith, To rest with child-like

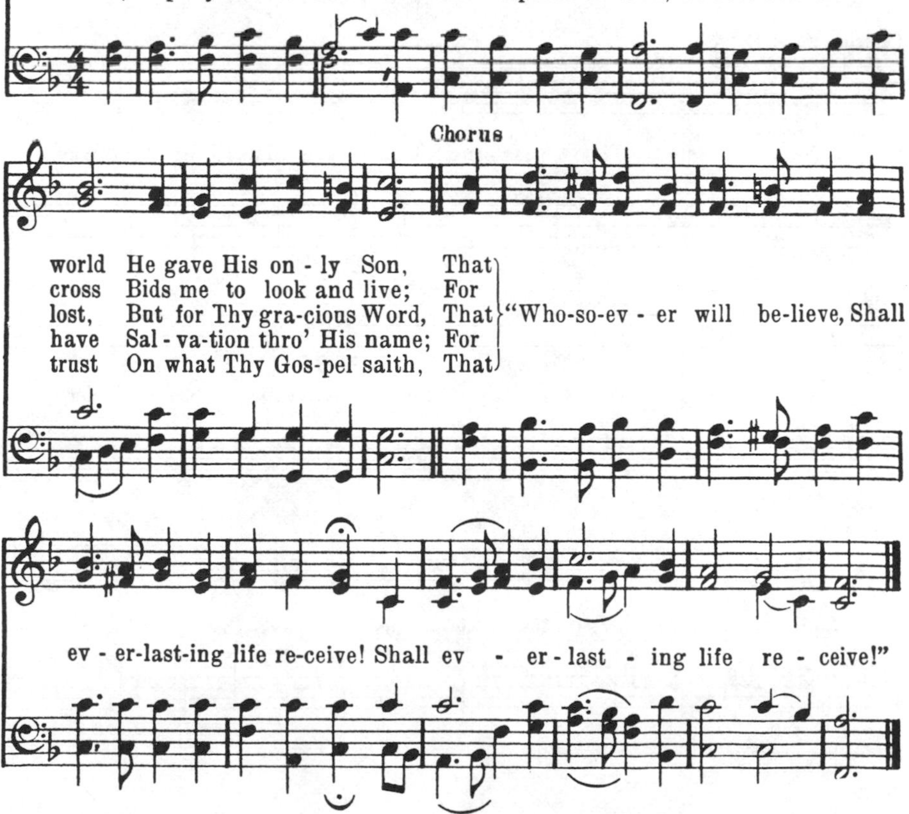

Chorus
world He gave His on-ly Son, That
cross Bids me to look and live; For
lost, But for Thy gra-cious Word, That
have Sal-va-tion thro' His name; For
trust On what Thy Gos-pel saith, That
"Who-so-ev-er will be-lieve, Shall
ev-er-last-ing life re-ceive! Shall ev-er-last-ing life re-ceive!"

426 Jesus Is Passing This Way

Fanny J. Crosby
Alt. by A. B. S.

Wm. H. Doane
Rewritten by Alfred B. Smith

Not rushed
1. Is there a heart that is wait - ing, Long-ing for par-don to - day?
2. Is there a heart that has wan-dered? Come with your bur-den to - day;
3. Is there a heart that is bro - ken? Wea - ry and sigh-ing for rest?
4. Come to this bless-ed Re-deem - er, Come to His in-fi-nite love;
Hear the glad mes-sage pro-claim - ing, Je - sus is pass-ing this way.
Mer - cy is ten-der - ly plead - ing, Je - sus is pass-ing this way.
Come to the arms of the Sav - iour, Lean wear-y one on His breast.
Come to the gate that is lead - ing Home-ward to man-sions a - bove.
Chorus- A. B. S.
Je - sus is pass - ing this way. Pass - ing this way,
pass - ing this way. Come with your bur - dens,
Come with your cares For Je - sus is pass - ing this way.

Jesus I Come

William T. Sleeper

George C. Stebbins

1. Out of my bond-age, sor - row and night, Je - sus, I come, Je - sus, I come;
2. Out of my shame-ful fail - ure and loss, Je - sus, I come, Je - sus, I come;
3. Out of un - rest and ar - ro-gant pride, Je - sus, I come, Je - sus, I come;
4. Out of the fear and dread of the tomb, Je - sus, I come, Je - sus, I come;
In - to Thy free - dom, glad-ness and light, Je - sus, I come to Thee.
In - to the glo - rious gain of Thy cross, Je - sus, I come to Thee.
In - to Thy bless - ed will to a - bide, Je - sus, I come to Thee.
In - to the joy and light of Thy home, Je - sus, I come to Thee.
Out of my sick-ness in - to Thy health, Out of my want and in - to Thy wealth,
Out of earth's sor-rows in - to Thy balm, Out of life's storms and in - to Thy calm,
Out of my-self to dwell in Thy love, Out of de-spair in-to rap-tures a - bove,
Out of the depths of ru - in un-told, In - to the peace of Thy shel-ter-ing fold,
Out of my sin and in - to Thy-self, Je - sus, I come to Thee.
Out of dis-tress to ju - bi - lant psalm, Je - sus, I come to Thee.
Up - ward for aye on wings like a dove, Je - sus, I come to Thee.
Ev - er Thy glo - rious face to be - hold, Je - sus, I come to Thee.

428 Lord, I'm Coming Home

William J. Kirkpatrick — William J. Kirkpatrick

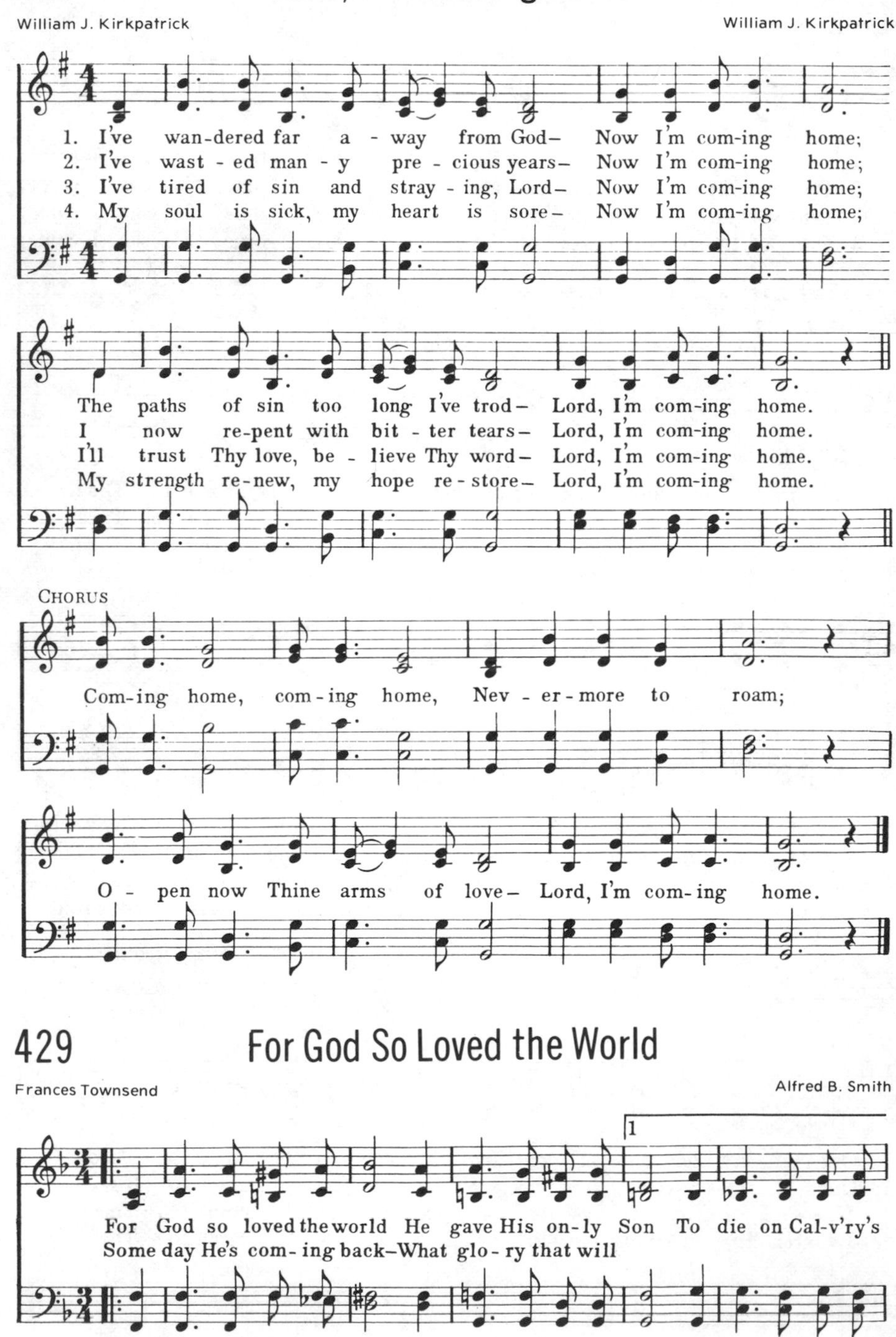
1. I've wan-dered far a - way from God— Now I'm com-ing home;
2. I've wast - ed man - y pre - cious years— Now I'm com-ing home;
3. I've tired of sin and stray - ing, Lord— Now I'm com-ing home;
4. My soul is sick, my heart is sore— Now I'm com-ing home;
The paths of sin too long I've trod— Lord, I'm com-ing home.
I now re-pent with bit - ter tears— Lord, I'm com-ing home.
I'll trust Thy love, be - lieve Thy word— Lord, I'm com-ing home.
My strength re-new, my hope re - store— Lord, I'm com-ing home.
CHORUS
Com-ing home, com - ing home, Nev - er - more to roam;
O - pen now Thine arms of love— Lord, I'm com - ing home.
429 For God So Loved the World
Frances Townsend
Alfred B. Smith
1
For God so loved the world He gave His on - ly Son To die on Cal-v'ry's
Some day He's com - ing back—What glo - ry that will

2
tree, From sin to set me free; be! Won-der-ful His love to me.
© Copyright 1938. Renewal 1966 by Alfred B. Smith. Assigned to Singspiration, Inc.
Arr. © 1968 by Singspiration, Inc. All rights reserved. Used by permission.
Look to the Lamb of God
430
H. G. Jackson
James M. Black
1. If you from sin are long-ing to be free, Look to the Lamb of God;
2. When Sa-tan tempts, and doubts and fears as-sail, Look to the Lamb of God;
3. Are you a-wea-ry, does the way seem long? Look to the Lamb of God;
4. Fear not when shad-ows on your path-way fall, Look to the Lamb of God;
He, to re-deem you, died on Cal-va-ry, Look to the Lamb of God.
You in His strength shall o-ver all pre-vail, Look to the Lamb of God.
His love will cheer and fill your heart with song, Look to the Lamb of God.
In joy or sor-row Christ is all in all, Look to the Lamb of God.
CHORUS
Look to the Lamb of God, Look to the Lamb of God,
the Lamb of God, the Lamb of God,
For He a-lone is a-ble to save you— Look to the Lamb of God.

431 Pass Me Not

Fanny J. Crosby

William H. Doane

1. Pass me not, O gen-tle Sav-ior- Hear my hum-ble cry!
2. Let me at a throne of mer-cy Find a sweet re-lief;
3. Trust-ing on-ly in Thy mer-it, Would I seek Thy face;
4. Thou the spring of all my com-fort, More than life to me!
While on oth-ers Thou art call-ing, Do not pass me by.
Kneel-ing there in deep con-tri-tion, Help my un-be-lief.
Heal my wound-ed, bro-ken spir-it, Save me by Thy grace.
Whom have I on earth be-side Thee? Whom in heav'n but Thee?
D.S.-While on oth-ers Thou art call-ing, Do not pass me by.

CHORUS
D.S.
Sav-ior, Sav-ior, Hear my hum-ble cry!

432 Here Am I

Alfred B. Smith

Alfred B. Smith

1. Here am I, send me. Here am I, send me. There is
2. Here am I, use me. Here am I, use me. There is

8va
work that must be done,There are vic-t'ries to be won;Here am I, bles-sed Lord,send me.
work that must be done,There are vic-t'ries to be won;Here am I, bles-sed Lord,use me.
Why Not Now?
433
Daniel W. Whittle
Charles C. Case
1. While we pray and while we plead, While you see your soul's deep need,
2. You have wan-dered far a - way– Do not risk an - oth - er day;
3. In the world you've failed to find Aught of peace for trou-bled mind;
4. Come to Christ, con-fes-sion make– Come to Christ and par-don take;
While your Fa-ther calls you home, Will you not, my broth-er, come?
Do not turn from God your face, But to-day ac-cept His grace.
Come to Christ, on Him be-lieve– Peace and joy you shall re-ceive.
Trust in Him from day to day– He will keep you all the way.
CHORUS
1
2
Why not now? why not now? Why not come to Je-sus now? Je-sus now?
Why not now? why not now?

434 Have You Any Room for Jesus?

Adapted by Daniel W. Whittle

C. C. Williams

1. Have you an - y room for Je - sus, He who bore your load of sin?
As He knocks and asks ad - mis - sion, Sin - ner, will you let Him in?

2. Room for pleas - ure, room for busi - ness, But for Christ the Cru - ci - fied,
Not a place that He can en - ter, In the heart for which He died?

3. Have you an - y room for Je - sus, As in grace He calls a - gain?
O, to - day is time ac - cept - ed, You will nev - er call in vain.

4. Room and time now give to Je - sus, Soon will pass God's day of grace;
Soon your heart left cold and si - lent, And the Sav - ior's plead - ing cease.

Refrain

Room for Je - sus, King of glo - ry! Has - ten now, His word o - bey;
Swing the heart's door wide - ly o - pen, Bid Him en - ter while you may.

What Will You Do With Jesus?

Albert B. Simpson

Mary L. Stocks

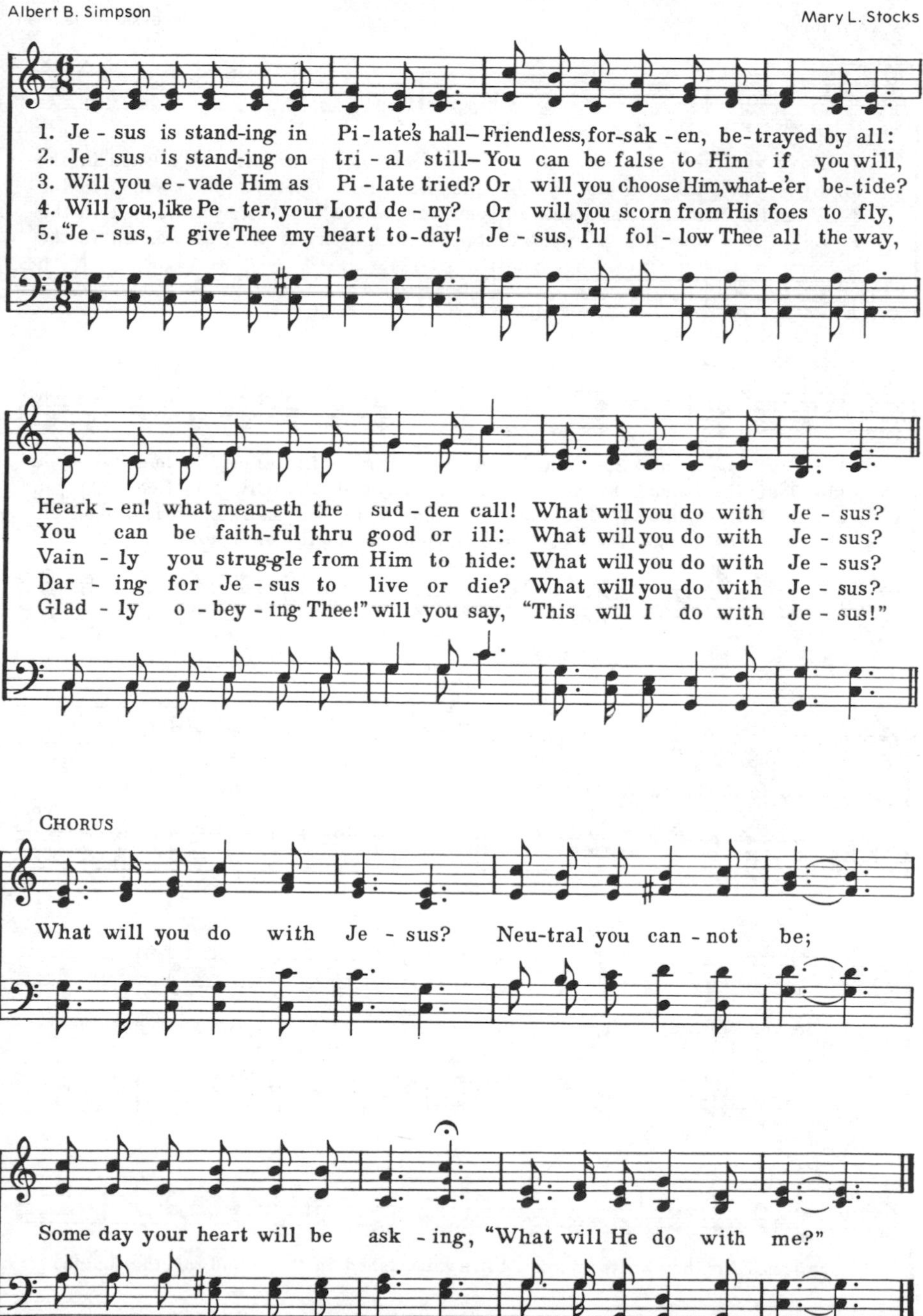
1. Je - sus is stand-ing in Pi - late's hall— Friendless, for-sak - en, be-trayed by all:
2. Je - sus is stand-ing on tri - al still— You can be false to Him if you will,
3. Will you e - vade Him as Pi - late tried? Or will you choose Him, what-e'er be-tide?
4. Will you, like Pe - ter, your Lord de - ny? Or will you scorn from His foes to fly,
5. "Je - sus, I give Thee my heart to-day! Je - sus, I'll fol - low Thee all the way,
Heark - en! what mean-eth the sud - den call! What will you do with Je - sus?
You can be faith-ful thru good or ill: What will you do with Je - sus?
Vain - ly you strug-gle from Him to hide: What will you do with Je - sus?
Dar - ing for Je - sus to live or die? What will you do with Je - sus?
Glad - ly o - bey - ing Thee!" will you say, "This will I do with Je - sus!"
CHORUS
What will you do with Je - sus? Neu-tral you can - not be;
Some day your heart will be ask - ing, "What will He do with me?"

436 Are You Washed in the Blood?

Elisha A. Hoffman | Elisha A. Hoffman

1. Have you been to Je-sus for the cleans-ing pow'r? Are you washed in the blood of the Lamb? Are you ful-ly trust-ing in His grace this hour? Are you washed in the blood of the Lamb?
2. Are you walk-ing dai-ly by the Sav-ior's side? Are you washed in the blood of the Lamb? Do you rest each mo-ment in the Cru-ci-fied? Are you washed in the blood of the Lamb?
3. When the Bride-groom com-eth will your robes be white? Are you washed in the blood of the Lamb? Will your soul be read-y for the man-sions bright And be washed in the blood of the Lamb?
4. Lay a-side the gar-ments that are stained with sin And be washed in the blood of the Lamb; There's a foun-tain flow-ing for the soul un-clean, O be washed in the blood of the Lamb?

CHORUS

Are you washed (Are you washed) in the blood, (in the blood,)
In the soul-cleans-ing blood of the Lamb? (of the Lamb?)
Are your gar-ments spot-less? Are they white as snow?
Are you washed in the blood of the Lamb?

Christ Receiveth Sinful Men

Erdmann Neumeister
Trans. by Emma F. Bevan

James McGranahan

1. Sin-ners Je-sus will re-ceive! Sound this word of grace to all
2. Come, and He will give you rest, Trust Him, for His word is plain;
3. Now my heart con-demns me not, Pure be-fore the law I stand;
4. Christ re-ceiv-eth sin-ful men, E-ven me with all my sin;
Who the heav'n-ly path-way leave, All who lin-ger, all who fall.
He will take the sin-ful-est, Christ re-ceiv-eth sin-ful men.
He who cleansed me from all spot Sat-is-fied its last de-mand.
Purged from ev-'ry spot and stain, Heav'n with Him I en-ter in.
CHORUS
Sing it o'er and o'er a-gain: Christ re-
Sing it o'er a-gain, Sing it o'er a-gain: Christ re-
ceiv-eth sin-ful men; Make the mes-
ceiv-eth sin-ful men, Christ re-ceiv-eth sin-ful men; Make the mes-sage
-sage clear and plain: Christ re-ceiv-eth sin-ful men.
plain, Make the mes-sage plain:

438 Let Jesus Come into Your Heart

Mrs. C. H. Morris | Mrs. C. H. Morris

1. If you are tired of the load of your sin, Let Je - sus come
2. If 'tis for pu - ri - ty now that you sigh, Let Je - sus come
3. If there's a tem - pest your voice can - not still, Let Je - sus come
4. If you would join the glad songs of the blest, Let Je - sus come
in - to your heart; If you de - sire a new life to be - gin,
in - to your heart; Foun-tains for cleans-ing are flow - ing near by,
in - to your heart; If there's a void this world nev - er can fill,
in - to your heart; If you would en - ter the man-sions of rest,
Let Je - sus come in - to your heart.
CHORUS
Just now, your doubt-ings give o'er; Just now, re - ject Him no more; Just now, throw o - pen the door; Let Je - sus come in - to your heart.

Only Trust Him

John H. Stockton | John H. Stockton

1. Come, ev - ery soul by sin op-pressed, There's mer - cy with the Lord,
2. For Je - sus shed His pre - cious blood, Rich bless - ings to be - stow;
3. Yes, Je - sus is the truth, the way That leads you in - to rest;
4. Come, then, and join this ho - ly band And on to glo - ry go,
And He will sure - ly give you rest By trust - ing in His word.
Plunge now in - to the crim - son flood That wash - es white as snow.
Be - lieve in Him with - out de - lay And you are ful - ly blest.
To dwell in that ce - les - tial land Where joys im - mor - tal flow.
Refrain
On - ly trust Him, on - ly trust Him, On - ly trust Him now;
He will save you, He will save you, He will save you now.

440 Safe in the Arms of Jesus

Fanny J. Crosby | William H. Doane

1. Safe in the arms of Je - sus, Safe on His gen-tle breast, There, by His
2. Safe in the arms of Je - sus, Safe from cor-rod-ing care, Safe from the
3. Je - sus, my heart's dear ref - uge, Je - sus has died for me; Firm on the
love o'er - shad - ed, Sweet-ly my soul shall rest. Hark! 'Tis the voice of
world's temp-ta - tions—Sin can-not harm me there. Free from the blight of
Rock of A - ges Ev - er my trust shall be. Here let me wait with
an - gels Borne in a song to me O - ver the fields of glo - ry,
sor - row, Free from my doubts and fears; On - ly a few more tri - als,
pa - tience, Wait till the night is o'er, Wait till I see the morn - ing
O - ver the jas - per sea.
On - ly a few more tears!
Break on the gold - en shore.
REFRAIN
Safe in the arms of Je - sus, Safe on His
gen - tle breast, There, by His love o'er - shad - ed, Sweet-ly my soul shall rest. A-MEN.

Oh, That Will Be Glory

Charles H. Gabriel — Charles H. Gabriel

1. When all my la - bors and tri - als are o'er And I am safe on that
2. When, by the gift of His in - fi - nite grace, I am ac - cord-ed in
3. Friends will be there I have loved long a - go; Joy like a riv - er a -
beau - ti - ful shore, Just to be near the dear Lord I a - dore
heav - en a place, Just to be there and to look on His face
round me will flow; Yet, just a smile from my Sav - iour, I know,
Will through the a - ges be glo - ry for me.
REFRAIN
Oh, that will be
Oh, that will
glo - ry for me, Glo-ry for me, glo-ry for me, When by His grace
be glo-ry for me, Glo-ry for me, glo-ry for me,
I shall look on His face, That will be glo - ry, be glo - ry for me.

442 Heaven at Last

Rev. M. B. Wharton
Rev. by A. B. S.

Alfred B. Smith

1. Heav'n at last– I've reached the har - bor, For whose calm I long have prayed. Filled with awe– I gaze in won - der– At the Things my Lord has made.
2. Heav'n at last– the Sav - iour liv - eth, See Him on His migh - ty throne. Crowns of life to each He giv - eth, Crowns, by faith, that we have won.
3. Heav'n at last, Our Loved ones gath - er, Tell - ing of the Joys on high, Tell - ing how our bless - ed Fa - ther, Wipes the tears from sor- rows eye.
4. Heav'n at last– Praise God– Like Je - sus, Ev - 'ry rap - tured saint I see, There we see Him as He sees us, Ev - er - more with Him to be!

Chorus

Hark! I hear the an - gels sing - ing morn - ing breaks, the night is past. And the heav'n - ly bells are ring - ing, Wel - come pil - grim– Home at last!

When We All Get to Heaven

443

Eliza E. Hewitt

Emily D. Wilson

1. Sing the won - drous love of Je - sus, Sing His mer - cy
2. While we walk the pil - grim path - way Clouds will o - ver -
3. Let us then be true and faith - ful, Trust - ing, serv - ing
4. On - ward to the prize be - fore us! Soon His beau - ty
and His grace; In the man - sions bright and bless - ed He'll pre -
spread the sky; But when trav - 'ling days are o - ver, Not a
ev - ery day; Just one glimpse of Him in glo - ry Will the
we'll be - hold; Soon the pearl - y gates will o - pen, We shall
Refrain
pare for us a place.
sha - dow, not a sigh. When we all get to heav - en,
toils of life re - pay. When we all
tread the streets of gold.
What a day of re - joic - ing that will be! When we
What a day of re - joic - ing that will be!
all see Je - sus, We'll sing and shout the vic - to - ry.
When we all and shout the vic - to - ry.

444 When the Roll Is Called Up Yonder

James M. Black James M. Black

1. When the trum-pet of the Lord shall sound, and time shall be no more, And the morn-ing breaks, e - ter - nal, bright and fair; When the saved of earth shall gath-er o - ver on the oth - er shore, And the roll is called up yon-der, I'll be there.
2. On that bright and cloud-less morn-ing when the dead in Christ shall rise, And the glo - ry of His res - ur - rec - tion share; When His cho - sen ones shall gath-er to their home be-yond the skies, And the roll is called up yon-der, I'll be there.
3. Let us la - bor for the Mas - ter from the dawn till set - ting sun, Let us talk of all His won-drous love and care; Then when all of life is o - ver, and our work on earth is done, And the roll is called up yon-der, I'll be there.
CHORUS
When the roll . . . . is called up yon - - - der, When the roll . . . . is called up yon - - der, When the roll . . . . . . is called up
When the roll is called up yon - der, I'll be there,
When the roll is called up yon-der, I'll be there,
When the roll is called up

yon - der, When the roll is called up yon - der, I'll be there.

He the Pearly Gates Will Open

445

Fred Blom
Trans. by N. Carlson

Elsie Ahlwen

1. Love di-vine, so great and won-drous, Deep and might-y, pure, sub-lime;
2. Like a dove when hunt-ed, fright-ened, As a wound-ed fawn was I;
3. Love di-vine, so great and won-drous– All my sins He then for-gave.
4. In life's e-ven-tide, at twi-light, At His door I'll knock and wait;
Com-ing from the heart of Je-sus– Just the same through tests of time.
Bro-ken-heart-ed, yet He healed me– He will heed the sin-ner's cry.
I will sing His praise for-ev-er For His blood, His power to save.
By the pre-cious love of Je-sus, I shall en-ter heav-en's gate.
Refrain
He the pear-ly gates will o-pen So that I may en-ter in;
For He pur-chased my re-demp-tion And for-gave me all my sin.

446 My Saviour First of All

Fanny J. Crosby John R. Sweney

1. When my life-work is end-ed and I cross the swell-ing tide,
2. O the soul-thrill-ing rap-ture when I view His bless-ed face
3. O the dear ones in glo-ry, how they beck-on me to come,
4. Thru the gates to the cit-y, in a robe of spot-less white,
When the bright and glo-rious morn-ing I shall see, I shall know my Re-
And the lus-ter of His kind-ly beam-ing eye; How my full heart will
And our part-ing at the riv-er I re-call; To the sweet vales of
He will lead me where no tears will ev-er fall; In the glad song of
deem-er when I reach the oth-er side, And His smile will be the
praise Him for the mer-cy, love and grace That pre-pare for me a
E-den they will sing my wel-come home- But I long to meet my
a-ges I shall min-gle with de-light- But I long to meet my
CHORUS
first to wel-come me.
man-sion in the sky. I shall know Him, I shall
Sav-ior first of all. I shall know Him,
Sav-ior first of all.
know Him, And re-deemed by His side I shall stand, I shall

know Him, I shall know Him By the print of the nails in His hand.
I shall know Him,
Face to Face
447
Carrie E. Breck
Grant C. Tullar
1. Face to face with Christ my Sav - ior, Face to face—what will it be—
2. On - ly faint - ly now I see Him, With the dark-ling veil be-tween;
3. What re - joic - ing in His pres - ence When are ban-ished grief and pain;
4. Face to face! O bliss-ful mo - ment! Face to face— to see and know;
When with rap - ture I be-hold Him, Je - sus Christ who died for me?
But a bless - ed day is com - ing When His glo - ry shall be seen.
When the crook - ed ways are straight-ened And the dark things shall be plain.
Face to face with my Re-deem - er, Je - sus Christ who loves me so.
Chorus
Face to face I shall be - hold Him, Far be - yond the star - ry sky;
Face to face in all His glo - ry, I shall see Him by and by!

448 Meet Me There

Fanny J. Crosby

William J. Kirkpatrick

1. On the hap-py, gold-en shore Where the faith-ful part no more, When the storms of life are o'er, Meet me there; Where the night dis-solves a-way In-to pure and per-fect day, I am go-ing home to stay— Meet me there.
2. Here our fond-est hopes are vain, Dear-est links are rent in twain, But in heav'n no throb of pain— Meet me there; By the riv-er spark-ling bright In the cit-y of de-light, Where our faith is lost in sight, Meet me there.
3. Where the harps of an-gels ring And the blest for-ev-er sing, In the pal-ace of the King, Meet me there; Where in sweet com-mun-ion blend Heart with heart and friend with friend, In a world that ne'er shall end, Meet me there.
CHORUS
Meet me there, Meet me there, Where the tree of life is bloom-ing, Meet me there; When the storms of life are o'er,
Meet me there, Meet me there,
Meet me there;

On the hap-py, gold-en shore, Where the faith-ful part no more, Meet me there.
Saved by Grace
449
Fanny J. Crosby
George C. Stebbins
Arr. by Norman Johnson
1. Some day the sil - ver cord will break, And I no more as now shall sing;
2. Some day my earth - ly house will fall - I can-not tell how soon 'twill be;
3. Some day, when fades the gold-en sun Be-neath the ros - y - tint-ed west,
4. Some day - till then I'll watch and wait, My lamp all trimmed and burn-ing bright,
But O the joy when I shall wake With-in the pal-ace of the King!
But this I know - my All in All Has now a place in heav'n for me.
My bless-ed Lord will say, "Well done!" And I shall en-ter in-to rest.
That when my Sav - ior opes the gate, My soul to Him may take its flight.
CHORUS
And I shall see Him face to face, And tell the sto - ry - Saved by grace;
And I shall see Him face to face, And tell the sto - ry - Saved by grace.

450 I Am Bound for the Promised Land

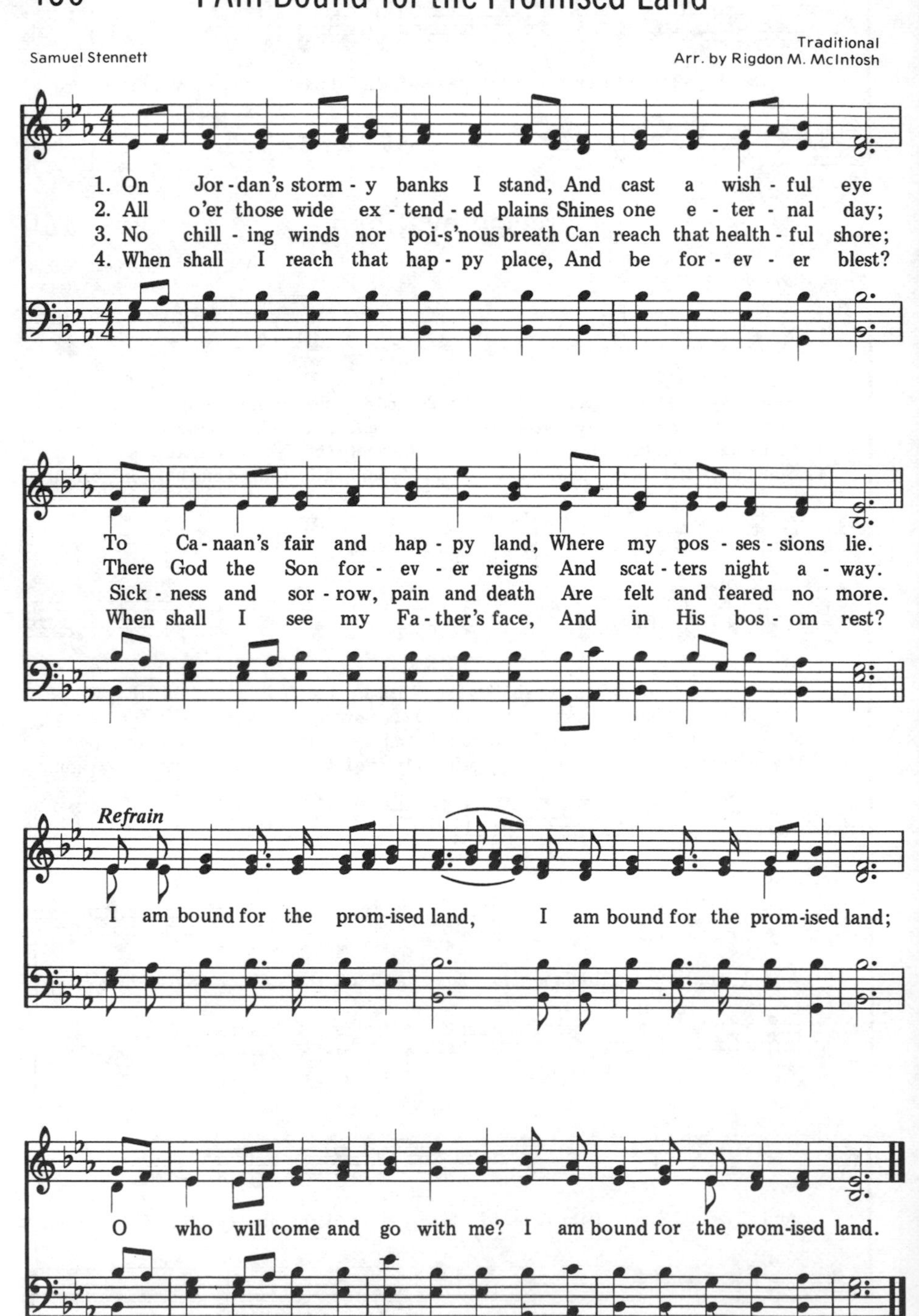
Samuel Stennett
Traditional
Arr. by Rigdon M. McIntosh
1. On Jor-dan's storm-y banks I stand, And cast a wish-ful eye
2. All o'er those wide ex-tend-ed plains Shines one e-ter-nal day;
3. No chill-ing winds nor poi-s'nous breath Can reach that health-ful shore;
4. When shall I reach that hap-py place, And be for-ev-er blest?
To Ca-naan's fair and hap-py land, Where my pos-ses-sions lie.
There God the Son for-ev-er reigns And scat-ters night a-way.
Sick-ness and sor-row, pain and death Are felt and feared no more.
When shall I see my Fa-ther's face, And in His bos-om rest?
Refrain
I am bound for the prom-ised land, I am bound for the prom-ised land;
O who will come and go with me? I am bound for the prom-ised land.

The Sands of Time Are Sinking

Anne R. Cousin

Chretien Urhan
Arr. by Edward F. Rimbault

1. The sands of time are sink - ing, The dawn of heav - en breaks;
2. O Christ! He is the foun - tain, The deep, sweet well of love!
3. O, I am my Be - lov - ed's, And my Be - lov - ed's mine!
4. The Bride eyes not her gar - ment, But her dear Bride-groom's face;
The sum - mer morn I've sighed for, The fair, sweet morn a - wakes:
The streams on earth I've tast - ed, More deep I'll drink a - bove:
He brings a poor vile sin - ner In - to His "house of wine."
I will not gaze at glo - ry But on my King of grace.
Dark, dark hath been the mid - night, But day - spring is at hand,
There to an o - cean ful - ness His mer - cy doth ex - pand,
I stand up - on His mer - it, I know no oth - er stand,
Not at the crown He giv - eth But on His pierc - ed hand,
And glo - ry, glo - ry dwell - eth In Im - man - uel's land.
And glo - ry, glo - ry dwell - eth In Im - man - uel's land.
Not e'en where glo - ry dwell - eth In Im - man - uel's land.
The Lamb is all the glo - ry Of Im - man - uel's land. A-men.

452 No Night There

John R. Clements — Hart P. Danks

1. In the land of fade - less day Lies the "cit - y four - square,"
2. All the gates of pearl are made, In the "cit - y four - square,"
3. And the gates shall nev - er close To the "cit - y four - square,"
4. There they need no sun - shine bright, In that "cit - y four - square,"
It shall nev - er pass a - way, And there is "no night there."
All the streets with gold are laid, And there is "no night there."
There life's crys - tal riv - er flows, And there is "no night there."
For the Lamb is all the light, And there is "no night there."
CHORUS
mf
God shall "wipe a-way all tears;" There's no death, no pain, nor fears;
God shall "wipe a - way all tears;" There's no death, no pain, nor fears;
f
dim.
mf
And they count not time by years, For there is "no night there."
And they count not time by years, by years, For there is "no night... there."

Sweet By and By 453

Sanford F. Bennett
Joseph P. Webster
1. There's a land that is fair - er than day, And by faith we can see it a - far; For the Fa - ther waits o - ver the way, To pre - pare us a dwell - ing-place there.
2. We shall sing on that beau - ti - ful shore The me - lo - di - ous songs of the blest, And our spir - its shall sor - row no more, Not a sigh for the bless - ing of rest.
3. To our boun - ti - ful Fa - ther a - bove, We will of - fer our trib - ute of praise, For the glo - ri - ous gift of His love, And the bless - ings that hal - low our days.
Chorus
In the sweet by and by, We shall meet on that beau - ti - ful shore; In the sweet by and by, We shall meet on that beau - ti - ful shore.
In the sweet by and by, by and by,
In the sweet by and by,

454 When His Face I See

Maud Frazer

Robert Harkness
Arr. by Donna Krieger

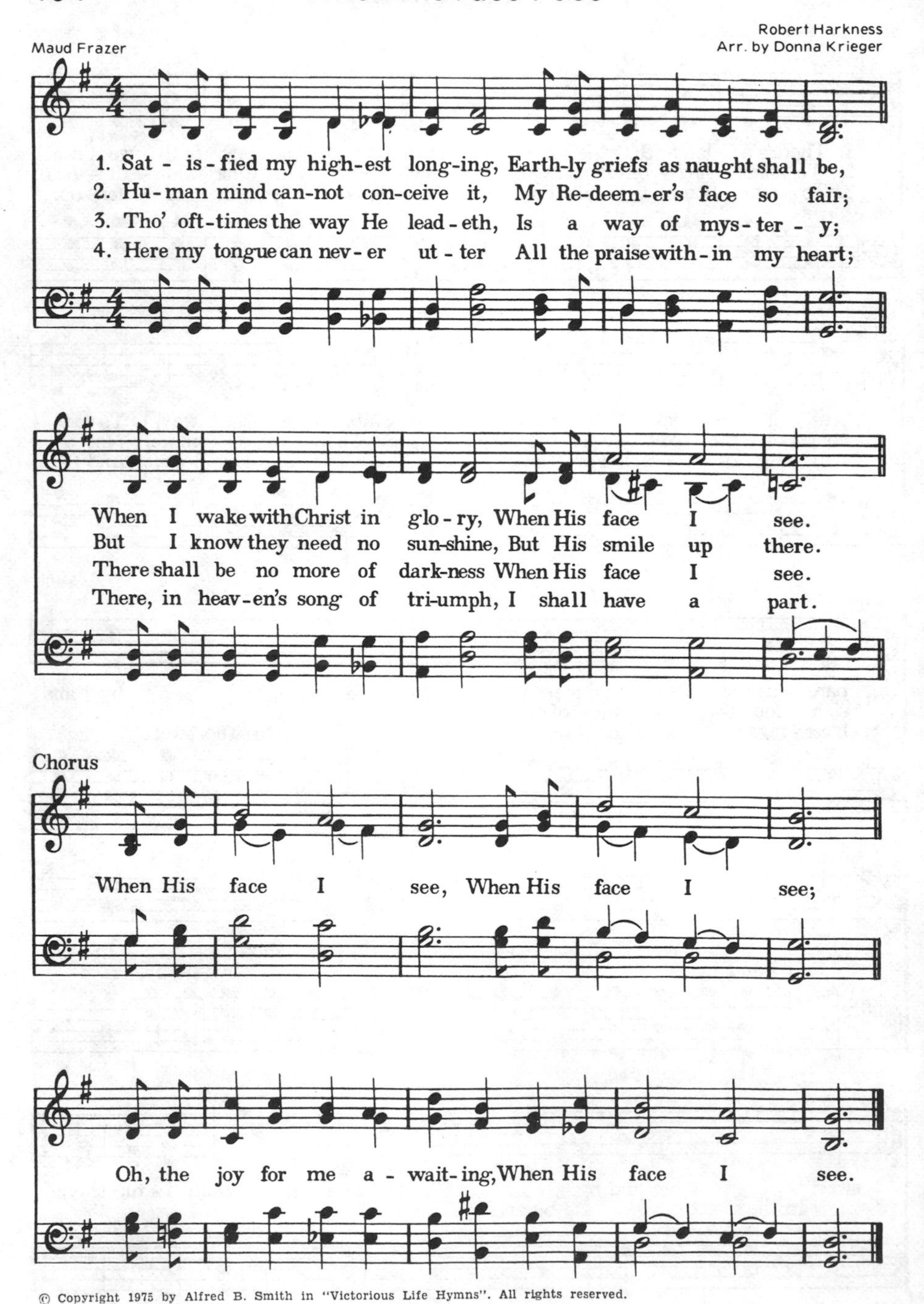
1. Sat - is - fied my high - est long - ing, Earth - ly griefs as naught shall be,
2. Hu - man mind can - not con - ceive it, My Re - deem - er's face so fair;
3. Tho' oft - times the way He lead - eth, Is a way of mys - ter - y;
4. Here my tongue can nev - er ut - ter All the praise with - in my heart;
When I wake with Christ in glo - ry, When His face I see.
But I know they need no sun - shine, But His smile up there.
There shall be no more of dark - ness When His face I see.
There, in heav - en's song of tri - umph, I shall have a part.
Chorus
When His face I see, When His face I see;
Oh, the joy for me a - wait - ing, When His face I see.

The Glorious Hope

Samuel Medley, Alt. A.B.S.
Alfred B. Smith
1. Oh, glo-rious hope of per-fect love! It lifts me up to
2. Re - joic - ing now in ear-nest hope, I stand, and from the
3. A land of corn, and wine, and oil; Fa-vored with God's pe -
4. Oh, that I might at once go up; No more on this side
Instrumental
8va
things a-bove; Ris - ing on ea-gles' wings.
moun-tain-top See all the land be - low.
cul - iar smile, With ev - 'ry bless-ing blest;
Jor - dan stop, But now the land pos - sess;
8va
It gives my thirst-y soul a taste, Pre-pares for me a heav'n-ly feast
Riv - ers of milk and hon-ey rise, And all the fruits of par - a-dise
There dwells the Lord our Right-eous-ness And keeps His own in per-fect peace,
This mo-ment end my pil-grim years, Sor-rows and sins, and doubts and fears,
Instrumental
8va
And gives a heart that sings.
In end-less plen - ty grow.
And ev - er - last - ing rest.
To dwell in bless-ed - ness.
8va

May also be sung without instrumental interludes.

456 Beulah Land

Edgar Page Stites

John R. Sweney

1. I've reached the land of corn and wine, And all its rich-es free-ly mine;
2. My Sav-ior comes and walks with me, And sweet com-mun-ion here have we;
3. A sweet per-fume up-on the breeze Is borne from ev-er-ver-nal trees
4. The zeph-yrs seem to float to me Sweet sounds of heav-en's mel-o-dy,

Here shines un-dimmed one bliss-ful day, For all my night has passed a-way.
He gen-tly leads me by His hand, For this is heav-en's bor-der-land.
And flow'rs that nev-er-fad-ing grow, Where streams of life for-ev-er flow.
As an-gels with the white-robed throng Join in the sweet Re-demp-tion song.

CHORUS

O Beu-lah Land, sweet Beu-lah Land! As on thy high-est mount I stand,

I look a-way a-cross the sea, Where man-sions are pre-pared for me,

And view the shin-ing glo-ry-shore— My heav'n, my home for-ev-er-more!

Hallelujah! Amen!

Fanny J. Crosby

Revised by Alfred B. Smith

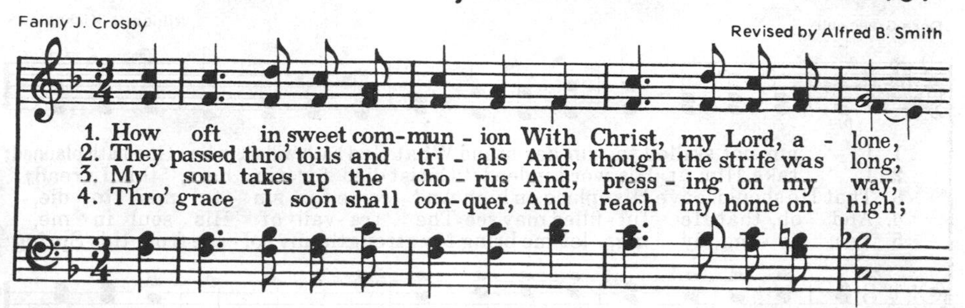
1. How oft in sweet com-mun-ion With Christ, my Lord, a-lone,
2. They passed thro' toils and tri-als And, though the strife was long,
3. My soul takes up the cho-rus And, press-ing on my way,
4. Thro' grace I soon shall con-quer, And reach my home on high;

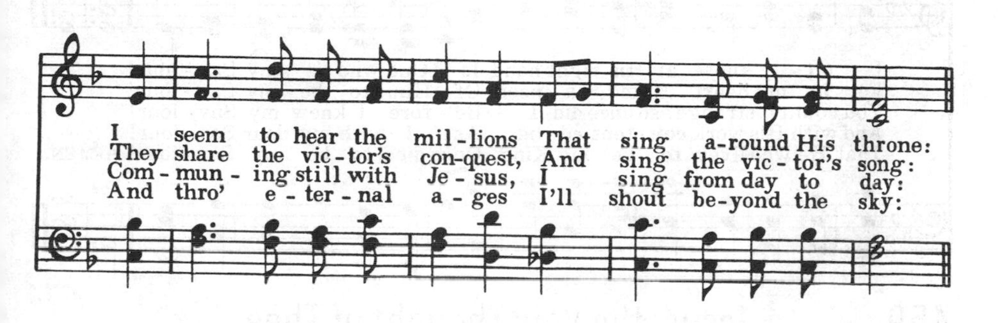
I seem to hear the mil-lions That sing a-round His throne:
They share the vic-tor's con-quest, And sing the vic-tor's song:
Com-mun-ing still with Je-sus, I sing from day to day:
And thro' e-ter-nal a-ges I'll shout be-yond the sky:

Chorus

Hal-le-lu-jah! A-men! Hal-le-lu-jah! A-men!

To God be the glo-ry! Hal-le-lu-jah! A-men!

458 I Am Not Skilled to Understand

Dora Greenwell | William J. Kirkpatrick

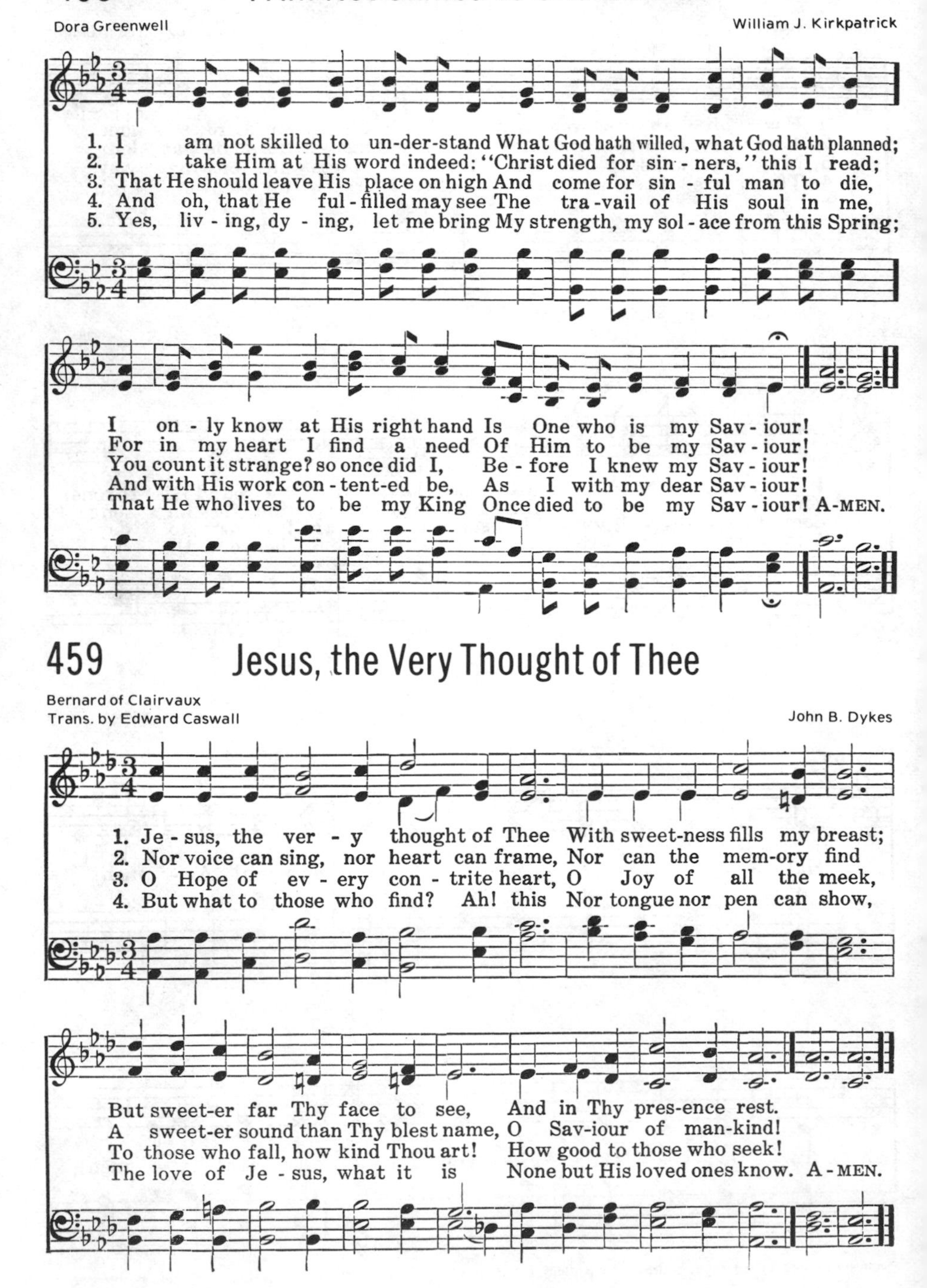
1. I am not skilled to un-der-stand What God hath willed, what God hath planned;
2. I take Him at His word indeed: "Christ died for sin-ners," this I read;
3. That He should leave His place on high And come for sin-ful man to die,
4. And oh, that He ful-filled may see The tra-vail of His soul in me,
5. Yes, liv-ing, dy-ing, let me bring My strength, my sol-ace from this Spring;
I on-ly know at His right hand Is One who is my Sav-iour!
For in my heart I find a need Of Him to be my Sav-iour!
You count it strange? so once did I, Be-fore I knew my Sav-iour!
And with His work con-tent-ed be, As I with my dear Sav-iour!
That He who lives to be my King Once died to be my Sav-iour! A-MEN.
459 Jesus, the Very Thought of Thee
Bernard of Clairvaux
Trans. by Edward Caswall
John B. Dykes
1. Je-sus, the ver-y thought of Thee With sweet-ness fills my breast;
2. Nor voice can sing, nor heart can frame, Nor can the mem-ory find
3. O Hope of ev-ery con-trite heart, O Joy of all the meek,
4. But what to those who find? Ah! this Nor tongue nor pen can show,
But sweet-er far Thy face to see, And in Thy pres-ence rest.
A sweet-er sound than Thy blest name, O Sav-iour of man-kind!
To those who fall, how kind Thou art! How good to those who seek!
The love of Je-sus, what it is None but His loved ones know. A-MEN.

Battle Hymn of the Republic

Julia Ward Howe

William Steffe, Arr.

1. Mine eyes have seen the glo - ry of the com - ing of the Lord; He is
2. I have seen Him in the watch-fires of a hun-dred cir-cling camps; They have
3. I have read a fier - y gos - pel writ in burn - ished rows of steel: "As ye
4. He has sound - ed forth the trum - pet that shall nev - er call re - treat; He is
5. In the beau - ty of the lil - ies Christ was born a - cross the sea, With a
tramp - ling out the vint - age where the grapes of wrath are stored; He hath loosed the
build - ed Him an al - tar in the eve - ning dews and damps; I can read His
deal with My con - tem-ners, so with you My grace shall deal; Let the He - ro,
sift - ing out the hearts of men be - fore His judg-ment seat; O be swift, my
glo - ry in His bos - om that trans-fig- ures you and me: As He died to
fate - ful light-ning of His ter - ri - ble swift sword: His truth is march-ing on.
right - eous sen-tence by the dim and flar - ing lamps: His day is march-ing on.
born of wo - man, crush the ser-pent with His heel, Since God is march-ing on."
soul, to an - swer Him! be ju - bi - lant, my feet! Our God is march-ing on.
make men ho - ly, let us die to make men free, While God is march-ing on.
REFRAIN (Last line of each stanza becomes last line of Refrain.)
Glo - ry! glo - ry! Hal - le - lu - jah! Glo - ry! glo - ry! Hal - le - lu - jah!
Glo - ry! glo - ry! Hal-le - lu - jah! His truth is march-ing on. A - men.

461 The Star-Spangled Banner

Frances Scott Key

John Stafford Smith

1. O say, can you see, by the dawn's ear-ly light, What so proud-ly we
2. O thus be it ev - er, when free men shall stand Be - tween their loved
hailed at the twi-light's last gleam-ing, Whose broad stripes and bright stars, thru the
homes and the war's des - o - la - tion! Blest with vic - t'ry and peace, may the
per - il - ous fight, O'er the ram-parts we watched, were so gal-lant-ly stream-ing?
heav'n-res-cued land Praise the Pow'r that hath made and pre-served us a na - tion!
And the rock-ets' red glare, the bombs burst-ing in air, Gave proof thru the
Then con-quer we must, when our cause it is just; And this be our
night that our flag was still there. O say, does that star-span-gled
mot - to: "In God is our trust!" And the star-span-gled ban - ner in

ban-ner yet wave O'er the land of the free and the home of the brave?
tri-umph shall wave O'er the land of the free and the home of the brave!
America
462
Samuel F. Smith
Henry Carey
1. My coun-try, 'tis of thee, Sweet land of lib-er-ty,
2. My na-tive coun-try, thee, Land of the no-ble free,
3. Let mu-sic swell the breeze, And ring from all the trees
4. Our fa-thers' God, to Thee, Au-thor of lib-er-ty,
Of thee I sing: Land where my fa-thers died, Land of the
Thy name I love: I love thy rocks and rills, Thy woods and
Sweet free-dom's song: Let mor-tal tongues a-wake, Let all that
To Thee we sing: Long may our land be bright With free-dom's
pil-grims' pride, From ev-'ry moun-tain side Let free-dom ring!
tem-pled hills; My heart with rap-ture thrills Like that a-bove.
breathe par-take; Let rocks their si-lence break, The sound pro-long.
ho-ly light; Pro-tect us by Thy might, Great God, our King!

463
If You Want Joy
J.D.C.
Brightly
Rev. Joseph Carlson
If you want joy, real joy, won-der-ful joy, Let Je-sus come
true joy,
in-to your heart; heart. Your sins He'll wash a-way,
your heart; your heart.
Fine
Your night He'll turn to day, Your life He'll make it o-ver a new;
a - new;
D. C.
464
On the Victory Side
W. J. C.
Walter J. Main
On the vic-t'ry side, On the vic-t'ry side! No foe can daunt me,
No fear can haunt me On the vic-t'ry side; On the vic-t'ry side, On the

vic - t'ry side! With Christ with-in, The fight we'll win, On the vic - t'ry side!
Sing It and Tell It Again
465
Unknown
Edit. by Anna Atwood
Unknown
Arr. by A. B. S.
1. Tell it a - gain, for some - one needs it,
2. Sing it a - gain, for some - one needs it,
Tell it a - gain. Tell it a - gain 'till
Sing it a - gain. Sing it a - gain 'till
some - one heeds it, Tell it a - gain. There's no oth - er
some - one heeds it, Sing it a - gain. There's no oth - er
stor - y that leads men to glo - ry; So
stor - y that leads men to glo - ry; So,
tell it and tell it, and tell it a - gain.
sing it and sing it, and sing it a - gain.
© Copyright 1975 by Alfred B. Smith in "Victorious Life Hymns". All rights reserved.

466 All Because of Calvary

W. P. L. Wendell P. Loveless

Two-Part Chorus
All my sins are gone, All because of Cal-va-ry;
All my sins are gone
Life is filled with song, All be-cause of Cal-va-ry;
Life is filled with song
Christ my Sav-iour lives, Lives from sin to set me free;
Christ my Sav-iour lives
Some day He's coming, O wondrous, blessed day, All, yes, all because of Cal-va-ry.

467 How Greatly Jesus Loved Me

J. W. Y. J. W. Young

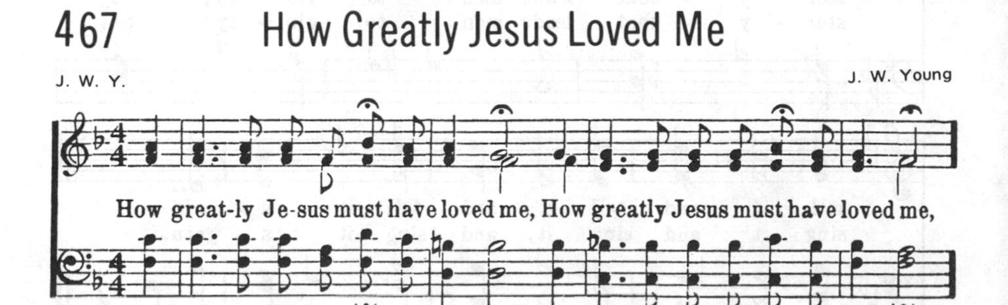
How great-ly Je-sus must have loved me, How greatly Jesus must have loved me,

To bear my sins, To bear my sins In His Bod-y on the Tree!
Vessels for the Master's Use
468
A. B. S.
(11 Tim. 2:21)
Alfred B. Smith
Filled to o-ver-flow-ing, Hearts a-glow and show-ing Christ to those who do not
(piano)
know Him; Sanc-ti-fied and ho-ly, Yield-ed to Him on-ly,
Fine
Ves-sels for the Mas-ter's use.___ O make my life___ a bless-ing,
D. C.
Lord. May it stand___ Thy test-ing, Lord.___

469 Only to Be What He Wants Me to Be

N. J. C. Norman J. Clayton

On-ly to be what He wants me to be, Ev-'ry mo-ment of ev-'ry day;
Yield-ed com-plete-ly to Je-sus a-lone, Ev-'ry step of this pil-grim way;
Just to be clay in the Pot-ter's hands, Read-y to do what His Word commands,
On-ly to be what He wants me to be, Ev-'ry mo-ment of ev-'ry day.

470 Rolled Away

W. D. K. Walter J. Kallenbach

Unison
Rolled a-way, rolled a-way, rolled a-way, Ev-'ry bur-den of my heart rolled a-

FINE
Men's voices, or full unison
D.S.
way; Ev-'ry sin had to go 'neath the crim - son flow,

Every Day With Jesus

471

Robert C. Loveless

Wendell P. Loveless

Ev - ery day with Je - sus Is sweet-er than the day be - fore;
Ev - ery day with Je - sus, I love Him more and more;
Je - sus saves and keeps me, And He's the One I'm wait-ing for:
Ev - ery day with Je - sus Is sweet-er than the day be - fore.

472 I Am the Resurrection and the Life

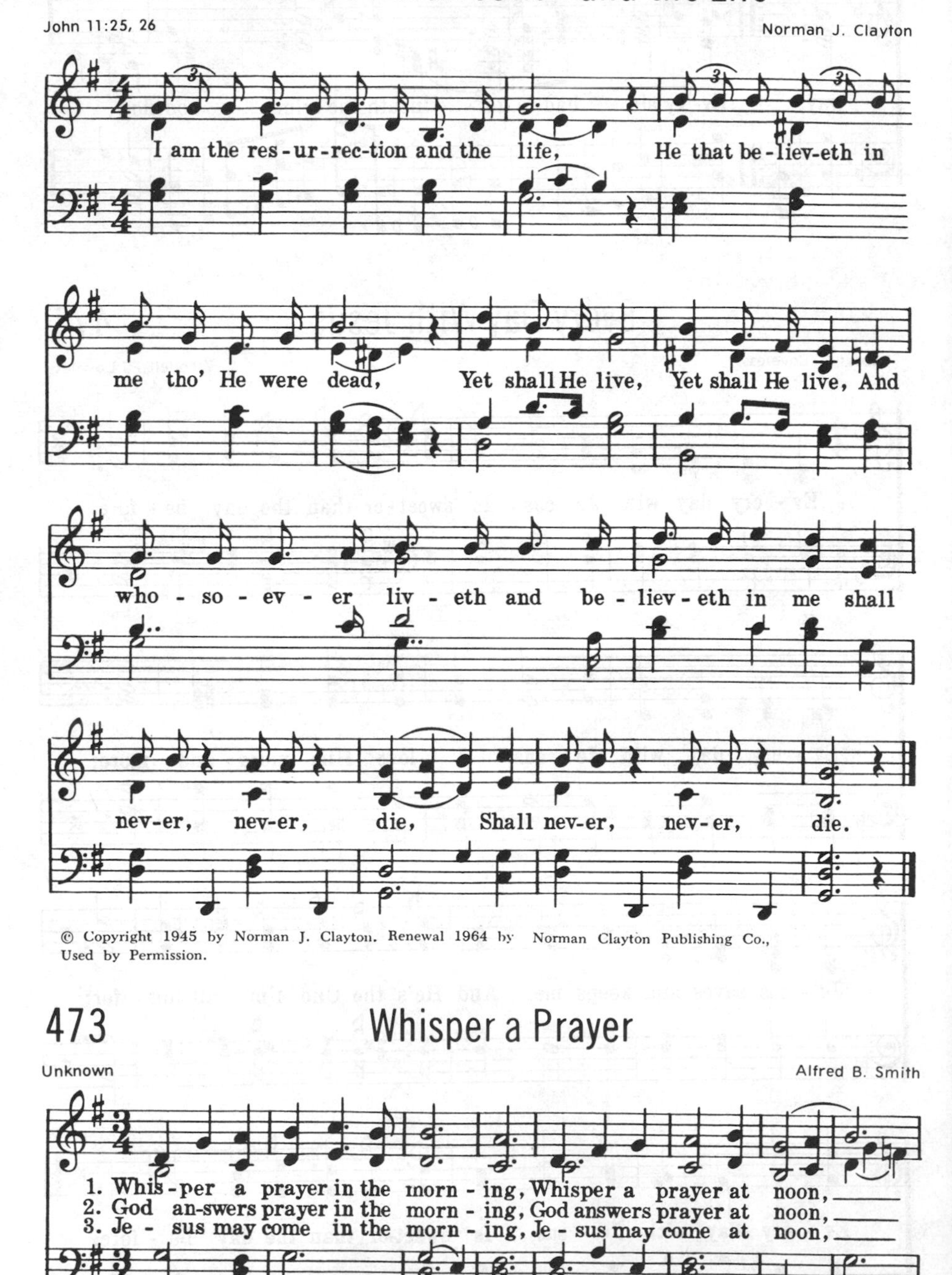
John 11:25, 26
Norman J. Clayton
I am the res-ur-rec-tion and the life,
He that be-liev-eth in
me tho' He were dead,
Yet shall He live,
Yet shall He live, And
who - so - ev - er liv - eth and be - liev - eth in me shall
nev-er, nev-er, die,
Shall nev-er, nev-er, die.
© Copyright 1945 by Norman J. Clayton. Renewal 1964 by Norman Clayton Publishing Co., Used by Permission.
473
Whisper a Prayer
Unknown
Alfred B. Smith
1. Whis-per a prayer in the morn - ing, Whisper a prayer at noon,
2. God an-swers prayer in the morn - ing, God answers prayer at noon,
3. Je - sus may come in the morn - ing, Je - sus may come at noon,

As sung in the air raid shelters in London, England during World War II.

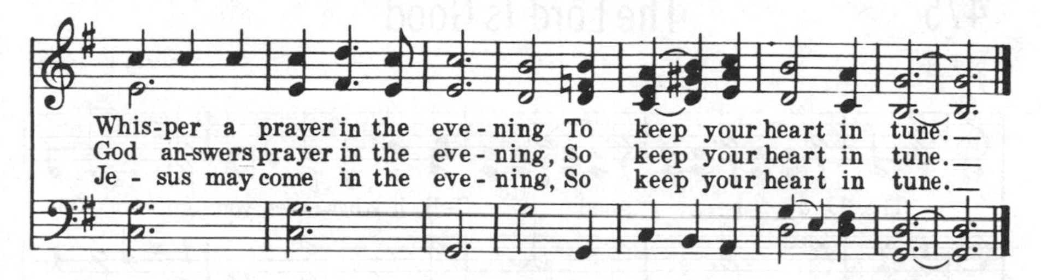
Whis-per a prayer in the eve-ning To keep your heart in tune.
God an-swers prayer in the eve-ning, So keep your heart in tune.
Je - sus may come in the eve-ning, So keep your heart in tune.

As Long as There Are Stars 474

A. B. S. Alfred B. Smith

As long as there are stars in the heav'ns a - bove, I
know that I'll be kept by His won - der - ful love; The
God Who made the world calms the storm - y sea, And I
know He cares for me.

475 The Lord Is Good

A. B. S. Alfred B. Smith

The Lord is good Tell it wher-ev-er you go, The
Lord is good Tell it that oth-ers may know; Tell of His
bless-ings and tell of His love, Tell how He's coming from heav-en a-
bove: The Lord is good Tell it wher-ev-er you go!

476 I Haven't Words to Tell

W. P. L. Wendell P. Loveless

I have-n't words to tell of the love of Je-sus,— His love is
won-der-ful, It fills each joy-ous day, Each step He leads me;

Oh, what a joy to tell all the world of Je - sus,___ Ah, yes, but
I have - n't words to tell of His love for me.___

Things Are Different Now 477

Stanton W. Gavitt

Stanton W. Gavitt

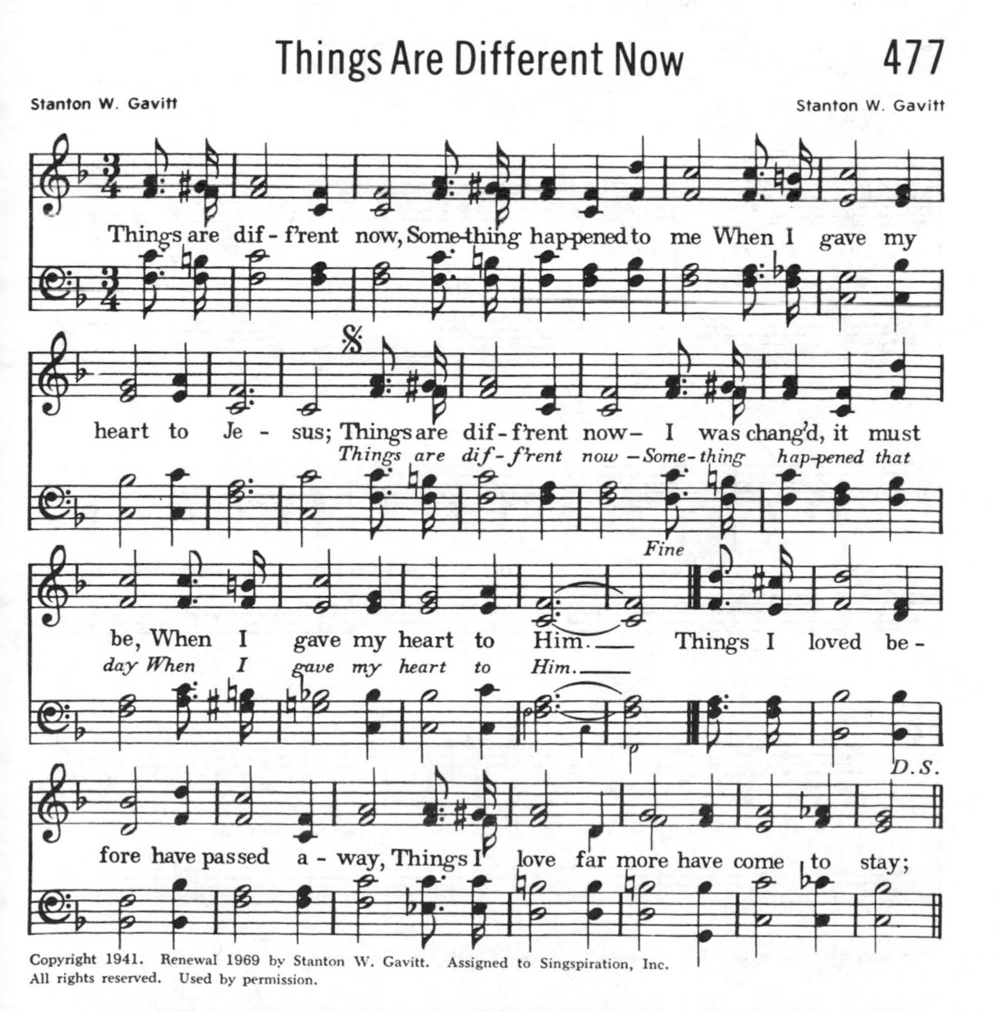
Things are dif - f'rent now, Some-thing hap-pened to me When I gave my
heart to Je - sus; Things are dif - f'rent now— I was chang'd, it must
Things are dif - f'rent now —Some - thing hap-pened that
be, When I gave my heart to Him.___ Things I loved be -
day When I gave my heart to Him.___
Fine
fore have passed a - way, Things I love far more have come to stay;
D.S.

478
Altogether Lovely
W. P. L.
Wendell P. Loveless
Al - to-geth - er love - ly, He is al - to-geth - er love - ly, And the fair - est of ten thou - sand, This won-der-ful Friend di - vine; He gave Him-self to save me, Now He lives in heav'n to keep me, He is al - to-geth - er love - ly, Is this won-der-ful Sav-iour of mine.

More Time Alone With Thee Lord Jesus 479

W. P. L.

Wendell P. Loveless

More time a - lone with Thee, Lord Je - sus, More time a lone with
Thee,—— More time to know Thy - self, Lord Je - sus Thou hast done
all for me.—— Deep is Thy love, Sweet is Thy peace.
Wondrous Thy grace, suf - fi - cient for ev - 'ry need, More time a - lone with
Thee, Lord Je - sus More time a - lone with Thee.——

480 I Will Sing of the Mercies of the Lord

Psa. 89:1

James H. Fillmore

I will sing of the mer-cies of the Lord for - ev-er, I will sing, I will
sing, I will sing of the mer-cies of the Lord for - ev - er, I will
sing of the mer-cies of the Lord. With my mouth will I make known Thy
faith-ful-ness, Thy faith-ful-ness, With my mouth will I make known Thy
faith-ful-ness to all gen - er - a - tions. I will sing of the mer-cies of the
Lord for - ev - er, I will sing of the mer-cies of the Lord.

Happiness Is The Lord

I. F. S. Ira F. Stamphill

Unison

1. Hap - pi - ness is to know the Sav - ior, Liv - ing a life with - in His fa - vor,
2. Hap - pi - ness is a new cre - a - tion—"Je - sus and me" in close re - la - tion,
3. Hap - pi - ness is to be for - giv - en, Liv - ing a life that's worth the liv - in',

Hav - ing a change in my be - hav - ior— Hap - pi - ness is the Lord;
Hav - ing a part in His sal - va - tion—
Tak - ing a trip that leads to heav - en—

1 *(to vs. 2)*

2 Hap - pi - ness is the Lord. Real joy is mine, no mat - ter if tear - drops start; I've found the se - cret— it's Je - sus in my heart!

D.C. (to vs. 3)

3 Hap - pi - ness is the Lord, Hap - pi - ness is the Lord, Hap - pi - ness is the Lord!

482 The Very, Very Sweetest Thing I Know

Mrs. W. G. T. | Mrs. Walter G. Taylor

Not too fast

It is the ver - y, ver - y, sweet-est thing I know, That Je - sus
I know,
is my lov - ing Sav - iour! And thru the days and years, He'll ever with me
go, This is the ver - y sweetest thing I know! To walk with Him,
To talk with Him, this is the ver - y, ver - y, sweetest thing I know!
O what a won-der that Je - sus found me, Out in the dark-ness, no

483 O What a Wonder

R. S. | Ralph Scherman

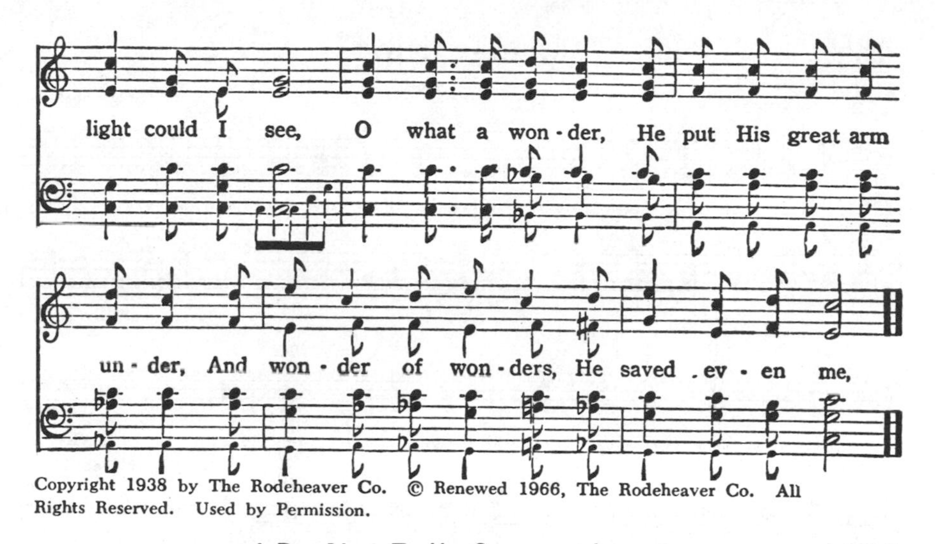
light could I see, O what a won - der, He put His great arm
un - der, And won - der of won - ders, He saved . ev - en me,

I Do Not Fully Comprehend 484

W. C. Martin & A.B.S. Alfred B. Smith

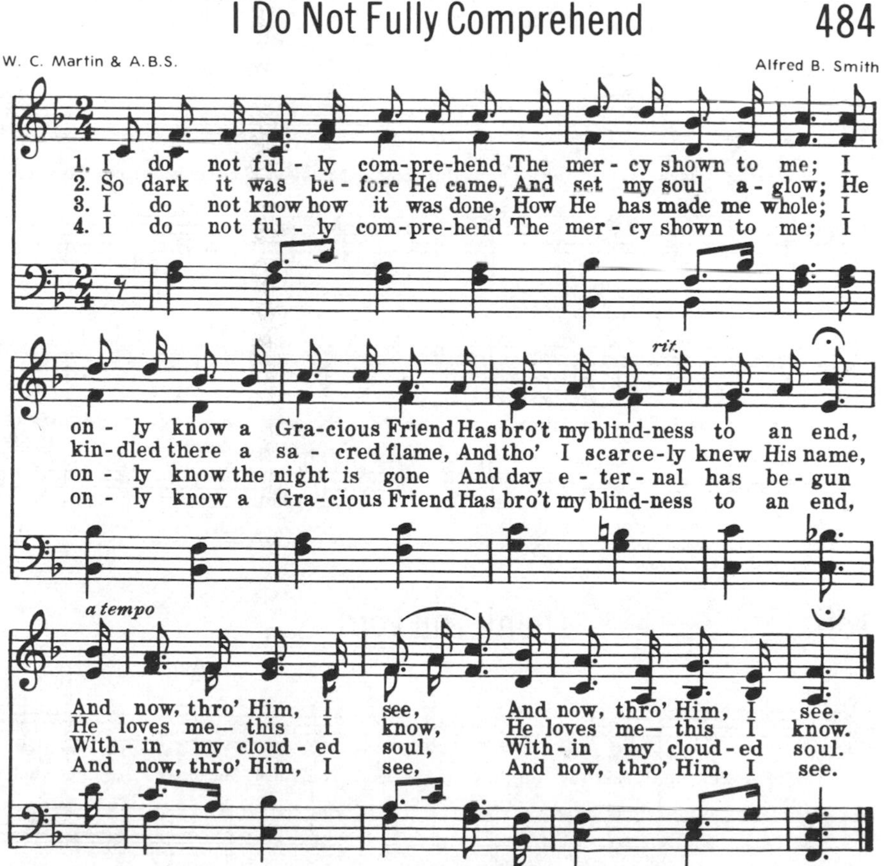
1. I do not ful - ly com-pre-hend The mer - cy shown to me; I
2. So dark it was be - fore He came, And set my soul a - glow; He
3. I do not know how it was done, How He has made me whole; I
4. I do not ful - ly com-pre-hend The mer - cy shown to me; I
on - ly know a Gra-cious Friend Has bro't my blind-ness to an end,
kin-dled there a sa - cred flame, And tho' I scarce-ly knew His name,
on - ly know the night is gone And day e - ter - nal has be - gun
on - ly know a Gra-cious Friend Has bro't my blind-ness to an end,
rit.
a tempo
And now, thro' Him, I see, And now, thro' Him, I see.
He loves me— this I know, He loves me— this I know.
With - in my cloud - ed soul, With - in my cloud - ed soul.
And now, thro' Him, I see, And now, thro' Him, I see.

485 Keep Praising

W. P. L. — Wendell P. Loveless

Keep prais-ing, keep prais-ing, When the days are dark and drear; Keep
and drear;
prais-ing, keep prais-ing, God will guide you, nev - er fear; Keep
nev - er fear;
prais-ing, keep prais - ing, Thank-ful hearts to Him be rais - ing; Has the
Lord not said, There is glo - ry on a-head—So keep on prais - ing Him.

486 Thank You Lord

Seth Sykes — Mr. and Mrs. Seth Sykes

Thank You, Lord, for sav - ing my soul; Thank You, Lord, for mak - ing me whole;

Thank You, Lord, for giv-ing to me Thy great sal - va - tion so rich and free.

Lead Me to Some Soul Today 487

Will H. Houghton

Wendell P. Loveless

Lead me to some soul to-day, O teach me, Lord, just what to say;
Friends of mine are lost in sin, And can-not find their way.
Few there are who seem to care, And few there are who pray;
who pray;
Melt my heart and fill my life, Give me one soul to - day.

488 Do You Wonder Why?

I. A. K. Ida A. Koritz

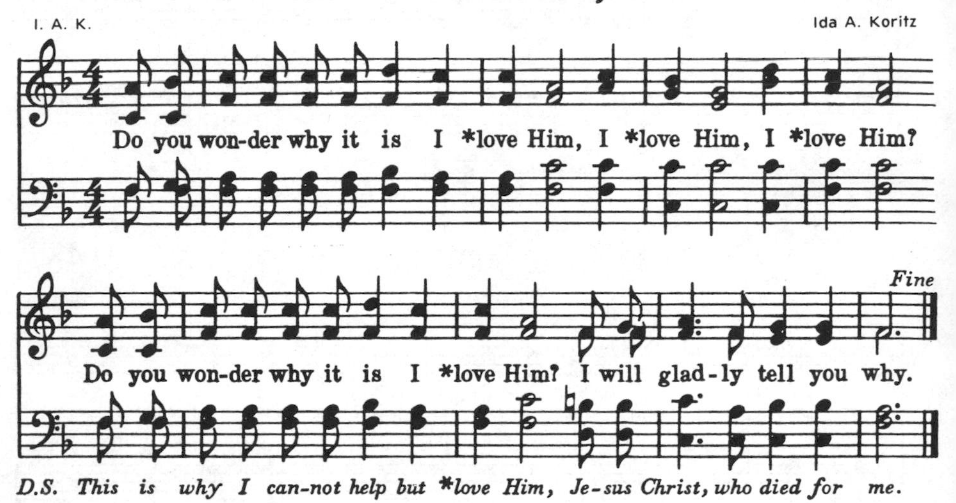

Do you won-der why it is I *love Him, I *love Him, I *love Him?
Fine
Do you won-der why it is I *love Him? I will glad-ly tell you why.
D.S. This is why I can-not help but *love Him, Je-sus Christ, who died for me.

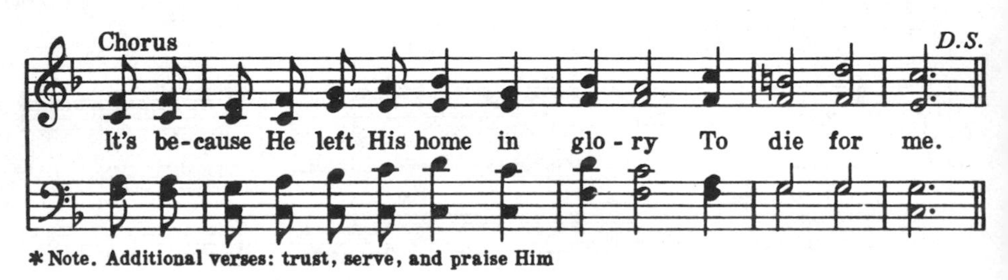

Chorus
D.S.
It's be-cause He left His home in glo-ry To die for me.

*Note. Additional verses: trust, serve, and praise Him

489 Following Jesus

English Arr. Donna J. Krieger

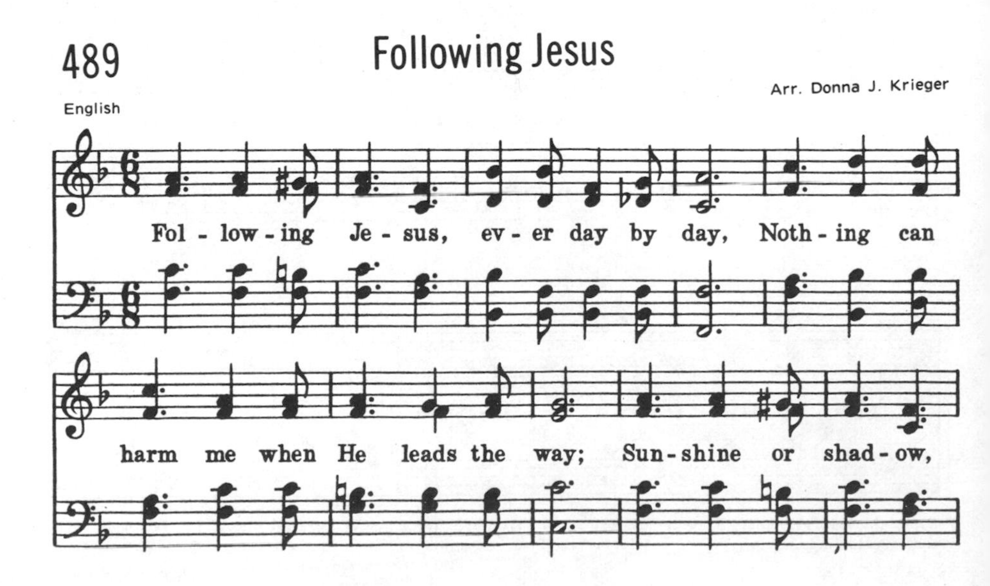

Fol-low-ing Je-sus, ev-er day by day, Noth-ing can
harm me when He leads the way; Sun-shine or shad-ow,

what-e'er be fall, Je-sus my Sav-ior is my All in All.
It's No Longer I
490
A. B. S.
Gal. 2:20
Arr. by Alfred B. Smith
It's no long-er I who liv-eth, But Christ who liv-eth in me.
It's no long-er I who liv-eth, But Christ who liv-eth in me.
In me, in me. Je-sus is a-live in me.
It's no long-er I who liv-eth, But Christ who liv-eth in me.

491 Are We Downhearted

R. H.

Robert Harkness

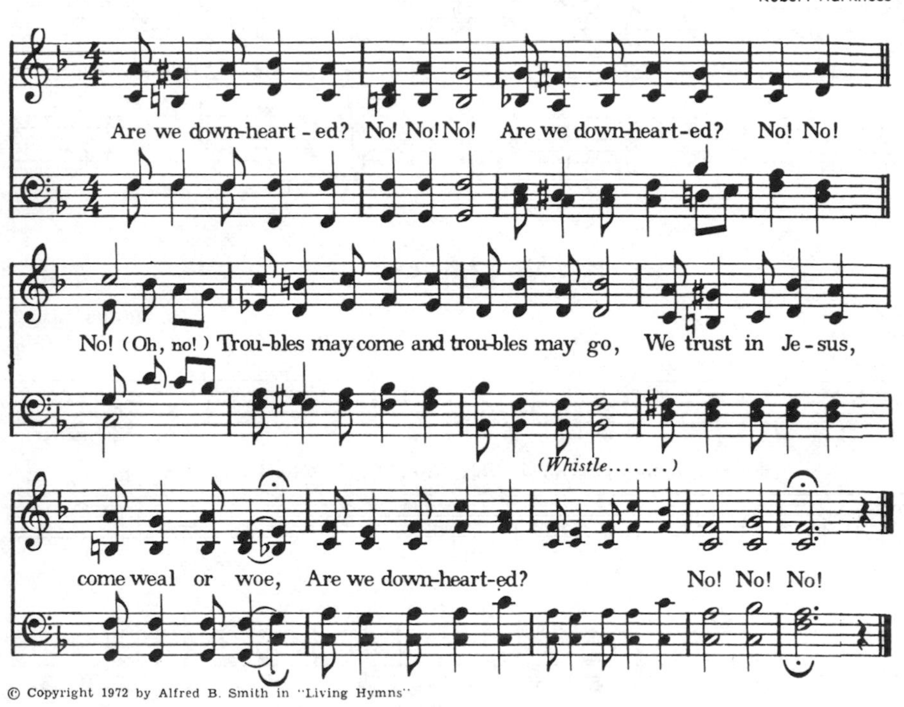

Are we down-heart - ed? No! No! No! Are we down-heart-ed? No! No!
No! (Oh, no!) Trou-bles may come and trou-bles may go, We trust in Je - sus,
(Whistle.......)
come weal or woe, Are we down-heart-ed? No! No! No!

492 Sweet Honey in the Rock

Unknown
Arr. by Alfred B. Smith

Sweet ho-ney in the rock — Sweet ho-ney in the rock. Je - sus
tastes like ho-ney in the rock. — Oh taste and see — that the Lord is
good For He tastes like ho - ney in the rock. —

They Say He Is Wonderful 493

Arr. by Alfred B. Smith

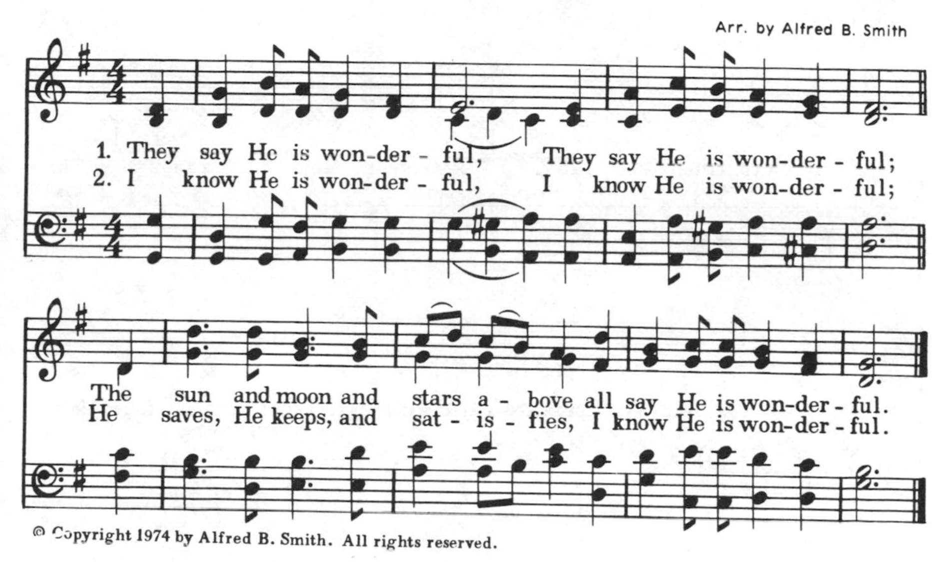

1. They say He is won-der - ful, They say He is won-der - ful;
2. I know He is won-der - ful, I know He is won-der - ful;
The sun and moon and stars a - bove all say He is won-der - ful.
He saves, He keeps, and sat - is - fies, I know He is won-der - ful.

Jesus, Let Me Hide My Soul in Thee 494

D. Hutton

Arr. by Alfred B. Smith

Not fast

Je - sus, Je - sus, Let my soul be lost in Thee. ___ Hide me in the Rock of A - ges; Hide me, hide me, Sav - iour, in Thee.

495 Take More Time to Pray

A. B. S. — Alfred B. Smith

Take more time to pray. Take more time to pray. The
world's in such a hur-ry, Hearts are filled with fear. Trust the Sav-iour, He's
al-ways near. Take more time to pray. Take more time to pray. Tho'
cares may sur-round you, They need not con-found you; Take more time to pray.

496 He's the One I Love

N. B. V. — N. B. Vandall

He's the One I love, He's the One I love,

8va
Fair-er is He than the lil-y to me, He's the One I love.
He Holds My Hand
497
N. J. C.
Norman J. Clayton
He holds my hand, Je-sus holds my hand; Safe-ly to
heav-en He leads the way, He is my keep-er from day to day;
He holds my hand, Je-sus holds my hand; The road may be
long, But my Sav-iour is strong, And He holds my hand.

I Will Serve Thee

William J. & Gloria Gaither

William J. Gaither

I will serve Thee
because I love Thee,
You have giv - en life to
me;
I was noth - ing
be - fore You found me,
You have giv - en life to
me.
Heart - aches,
bro - ken piec - es,
Ru - ined lives are

why You died on Cal-v'ry; Your touch is what I longed for;
You have giv-en life to me.
me.
1.
2.
Fine
With eternity's Values in View
499
A. B. S.
Alfred B. Smith
With e-ter-ni-ty's val-ues in view, Lord, With e-ter-ni-ty's val-ues in view; May I do each day's work for Je-sus, With e-ter-ni-ty's val-ues in view.

500 The Family of God

William J. & Gloria Gaither — William J. Gaither

With thankfulness

I'm so glad I'm a part of the fam-'ly of God; I've been washed in the foun-tain,— cleansed by His blood! Joint heirs with Je-sus as we tra-vel this sod, For I'm part of the fam-'ly,— the fam-'ly of

1. God! ——— I'm so

2. God! ———

Fine

My God's A Great God

H. B. Harry Bollback

Majesticly
My God's a Great God and wor - thy to be praised.
My God's a Great God, oh praise His Ho - ly name. He made the world so
1.
great. He keeps me by His grace. And soon I'll see His face.
My God's so great!
2.
name. He made the world so great, He
keeps me by His grace, and soon I'll see His face My God's so great!

502 God Be With You

Jeremiah E. Raukin
William G. Tomen
1. God be with you till we meet a - gain, By His coun-sels guide, up - hold you, With His sheep se - cure - ly fold you—
2. God be with you till we meet a - gain, 'Neath His wings pro - tect - ing hide you, Dai - ly man - na still pro - vide you—
3. God be with you till we meet a - gain, When life's per - ils thick con - found you, Put His arms un - fail - ing round you—
4. God be with you till we meet a - gain, Keep love's ban - ner float - ing o'er you; Smite death's threat'ning wave be - fore you—
God be with you till we meet a - gain.
CHORUS
Till we meet, till we meet, Till we meet at Je - sus' feet,
till we meet,
Till we meet, till we meet— God be with you till we meet a - gain.

RESPONSIVE READINGS

The House of God 1
Delight in the House of God 2
God the Creator 3
The Glory of God 4
Divine Greatness 5
The Goodness of God 6
The Divine Shepherd 7
The Holy Scriptures 8
The Commandments 9
The Christ of Prophecy 10
Divine Love 11
Divine Blessings 12
Divine Care 13
Divine Protection 14
Divine Comfort 15
Thanksgiving 16
Joyful Worship 17
Song of Deliverance 18
A Psalm of Praise 19
Benefits of Wisdom 20
The Gracious Invitation 21
The Prayer of the Penitent 22
The Path of Obedience 23
Thirsting for God 24
The All-Knowing God 25
A Hymn of Eternity 26
Great Commission 27
Confidence in God 28
The Beatitudes 29
Jesus Teaches Prayer 30
The Vine and the Branches 31
Witness of the Spirit 32
Consecration and Service 33
Stewardship 34
The More Excellent Way 35
Christian Warfare 36
Victorious Faith 37
The Way Home 38
The Victories of Faith 39
Highway to Zion 40
Christmas 41
The Triumphal Entry 42
The Promised Comforter 43
The Crucifixion 44
The Risen Savior 45
Resurrection 46
Pentecost 47
The Lord's Return 48
Temperance 49
Missions 50
God's Mercy Endureth Forever . . 51

The Apostles' Creed

I believe in GOD THE FATHER Almighty, Maker of heaven and earth:

And in JESUS CHRIST his only Son, our Lord; who was conceived by the Holy Ghost, born of the Virgin Mary, suffered under Pontius Pilate, was crucified, dead, and buried; he descended into hell; the third day he rose again from the dead; he ascended into heaven, and sitteth on the right hand of God the Father Almighty; from thence he shall come to judge the quick and the dead.

I believe in the HOLY GHOST; the holy Catholic Church; the communion of saints; the forgiveness of sins; the resurrection of the body; and the life everlasting. Amen.

SELECTIONS FOR RESPONSIVE READING

1 *The House of God*

I was glad when they said unto me, Let us go into the house of the Lord.

Our feet shall stand within thy gates, O Jerusalem!

Jerusalem is builded as a city that is compact together.

Whither the tribes go up, the tribes of the Lord, unto the testimony of Israel, to give thanks unto the name of the Lord.

For there are set thrones of judgment, the thrones of the house of David.

Pray for the peace of Jerusalem: they shall prosper that love thee.

Peace be within thy walls, and prosperity within thy palaces.

For my brethren and companions' sakes, I will now say, Peace be within thee.

Because of the house of the Lord our God I will seek thy good.

O come, let us sing unto the Lord; let us make a joyful noise to the Rock of our salvation.

Let us come before his presence with thanksgiving, and make a joyful noise unto him with psalms.

For the Lord is a great God, and a great King above all gods.

O come, let us worship and bow down: let us kneel before the Lord, our Maker.

—Psalm 122; 95:1, 2, 3, 6

2 *Delight in the House of God*

How amiable are thy tabernacles, O Lord of hosts!

My soul longeth, yea, even fainteth for the courts of the Lord:

My heart and my flesh crieth out for the living God.

Yea, the sparrow hath found an house, and the swallow a nest for herself, where she may lay her young,

Even thine altars, O Lord of hosts, my King and my God!

Blessed are they that dwell in thy house: they will be still praising thee.

Blessed is the man whose strength is in thee; in whose heart are the ways of them.

They go from strength to strength, every one of them in Zion appeareth before God.

O Lord God of hosts, hear my prayer; give ear, O God of Jacob.

Behold, O God our Shield! and look upon the face of thine Anointed.

For a day in thy courts is better than a thousand.

I had rather be a doorkeeper in the house of my God, than to dwell in the tents of wickedness.

For the Lord God is a Sun and Shield.

O Lord of hosts! blessed is the man that trusteth in thee.

—Psalm 84

3 *God the Creator*

In the beginning God created the heaven and the earth.

And the earth was without form, and void; and darkness was upon the face of the deep. And the Spirit of God moved upon the face of the waters.

And God said, Let there be light: and there was light.

And God saw the light, that it was good: and God divided the light from the darkness.

And God called the light Day, and the darkness he called Night. And the evening and the morning were the first day.

And God said, Let there be a firmament in the midst of the waters, and let it divide the waters from the waters.

And God made two great lights; the greater light to rule the day, and the lesser light to rule the night: he made the stars also.

And God created great whales, and every living creature that moveth, which the waters brought forth abundantly, after their kind, and every winged fowl after his kind: and God saw that it was good.

And God made the beast of the earth after his kind, and cattle after their kind, and every thing that creepeth upon the earth after his kind: and God saw that it was good.

And God said, Let us make man in our image, after our likeness: and let them have dominion over the fish of the sea, and over the fowl of the air, and over the cattle, and over all the earth, and over every creeping thing that creepeth upon the earth.

So God created man in his own image, in the image of God created he him; male and female created he them.

And God saw every thing that he had made, and, behold, it was very good. And the evening and the morning were the sixth day.

—Genesis 1:1-6, 16, 21, 25-27, 31

4 *The Glory of God*

The heavens declare the glory of God, and the firmament sheweth his handywork.

Day unto day uttereth speech, and night unto night sheweth knowledge.

There is no speech nor language, where their voice is not heard.

Their line is gone out through all the earth, and their words to the end of the world.

In them hath he set a tabernacle for the sun, which is as a bridegroom coming out of his chamber, and rejoiceth as a strong man to run a race.

His going forth is from the end of the heaven, and his circuit unto the ends of it: and there is nothing hid from the heat thereof.

The law of the Lord is perfect, converting the soul:

The testimony of the Lord is sure, making wise the simple:

The statutes of the Lord are right, rejoicing the heart:

The commandment of the Lord is pure, enlightening the eyes: The fear of the Lord is clean, enduring for ever:

The judgments of the Lord are true and righteous altogether.

More to be desired are they than gold, yea, than much fine gold; sweeter also than honey and the honeycomb.

Moreover, by them is thy servant warned, and in keeping of them there is great reward.

Who can understand his errors? cleanse thou me from secret faults.

Keep back thy servant also from presumptuous sins: let them not have dominion over me:

Then shall I be upright, and I shall be innocent from the great transgression.

Let the words of my mouth, and the meditation of my heart, be acceptable in thy sight, O Lord, my strength and my redeemer.

—Psalm 19

5 *Divine Greatness*

Bless the Lord, O my soul. O Lord my God, thou art very great; thou art clothed with honour and majesty.

Who coverest thyself with light as with a garment; who stretchest out the heavens like a curtain:

Who layeth the beams of his chambers in the waters: who maketh the clouds his chariot: who walketh upon the wings of the wind:

Who maketh his angels spirits; his ministers a flaming fire:

Who laid the foundations of the earth, that it should not be removed for ever.

Thou coveredst it with the deep as with a garment: the waters stood above the mountains.

At thy rebuke they fled; at the voice of thy thunder they hasted away.

They go up by the mountains; they go down by the valleys unto the place which thou hast founded for them.

Thou hast set a bound that they may not pass over, that they turn not again to cover the earth.

He sendeth the springs into the valleys, which run among the hills.

They give drink to every beast of the field; the wild asses quench their thirst.

He appointed the moon for seasons: the sun knoweth his going down.

Thou makest darkness, and it is night, wherein all the beasts of the forest do creep forth.

The young lions roar after their prey, and seek their meat from God.

O Lord, how manifold are thy works! in wisdom hast thou made them all: the earth is full of thy riches.

The glory of the Lord shall endure for ever: the Lord shall rejoice in his works.

He looketh on the earth, and it trembleth: he toucheth the hills, and they smoke.

I will sing unto the Lord as long as I live: I will sing praise to my God while I have my being.

—Psalm 104:1-11, 19-21, 24, 31-33

6 The Goodness of God

I will bless the Lord at all times: his praise shall continually be in my mouth.

My soul shall make her boast in the Lord: the humble shall hear thereof, and be glad.

O magnify the Lord with me, and let us exalt his name together.

I sought the Lord, and he heard me, and delivered me from all my fears.

They looked unto him, and were lightened; and their faces were not ashamed.

This poor man cried, and the Lord heard him, and saved him out of all his troubles.

The angel of the Lord encampeth round about them that fear him, and delivereth them.

O taste and see that the Lord is good: blessed is the man that trusteth in him.

O fear the Lord, ye his saints: for there is no want to them that fear him.

The young lions do lack and suffer hunger; but they that seek the Lord shall not want any good thing.

The righteous cry, and the Lord heareth, and delivereth them out of all their troubles.

The Lord is nigh unto them that are of a broken heart; and saveth such as be of a contrite spirit.

Many are the afflictions of the righteous: but the Lord delivereth him out of them all.

The Lord redeemeth the soul of his servants; and none of them that trust in him shall be desolate.

—*Psalm 34:1-10, 17-19, 22*

7 The Divine Shepherd

The Lord is my shepherd; I shall not want.

He maketh me to lie down in green pastures: he leadeth me beside the still waters.

He restoreth my soul: he leadeth me in the paths of righteousness for his name's sake.

Yea, though I walk through the valley of the shadow of death, I will fear no evil:

For thou art with me; thy rod and thy staff they comfort me.

Thou preparest a table before me in the presence of mine enemies:

Thou anointest my head with oil; my cup runneth over.

Surely goodness and mercy shall follow me all the days of my life; and I will dwell in the house of the Lord for ever. —*Psalm 23*

8 The Holy Scriptures

Wherewithal shall a young man cleanse his way? by taking heed thereto according to thy word.

With my whole heart have I sought thee: O let me not wander from thy commandments.

Thy word have I hid in mine heart, that I might not sin against thee.

Open thou mine eyes, that I may behold wondrous things out of thy law.

Thy testimonies are wonderful: therefore doth my soul keep them.

The entrance of thy words giveth

light: it giveth understanding unto the simple.

—Psalm 119:9-11, 18, 129, 130

All scripture is given by inspiration of God, and is profitable for doctrine, for reproof, for correction, for instruction in righteousness.

That the man of God may be perfect, throughly furnished unto all good works.

Study to show thyself approved unto God, a workman that needeth not to be ashamed, rightly dividing the word of truth.

—2 Timothy 3:16, 17; 2:15

For the prophecy came not in old time by the will of man:

But holy men of God spake as they were moved by the Holy Ghost.

—2 Peter 1:21

The word of God is quick, and powerful, and sharper than any twoedged sword, piercing even to the dividing asunder of soul and spirit, and of the joints and marrow, and is a discerner of the thoughts and intents of the heart. *—Hebrews 4:12*

9 *The Commandments*

And God spake all these words, saying, I am the Lord thy God, which have brought thee out of the land of Egypt, out of the house of bondage.

(I) Thou shalt have no other gods before me.

(II) Thou shalt not make unto thee any graven image, or any likeness of any thing that is in heaven above, or that is in the earth beneath, or that is in the water under the earth:

Thou shalt not bow down thyself to them, nor serve them: for I the Lord thy God am a jealous God, visiting the iniquity of the fathers upon the children unto the third and fourth generation of them that hate me; and showing mercy unto thousands of them that love me, and keep my commandments.

(III) Thou shalt not take the name of the Lord thy God in vain: for the Lord will not hold him guiltless that taketh his name in vain.

(IV) Remember the sabbath day, to keep it holy. Six days shalt thou labour, and do all thy work; but the seventh day is the sabbath of the Lord thy God: in it thou shalt not do any work, thou, nor thy son, nor thy daughter, thy manservant, nor thy maidservant, nor thy cattle, nor thy stranger that is within thy gates.

For in six days the Lord made heaven and earth, the sea, and all that in them is, and rested the seventh day: wherefore the Lord blessed the sabbath day, and hallowed it.

(V) Honour thy father and thy mother: that thy days may be long upon the land which the Lord thy God giveth thee.

(VI) Thou shalt not kill.

(VII) Thou shalt not commit adultery.

(VIII) Thou shalt not steal.

(IX) Thou shalt not bear false witness against thy neighbour.

(X) Thou shalt not covet thy neighbour's house, thou shalt not covet thy neighbour's wife, nor his manservant, nor his maidservant, nor his ox, nor his ass, nor any thing that is thy neighbour's.

—Exodus 20:1

10 *The Christ of Prophecy*

And there shall come forth a rod out of the stem of Jesse, and a Branch shall grow out of his roots:

And the spirit of the Lord shall rest upon him, the spirit of wisdom and understanding, the spirit of counsel and might, the spirit of knowledge, and of the fear of the Lord;

And shall make him of quick understanding in the fear of the Lord: and he shall not judge after the sight of his eyes, neither reprove after the hearing of his ears:

But with righteousness shall he judge the poor, and reprove with equity for the meek of the earth: and he shall smite the earth with the rod of his mouth, and with the breath of his lips shall he slay the wicked.

And righteousness shall be the girdle of his loins, and faithfulness the girdle of his reins.

Behold my servant, whom I uphold; mine elect, in whom my soul delighteth; I have put my spirit upon him: he shall bring forth judgment to the Gentiles.

He shall not cry, nor lift up, nor cause his voice to be heard in the street.

A bruised reed shall he not break, and the smoking flax shall he not quench: he shall bring forth judgment unto truth.

He shall not fail nor be discouraged, till he have set judgment in the earth: and the isles shall wait for his law.

Go through, go through the gates; prepare ye the way of the people; cast up, cast up the highway; gather out the stones; lift up a standard for the people.

Behold, the Lord hath proclaimed unto the end of the world, Say ye to the daughter of Zion, Behold, thy salvation cometh; behold, his reward is with him, and his work before him.

—*Isaiah 11:1-5; 42:1-4; 62:10, 11*

Behold, the days come, saith the Lord, that I will raise unto David a righteous Branch, and a King shall reign and prosper, and shall execute judgment and justice in the earth.

In his days Judah shall be saved, and Israel shall dwell safely; and this is his name whereby he shall be called, THE LORD OUR RIGHTEOUSNESS.

—*Jeremiah 23:5, 6*

Unto you that fear my name shall the Sun of righteousness arise with healing in his wings. —*Malachi 4:2*

11 *Divine Love*

And as Moses lifted up the serpent in the wilderness, even so must the Son of man be lifted up: that whosoever believeth in him should not perish, but have eternal life.

For God so loved the world, that he gave his only begotten Son, that whosoever believeth in him should not perish, but have everlasting life.

For God sent not his Son into the world to condemn the world; but that the world through him might be saved.

He that believeth on him is not condemned: but he that believeth not is condemned already, because he hath not believed in the name of the only begotten Son of God.

And this is the condemnation, that light is come into the world, and men loved darkness rather than light, because their deeds were evil.

For every one that doeth evil hateth the light, neither cometh to the light, lest his deeds should be reproved.

But he that doeth truth cometh to the light, that his deeds may be made manifest, that they are wrought in God.

He that believeth on the Son hath everlasting life: and he that believeth not the Son shall not see life; but the wrath of God abideth on him.

—John 3:14-21, 36

Beloved, let us love one another: for love is of God; and every one that loveth is born of God, and knoweth God.

He that loveth not knoweth not God; for God is love.

In this was manifested the love of God toward us, because that God sent his only begotten Son into the world, that we might live through him.

Herein is love, not that we loved God, but that he loved us, and sent his Son to be the propitiation for our sins.

—1 John 4:7-10

12 Divine Blessings

Bless the Lord, O my soul; and all that is within me, bless his holy name.

Bless the Lord, O my soul, and forget not all his benefits:

Who forgiveth all thine iniquities; who healeth all thy diseases.

Who redeemeth thy life from destruction; who crowneth thee with lovingkindness and tender mercies;

Who satisfieth thy mouth with good things; so that thy youth is renewed like the eagle's.

The Lord executeth righteousness and judgment for all that are oppressed.

He made known his ways unto Moses, his acts unto the children of Israel.

The Lord is merciful and gracious, slow to anger, and plenteous in mercy.

He will not always chide: neither will he keep his anger for ever.

He hath not dealt with us after our sins, nor rewarded us according to our iniquities.

For as the heaven is high above the earth, so great is his mercy toward them that fear him.

As far as the east is from the west, so far hath he removed our transgressions from us.

Like as a father pitieth his children, so the Lord pitieth them that fear him.

For he knoweth our frame; he remembereth that we are dust.

As for man, his days are as grass: as a flower of the field, so he flourisheth.

For the wind passeth over it, and it is gone; and the place thereof shall know it no more.

But the mercy of the Lord is from everlasting to everlasting upon them that fear him, and his righteousness unto children's children.

To such as keep his covenant, and to

those that remember his commandments to do them.

The Lord hath prepared his throne in the heavens; and his kingdom ruleth over all.

Bless the Lord, ye his angels, that excel in strength, that do his commandments, hearkening unto the voice of his word.

Bless ye the Lord, all ye his hosts; ye ministers of his that do his pleasure.

Bless the Lord, all his works, in all places of his dominion: bless the Lord, O my soul. —*Psalm 103*

13 Divine Care

Lay not up for yourselves treasures upon earth, where moth and rust doth corrupt, and where thieves break through and steal:

But lay up for yourselves treasures in heaven, where neither moth nor rust doth corrupt, and where thieves do not break through nor steal:

For where your treasure is, there will your heart be also.

No man can serve two masters: for either he will hate the one, and love the other; or else he will hold to the one and despise the other. Ye cannot serve God and mammon.

Therefore I say unto you, Take no thought for your life, what ye shall eat, or what ye shall drink; nor yet for your body, what ye shall put on.

Is not the life more than meat, and the body than raiment?

Behold the fowls of the air: for they sow not, neither do they reap, nor gather into barns; yet your heavenly Father feedeth them.

Are ye not much better than they?

Which of you by taking thought can add one cubit unto his stature?

And why take ye thought for raiment? Consider the lilies of the field, how they grow; they toil not, neither do they spin:

And yet I say unto you, That even Solomon in all his glory was not arrayed like one of these.

Wherefore, if God so clothe the grass of the field, which today is, and tomorrow is cast into the oven, shall he not much more clothe you, O ye of little faith?

Therefore take no thought, saying, What shall we eat? or, What shall we drink? or, Wherewithal shall we be clothed?

For after all these things do the Gentiles seek: for your heavenly Father knoweth that ye have need of all these things.

But seek ye first the kingdom of God, and his righteousness; and all these things shall be added unto you.

Take therefore no thought for the morrow: for the morrow shall take thought for the things of itself. Sufficient unto the day is the evil thereof.

—*Matthew 6:19-21, 24-34*

14 Divine Protection

He that dwelleth in the secret place of the most High shall abide under the shadow of the Almighty.

I will say of the Lord, He is my refuge and my fortress: my God; in him will I trust.

Surely he shall deliver thee from

the snare of the fowler, and from the noisome pestilence.

He shall cover thee with his feathers, and under his wings shalt thou trust: his truth shall be thy shield and buckler.

Thou shalt not be afraid for the terror by night; nor for the arrow that flieth by day;

Nor for the pestilence that walketh in darkness; nor for the destruction that wasteth at noonday.

A thousand shall fall at thy side, and ten thousand at thy right hand; but it shall not come nigh thee.

Only with thine eyes shalt thou behold and see the reward of the wicked.

Because thou hast made the Lord, which is my refuge, even the most High, thy habitation.

There shall no evil befall thee, neither shall any plague come nigh thy dwelling.

For he shall give his angels charge over thee, to keep thee in all thy ways.

They shall bear thee up in their hands, lest thou dash thy foot against a stone.

Thou shalt tread upon the lion and adder: the young lion and the dragon shalt thou trample under feet.

Because he hath set his love upon me, therefore will I deliver him: I will set him on high, because he hath known my name.

He shall call upon me, and I will answer him: I will be with him in trouble; I will deliver him, and honour him.

With long life will I satisfy him, and show him my salvation.

—Psalm 91

15 Divine Comfort

Comfort ye, comfort ye my people, saith your God.

Speak ye comfortably to Jerusalem, and cry unto her, that her warfare is accomplished, that her iniquity is pardoned: for she hath received of the Lord's hand double for all her sins.

The voice of him that crieth in the wilderness, Prepare ye the way of the Lord, make straight in the desert a highway for our God.

Every valley shall be exalted, and every mountain and hill shall be made low: and the crooked shall be made straight, and the rough places plain:

And the glory of the Lord shall be revealed, and all flesh shall see it together: for the mouth of the Lord hath spoken it.

The voice said, Cry. And he said, What shall I cry? All flesh is grass, and all the goodliness thereof is as the flower of the field:

The grass withereth, the flower fadeth: because the Spirit of the Lord bloweth upon it: surely the people is grass.

The grass withereth, the flower fadeth: but the word of our God shall stand for ever.

O Zion, that bringest good tidings, get thee up into the high mountain; O Jerusalem, that bringest good tidings, lift up thy voice with strength; lift it up, be not afraid; say unto the cities of Judah, Behold your God!

Behold, the Lord God will come with strong hand, and his arm shall rule for him; behold, his reward is with him, and his work before him.

He shall feed his flock like a shepherd: he shall gather the lambs with his arm, and carry them in his bosom, and shall gently lead those that are with young.

He giveth power to the faint; and to them that have no might he increaseth strength.

Even the youths shall faint and be weary, and the young men shall utterly fall:

But they that wait upon the Lord shall renew their strength; they shall mount up with wings as eagles; they shall run, and not be weary; and they shall walk and not faint.

—Isaiah 40:1-11, 29-31

16 *Thanksgiving*

I love the Lord, because he hath heard my voice and my supplications.

Because he hath inclined his ear unto me, therefore will I call upon him as long as I live.

The sorrows of death compassed me, and the pains of hell gat hold upon me: I found trouble and sorrow.

Then called I upon the name of the Lord: O Lord, I beseech thee, deliver my soul.

Gracious is the Lord, and righteous; yea, our God is merciful.

The Lord preserveth the simple: I was brought low, and he helped me.

Return unto thy rest, O my soul; for the Lord hath dealt bountifully with thee.

For thou hast delivered my soul from death, mine eyes from tears, and my feet from falling.

I will walk before the Lord in the land of the living.

What shall I render unto the Lord for all his benefits toward me?

I will take the cup of salvation, and call upon the name of the Lord.

I will pay my vows unto the Lord now in the presence of all his people.

Precious in the sight of the Lord is the death of his saints.

O Lord, truly I am thy servant; I am thy servant, and the son of thine handmaid: thou hast loosed my bonds.

I will offer to thee the sacrifice of thanksgiving, and will call upon the name of the Lord.

I will pay my vows unto the Lord now in the presence of all his people.

—Psalm 116:1-9, 12-18

17 *Joyful Worship*

I was glad when they said unto me, Let us go into the house of the Lord.

Our feet shall stand within thy gates, O Jerusalem.

Jerusalem is builded as a city that is compact together:

Whither the tribes go up, the tribes of the Lord, unto the testimony of Israel, to give thanks unto the name of the Lord.

For there are set thrones of judgment, the thrones of the house of David.

Pray for the peace of Jerusalem: they shall prosper that love thee.

Peace be within thy walls, and prosperity within thy palaces.

For my brethren and companions' sakes, I will now say, Peace be within thee.

Because of the house of the Lord our God I will seek thy good.

I was glad when they said unto me, Let us go into the house of the Lord.

—Psalm 122

I will praise thee with my whole heart: before the gods will I sing praise unto thee.

I will worship toward thy holy temple, and praise thy name for thy lovingkindness and for thy truth: for thou hast magnified thy word above all thy name.

In the day when I cried thou answeredst me, and strengthenedst me with strength in my soul.

All the kings of the earth shall praise thee, O Lord, when they hear the words of thy mouth.

Yea, they shall sing in the ways of the Lord: for great is the glory of the Lord.

Though the Lord be high, yet hath he respect unto the lowly: but the proud he knoweth afar off.

Though I walk in the midst of trouble, thou wilt revive me: thou shalt stretch forth thine hand against the wrath of mine enemies, and thy right hand shall save me.

The Lord will perfect that which concerneth me: thy mercy, O Lord, endureth for ever: forsake not the works of thine own hands.

—Psalm 138

18 Song of Deliverance

I waited patiently for the Lord; and he inclined unto me, and heard my cry.

He brought me up also out of an horrible pit, out of the miry clay, and set my feet upon a rock, and established my goings.

And he hath put a new song in my mouth, even praise unto our God: many shall see it, and fear, and shall trust in the Lord.

Blessed is that man that maketh the Lord his trust, and respecteth not the proud, nor such as turn aside to lies.

Many, O Lord my God, are thy wonderful works which thou hast done, and thy thoughts which are to us-ward:

They cannot be reckoned up in order unto thee: if I would declare and speak of them, they are more than can be numbered.

Sacrifice and offering thou didst not desire; mine ears hast thou opened: burnt offering and sin offering hast thou not required.

Then said I, Lo, I come: in the volume of the book it is written of me,

I delight to do thy will, O my God: yea, thy law is within my heart.

I have preached righteousness in the great congregation: lo, I have not refrained my lips, O Lord, thou knowest.

I have not hid thy righteousness within my heart; I have declared thy faithfulness and thy salvation:

I have not concealed thy lovingkindness and thy truth from the great congregation.

Withhold not thou thy tender mercies from me, O Lord: let thy lovingkindness and thy truth continually preserve me.

For innumerable evils have compassed me about: mine iniquities have taken hold upon me, so that I am not able to look up: they are more than the hairs of mine head: therefore my heart faileth me.

Be pleased, O Lord, to deliver me: O Lord, make haste to help me.

Let all those that seek thee rejoice and be glad in thee: let such as love thy salvation say continually, The Lord be magnified.

—*Psalm 40:1-13, 16*

19 *A Psalm of Praise*

I will extol thee, my God, O King; and I will bless thy name for ever and ever.

Every day will I bless thee; and I will praise thy name for ever and ever.

Great is the Lord, and greatly to be praised; and his greatness is unsearchable.

One generation shall praise thy works to another, and shall declare thy mighty acts.

I will speak of the glorious honour of thy majesty, and of thy wondrous works.

And men shall speak of the might of thy terrible acts: and I will declare thy greatness.

They shall abundantly utter the memory of thy great goodness, and shall sing of thy righteousness.

The Lord is gracious and full of compassion; slow to anger, and of great mercy.

The Lord is good to all; and his tender mercies are over all his works.

All thy works shall praise thee, O Lord; and thy saints shall bless thee.

They shall speak of the glory of thy kingdom, and talk of thy power;

To make known to the sons of men his mighty acts, and the glorious majesty of his kingdom.

Thy kingdom is an everlasting kingdom, and thy dominion endureth throughout all generations.

The Lord upholdeth all that fall, and raiseth up all those that be bowed down.

The eyes of all wait upon thee; and thou givest them their meat in due season.

Thou openest thine hand, and satisfiest the desire of every living thing.

The Lord is righteous in all his ways, and holy in all his works.

The Lord is nigh unto all them that call upon him, to all that call upon him in truth.

He will fulfil the desire of them that fear him: he also will hear their cry, and will save them.

The Lord preserveth all them that love him: but all the wicked will he destroy. My mouth shall speak the praise of the Lord; and let all flesh bless his holy name for ever and ever.

—*Psalm 145*

20 *Benefits of Wisdom*

My son, forget not my law; but let thine heart keep my commandments:

For length of days, and long life, and peace, shall they add to thee.

Let not mercy and truth forsake thee: bind them about thy neck;

write them upon the table of thine heart:

So shalt thou find favour and good understanding in the sight of God and man.

Trust in the Lord with all thine heart; and lean not unto thine own understanding.

In all thy ways acknowledge him, and he shall direct thy paths.

Happy is the man that findeth wisdom, and the man that getteth understanding.

For the merchandise of it is better than the merchandise of silver, and the gain thereof than fine gold.

She is more precious than rubies: and all the things thou canst desire are not to be compared unto her.

Length of days is in her right hand; and in her left hand riches and honour.

Her ways are ways of pleasantness, and all her paths are peace.

She is a tree of life to them that lay hold upon her: and happy is every one that retaineth her.

The Lord by wisdom hath founded the earth; by understanding hath he established the heavens.

By his knowledge the depths are broken up, and the clouds drop down the dew.

My son, let not them depart from thine eyes: keep sound wisdom and discretion:

So shall they be life unto thy soul, and grace to thy neck.

Then shalt thou walk in thy way safely, and thy foot shall not stumble.

When thou liest down, thou shalt not be afraid: yea, thou shalt lie down, and thy sleep shall be sweet.

Be not afraid of sudden fear, neither of the desolation of the wicked, when it cometh.

For the Lord shall be thy confidence, and shall keep thy foot from being taken. —*Proverbs 3:1-6, 13-26*

21 The Gracious Invitation

Ho, every one that thirsteth, come ye to the waters, and he that hath no money; come ye, buy, and eat; yea, come, buy wine and milk without money and without price.

Wherefore do ye spend money for that which is not bread? and your labour for that which satisfieth not? hearken diligently unto me, and eat ye that which is good, and let your soul delight itself in fatness.

Incline your ear, and come unto me: hear, and your soul shall live; and I will make an everlasting covenant with you, even the sure mercies of David.

Behold, I have given him for a witness to the people, a leader and commander to the people.

Behold, thou shalt call a nation that thou knowest not, and nations that knew not thee shall run unto thee because of the Lord thy God, and for the Holy One of Israel; for he hath glorified thee.

Seek ye the Lord while he may be found, call ye upon him while he is near:

Let the wicked forsake his way, and the unrighteous man his thoughts: and let him return unto the Lord, and he will have mercy upon him;

and to our God, for he will abundantly pardon.

For my thoughts are not your thoughts, neither are your ways my ways, saith the Lord.

For as the heavens are higher than the earth, so are my ways higher than your ways, and my thoughts than your thoughts.

For as the rain cometh down, and the snow from heaven, and returneth not thither, but watereth the earth, and maketh it bring forth and bud, that it may give seed to the sower, and bread to the eater:

So shall my word be that goeth forth out of my mouth: it shall not return unto me void, but it shall accomplish that which I please, and it shall prosper in the thing whereto I sent it.

For ye shall go out with joy, and be led forth with peace: the mountains and the hills shall break forth before you into singing, and all the trees of the field shall clap their hands.

Instead of the thorn shall come up the fir tree, and instead of the brier shall come up the myrtle tree:

And it shall be to the Lord for a name, for an everlasting sign that shall not be cut off.

—*Isaiah* 55

22 *Prayer of the Penitent*

Have mercy upon me, O God, according to thy lovingkindness;

According unto the multitude of thy tender mercies blot out my transgressions.

Wash me throughly from mine iniquity, and cleanse me from my sin.

For I acknowledge my transgressions; and my sin is ever before me.

Against thee, thee only, have I sinned, and done this evil in thy sight: that thou mightest be justified when thou speakest, and be clear when thou judgest.

Behold, I was shapen in iniquity; and in sin did my mother conceive me.

Behold, thou desirest truth in the inward parts; and in the hidden part thou shalt make me to know wisdom.

Purge me with hyssop, and I shall be clean: wash me, and I shall be whiter than snow.

Make me to hear joy and gladness; that the bones which thou hast broken may rejoice.

Hide thy face from my sins, and blot out all mine iniquities.

Create in me a clean heart, O God; and renew a right spirit within me.

Cast me not away from thy presence; and take not thy holy Spirit from me.

Restore unto me the joy of thy salvation; and uphold me with thy free Spirit:

Then will I teach transgressors thy ways; and sinners shall be converted unto thee.

Deliver me from bloodguiltiness, O God, thou God of my salvation; and my tongue shall sing aloud of thy righteousness.

O Lord, open thou my lips; and my mouth shall shew forth thy praise.

For thou desirest not sacrifice; else would I give it: thou delightest not in burnt offering.

The sacrifices of God are a broken

spirit: a broken and a contrite heart, O God, thou wilt not despise.

—Psalm 51:1-17

I will delight myself in thy statutes: I will not forget thy word.

—Psalm 119:1-16

23 The Path of Obedience

Blessed are the undefiled in the way, who walk in the law of the Lord.

Blessed are they that keep his testimonies and that seek him with the whole heart.

They also do no iniquity: they walk in his ways.

Thou hast commanded us to keep thy precepts diligently.

O that my ways were directed to keep thy statutes!

Then shall I not be ashamed, when I have respect unto all thy commandments.

I will praise thee with uprightness of heart, when I shall have learned thy righteous judgments.

I will keep thy statutes: O forsake me not utterly.

Wherewithal shall a young man cleanse his way? By taking heed thereto according to thy word.

With my whole heart have I sought thee: O let me not wander from thy commandments.

Thy word have I hid in mine heart, that I might not sin against thee.

Blessed art thou, O Lord: teach me thy statutes.

With my lips have I declared all the judgments of thy mouth.

I have rejoiced in the way of thy testimonies, as much as in all riches.

I will meditate in thy precepts, and have respect unto thy ways.

24 Thirsting for God

As the hart panteth after the water brooks,

So panteth my soul after thee, O God.

My soul thirsteth for God, for the living God:

When shall I come and appear before God?

My tears have been my meat day and night,

While they continually say unto me, Where is thy God?

Why art thou cast down, O my soul?

And why art thou disquieted in me?

Hope thou in God:

For I shall yet praise him for the help of his countenance.

Deep calleth unto deep at the noise of thy waterspouts:

All thy waves and thy billows are gone over me.

Yet the Lord will command his lovingkindness in the daytime,

And in the night his song shall be with me, and my prayer unto the God of my life.

Judge me, O God, and plead my cause against an ungodly nation:

O deliver me from the deceitful and unjust man.

O send out thy light and thy truth: let them lead me;

Let them bring me unto thy holy hill, and to thy tabernacles.

Then will I go unto the altar of God, unto God my exceeding joy:

Yea, upon the harp will I praise thee, O God, my God.

Why art thou cast down, O my soul?

And why art thou disquieted within me?

Hope in God:

For I shall yet praise him, who is the health of my countenance, and my God.

—Psalms 42:1-3, 5, 7-8; 43:1, 3-5

25 The All-Knowing God

O Lord, thou hast searched me, and known me.

Thou knowest my downsitting and mine uprising; thou understandest my thought afar off.

Thou compassest my path and my lying down, and art acquainted with all my ways.

Such knowledge is too wonderful for me; it is high, I cannot attain unto it.

Whither shall I go from thy Spirit?

Or whither shall I flee from thy presence?

If I ascend up into heaven, thou art there:

If I make my bed in hell, behold, thou art there.

If I take the wings of the morning, and dwell in the uttermost parts of the sea;

Even there shall thy hand lead me, and thy right hand shall hold me.

If I say, Surely the darkness shall cover me; even the night shall be light about me.

Yea, the darkness hideth not from thee;

But the night shineth as the day:

The darkness and the light are both alike to thee.

How precious also are thy thoughts unto me, O God!

How great is the sum of them!

If I should count them, they are more in number than the sand:

When I awake, I am still with thee.

Search me, O God, and know my heart:

Try me, and know my thoughts:

And see if there be any wicked way in me,

And lead me in the way everlasting.

—Psalm 139:1-3, 6-12, 17, 18, 23, 24.

26 A Hymn of Eternity

Lord, thou hast been our dwelling place in all generations.

Before the mountains were brought forth, or ever thou hadst formed the earth and the world,

Even from everlasting to everlasting thou art God.

Thou turnest man to destruction; and sayest, Return, ye children of men.

For a thousand years in thy sight are but as yesterday when it is past, and as a watch in the night.

Thou carriest them away as with a flood; they are as a sleep:

In the morning they are like grass which groweth up.

In the morning it flourisheth, and

groweth up; in the evening it is cut down, and withereth.

We spend our years as a tale that is told.

So teach us to number our days, that we may apply our hearts unto wisdom.

Return, O Lord, how long? and let it repent thee concerning thy servants.

O satisfy us early with thy mercy; that we may rejoice and be glad all our days.

Make us glad according to the days wherein thou hast afflicted us, and the years wherein we have seen evil.

Let thy work appear unto thy servants, and thy glory unto their children.

And let the beauty of the Lord our God be upon us:

And establish thou the work of our hands upon us; yea, the work of our hands establish thou it.

—Psalm 90:1-6, 9b, 12-17

27 Great Commission

Then the eleven disciples went away into Galilee, into a mountain where Jesus had appointed them.

And when they saw him, they worshipped him: but some doubted.

And Jesus came and spake unto them, saying, All power is given unto me in heaven and in earth.

Go ye therefore, and teach all nations, baptizing them in the name of the Father, and of the Son, and of the Holy Ghost;

Teaching them to observe all things whatsoever I have commanded you: and, lo, I am with you alway, even unto the end of the world.

—Matthew 28:16-20

Jesus said unto them, Thus it is written, and thus it behoved Christ to suffer, and to rise from the dead the third day:

And that repentance and remission of sins should be preached in his name among all nations, beginning at Jerusalem.

And ye are witnesses of these things.

And, behold, I send the promise of my Father upon you: but tarry ye in the city of Jerusalem, until ye be endued with power from on high.

—Luke 24:46-49

They asked of him, saying, Lord, wilt thou at this time restore again the kingdom of Israel?

And he said unto them, It is not for you to know the times or the seasons, which the Father hath put in his own power.

But ye shall receive power, after that the Holy Ghost is come upon you:

And ye shall be witnesses unto me both in Jerusalem, and in all Judaea, and in Samaria, and unto the uttermost part of the earth.

And when he had spoken these things, while they beheld, he was taken up; and a cloud received him out of their sight. *—Acts 1:6-9*

28 Confidence in God

Fret not thyself because of evildoers, neither be thou envious against the workers of iniquity.

For they shall soon be cut down like the grass, and wither as the green herb.

Trust in the Lord, and do good; so shalt thou dwell in the land, and verily thou shalt be fed.

Delight thyself also in the Lord, and he shall give thee the desires of thine heart.

Commit thy way unto the Lord; trust also in him; and he shall bring it to pass.

And he shall bring forth thy righteousness as the light, and thy judgment as the noonday.

Rest in the Lord, and wait patiently for him: fret not thyself because of him who prospereth in his way, because of the man who bringeth wicked devices to pass.

Cease from anger, and forsake wrath: fret not thyself in any wise to do evil.

For evildoers shall be cut off: but those that wait upon the Lord, they shall inherit the earth.

For yet a little while, and the wicked shall not be: yea, thou shalt diligently consider his place, and it shall not be.

But the meek shall inherit the earth, and shall delight themselves in the abundance of peace.

The steps of a good man are ordered by the Lord; and he delighteth in his way.

Though he fall, he shall not be utterly cast down: for the Lord upholdeth him with his hand.

I have been young, and now am old; yet have I not seen the righteous forsaken, nor his seed begging bread.

I have seen the wicked in great power, and spreading himself like a green bay tree.

Yet he passed away, and, lo, he was not: yea, I sought him, but he could not be found

Mark the perfect man, and behold the upright: for the end of that man is peace.

—Psalm 37:1-11, 23-25, 35-37

29 *The Beatitudes*

And seeing the multitudes, he went up into a mountain: and when he was set, his disciples came unto him:

And he opened his mouth, and taught them, saying,

Blessed are the poor in spirit: for theirs is the kingdom of heaven.

Blessed are they that mourn: for they shall be comforted.

Blessed are the meek: for they shall inherit the earth.

Blessed are they which do hunger and thirst after righteousness: for they shall be filled.

Blessed are the merciful: for they shall obtain mercy.

Blessed are the pure in heart: for they shall see God.

Blessed are the peacemakers: for they shall be called the children of God.

Blessed are they which are persecuted for righteousness' sake: for theirs is the kingdom of heaven.

Blessed are ye, when men shall revile you, and persecute you, and shall say all manner of evil against you falsely, for my sake.

Rejoice, and be exceeding glad: for great is your reward in heaven:

For so persecuted they the prophets which were before you.

Ye are the salt of the earth: but if the salt have lost his savour, wherewith shall it be salted?

—Matthew 5:1-12

30 *Jesus Teaches Prayer*

And it came to pass, that, as he was praying in a certain place, when he ceased, one of his disciples said unto him, Lord, teach us to pray, as John also taught his disciples.

And he said unto them, When ye pray, say, Our Father which art in heaven, Hallowed be thy name. Thy kingdom come. Thy will be done, as in heaven, so in earth.

Give us day by day our daily bread.

And forgive us our sins; for we also forgive every one that is indebted to us.

And lead us not into temptation; but deliver us from evil.

And he said unto them, Which of you shall have a friend, and shall go unto him at midnight, and say unto him, Friend, lend me three loaves;

For a friend of mine in his journey is come to me, and I have nothing to set before him?

And he from within shall answer and say, Trouble me not: the door is now shut, and my children are with me in bed; I cannot rise and give thee.

I say unto you, Though he will not rise and give him, because he is his friend, yet because of his importunity he will rise and give him as many as he needeth.

And I say unto you, Ask, and it shall be given you; seek, and ye shall find; knock, and it shall be opened unto you.

For every one that asketh receiveth; and he that seeketh findeth; and to him that knocketh it shall be opened.

If a son shall ask bread of any of you that is a father, will he give him a stone? or if he ask a fish, will he for a fish give him a serpent?

Or if he shall ask an egg, will he offer him a scorpion?

If ye then, being evil, know how to give good gifts unto your children: how much more shall your heavenly Father give the Holy Spirit to them that ask him? *—Luke 11:1-13*

31 *The Vine and the Branches*

I am the true vine, and my Father is the husbandman.

Every branch in me that beareth not fruit he taketh away: and every branch that beareth fruit, he purgeth it, that it may bring forth more fruit.

Now ye are clean through the word which I have spoken unto you.

Abide in me, and I in you. As the branch cannot bear fruit of itself, except it abide in the vine; no more can ye, except ye abide in me.

I am the vine, ye are the branches: he that abideth in me, and I in him, the same bringeth forth much fruit: for without me ye can do nothing.

If a man abide not in me, he is cast forth as a branch, and is withered;

and men gather them, and cast them into the fire, and they are burned.

If ye abide in me, and my words abide in you, ye shall ask what ye will, and it shall be done unto you.

Herein is my Father glorified, that ye bear much fruit; so shall ye be my disciples.

As the Father hath loved me, so have I loved you: continue ye in my love.

If ye keep my commandments, ye shall abide in my love; even as I have kept my Father's commandments, and abide in his love.

These things have I spoken unto you, that my joy might remain in you, and that your joy might be full.

This is my commandment, That ye love one another, as I have loved you.

Greater love hath no man than this, that a man lay down his life for his friends.

Ye are my friends, if ye do whatsoever I command you.

—John 15:1-14

32 *Witness of the Spirit*

There is therefore now no condemnation to them which are in Christ Jesus, who walk not after the flesh, but after the Spirit.

For as many as are led by the Spirit of God, they are the sons of God.

For ye have not received the spirit of bondage again to fear: but ye have received the Spirit of adoption, whereby we cry, Abba, Father.

The Spirit itself beareth witness with our spirit, that we are the children of God:

And if children, then heirs; heirs of God, and joint-heirs with Christ; if so be that we suffer with him, that we may be also glorified together.

For I reckon that the sufferings of this present time are not worthy to be compared with the glory which shall be revealed in us.

And we know that all things work together for good to them that love God, to them who are the called according to his purpose.

For whom he did foreknow, he also did predestinate to be conformed to the image of his Son, that he might be the firstborn among many brethren.

Moreover whom he did predestinate, them he also called: and whom he called, them he also justified: and whom he justified, them he also glorified.

What shall we then say to these things? If God be for us, who can be against us?

He that spared not his own Son, but delivered him up for us all, how shall he not with him also freely give us all things?

Who shall lay any thing to the charge of God's elect? It is God that justifieth.

Who is he that condemneth? It is Christ that died, yea rather, that is risen again, who is even at the right hand of God, who also maketh intercession for us.

Who shall separate us from the love of Christ? shall tribulation, or distress, or persecution, or famine, or nakedness, or peril or sword?

As it is written, For thy sake we are

killed all the day long; we are accounted as sheep for the slaughter.

Nay, in all these things we are more than conquerors through him that loved us.

For I am persuaded, that neither death, nor life, nor angels, nor principalities, nor powers, nor things present, nor things to come,

Nor height, nor depth, nor any other creature, shall be able to separate us from the love of God, which is in Christ Jesus our Lord.

—*Romans 8:1, 14-18, 28-39*

33 Consecration and Service

I beseech you therefore, brethren, by the mercies of God, that ye present your bodies a living sacrifice, holy, acceptable unto God, which is your reasonable service.

And be not conformed to this world: but be ye transformed by the renewing of your mind, that ye may prove what is that good, and acceptable, and perfect will of God.

For I say, through the grace given unto me, to every man that is among you, not to think of himself more highly than he ought to think;

But to think soberly, according as God hath dealt to every man the measure of faith.

For as we have many members in one body, and all members have not the same office;

So we, being many, are one body in Christ, and every one members one of another.

Having then gifts differing according to the grace that is given to us, whether prophecy, let us prophesy according to the proportion of faith;

Or ministry, let us wait on our ministering: or he that teacheth, on teaching;

Or he that exhorteth, on exhortation: he that giveth, let him do it with simplicity; he that ruleth, with diligence; he that sheweth mercy, with cheerfulness.

Let love be without dissimulation. Abhor that which is evil; cleave to that which is good.

Be kindly affectioned one to another with brotherly love; in honour preferring one another;

Not slothful in business; fervent in spirit; serving the Lord;

Rejoicing in hope; patient in tribulation; continuing instant in prayer;

Distributing to the necessity of saints; given to hospitality.

Bless them which persecute you: bless, and curse not.

Rejoice with them that do rejoice, and weep with them that weep.

Be of the same mind one toward another. Mind not high things, but condescend to men of low estate. Be not wise in your own conceits.

Recompense to no man evil for evil. Provide things honest in the sight of all men.

If it be possible, as much as lieth in you, live peaceably with all men.

Dearly beloved, avenge not yourselves, but rather give place unto wrath: for it is written, Vengeance is mine; I will repay, saith the Lord.

Therefore if thine enemy hunger, feed him; if he thirst, give him drink: for in so doing thou shalt heap coals of fire on his head.

Be not overcome of evil, but overcome evil with good.

—Romans 12

34 Stewardship

Honour the Lord with thy substance, and with the firstfruits of all thine increase:

So shall thy barns be filled with plenty, and thy presses shall burst out with new wine.

—Proverbs 3:9, 10

Bring ye all the tithes into the storehouse, that there may be meat in mine house, and prove me now herewith, saith the Lord of hosts, if I will not open you the windows of heaven, and pour you out a blessing, that there shall not be room enough to receive it.

—Malachi 3:10

This I say, He which soweth sparingly, shall reap also sparingly; and he which soweth bountifully shall reap also bountifully.

Every man according as he purposeth in his heart, so let him give; not grudgingly, or of necessity: for God loveth a cheerful giver.

And God is able to make all grace abound toward you; that ye, always having all sufficiency in all things, may abound to every good work.

—2 Corinthians 9:6-8

Above all things have fervent charity among yourselves: for charity shall cover the multitude of sins.

Use hospitality one to another without grudging.

As every man hath received the gift, even so minister the same one to another, as good stewards of the manifold grace of God.

—1 Peter 4:8-10

35 The More Excellent Way

Though I speak with the tongues of men and of angels, and have not love, I am become as sounding brass, or a tinkling cymbal.

And though I have the gift of prophecy, and understand all mysteries, and all knowledge; and though I have all faith, so that I could remove mountains, and have not love, I am nothing.

And though I bestow all my goods to feed the poor, and though I give my body to be burned, and yet have not love, it profiteth me nothing.

Love suffereth long, and is kind; love envieth not; love vaunteth not itself, is not puffed up,

Doth not behave itself unseemly, seeketh not her own, is not easily provoked, thinketh no evil;

Rejoiceth not in iniquity, but rejoiceth in the truth;

Beareth all things, believeth all things, hopeth all things, endureth all things.

Love never faileth: but whether there be prophecies, they shall fail; whether there be tongues, they shall cease; whether there be knowledge, it shall vanish away.

For we know in part, and we prophesy in part.

But when that which is perfect is come, then that which is in part shall be done away.

When I was a child, I spake as a child, I understood as a child, I thought as a child: but when I became a man, I put away childish things.

For now we see through a glass, darkly; but then face to face:

Now I know in part; but then shall I know even as also I am known.

And now abideth faith, hope, love, these three; but the greatest of these is love. *—1 Corinthians 13*

36 *Christian Warfare*

Thou therefore, my son, be strong in the grace that is in Christ Jesus.

And the things that thou hast heard of me among many witnesses, the same commit thou to faithful men, who shall be able to teach others also.

Thou therefore endure hardness, as a good soldier of Jesus Christ.

No man that warreth entangleth himself with the affairs of this life; that he may please him who hath chosen him to be a soldier.

And if a man also strive for masteries, yet is he not crowned, except he strive lawfully.

—2 Timothy 2:1-5

Finally, my brethren, be strong in the Lord, and in the power of his might.

Put on the whole armour of God, that ye may be able to stand against the wiles of the devil.

For we wrestle not against flesh and blood, but against principalities, against powers, against the rulers of the darkness of this world, against spiritual wickedness in high places.

Wherefore take unto you the whole armour of God, that ye may be able to withstand in the evil day, and having done all, to stand.

Stand therefore, having your loins girt about with truth, and having on the breastplate of righteousness;

And your feet shod with the preparation of the gospel of peace;

Above all, taking the shield of faith, wherewith ye shall be able to quench all the fiery darts of the wicked.

And take the helmet of salvation, and the sword of the Spirit, which is the word of God:

Praying always with all prayer and supplication in the Spirit, and watching thereunto with all perseverance and supplication for all saints.

—Ephesians 6:10-18

37 *Victorious Faith*

The Lord is my light and my salvation; whom shall I fear? the Lord is the strength of my life; of whom shall I be afraid?

When the wicked, even mine enemies and my foes, came upon me to eat up my flesh, they stumbled and fell.

Though an host should encamp against me, my heart shall not fear: though war should rise against me, in this will I be confident.

One thing have I desired of the Lord, that will I seek after: that I may dwell in the house of the Lord all the days of my life, to behold the beauty of the Lord, and to enquire in his temple.

For in the time of trouble he shall hide me in his pavilion: in the secret of his tabernacle shall he hide me: he shall set me up upon a rock.

And now shall mine head be lifted up above mine enemies round about me: therefore will I offer in his tabernacle sacrifices of joy; I will sing, yea, I will sing praises unto the Lord.

Hear, O Lord, when I cry with my voice: have mercy also upon me, and answer me.

When thou saidst, Seek ye my face; my heart said unto thee, Thy face, Lord, will I seek.

Hide not thy face far from me; put not thy servant away in anger: thou hast been my help; leave me not, neither forsake me, O God of my salvation.

When my father and my mother forsake me, then the Lord will take me up.

Teach me thy way, O Lord, and lead me in a plain path, because of mine enemies.

Deliver me not over unto the will of mine enemies: for false witnesses are risen up against me, and such as breathe out cruelty.

I had fainted, unless I had believed to see the goodness of the Lord in the land of the living.

Wait on the Lord: be of good courage, and he shall strengthen thine heart: wait, I say, on the Lord.

—Psalm 27

38 *The Way Home*

Let not your heart be troubled: ye believe in God, believe also in me.

In my Father's house are many mansions: if it were not so I would have told you. I go to prepare a place for you.

And if I go and prepare a place for you, I will come again, and receive you unto myself; that where I am, there ye may be also.

And whither I go ye know, and the way ye know.

Thomas saith unto him, Lord, we know not whither thou goest; and how can we know the way?

Jesus saith unto him, I am the way, the truth, and the life: no man cometh unto the Father but by me.

If ye had known me, ye should have known my Father also: and from henceforth ye know him, and have seen him.

Philip saith unto him, Lord, show us the Father, and it sufficeth us.

Jesus saith unto him, Have I been so long time with you, and yet hast thou not known me, Philip? he that hath seen me hath seen the Father; and how sayest thou then, Show us the Father?

Believest thou not that I am in the Father, and the Father in me? the words that I speak unto you I speak not of myself: but the Father that dwelleth in me, he doeth the works.

Believe me that I am in the Father, and the Father in me: or else believe me for the very works' sake.

Verily, verily, I say unto you, He that believeth on me, the works that I do shall he do also; and greater works than these shall he do; because I go unto my Father.

And whatsoever ye shall ask in my name, that will I do, that the Father may be glorified in the Son.

If ye shall ask anything in my name, I will do it. *—John 14:1-14*

39 *The Victories of Faith*

Now faith is the substance of things hoped for, the evidence of things not seen.

For by it the elders obtained a good report.

Through faith we understand that the worlds were framed by the word of God, so that things which are seen were not made of things which do appear.

By faith Abel offered unto God a more excellent sacrifice than Cain, by which he obtained witness that he was righteous, God testifying of his gifts: and by it he being dead yet speaketh.

By faith Enoch was translated that he should not see death; and was not found, because God had translated him: for before his translation he had this testimony, that he pleased God.

But without faith it is impossible to please him: for he that cometh to God must believe that he is, and that he is a rewarder of them that diligently seek him.

By faith Abraham, when he was called to go out into a place which he should after receive for an inheritance, obeyed; and he went out, not knowing whither he went.

By faith he sojourned in the land of promise, as in a strange country, dwelling in tabernacles with Isaac and Jacob, the heirs with him of the same promise:

For he looked for a city which hath foundations, whose builder and maker is God.

Through faith also Sara herself received strength to conceive seed, and was delivered of a child when she was past age, because she judged him faithful who had promised.

Therefore sprang there even of one, and him as good as dead, so many as the stars of the sky in multitude, and as the sand which is by the sea shore innumerable.

These all died in faith, not having received the promises, but having seen them afar off, and were persuaded of them, and embraced them, and confessed that they were strangers and pilgrims on the earth.

For they that say such things declare plainly that they seek a country.

And truly, if they had been mindful of that country from whence they came out, they might have had opportunity to have returned.

But now they desire a better country, that is, an heavenly: wherefore God is not ashamed to be called their God: for he hath prepared for them a city.

By faith Moses, when he was come to years, refused to be called the son of Pharaoh's daughter;

Choosing rather to suffer affliction with the people of God, than to enjoy the pleasures of sin for a season;

Esteeming the reproach of Christ greater riches than the treasures in Egypt: for he had respect unto the recompence of the reward.

Wherefore seeing we also are compassed about with so great a cloud of witnesses, let us lay aside every weight, and the sin which doth so easily beset us, and let us run with patience the race that is set before us.

Looking unto Jesus the author and finisher of our faith; who for the joy that was set before him endured the cross, despising the shame, and is set down at the right hand of the throne of God.

—Hebrews 11:1-6, 8-16, 24-26; 12:1-2

40 Highway to Zion

The wilderness and the solitary place shall be glad for them; and the desert shall rejoice, and blossom as the rose.

It shall blossom abundantly, and rejoice even with joy and singing: the glory of Lebanon shall be given unto it, the excellency of Carmel and Sharon, they shall see the glory of the Lord, and the excellency of our God.

Strengthen ye the weak hands, and confirm the feeble knees.

Say to them that are of a fearful heart, Be strong, fear not: behold, your God will come with vengeance, even God with a recompence; he will come and save you.

Then the eyes of the blind shall be opened, and the ears of the deaf shall be unstopped.

Then shall the lame man leap as an hart, and the tongue of the dumb sing: for in the wilderness shall waters break out, and streams in the desert.

And the parched ground shall become a pool, and the thirsty land springs of water: in the habitation of dragons, where each lay, shall be grass with reeds and rushes.

And an highway shall be there, and a way, and it shall be called The way of holiness; the unclean shall not pass over it; but it shall be for those: the wayfaring men, though fools, shall not err therein.

No lion shall be there, nor any ravenous beast shall go up thereon, it shall not be found there; but the redeemed shall walk there:

And the ransomed of the Lord shall return, and come to Zion with songs and everlasting joy upon their heads: they shall obtain joy and gladness, and sorrow and sighing shall flee away. *—Isaiah 35*

41 Christmas

And it came to pass in those days, that there went out a decree from Caesar Augustus, that all the world should be taxed.

(And this taxing was first made when Cyrenius was governor of Syria.)

And all went to be taxed, every one into his own city.

And Joseph also went up from Galilee out of the city of Nazareth, into Judaea, unto the city of David, which is called Bethlehem; (because he was of the house and lineage of David:)

To be taxed with Mary his espoused wife, being great with child.

And so it was, that, while they were there, the days were accomplished that she should be delivered.

And she brought forth her firstborn son, and wrapped him in swaddling clothes, and laid him in a manger;

because there was no room for them in the inn.

And there were in the same country shepherds abiding in the field, keeping watch over their flock by night.

And, lo, the angel of the Lord came upon them, and the glory of the Lord shone round about them: and they were sore afraid.

And the angel said unto them, Fear not: for, behold, I bring you good tidings of great joy, which shall be to all people.

For unto you is born this day in the city of David a Saviour, which is Christ the Lord.

And this shall be a sign unto you; Ye shall find the babe wrapped in swaddling clothes, lying in a manger.

And suddenly there was with the angel a multitude of the heavenly host praising God, and saying,

Glory to God in the highest, and on earth peace, good will toward men.

And it came to pass, as the angels were gone away from them into heaven, the shepherds said one to another, Let us now go even unto Bethlehem, and see this thing which is come to pass, which the Lord hath made known unto us.

And they came with haste, and found Mary, and Joseph, and the babe lying in a manger.

And when they had seen it, they made known abroad the saying which was told them concerning this child.

And all they that heard it wondered at those things which were told them by the shepherds. —*Luke 2:1-18*

42 The Triumphal Entry

And when they came nigh to Jerusalem, unto Bethphage and Bethany, at the mount of Olives, he sendeth forth two of his disciples, and saith unto them,

Go your way into the village over against you: and as soon as ye be entered into it, ye shall find a colt tied, whereon never man sat; loose him and bring him.

And if any man say unto you, Why do ye this? say ye that the Lord hath need of him; and straightway he will send him hither.

And they went their way, and found the colt tied by the door without in a place where two ways met: and they loose him.

And certain of them that stood there said unto him, What do ye, loosing the colt?

And they said unto them even as Jesus had commanded: and they let them go.

And they brought the colt to Jesus, and cast their garments on him; and he sat upon him.

And many spread their garments in the way: and others cut down branches of the trees, and strawed them in the way.

And they that went before, and they that followed, cried, saying, Hosanna; Blessed is he that cometh in the name of the Lord.

Blessed be the kingdom of our father David, that cometh in the name of the Lord: Hosanna in the highest. And Jesus entered into Jerusalem, and into the temple.

—*Mark 11:1-11*

43 *The Promised Comforter*

If ye love me, keep my commandments.

And I will pray the Father, and he shall give you another Comforter, that he may abide with you for ever;

Even the Spirit of truth; whom the world cannot receive, because it seeth him not, neither knoweth him:

But ye know him; for he dwelleth with you, and shall be in you.

I will not leave you comfortless: I will come to you.

Yet a little while, and the world seeth me no more; but ye see me: because I live, ye shall live also.

At that day ye shall know that I am in my Father, and ye in me, and I in you.

But now I go my way to him that sent me; and none of you asketh me, Whither goest thou?

But because I have said these things unto you, sorrow hath filled your heart.

Nevertheless I tell you the truth: It is expedient for you that I go away:

For if I go not away, the Comforter will not come unto you; but if I depart, I will send him unto you.

And when he is come he will reprove the world of sin, and of righteousness, and of judgment:

Of sin, because they believe not on me;

Of righteousness, because I go to my Father, and ye see me no more;

Of judgment, because the prince of this world is judged.

I have yet many things to say unto you, but ye cannot bear them now.

Howbeit when he, the Spirit of truth, is come, he will guide you into all truth:

For he shall not speak of himself; but whatsoever he shall hear, that shall he speak: and he will show you things to come.

He shall glorify me: for he shall receive of mine, and shall show it unto you.

These things I have spoken unto you, that in me ye might have peace. In the world ye shall have tribulation: but be of good cheer; I have overcome the world.

—John 14:15-20; 16:5-14, 33

44 *The Crucifixion*

He is despised and rejected of men; a man of sorrows, and acquainted with grief: and we hid as it were our faces from him; he was despised, and we esteemed him not.

Surely he hath borne our griefs, and carried our sorrows: yet we did esteem him stricken, smitten of God, and afflicted.

But he was wounded for our transgressions, he was bruised for our iniquities: the chastisement of our peace was upon him; and with his stripes we are healed.

All we like sheep have gone astray; we have turned every one to his own way; and the Lord hath laid on him the iniquity of us all.

—Isaiah 53:3-6

Then Pilate therefore took Jesus, and scourged him.

And the soldiers platted a crown of

thorns, and put it on his head, and they put on him a purple robe,

And said, Hail, King of the Jews! and they smote him with their hands.

Pilate therefore went forth again, and saith unto them, Behold, I bring him forth to you, that ye may know that I find no fault in him.

Then came forth Jesus, wearing the crown of thorns, and the purple robe. And Pilate saith unto them, Behold the man!

When the chief priests therefore and officers saw him, they cried out, saying, Crucify him, crucify him. Pilate saith unto them, Take ye him, and crucify him: for I find no fault in him.

Then delivered he him therefore unto them to be crucified. And they took Jesus, and led him away.

And he bearing his cross went forth into a place called the place of a skull, which is called in the Hebrew Golgotha:

Where they crucified him, and two other with him, on either side one, and Jesus in the midst.

And Pilate wrote a title, and put it on the cross. And the writing was, Jesus of Nazareth the King of the Jews.

—John 19:1-6, 16-19

45 The Risen Saviour

In the end of the sabbath, as it began to dawn toward the first day of the week, came Mary Magdalene and the other Mary to see the sepulchre.

And, behold, there was a great earthquake: for the angel of the Lord descended from heaven, and came and rolled back the stone from the door, and sat upon it.

His countenance was like lightning, and his raiment white as snow:

And for fear of him the keepers did shake, and became as dead men.

And the angel answered and said unto the women, Fear not ye: for I know that ye seek Jesus, which was crucified.

He is not here: for he is risen, as he said. Come, see the place where the Lord lay.

And go quickly, and tell his disciples that he is risen from the dead; and, behold, he goeth before you into Galilee; there shall ye see him: lo, I have told you.

And they departed quickly from the sepulchre with fear and great joy; and did run to bring his disciples word.

And as they went to tell his disciples, behold, Jesus met them, saying, All hail. And they came and held him by the feet, and worshipped him.

Then said Jesus unto them, Be not afraid: go tell my brethren that they go into Galilee, and there shall they see me.

—Matthew 28:1-10

Then the same day at evening, being the first day of the week, when the doors were shut where the disciples were assembled for fear of the Jews, came Jesus and stood in the midst, and saith unto them, Peace be unto you.

And when he had so said, he shewed unto them his hands and his side.

Then were the disciples glad, when they saw the Lord.

And after eight days again his disciples were within, and Thomas with them: then came Jesus, the doors being shut, and stood in the midst, and said, Peace be unto you.

Then saith he to Thomas, Reach hither thy finger, and behold my hands; and reach hither thy hand, and thrust it into my side: and be not faithless, but believing.

And Thomas answered and said unto him, My Lord and my God.

Jesus saith unto him, Thomas, because thou hast seen me, thou hast believed: blessed are they that have not seen, and yet have believed.

—*John 20:19, 20, 26-29*

I am he that liveth, and was dead; and, behold, I am alive for evermore, Amen; and have the keys of hell and of death.

—*Revelation 1:18*

46 Resurrection

Now is Christ risen from the dead, and become the firstfruits of them that slept.

For since by man came death, by man came also the resurrection of the dead.

For as in Adam all die, even so in Christ shall all be made alive.

But every man in his own order: Christ the firstfruits; afterward they that are Christ's at his coming.

Then cometh the end, when he shall have delivered up the kingdom to God, even the Father; when he shall have put down all rule and all authority and power.

For he must reign, till he hath put all enemies under his feet.

The last enemy that shall be destroyed is death.

There is one glory of the sun, and another glory of the moon, and another glory of the stars: for one star differeth from another star in glory.

So also is the resurrection of the dead. It is sown in corruption; it is raised in incorruption:

It is sown in dishonour; it is raised in glory; it is sown in weakness; it is raised in power:

It is sown a natural body; it is raised a spiritual body. There is a natural body, and there is a spiritual body.

And so it is written, The first man Adam was made a living soul; the last Adam was made a quickening spirit.

The first man is of the earth, earthy: the second man is the Lord from heaven.

As is the earthy, such are they also that are earthy: and as is the heavenly, such are they also that are heavenly.

And as we have borne the image of the earthy, we shall also bear the image of the heavenly.

For this corruptible must put on incorruption, and this mortal must put on immortality.

So when this corruptible shall have put on incorruption, and this mortal shall have put on immortality, then shall be brought to pass the saying that is written, Death is swallowed up in victory.

O death, where is thy sting? O grave, where is thy victory?

The sting of death is sin, and the strength of sin is the law.

But thanks be to God, which giveth us the victory through our Lord Jesus Christ.

—1 Corinthians 15:20-26, 41-45, 47-49, 53-57

47 Pentecost

And, behold, I send the promise of my Father upon you: but tarry ye in the city of Jerusalem, until ye be endued with power from on high.

And he led them out as far as Bethany, and he lifted up his hands, and blessed them.

And it came to pass, while he blessed them, he was parted from them, and carried up into heaven.

And they worshipped him, and returned to Jerusalem with great joy.

And were continually in the temple, praising and blessing God. Amen.

—Luke 24:49-53

And when the day of Pentecost was fully come, they were all with one accord in one place.

And suddenly there came a sound from heaven as of a rushing mighty wind, and it filled all the house where they were sitting.

And there appeared unto them cloven tongues like as of fire, and it sat upon each of them.

And they were all filled with the Holy Ghost, and began to speak with other tongues, as the Spirit gave them utterance.

And there were dwelling at Jerusalem Jews, devout men, out of every nation under heaven.

Now when this was noised abroad, the multitude came together, and were confounded, because that every man heard them speak in his own language.

And they were all amazed and marvelled, saying one to another, Behold, are not all these which speak Galileans?

And how hear we every man in our own tongue, wherein we were born?

Parthians, and Medes, and Elamites, and the dwellers in Mesopotamia, and in Judaea, and Cappadocia, in Pontus, and Asia.

Phrygia, and Pamphylia, in Egypt, and in the parts of Libya about Cyrene, and strangers of Rome, Jews and proselytes,

Cretes and Arabians, we do hear them speak in our tongues the wonderful works of God.

And they were all amazed, and were in doubt, saying one to another, What meaneth this?

Others mocking said, These men are full of new wine.

But Peter, standing up with the eleven, lifted up his voice, and said unto them, Ye men of Judaea, and all ye that dwell in Jerusalem, be this known unto you, and hearken to my words:

For these are not drunken, as ye suppose, seeing it is but the third hour of the day.

But this is that which was spoken by the prophet Joel;

And it shall come to pass in the last

days, saith God, I will pour out of my Spirit upon all flesh: and your sons and your daughters shall prophesy, and your young men shall see visions, and your old men shall dream dreams:

And on my servants and on my handmaidens I will pour out in those days of my Spirit; and they shall prophesy:

And I will shew wonders in heaven above, and signs in the earth beneath; blood, and fire, and vapour of smoke:

The sun shall be turned into darkness, and the moon into blood, before that great and notable day of the Lord come:

And it shall come to pass, that whosoever shall call on the name of the Lord shall be saved.

—Acts 2:1-21

48 *The Lord's Return*

But I would not have you to be ignorant, brethren, concerning them which are asleep, that ye sorrow not, even as others which have no hope.

For if we believe that Jesus died and rose again, even so them also which sleep in Jesus will God bring with him.

For this we say unto you by the word of the Lord, that we which are alive and remain unto the coming of the Lord shall not precede them which are asleep.

For the Lord himself shall descend from heaven with a shout, with the voice of the archangel, and with the trump of God: and the dead in Christ shall rise first:

Then we which are alive and remain shall be caught up together with them in the clouds, to meet the Lord in the air: and so shall we ever be with the Lord.

Wherefore comfort one another with these words.

But of the times and the seasons, brethren, ye have no need that I write unto you.

For yourselves know perfectly that the day of the Lord so cometh as a thief in the night.

For when they shall say, Peace and safety; then sudden destruction cometh upon them, as travail upon a woman with child; and they shall not escape.

But ye, brethren, are not in darkness, that that day should overtake you as a thief.

Ye are all the children of light, and the children of the day: we are not of the night, nor of darkness.

Therefore let us not sleep, as do others; but let us watch and be sober.

For they that sleep sleep in the night; and they that be drunken are drunken in the night.

But let us, who are of the day, be sober, putting on the breastplate of faith and love; and for an helmet, the hope of salvation.

For God hath not appointed us to wrath, but to obtain salvation by our Lord Jesus Christ,

Who died for us, that, whether we wake or sleep, we should live together with him.

—1 Thessalonians 4:13-18; 5:8-10

49 Temperance

Wine is a mocker, strong drink is raging: and whosoever is deceived thereby is not wise.

Who hath woe? who hath sorrow? who hath contentions? who hath babbling? who hath wounds without cause? who hath redness of eyes?

They that tarry long at the wine; they that go to seek mixed wine.

Look not thou upon the wine when it is red, when it giveth his colour in the cup, when it moveth itself aright.

At the last it biteth like a serpent, and stingeth like an adder.
—*Proverbs 20:1; 23:29-32*

Woe unto them that rise up early in the morning, that they may follow strong drink; that continue until night, till wine inflame them!

Woe unto them that are mighty to drink wine, and men of strength to mingle strong drink:

Which justify the wicked for reward, and take away the righteousness of the righteous from him!
—*Isaiah 5:11, 22, 23*

This I say then, Walk in the Spirit, and ye shall not fulfil the lust of the flesh.

For the flesh lusteth against the Spirit, and the Spirit against the flesh: and these are contrary the one to the other: so that ye cannot do the things that ye would.

But if ye be led of the Spirit, ye are not under the law.

Now the works of the flesh are manifest, which are these; Adultery, fornication, uncleanness, lasciviousness.

Idolatry, witchcraft, hatred, variance, emulations, wrath, strife, seditions, heresies,

Envyings, murders, drunkenness, revellings, and such like:

Of the which I tell you before, as I have also told you in time past, that they which do such things shall not inherit the kingdom of God.
—*Galatians 5:16-21*

50 Missions

O sing unto the Lord a new song: sing unto the Lord, all the earth.

Sing unto the Lord, bless his name; shew forth his salvation from day to day.

Declare his glory among the heathen, his wonders among all people.

For the Lord is great, and greatly to be praised: he is to be feared above all gods.

For all the gods of the nations are idols: but the Lord made the heavens.

Honour and majesty are before him: strength and beauty are in his sanctuary.

Give unto the Lord, O ye kindreds of the people, give unto the Lord glory and strength.

Give unto the Lord the glory due unto his name: bring an offering, and come into his courts.

O worship the Lord in the beauty of holiness: fear before him, all the earth.

Say among the heathen that the Lord reigneth: the world also shall be established that it shall not be moved: he shall judge the people righteously.

Let the heavens rejoice, and let the earth be glad; let the sea roar, and the fulness thereof.

Let the field be joyful, and all that is therein: then shall all the trees of the wood rejoice

Before the Lord: for he cometh, for he cometh to judge the earth: he shall judge the world with righteousness, and the people with his truth.

—Psalm 96

51 God's Mercy Endureth For ever

O give thanks unto the Lord; for he is good:

For his mercy endureth for ever.

O give thanks unto the God of gods:

For his mercy endureth for ever.

O give thanks to the Lord of lords:

For his mercy endureth for ever.

To him who alone doeth great wonders:

For his mercy endureth for ever.

To him that by wisdom made the heavens:

For his mercy endureth for ever.

To him that stretched out the earth above the waters:

For his mercy endureth for ever.

To him that made great lights:

For his mercy endureth for ever.

The sun to rule by day:

For his mercy endureth for ever.

The moon and stars to rule by night:

For his mercy endureth for ever.

To him that smote Egypt in their firstborn:

For his mercy endureth for ever.

And brought out Israel from among them:

For his mercy endureth for ever.

With a strong hand, and with a stretched out arm:

For his mercy endureth for ever.

Who remembered us in our low estate:

For his mercy endureth for ever.

And hath redeemed us from our enemies:

For his mercy endureth for ever.

Who giveth food to all flesh:

For his mercy endureth for ever.

O give thanks unto the God of heaven:

For his mercy endureth for ever.

—Psalm 136

TOPICAL INDEX

ABIDING IN CHRIST
Accepted in the beloved 375
How tedious and tasteless 342
I Have learned the 336
It's no longer I 490
Jesus Only Let me see 330

ABUNDANT LIFE
Count your blessings 297
Dwelling in Beulah land 350
Give of your best 322
How tedious and tasteless 342
Let the Lower lights 298
Look to the lamb 430
My soul, be on thy 407
O what a Savior 325
Take time to be holy 354
Trust and obey 234
Turn your eyes upon Jesus 418
See: challenge, invitation, service, warnings

ADORATION
Be Thou Exalted 5
Give me Jesus 320
Hallelujah to the lamb 48
Heavenly Father I glorify 42
Holy, Holy, Holy 22
How great Thou art 27
I am His and He 243
Immortal, Invisible, God 15
Jesus, I am resting 262
Jesus is the sweetest 81
Jesus! Jesus! Jesus! 64
Jesus, the very thought 459
Jesus, wondrous Savior 33
Join all the glorious 79
Lord, with glowing heart 36
Majestic sweetness 196
May Jesus Christ be praised 41
My Jesus, I love thee 65
O could I speak the 13
O God, Our help in ages 301
O Jesus, king, most wonderful 67
O my soul, bless thou 18
O sacred head now 107
O the deep, deep love 26
O what a Savior 325
Sweet Name Come down 63
The great physician 289
There's a wonderful name 98
Wonderful Jesus 230
Wonderful Savior 34
Worthy is the Lamb 17
See: devotion, praise, worship

ASSENSION AND REIGN
See: Jesus Our Savior

ASSURANCE
Accepted in the beloved 375
A child of the king 238
A mighty fortress 29
A shelter in the 278
Blessed Assurance 200
Blessed quietness 152
Day by day 266
God will take care of you 281
Have faith in God 231
He hideth my soul 272
He is able to deliver 235
He leadeth me 276
He the pearly gates 445
He's the one 496
Hiding in thee 203
How firm a foundation 170
I am His, and He is mine 243
I am not skilled to 458
I am trusting thee 247
I belong to the king 239
I have a Savior who 299
I know whom I have 341
I shall know Him 446
I walk with the king 339
I will sing the wondrous 60
I've found a friend 222
In the garden 228
Ivory Palaces 362
Jesus I am resting 262
Jesus my all 345
Jesus Never Has failed me 202
Jesus never fails 250
Jesus understands 264
Join all the glorious 79
Just when I need Him 201
Lead on o king eternal 394
Leaning on the everlast 206
Like a river glorious 265
Moment by moment 285
More secure is noone 258
My anchor holds 290
My faith has found 183
My Saviour first of all 446
No blood, no altar now 130
No night there 452
No not one 208
Nor silver, nor gold 127
O God, Our help in 301
O happy Day 369
Only a touch 227
Only believe 245
Standing on the promises 171
Sometime we'll understand 249
Surely goodness and mercy 286
The haven of rest 240
The Lord's my shepherd 293
The Solid rock 232
'Tis so sweet to trust 251
Trust and Obey 234
Trusting Jesus 233
Under His Wings 241
We have an anchor 279
Yesterday, Today 257
See: faith, heaven, hope, trust

ATONEMENT
Alas, and did 121
All my sins have been 242
Arise, my soul, arise 6
At the cross 131
Hallelujah! what a Savior 119
Majestic Sweetness 196
Opened for me 109
Rock of Ages 275
To God be the glory 4
What a Wonderful Saviour 70
See: blood, cross, Jesus death and suffering

BAPTISM
I'll live for Him 313
Jesus, I my cross 311
O Happy Day! 369
O master let me 403
Trust and Obey 234
Where He leads me 410
See: commitment, discipleship

BIBLE
Break thou the bread 166
Holy Bible Book divine 167
I am standing on the word 164
More about Jesus 361
O word of God incarnate 163
Standing on the promises 171
The old book and the old 169
Thy word have I hid 165
Wonderful words of life 168

BLESSINGS
Count your blessings 297
Dwelling in Beulah land 350
Go to the deeps of Gods 374
God is here 151
Sweet Honey in the Rock 492
His yoke is easy 351
I am not skilled 458
Jesus my all 345
Showers of blessings 284

BLOOD
Alas and did my Savior 121
Are you washed in the 436
Blessed be the fountain 123
Covered by the blood 114
Complete in Thee 373
Glory to His name 75
Hallelujah for the blood 118
I will praise Him 35
It cleanseth me 116
No blood, no altar now 130
Nothing but the blood 122
Opened for me 109
Saved by the blood 72
The blood will never lose 126
There is a fountain 129
Power in the Blood 125
See: cleansing, Jesus death and suffering, salvation

BURDEN
See: comfort

CALVARY
See: atonement, blood

CAROLS
See: Christmas

CHALLENGE
Bring Them in 390
Count your blessings 297
Give of your best 322
I gave my life 421
I would be true 366
Is your all on the 319
Jesus calls us 386
Jesus only let me see 330
Lead on, O king eternal 394
Let the lower lights 298
Rescue the perishing 412
Stand up for Jesus 368
Take time to be holy 354
The fight is on 409
Who is on the Lord's 383

CHILDREN'S HYMNS
Hosanna, loud hosanna 100
I love to tell the 401
Jesus loves even me 254
Jesus loves me 256
O how I love Jesus 253
Onward christian soldiers 384
Praise Him! Praise Him! 31
Savior, like a shepherd 236
Tell me the story of 86
This is my Father's world 21
When He cometh 140

CHOIR
And can it be 10
Arise, my soul arise 6
Be thou exalted 5
Behold the Lamb of 105
Full consecration 327
Heaven Came down 259
How great thou art 27
I have a Savior who 299
It cleanseth me 116
Jesus has loved me 44
Jesus is coming again 139
Jesus! Jesus! Jesus! 64
Lord, with glowing heart 36
Love, wonderful love 173
Make me a blessing 382
My anchor holds 290
My Father planned it 288
My hope is in the Lord
O sacred head now 107
Surely goodness and 286
That beautiful name 85
The fight is on 409
The old book and the 169
Till the whole world 395

CHORUSES
See: Gospel choruses

CHRIST
See: Jesus; Our Savior

CHRISTIAN WARFARE
A mighty fortress 29
Battle Hymn of the 460
Faith Is the victory 205
He is able to deliver 235
Lead on, O king 394
My soul be on thy 407
Onward christian soldiers 384
Stand up for Jesus 368
The banner of the cross 379
The battle is the Lord's 400
The fight is on 409
The strife is o'er 111
True-hearted, whole-hearted 315
Who is on the Lord's side 383
See: church, loyalty, victory

CHRISTLIKENESS
I would be like Jesus 303
Jesus only let me see 330
Make me a blessing 382
More Like my Savior 306
O to be like thee 358

CHRISTMAS
Angels we have heard 96
Away in a manger 92
It Came upon the 95
O come all ye faithful 94
O come, o come Emmanuel 93
Silent night, Holy night 90
What child is this 97

CHURCH
A mighty fortress 29
Faith of our fathers 246
I love Thy kingdom 160
I love to tell the 401
O breath of life 159
O day of rest and 14
O for a thousand 23
O word of God incarnate 163
Onward Christian soldiers 384
The Church's one foundation 161
The son of God goes 393
See: Christian warfare, fellowship

CLEANSING
Are you washed in the 436
Blessed be the fountain 123
Channels only 309
Cleanse me 316
It cleanseth me 116
Jesus paid it all 194
Let Jesus come into 438
Nothing but the blood
Opened for me 109
Power in the blood 125
There is a fountain 129

TOPICAL INDEX

LOSING HYMNS
ìod Be With You 502
ake the name of Jesus . . . 83

OMFORT
oes Jesus care 267
rom every stormy wind . . 214
od leads us along 277
liding in thee 203
lold thou my hand 296
low firm a foundation . . . 170
heard the voice of Jesus . . 335
must tell Jesus 211
am not skilled to 458
n the heart of Jesus 174
t's just like His 184
vory palaces 490
esus, lover of my soul . . . 274
esus never fails 250
esus never has failed me . . 202
esus understands 264
ust when I need him 201
ike a river glorious 265
loment by moment 285
lear to the heart 216
lo night there 452
) God, our help in ages . . . 301
nly a touch 227
ometime we'll understand . 249
'ake the name of Jesus . . . 83
eaning on the everlasting . 206
'he great physician 289
'he Lord's my shepherd . . 293
'he name of Jesus 84
Tis the blessed Holy Spirit . 149
Jnder His wings 241

COMMITMENT
)raw me nearer 357
ive me Jesus 320
lave thine own way 328
surrender all 305
'll live for Him 313
esus, I my cross 311
ead me to calvary 318
peak, My Lord 391
'ake my life and 314
'ake the world but 320
'rue-hearted, whole-hearted 315
'hy will be done 323
Vhere He leads me 410
'ielded to God 376
ee: consecration, dedication, discipleship

COMMUNION
ee: Service music, Lord's supper

COMMUNION OF SAINTS
ee: fellowship with believers fellowship with God

CONFIDENCE
ccepted in the beloved . . 375
esus never fails 250
esus never has failed 202
esus Understands 264
Ay father planned it all . . . 288
Io not one 208
Iothing but the blood . . .
) believe it 424
Iow firm a foundation . . . 170
Iow tedious and tasteless . . 342
am not skilled 458

CONFESSION
ee: repentance

CONSECRATION
Breathe on me, Breath of . . 155
cleanse me 316
Draw me nearer 357
Following Jesus 489
Full consecration 327
Give me Jesus 320
I'll live for Him 313
Is your all on the 319
Jesus calls us 386
Jesus only let me see 330
Lord, search my life 310
Make me a captive Lord . . . 332
My goal is God, himself . . . 372
Nearer, still nearer 307
Not I, but christ 338
O Jesus, king most 67
O to be kept for Jesus 308
Only one life to offer 331
Open my eyes 156
Something for thee 312
Take my life and let 314
Take the world but 320
When I survey the 110
Where He leads me 410
Yielded to God 376
See: commitment, discipleship

CONSOLATION
See: comfort

COURAGE
Faith is the victory 205
Faith of our fathers 246
Jesus never has failed 202
Lead on o king eternal . . . 394
Just when I need him 201
O love that wilt not 181
Stand up for Jesus 368
The son of God goes 393
See: challenge, Christian warfare,

CROSS
At calvary 128
At the cross 131
Behold the Lamb of God . . 105
Beneath the cross 363
Covered by the blood 114
Glory to his name 75
In the cross of Christ 102
Jesus I my Cross have 311
Lead me to Calvary 318
Must Jesus bear the cross . . 124
Nailed to the cross 347
Opened for me 109
The banner of the cross . . . 379
The old rugged cross 104
When I survey the 110
The blood will never lose . . 126
See: Jesus death and suffering

DECISION
See: dedication, commitment, invitation, salvation

DEDICATION
Do thy work through me . . 283
Draw me nearer 357
Following Jesus 489
Full Surrender 326
Give me Jesus 320
I surrender all 305
I would be like Jesus 303
I'll live for Him 313
Jesus calls us 386
Jesus only let me see 330
Make me a captive lord . . . 332
O the bitter pain and 333
Speak, my Lord 391
Sweet name come down . . . 63
Take the world but give . . . 320
Yielded to God 376
See: commitment

DEDICATION OF CHILDREN
Children of the Heavenly . . 258
Hosanna, loud hosanna . . . 100
Jesus Loves me 256
Savior Like a shepherd . . . 236
When He cometh 140

DEDICATION OF CHRISTIAN WORKERS
Channels only 309
If Jesus goes with me 295
I'll go where you want . . . 380
So send I you 391
See: commitment, service

DEEPER LIFE
Accepted in the beloved . . 375
Channels only 309
Complete in thee 373
Draw me nearer 357
Every day with Jesus 350
Full consecration 327
Give me Jesus 320
He is so precious to me . . . 68
I have learned the wondrous 336
I heard the voice of Jesus . . 335
I surrender all 305
I would be like Jesus 303
In tenderness he sought me . 186
Is your all on the altar 319
Jesus calls us 386
Jesus, I am resting, resting . 262
Jesus, I my cross have 311
Jesus, lover of my soul . . . 274
Jesus, the very thought . . . 459
Living for Jesus 317
Lord, search my life 310
Love, life and everlasting . . 32
Moment by moment 285
May the mind of Christ . . . 287
My goal is God 372
Near the cross 347
Not I, but Christ 338
O Jesus, King most 67
O the bitter pain and sorrow 333
Open my eyes 156
Stir me, O stir me 389
'Tis the blessed Holy 149
Yielded to God 376
See: Victorious Life

DEPENDENCE ON GOD
Great is thy faithfulness . . . 28
How tedious and tasteless . . 342
I need thee every hour . . . 292
Jesus, lover of my soul . . . 274
Leaning on the everlasting . 206
Not I, but Christ 338

DEVOTIONAL
Alas! and did my Savior . . . 121
At the cross I was 300
Cleanse me 316
Close to thee 294
Go to the deeps of 374
I am His and He is mine . . . 243
I heard the voice of 335
I need thee every hour . . . 292
I would be like Jesus 303
Jesus has loved me 44
Jesus, lover of my 274
Jesus, Savior pilot me 291
Jesus, the very thought . . . 459
More about Jesus 361
My faith look up to thee . . 248
My savior first of all 446
Near the cross 347
Near to the heart 216
Nearer, still nearer 307
O love that wilt 181
O to be like thee 358
Only one life 331
Rock of ages 275
Savior, Breathe an evening . 221
Something for Thee 312
Sun of my soul 302
The old rugged cross 104
Turn your eyes upon 418
See: adoration, fellowship, prayer

DISCIPLESHIP
Do thy work through me . . 283
Every day with Jesus 350
I'll live for Him 313
Jesus calls us 386
Jesus, I my cross 311
Stepping in the light 352
His yoke is easy 351
The son of God goes 393
Where he leads, I'll follow . 410

DUETS
Cleanse me 316
Love divine, all loves 25
Nailed to the cross 117
Whom having not seen . . . 223

EASTER
Christ arose 133
Christ the Lord is Risen . . . 132
One Day 337
Hosanna, Loud Hosanna . . 100
The Lord is risen 136
See: Jesus resurrection

ENCOURAGEMENT
He is able to deliver thee . . 235
Jesus never has failed 202
Jesus never fails 250
See: assurance, trust

ETERNAL HOME
See: Heaven

EVENING HYMNS
Savior, breathe an evening . 221
Sun of my soul 302

FAITH
At the cross, I was 300
Faith is the victory 205
Faith of our fathers 246
Great is thy faithfulness . . . 28
Have faith in God 231
Just when I need Him 201
On the victory side 464
Only believe 245
O believe it 424
The old book and the old . . 169
Thou wilt keep Him 263
Trust Him 185
Sometime we'll understand . 249
See: assurance, trust

FATHER'S DAY
Faith of our fathers 246

FELLOWSHIP WITH BELIEVERS
From every stormy wind . . 214
Leaning on the everlasting . 206
Near to the Heart of God . . 216
Onward Christian soldiers . . 384
See: Christian unity, church

FELLOWSHIP WITH GOD
Beulah land 455
Dwelling in Beulah land . . . 350
Deeper and deeper 334

Everyday with Jesus 471
He lives 137
I would be true 366
I've found a friend 222
In the garden 228
Leaning on the everlasting . 206
O master let me walk 403
Still sweeter every day ... 54
The glory of His presence .. 225
Trust and Obey 234

FORGIVING
See: salvation

FUNERAL HYMNS
He the pearly gates 445
Meet me there 448
Leaning on the everlasting . 206
My Savior first of all 446
No night there 452
Saved by Grace 449
Sweet by and by 453
See: comfort heaven, resurrection

GLORY
See: Heaven

GOD SOVEREIGNTY
My God's a Great God 501

GOD IN CREATION
Fairest Lord Jesus 113
How Great thou art 27
Immortal, invisible 15
O worship the king 24
This is my father's world .. 21
We praise Thee, O God ... 53
The spacious firmament ... 19

GOD THE FATHER
A Child of the King 238
A mighty fortress 29
Be Thou Exalted 5
For God so loved 428
God is so good 43
Guide me, O thou 273
How great thou art 27
Immortal, invisible 15
O God, our help 301
to God be the glory 4
this is my father's world .. 21
See: trinity, worship

GOSPEL
See: invitation, warning

GOSPEL CHORUSES
Are we down-hearted 491
Do you wonder why? 487
Every day with Jesus 471
Following Jesus 489
For God so loved 428
God is so Good 43
Happiness is to know 261
He holds my hand 497
It's No Longer I 490
Jesus Christ is the way ... 255
My God's a Great God 501
On the victory side 464
Thou wilt keep him 263
They say he is wonderful .. 493
Trust Him 185
With Eternity's values 499

GRACE
Amazing grace 77
At calvary 128
Come Thou fount 12
Grace Greater than our sins . 190
Grace 'tis a charming 193
Great God of wonders 20
Jesus Lover of my soul ... 274
Jesus paid it all 194
Jesus saves 388
No Blood, no altar 130
Nor silver, nor gold 127
O for a thousand 23
Only a sinner 191
Saved by grace 449
See: mercy, salvation

GUIDANCE AND CARE
All the way my Saviour ... 237
Children of the Heavenly .. 258
Close to Thee 294
Day by day 266
Every day with Jesus 471
God Be With You 502
God leads us along 277
God will take care of you .. 281
Guide me, O thou 273
Have faith in God 231
He leadeth me 276
Hold thou my hand 296
Holy Spirit, faithful 154
I have a Saviour 219
Jesus Never has failed 202
Jesus, Saviour, pilot me ... 291
Lead on, O king eternal ... 394
Moment by moment 285
My father planned it 288
O God, our help 301
Only a touch 227
Saviour like a shepherd ... 236
Saviour more than life 294
Surely goodness and mercy . 286
The Lord's my Shepherd .. 293
Trusting Jesus 233
Where He heads, I'll 410
See: faith and trust

HEAVEN
A child of the king 238
Beulah land 455
Face to face 447
Guide me, o thou 273
Hallelujah! amen! 457
He the pearly gates 445
Heaven at last 442
I love to tell the 401
I shall know Him 446
In the heart of Jesus 174
Love, wonderful love 173
Meet me there 448
Must Jesus bear the 124
My Savior first of all 446
No night there 452
Saved by grace 449
Sometime We'll Understand 249
Surely goodness and 286
The glorious hope 455
The sands of time 451
We're marching to Zion ... 49
When the roll is called 444
Whom having not seen ... 223
See: Jesus return, second coming

HOLINESS
Breathe on me, breath 155
Channels only 309
Fill all my vision 353
More holiness give me 356
O to be like Thee 358
Take time to be holy 354
Thy word have I hid 165
See: cleansing, consecration, Holy Spirit

HOLY SPIRIT
Be Thou Exalted 5
Blessed quietness 152
Breathe on me, breath 155
Channels only 309
Cleanse me 316
Holy Spirit, faithful 154
O breath of life 159
Open my eyes, that I 156
Pentecostal power 157
Spirit of God 150
The comforter has come .. 148
Thou art calling me 153
'Tis the blessed Holy 149

HOPE
Have faith in God 231
My hope is in the Lord ... 1
No blood, no altar 130
O God, our help 301
The glorious hope 455
See: assurance, heaven, Jesus return, second coming

INSTALLATION FOR CHRISTIAN SERVICE
See: challenge, missions

INVITATION-SALVATION
Almost persuaded 423
But as many as received ... 197
For you I am praying 219
Choose now 417
Have you any room 434
I am coming to the cross .. 195
Jesus I come 427
I love to tell the story 401
Jesus Is passing this 426
Just as I am 422
Let Jesus come into 438
Lord, I'm coming home ... 428
My faith looks up to 248
Pass me not 431
Softly and tenderly 420
The great physician 289
The light of the world 415
Turn your eyes upon 418
What will you do 435
Whosoever will believe ... 425
Why not now? 433
See: warning

INVITATION TO CONSECRATION
Channels only 309
Cleanse me 316
Full surrender 326
I surrender all 305
If Jesus goes with me 295
I'll go where you 380
I'll live for Him 313
Is your all on the 319
Jesus calls us 386
Love divine, all loves 25
Make me a blessing 382
More like my Savior 306
Must Jesus bear the 124
Near the cross 347
Something for Thee 312
Take my life and let 314
Turn your eyes upon 418
Where He leads me 410

JESUS – OUR SAVIOR
Jesus never fails 250
Jesus Saves 388
Jesus, wondrous Savior ... 33
One day 337
Our great Savior 30

JESUS – ADVENT
See: Christmas

JESUS ASSENSION AND REIGN
All hail the power 8
All hail the power (diadem) 9
Arise, my soul, arise 6
Crown Him with many ... 7
I shall know Him 446
Rejoice the Lord is King .. 45

JESUS BIRTH
See: Christmas

JESUS EARTHLY MINISTRY
One day 337
Tell me the story 86
That beautiful name 85

JESUS: HIS FELLOWSHIP
All the way along 226
I must tell Jesus 211
I love to walk 229
If Jesus goes with me 295
In the garden 228
In the heart of Jesus 174
It's just like His 184
I've found a friend 222
Jesus, the very thought ... 459
Near to the heart 216
No not one 208
Speak, Lord, in the 217
Still sweeter every day ... 54
Sweet name come down .. 63
See: fellowship

JESUS: HIS NAME
All hail the power 8
All hail the power (diadem) 9
Glory to His name 75
Jesus! Jesus! Jesus! 64
Join all the Glorious 79
O how I love Jesus 253
Sweet name come down .. 63
Take the Name of Jesus ... 83
That beautiful name 85
The great physician 289
The name of Jesus 84

JESUS ASSENSION
JESUS RESURRECTION
Christ arose 133
Christ liveth in me 360
Christ the Lord is 132
Crown Him with 7
He lives 137
One Day 337
The Lord is Risen 136

JESUS RETURN
Coming Soon 146
For God so loved 428
Hallelujah! What a Savior .. 119
How great thou art 27
Jesus Is coming again 139
Lo He comes, with 145
O come, O come, ... 93
One day 337
When He cometh 140
Wounded for me 120
See: second coming

JESUS DEATH AND SUFFERING
And can it be 10
At Calvary 128
At the cross 131
Blessed be the fountain ... 123
For God so loved 428
Hallelujah, what a 119
He was wounded 108
I gave my life for 421

TOPICAL INDEX

the cross of Christ 102
sus paid it all. 194
y Redeemer 56
y Savior's love 176
ailed to the cross 117
ear the cross 347
or silver, nor gold 127
sacred head, now 107
ne day 337
ock of ages 275
he old rugged cross 104
here is a fountain 129
here is a green hill 103
s midnight, and on 101
hat will you do 435
hen I survey the 110
ounded for me 120

SUS: WORSHIP OF
ll hail the power 8
ll hail the power (diadem) 9
e Thou Exalted 5
rown Him with many . . . 7
airest Lord Jesus 113
am His and He is 243
know no other Jesus 115
sus! Jesus! Jesus! 64
sus, I am resting 262
sus, the very thought . . . 459
for a thousand 23
aise the Savior, ye 66
ake the name of Jesus . . . 83
he name of Jesus 84
ee: Jesus assension and reign

OY
ll the way along 226
re we down-hearted 491
eulah Land 455
e keeps me singing 260
the garden 228
sus is the joy 367
sus loves even me 254
sus saves 388
oy in serving Jesus 387
happy day 369
n the victory side 464
nly a touch 227
edeemed 57
ing the bells of 413
unshine in my soul 268
e're marching to Zion . . . 49
hen love shines in 180
hen we all get to 443
onderful Jesus 230
ee: gospel choruses, praise, testimony

ORD'S DAY
day of rest and 14

ORD'S SUPPER
t the cross 131
rom every stormy 214
esus paid it all 194
y faith has found 183
ear the cross 347
he old rugged cross 104
here is a fountain 129
'is midnight and on 101
hen I survey the 110
ounded for me 120
ee: blood, cross, Jesus death

OVE

OD'S LOVE
nd can it be 10
ehold at love 172
Lamb 105
leeper 334

For god so loved 428
He the pearly gates 445
He's a wonderful Savior . . . 58
I am His and He 243
I love thee, Lord Jesus . . . 112
It's just like His 184
Ivory palaces 490
Jesus has loved me 44
Jesus, I am resting 262
Jesus lover of my 274
Jesus loves even me 254
Jesus loves me 256
Love divine, all loves 25
Love found a way 178
Love lifted me 177
Love wonderful love 173
Loving care 282
My Saviour's love 176
O love that wilt not 181
O the deep, deep love 26
Seeking for me 87
Since the fullness of His . . . 40
The greatest thing is 182
Then Jesus came 59
There's a wideness 207
When I survey the 110
See: Christian unity, fellowship

OUR LOVE FOR GOD
I love thee, Lord 112
Jesus, the very thought . . . 459
My Jesus, I love thee 65
O how I love Jesus 253
Once it was the blessing . . . 304
Spirit of God, descend . . . 150
That's why I love 69
There is a green hill 103

OUR LOVE FOR OTHERS
Faith of our fathers 246
I love thy Kingdom 160
More like my Saviour 306
Rescue the perishing 412
Something for Thee 312
When love shines in 180
See: Christian unity, fellowship

LOYALTY
Give of your best 322
I would be true 366
Speak just a word 396
The banner of the 379
True-hearted, whole-hearted 315
True to the end 321
Who is on the Lord's 383
See: Christian warfare, courage, zeal

MERCY
And can it be 10
Come thou fount 12
There's a wideness 207
O take the gift of mercy . . 192
See: grave, love

MISSIONS
Anywhere with Jesus 398
Go ye into all the 402
Here Am I 432
If Jesus goes with me 295
I'll go where you 380
Lead on, O king 394
Let there be light 406
O Zion haste 399
So send I you 391
Stir me, oh, stir 398
The call for reapers 405
See: Christian warfare, service, soul-winning

NEW BIRTH
See: salvation

PARDON
Nor silver, nor gold 127

PATRIOTIC
America 462
Battle Hymn of the 460
The Star-spangled banner . . 461

PEACE
Blessed quietness 152
He's the one 496
I am His and He is 243
It is well with 270
Like a river glorious 265
Near to the heart 216
Peace, perfect peace 189
Wonderful peace 271
See: comfort, security

PENTECOST
See: Holy Spirit

PRAISE
All the way along 226
Be thou exalted 5
Blessed assurance 200
Come thou fount 12
Glory to His name 75
Guide me O thou 273
Hallelujah to the Lamb . . . 48
He is so precious 68
He's a wonderful Savior . . . 58
How great Thou art 27
I Walk with the King 339
I will praise Him 35
Jesus is all the world 78
Jesus is the joy 367
Join all the glorious 79
Lift up the gates 11
Lord with glowing 36
My redeemer 56
O could I speak 13
O for a thousand 23
O happy day 369
Only a sinner 191
Praise Him, praise Him . . . 31
Rejoice the Lord is 45
Revive us again 53
The God of abraham 39
The name of Jesus 84
Thine is the glory 134
To God be the glory 4
See: adoration, worship

PRAYER OR PRAYER MEETING
Deeper and Deeper 334
For you I am praying 219
From every stormy wind . . 214
Glory be to Him 16
Go to the deeps 374
God is here 151
I am praying blessed 212
I must tell Jesus 211
In the garden 228
Keep praising 485
Lord search my life 310
Make me a blessing 382
May Jesus Christ be praised . 41
More holiness give me 356
My faith looks up to thee . . 248
Near to the Heart of 216
O What a Savior 325
Open my eyes 156
Praise ye the triune 47
Speak Lord in the 217
Take time to be Holy 354
Teach me to pray 210

There's a wonderful name . 98
We come, O christ, to 67
Wonderful Savior 34
Worthy Is the Lamb 17
See: devotional, Holy Spirit, revival

PROMISES
Go to the deeps 374
O God, we want to 213
Standing on the promises . . 171
Thou wilt keep Him 263
'Tis so sweet to 251

PROVIDENCE
A mighty fortress 29
A shelter in the 278
Children of the Heavenly . . 258
Day by Day 266
God leads us along 277
God will take care of 281
He is able to deliver 235
Jesus Understands 264
My Father planned it 288
Loving care 282
O God, our help 301
O worship the King 24
We praise thee, O God 53
See: God our Father, guidance, care, Thanksgiving

PSALM ADAPTATIONS
How great thou art 27
O My Soul Bless Thou Jehovah 18
Surely, Goodness and Mercy 286
The Lord is my Shepherd . . 293

REDEMPTION
Nor silver, nor gold 127
Redeemed 57
See: atonement, cross, salvation

REJOICING
O happy day 369
Singing I go 61
See: victory

REPENTANCE
At calvary 128
Jesus I come 427
Just as I am 422
Only a Sinner 191
Pass me not 431
Rock of ages 275
See: cleansing, invitation

RESURRECTION
He is risen 136
See: Jesus return

REVIVAL
Cleanse me 316
God is here 151
O breath of Life 159
Revival prayer 218
Revive us again 53
See: consecration, holiness, Holy Spirit

REWARD
No blood, no altar 130
Shall I Empty-handed be . . 378

SALVATION
Amazing grace 77
And can it be 10
Are you washed in 436

TOPICAL INDEX

Arise, my soul, arise 6
At calvary 128
Blessed be the fountain 123
But as many as received 197
Choose now 417
Christ receiveth sinful 437
Complete in Thee 373
For God so loved 428
Glory to His name 75
Grace 'tis a charming 193
He is able to deliver 235
He was wounded 108
How greatly Jesus must 467
I heard the voice 335
I know whom I have 341
I will sing the 60
Jesus Christ is the way 255
Jesus Saves 388
Look to the lamb 430
Love Found a way 178
Love wonderful love 173
My faith has found 183
My redeemer 56
My Saviour's love 176
Nor silver, nor gold 127
Nothing but the blood 122
O happy day 369
O take the gift of mercy 192
One God and one 346
Only a sinner 191
Pass me not 431
Power in the blood 125
Redeemed 57
Saved by the blood 72
Saved, saved 73
Saved, Saved, saved 74
Since Jesus came into 71
Showers of blessings 284
The light of the world 415
There is a fountain 129
Turn your eyes 418
Verily, verily 52
We are by Christ 204
What a wonderful Savior 70
Whosoever will 198
Whosoever will believe 425
Wonderful words of life 168
Ye must be born again 416
See: invitation, Jesus death and suffering

SANCTIFICATION
Not I, but Christ 338
Open my eyes 156
See: holiness, Holy Spirit

SCRIPTURES
See: Bible

SECOND COMING
Christ Is coming back 143
Coming soon 146
Coming again 139
He is coming again 141
I know whom I have 341
I shall know Him 446
Is it the crowning 142
It is well with 270
Jesus is coming again 139
O my soul bless thou 18
O that will be glory 441
One day 337
The glorious hope 455

SECURITY
A mighty fortress 29
A shelter in the 278
Anywhere with Jesus 398
Children of the heavenly 258
He hideth my soul 272
He will hold me fact 280
Hiding in Thee 203
I belong to the King 239
I know whom I 341
Just when I need Him 201
Leaning on the everlasting 206
Loving care 282
My anchor holds 290
O God, our help 301
O love that wilt 181
Only believe 245
Praise the Savior 66
Rock of Ages 275
The haven of rest 240
The solid rock 232
Under His wings 241
Undergirded 299
We have an anchor 279

SERVICE FOR GOD
A passion for souls 411
Do thy work through me 283
I'll go where you 380
Lord, search my life 310
Lord, speak to me 215
Make me a blessing 382
More like my Savior 306
O master let me walk 403
O to be kept for 308
Rescue the perishing 412
Shall I empty-handed 378
Speak just a word 396
To the work 377
With eternity's values 499

SERVICE MUSIC

BENEDICTION
God be with you 501

CALL TO WORSHIP
God is here 151
Speak Lord, in the stillness 217
Spirit of God, descend 150

COMMUNION
See: Lord's supper

DOXOLOGIES
Keswick doxology 38
Praise God from whom 37

OFFERTORY
Take my life and let 314
We give thee but thine 355

PRAYER
Speak Lord, in the stillness 217
Revival prayer 218

SOLOS
A passion for souls 411
Be thou exalted 5
Complete in Thee 373
Fill all my vision 353
God leads us along 277
He's the one 496
I belong to the King 239
I have learned thee 336
I walk with the king 339
Look and live 414
Now I belong to Jesus 179
Once it was the 304
Only one life 331
Satisfied 209
Singing I go 61
So send I you 391
Stir me, o, stir me 389
Teach me to pray 210
The song of a soul 76
'tis the blessed Holy 149
What will you do with 435

SOUL WINNING
A passion for souls 411
Bring them in 390
Let the lower lights 298
Let there be light 406
O zion haste 399
Rescue the perishing 412
Stir me, oh, stir 398
'tis the blessed Holy 149
The call for reapers 405
See: missions, service

SOVEREIGNTY
See: God's sovereignty

STEWARDSHIP OF LIFE AND TALENTS
Give of your best 322
I'll go where you 380
Jesus calls us 386
Lord, Speak to me 215
Only one life 331
Something for Thee 312
Take my life and let 314
Take time to be holy 354
When I survey the 110
See: commitment, consecration, discipleship

STEWARDSHIP OF POSSESSIONS
Jesus calls us 386
Take my life and let 314
We give thee but thine 355
See: commitment, consecration, discipleship

SURRENDER
Channels only 309
Cleanse me 316
I surrender all 305
Is your all on the altar 319
See: commitment, consecration

TESTIMONY
A child of the King 238
All the way along 226
Amazing grace 77
At calvary 128
At the cross, I was 300
Beulah land 455
Christ liveth in me 360
Full surrender 326
Glory to His name 75
He brought me out 348
He holds my hand 497
He is so precious to me 68
He keeps me singing 260
He lifted me 359
Heaven came down 259
He's a wonderful Savior 58
He's the one 496
How greatly Jesus must 467
I am His and He is 243
I belong to the king 239
I know whom I have 341
I love thee, Lord Jesus 112
I love to tell the story 458
I love to walk with Jesus 229
I walk with the King 339
I will Praise Him 35
I will sing the wondrous 60
I'll live for Him 313
I've found a friend 222
It is well with 270
It's just like His great 184
Jesus Christ is the way 255
Jesus has loved me 44
Jesus, I am resting 262
Jesus is all the 78
Jesus is the joy of 367
Jesus is the sweetest 81
Jesus loves even me 25
Jesus loves me 25
Jesus never fails 25
Joy in serving Jesus 38
Leaning on the 20
Lord with glowing heart 3
Love lifted me 17
My anchor holds 29
My faith has found 18
My God's a Great God 50
My redeemer 5
My Saviour's love 17
No not one 20
Nor silver, nor gold 12
Not I, but Christ 33
Now I belong to Jesus 17
O could I speak 1
O happy day 36
O how I love Jesus 25
O the unsearchable riches 5
O it is wonderful 6
On the victory side 46
Only a sinner 19
Only one life 33
Praise Him, Praise 3
Redeemed 5
Revive us again 5
Ring the bells of 41
Saved, saved, saved 7
Satisfied 20
The song of a soul set 7
To god be the glory
Trust Him 18
What a wonderful Savior 7
Why do I sing about Jesus 5
See: joy, peace

THANKFULNESS
Count your blessings 29
We give thee but 35
We praise thee o God 5

THANKSGIVING
See: thankfulness

TRINITY
Be thou exalted
Holy, holy, holy 2
O day of rest and gladness 1
O my soul bless 1
Praise God from whom 3
Revive us again 5
The church's one foundation 16

TRUST
Anywhere with Jesus 39
He hold's my hand 49
He is able to deliver 23
I am trusting thee 24
It is well with my 27
Jesus I am resting 26
On the victory side 46
Only a touch 22
Only trust Him 43
Safe in the arms 24
Thou wilt keep him 26
Trust and obey 23
Trust Him 18
Trusting Jesus 23
See: assurance, care, faith, guidance

VICTORIOUS LIFE
Beulah land 45
Christ liveth in me 36
I love thee, Lord Jesus 11
I must tell Jesus 21
I walk with the king 33
I will praise Him 3
It's just like His great 18
Love life and everlasting 3
No Blood, no altar now 13

TOPICAL INDEX

O what a Savior 325
Once it was the 304
Our great Savior 30
Rise with thy risen 371
Satisfied 209
Since the fullness 40
'Tis the blessed Holy 149
See: church

VICTORY
A mighty fortress 29
Faith is the victory 205
He is able to 235
He is so precious 68
Singing I go 61
Stand up for Jesus 368
Victory all the time 349
We may not climb the 329
See: Christian warfare

WARNINGS
See: admonition

WEDDINGS
Saviour like a shepherd . . . 236

WITNESSING
Speak just a word 396
See: soul winning

WORD OF GOD
See: Bible

WORSHIP
A mighty fortress 29
All hail the power 8
All hail the power (diadem) 9
And can it be 10
Arise, my soul, arise 6
Be thou exalted 5
Crown him with many . . . 7
Glorious things of thee . . . 162
Hallelujah to the lamb 48
Heavenly father 42
Holy, holy, holy 22
How Great thou art 27
Immortal, invisible 15
Jesus the very thought . . . 459
Lift up the gates of 11
Like a river glorious 265
Love divine, all loves 25
My faith has found 183
O day of rest and 14
O God, our help 301
O Jesus, King most 67
O worship the king 24
Praise ye the triune God . . 47
Revival Prayer 218
The church's one foundation 161
This is my Father's 21
To God be the glory 4
Welcome Happy morning . . 135
Worthy in the Lamb 17

YIELDING
See: consecration, surrender

YOUTH
All the way along 226
Battle hymn of the 460
Beulah land 455
Bring them in 390
Channels only 309
Cleanse me 316
Fairest Lord Jesus 113
For God so loved 428
Give of your best 322
Glory to His name 75
He lives 137
He's a wonderful Savior . . . 58
Heaven came down 259
I am bound for the 450
I have a Savior who 299
I know a fount 106
I love thee, Lord Jesus . . . 112
I would be like Jesus 303
I would be true 366
It's just like His great 184
Jesus is coming again 139
Jesus is the joy of 367
Living for Jesus 317
Lord, search my life 310
Love, wonderful love 173
Make me a blessing 382
More like my Savior 306
Must I go and 404
My father planned it 288
My Hope is in the Lord . . . 1
Now I belong to Jesus 179
O it is wonderful 62
Only believe 245
Only one life 331
Onward Christian 384
Rescue the Perishing 412
Savior like a shepherd 236
Since Jesus came into 71
Speak just a word 396
Stand up for Jesus 368
Stepping in the light 352
Surely goodness and mercy . 286
Thank you Lord 486
That beautiful name 85
The future is exciting 324
The king's business 397
Thy word have I hid 165
Till the whole world knows . 395
True-hearted, whole-hearted 315
Turn your eyes upon 418
What will you do 435
Wounded for me 120
Ye must be born again . . . 416
See: children's hymns, gospel, Gospel choruses

ZEAL
Give of your best 322
My faith looks up 248
O Zion haste 399
To the work 377
True-hearted, whole-hearted 315
See: Christian warfare, courage, loyalty, victory

ACKNOWLEDGMENT

Grateful acknowledgment is given to those who have granted permission for the use of their hymns and tunes. Every effort has been made to properly accredit these in the body of the book. If, through inadvertence, any omissions occur, upon written notification acknowledgment will be included in future editions.

GENERAL INDEX

Index of First Lines, Titles, and Choruses
Titles are in CAPITALS; first lines in lower case type; first line of chorus in *italics*

A CHILD OF THE KING 238
A friend have I, who 223
A friend I have called 184
A MIGHTY FORTRESS IS OUR GOD . . 29
A moment more and I may 147
A PASSION FOR SOULS 411
A pilgrim was I and a 286
A ruler once came to Jesus 416
A SHELTER IN THE TIME OF STORM . 278
A wonderful Saviour is 272
ACCEPTED IN THE BELOVED 375
ALAS! AND DID MY SAVIOUR BLEED 121
ALL HAIL THE POWER (coro.) 8
ALL HAIL THE POWER (miles lane) . . . 8
ALL HAIL THE POWER (diadem) 9
All in all forever 304
All my life long I had 209
ALL MY SINS HAVE BEEN FORGIVEN 242
All power is given unto me 402
All praise to Him who 80
ALL THE WAY ALONG 226
ALL THE WAY MY SAVIOUR LEADS ME 237
All to Jesus, I surrender 305
ALMOST PERSUADED 423
ALTOGETHER LOVELY 478
AMAZING GRACE 77
Amazing love, how can it be 10
AMERICA 462
AND CAN IT BE 10
And I shall see Him face 449
And it holds, my anchor 290
ANGELS WE HAVE HEARD ON HIGH . 96
Anywhere, anywhere, fear I 398
ANYWHERE WITH JESUS 398
ARE YOU WASHED IN THE BLOOD? . 436
ARE WE DOWNHEARTED? 491
ARISE, MY SOUL, ARISE 6
As I tread life's tangled 282
As I travel life's pathway 202
As the father has sent me 392
AS WITH GLADNESS MEN OF OLD . . 91
Ask the Saviour to help you 370
AT CALVARY 128
AT THE CROSS 131
At the cross I was kneeling 300
AWAY IN A MANGER 92

BATTLE HYMN OF THE REPUBLIC . . 460
Be like Jesus, this my song 303
Be not dismayed whate'er 281
BE THOU EXALTED 5
BEHOLD THE LAMB OF GOD 105
BEHOLD WHAT LOVE 172
Behold, what manner of love, ... 172
BENEATH THE CROSS OF JESUS 363
BEULAH LAND 455
BLESS THE LORD, MY SOUL 3
BLESSED ASSURANCE 200
BLESSED BE THE FOUNTAIN 123
BLESSED QUIETNESS 152
Bowed 'neath your burden 264
BREAK THOU THE BREAD OF LIFE . . 166
BREATHE ON ME, BREATH OF GOD . 155
BRING THEM IN 390
BUT, AS MANY AS RECIEVED HIM . . . 197

CALLING TODAY 419
CHANNELS ONLY 309
CHILDREN OF THE HEAVENLY FATHER 258
CHOOSE NOW 417
CHRIST AROSE 133
Christ has for sin atoned 70
CHRIST IS COMING BACK AGAIN . . . 143
CHRIST LIVETH IN ME 360
CHRIST RECEIVETH SINFUL MEN . . . 437
CHRIST THE LORD IS RISEN TODAY . 132
CLEANSE ME 316
CLOSE TO THEE 294
Come every soul by sin 439
Come, home, come home 420
Come, let us join our 48
COME THOU FOUNT 12
Coming again, coming again 139
COMING SOON 146
COMPLETE IN THEE 373
COUNT YOUR BLESSINGS 297
COVERED BY THE BLOOD 114
CROWN HIM WITH MANY CROWNS . . 7

DAY BY DAY 266
Deep in my heart there's 51
DEEPER AND DEEPER 334
DO THY WORK THROUGH ME 283
Do you ever feel downhearted 231
DO YOU WONDER WHY? 488
DOES JESUS CARE? 267
DRAW ME NEARER 357
DWELLING IN BEULAH LAND 350
Dying with Jesus, by death 285

Earthly friends may prove 250
Earthly pleasures vainly 303

GENERAL INDEX

Encamped along the hills 205
EVERY DAY WITH JESUS 471

FACE TO FACE 447
FAIREST LORD JESUS 113
Fairest of ten thousand 76
FAITH IS THE VICTORY 205
FAITH OF OUR FATHERS 246
Far away in the depths 271
Far away the noise of 350
Far, far away, in heathen 402
Fear not, little flock 245
FILL ALL MY VISION 353
Fill me, Holy Spirit, fill 153
FOLLOWING JESUS 489
FOR GOD SO LOVED THE WORLD . . . 428
For me He died 1
For salvation full and free 330
For there is one God and 346
FOR YOU I AM PRAYING 219
Free from the law, o happy 199
FROM EVERY STORMY WIND 216
FULL CONSECRATION 327
FULL SURRENDER 326

Give me a passion for souls 411
GIVE ME JESUS 320
GIVE OF YOUR BEST TO THE MASTER 322
Glad day, glad day 142
Gloria! in excellis deo 96
GLORIOUS THINGS OF THEE ARE SPOKEN 162
GLORY BE TO HIM WHO LOVED US . . 16
Glory, glory, how the angels 413
GLORY TO HIS NAME 75
GO TO THE DEEPS OF GOD'S PROMISE 374
GO YE INTO ALL THE WORLD 402
GOD BE WITH YOU 502
GOD IS HERE 151
GOD IS SO GOOD 43
GOD LEADS US ALONG 277
GOD WILL TAKE CARE OF YOU 281
GRACE GREATER THAN OUR SINS . . 190
GRACE 'TIS A CHARMING SOUND . . . 193
GREAT GOD OF WONDERS 20
GREAT IS THY FAITHFULNESS 28
GUIDE ME, O THOU GREAT JEHOVAH 273

HALLELUJAH! AMEN! 457
HALLELUJAH FOR THE BLOOD 118
HALLELUJAH! PRAISE JEHOVAH . . . 2
Hallelujah! prince of peace 143
Hallelujah! thine the glory 53
Hallelujah 'tis the blood 116
HALLELUJAH TO THE LAMB 48
HALLELUJAH! WHAT A SAVIOUR! . . . 119
Happiness is the lord 481
HAPPINESS IS TO KNOW THE SAVIOUR 481
happy day, happy day 369
HAPPY IN JESUS 261
Hark, I hear the angels 442
Hark, 'tis the Shepherd's 390
HAVE FAITH IN GOD 231
HAVE THINE OWN WAY, LORD 328
HAVE YOU ANY ROOM FOR JESUS? . . 434
Have you been to Jesus 436
HE BROUGHT ME OUT 348
HE HIDETH MY SOUL 272
HE HOLDS MY HAND 497
HE IS ABLE TO DELIVER THEE 235
HE IS COMING AGAIN 141
HE IS SO PRECIOUS TO ME 68
HE KEEPS ME SINGING 260
HE LEADETH ME 276
HE LIFTED ME 359
HE LIVES 137
HE THE PEARLY GATES WILL OPEN . 445
HE WAS WOUNDED FOR OUR TRANSGRESSIONS 108
He will come the Lord of 143
HE WILL HOLD ME FAST 280
HE'S A WONDERFUL SAVIOUR TO ME 58
HE'S THE ONE I LOVE 496
Hear the Lord of harvest 391
HEAVEN AT LAST 442
HEAVEN CAME DOWN 259
HEAVENLY FATHER, I GLORIFY YOU 42
HEAVENLY SUNSHINE 269
HERE AM I 432
HIDING IN THEE 203
HIS YOKE IS EASY 351
HOLD THOU MY HAND 296
HOLY BIBLE, BOOK DIVINE 167
HOLY, HOLY, HOLY 22
HOLY SPIRIT, FAITHFUL GUIDE . . . 154
HOSANNA, LOUD HOSANNA 100
How beautiful to walk in 352
HOW FIRM A FOUNDATION 170
HOW GREAT THOU ART 27
HOW GREATLY JESUS MUST HAVE LOVED US 467
How I praise thee, precious 309
How oft in sweet communion 457
HOW TEDIOUS AND TASTELESS THE HOURS 342

I am a stranger here 397
I AM BOUND FOR THE PROMISED LAND 450
I AM COMING TO THE CROSS 195
I AM HIS AND HE IS MINE 243
I AM NOT SKILLED TO UNDERSTAND 458
I AM PRAYING BLESSED SAVIOUR . . 212
I am so glad that our father 254
I am standing on the mighty 164
I AM STANDING ON THE WORD 164
I am redeemed but not with 127
I am thine, o Lord, I have 357
I AM TRUSTING THEE, LORD JESUS . 247
I BELONG TO THE KING 239

GENERAL INDEX

I can hear my Saviour calling 410
I can never tell how much 40
I come to the garden alone 228
I GAVE MY LIFE FOR THEE 421
I have a Saviour, He's pleading 219
I have a Saviour, who lifted 299
I have a song that Jesus 50
I have found a friend 224
I have found a wondrous 367
I HAVE LEARNED THE WONDROUS . 336
I have walked alone with Jesus 225
I hear my Saviour say 194
I HEARD THE VOICE OF JESUS SAY . . 335
I KNOW A FOUNT 106
I know a name 85
I KNOW NO OTHER JESUS 115
I know not why God's 341
I KNOW WHOM I HAVE BELIEVED . . . 341
I LOVE THEE, LORD JESUS 112
I LOVE THY KINGDOM, LORD 160
I LOVE TO TELL THE STORY 401
I LOVE TO WALK WITH JESUS 229
I MUST TELL JESUS 211
I NEED JESUS 340
I need no other argument 183
I NEED THEE EVERY HOUR 292
I need thee, O, I need 292
I serve a risen Saviour 137
I shall know Him, I shall 446
I sing through the shade 288
I stand all amazed 62
I stand all amazed in the 176
I SURRENDER ALL 305
I WALK WITH THE KING 339
I WAS A WANDERING SHEEP 365
I was lost in sin 58
I was sinking deep in sin 177
I WILL PRAISE HIM! 35
I WILL SERVE THEE 498
I WILL SING OF THE MERCIES OF THE LORD 480
I WILL SING THE WONDROUS STORY 60
I WOULD BE LIKE JESUS 303
I WOULD BE TRUE 366
I would trust Him in the 85
IF I GAINED THE WORLD 343
IF JESUS GOES WITH ME 295
If you are tired of the 438
If you from sin are longing 430
I'LL GO WHERE YOU WANT ME TO GO 380
I'LL LIVE FOR HIM 313
IMMORTAL, INVISIBLE 15
IN A MOMENT 147
In loving kindness Jesus 359
IN MY HEART THERE RINGS A MELODY 50
In shady green pastures 277
In sorrow I wandered 339
IN TENDERNESS HE SOUGHT ME . . . 186
In the beloved, accepted 375
IN THE CROSS OF CHRIST I GLORY . . 102
IN THE GARDEN 228
IN THE HEART OF JESUS 174
In the land of fadeless day 453
In the sweet by and by 453
Into the heart of Jesus 334
IS IT THE CROWNING DAY? 142
Is there a heart that is 426
IS YOUR ALL ON THE ALTAR? 319
IT CAME UPON THE MIDNIGHT CLEAR 95
IT CLEANSETH ME 116
IT IS WELL WITH MY SOUL 270
It may be at morn 144
It may be in the valley 295
It may not be on the mount 380
It will never lose it's 126
It is not your repentance 192
I'll tell to all that God 395
I'm a child of the King 328
I'm pressing on the upward 244
IT'S JUST LIKE HIS GREAT LOVE . . . 184
IT'S NO LONGER I 490
I've a message from the 414
I've anchored my soul 240
I'VE FOUND A FRIEND 222
I've found a friend, who 73
I've reached the land of 456
I've wandered far away 428
IVORY PALACES 362

JESUS CALLS US 386
Jesus came to earth by a 197
JESUS CHRIST IS THE WAY 255
Jesus comes with power 180
Jesus found me when a far 187
JESUS HAS LOVED ME 44
Jesus has promised my 69
JESUS, I AM RESTING RESTING 262
JESUS, I COME 427
Jesus, I long, I long to be 411
JESUS, I MY CROSS HAVE TAKEN . . . 411
JESUS IS ALL THE WORLD TO ME . . . 78
JESUS IS COMING AGAIN 139
JESUS IS MINE 138
JESUS IS PASSING THIS WAY 426
Jesus is standing in Pilate's 435
Jesus is tenderly calling 419
JESUS IS THE JOY OF LIVING 367
JESUS IS THE SWEETEST NAME I KNOW 81
Jesus, Jesus, how I trust 251
JESUS! JESUS! JESUS! 64
Jesus, Jesus, Jesus, sweetest 260
Jesus keep me near the cross 347
JESUS, LET ME HIDE MY SOUL IN THEE 49
JESUS, LOVER OF MY SOUL 274
JESUS LOVES EVEN ME 254
JESUS LOVES ME 256
Jesus may come today 142

GENERAL INDEX

JESUS MY ALL 345
Jesus my King, my 34
Jesus my Lord will love 179
Jesus my Prophet stands 345
Jesus, my saviour to 87
JESUS NEVER FAILS 250
JESUS NEVER HAS FAILED ME YET . 202
Jesus, oh how sweet the name 84
JESUS ONLY LET ME SEE 330
JESUS PAID IT ALL 194
JESUS SAVES 388
JESUS, SAVIOUR, PILOT ME 291
JESUS SHALL REIGN 46
JESUS STAND AMONG US 252
JESUS, THE VERY THOUGHT OF THEE 459
JESUS UNDERSTANDS 264
JESUS, WONDROUS SAVIOUR 33
JOIN ALL THE GLORIOUS NAMES . . . 79
JOY IN SERVING JESUS 387
JOY TO THE WORLD 88
Joys are flowing like a 152
JUST AS I AM 422
JUST WHEN I NEED HIM MOST 201

KEEP PRAISING 485
KESWICK DOXOLOGY 38
King of my life I crown 318

LEAD ME TO CALVARY 318
LEAD ME TO SOME SOUL TODAY . . . 487
LEAD ON, O KING ETERNAL 394
LEANING ON THE EVERLASTING ARMS 206
Let it come, O Lord, we 151
LET JESUS COME INTO YOUR HEART 438
LET THERE BE LIGHT 406
LET THE LOWER LIGHTS BE BURNING 298
LIFT UP THE GATES OF PRAISE 11
Lift up your heads, pilgrim 141
LIKE A RIVER GLORIOUS 265
like the stars of the 140
LIVING FOR JESUS 317
Living in Thee, and thou 210
LO, HE COMES WITH CLOUDS DESCENDING 145
LOOK AND LIVE 414
LOOK TO THE LAMB OF GOD 430
Lord as of old at pentecost 157
Lord, hear my prayer 310
LORD, I'M COMING HOME 428
Lord Jesus, I long to 364
Lord lift me up and let me 244
LORD OF THE LIVING HARVEST . . . 408
LORD, SEARCH MY LIFE 310
LORD, SPEAK TO ME 215
LORD, WITH GLOWING HEART I'D PRAISE THEE 36
LORD DIVINE, ALL LOVES EXCELLING 25
Love divine so great and 445
LOVE FOUND A WAY 178
LOVE, LIFE AND EVERLASTING JOY 32
LOVE LIFTED ME 177
LOVE, WONDERFUL LOVE 173
Loved with everlasting love 243
LOVING CARE 282
Low in the grave he lay 133

MAJESTIC SWEETNESS SITS ENTHRONED 196
Man of sorrows, what a name 119
MAKE ME A BLESSING 382
MAKE ME A CAPTIVE, LORD 332
Marching on, marching on 379
Marvelous grace of our loving 190
Marvelous message we bring 139
MAY JESUS CHRIST BE PRAISED . . . 41
MAY THE MIND OF CHRIST MY SAVIOUR 287
MEET ME THERE 448
mercy there was great and 128
Mid the storms of doubt 169
Mine eyes have seen the glory 460
MOMENT BY MOMENT 285
MORE ABOUT JESUS 361
MORE HOLINESS GIVE ME 356
MORE LIKE MY SAVIOUR 306
More secure is no one ever 258
MUST I GO AND EMPTY-HANDED . . . 404
MUST JESUS BEAR THE CROSS ALONE 124
MY ANCHOR HOLDS 290
My country 'tis of thee 462
MY FAITH HAS FOUND A RESTING PLACE 183
MY FAITH LOOKS UP TO THEE 248
My father is rich in 238
MY FATHER PLANNED IT ALL 288
MY GOAL IS GOD HIMSELF 372
MY GOD'S A GREAT GOD 501
My heart in fear 348
MY HEART'S PRAYER 220
My hope is built on 232
MY HOPE IS IN THE LORD 1
MY JESUS I LOVE THEE 65
My life, my love, I give 313
MY LORD AND I 224
My Lord has garments so 362
MY REDEEMER 56
MY SAVIOUR FIRST OF ALL 446
MY SAVIOUR'S LOVE 176
My sins laid open 122
MY SOUL BE ON THY GUARD 407
MY SOUL IS FILLED WITH GLORY . . 187
My soul in sad exile 240

NAILED TO THE CROSS 117
NAME OF JESUS 344
Naught have I gotten 191
NEAR THE CROSS 347

GENERAL INDEX

NEAR TO THE HEART OF GOD 214
NEARER, STILL NEARER 307
NO BLOOD, NO ALTAR NOW 130
NO NIGHT THERE 452
NO NOT ONE 208
None but Christ can satisfy 32
NOR SILVER, NOR GOLD 127
NOT I, BUT CHRIST 338
Not now, but in the coming 249
NOTHING BUT THE BLOOD 122
NOW I BELONG TO JESUS 179

O BELIEVE IT 424
O Beulah land 456
O BREATH OF LIFE 159
O Christ, in Thee my soul 32
O COME ALL YE FAITHFUL 94
O come let us adore Him 94
O COME, O COME EMMANUEL 93
O COULD I SPEAK THE MATCHLESS WORTH 13
O DAY OF REST AND GLADNESS . . . 14
O FOR A THOUSAND TONGUES 23
O GOD, OUR HELP IN AGES PAST . . . 301
O GOD, WE WANT TO THANK YOU . . 213
O HAPPY DAY 369
O He is the only perfect 263
O HOLY SPIRIT 158
O HOW I LOVE JESUS 253
O how sweet the glorious 257
O IT IS WONDERFUL 62
O Jesus is a rock in a 278
O JESUS, KING MOST WONDERFUL . . 67
O Jesus, Lord and Saviour 317
O LITTLE TOWN OF BETHLEHEM . . . 89
O LOVE THAT WILT NOT LET ME GO . 181
O MASTER LET ME WALK WITH THEE 403
O matchless love, how can 182
O MY SOUL BLESS THOU JEHOVAH . . 18
O PRAISE THE GOD OF LOVE 175
O precious is the flow 122
O SACRED HEAD NOW WOUNDED . . . 107
O say can you see 461
O soul are you weary 418
O spread the tidings 148
O TAKE THE GIFT OF MERCY 192
O THAT WILL BE GLORY 441
O THE BITTER PAIN AND SORROW . . 333
O THE DEEP, DEEP LOVE OF JESUS . . 26
O the unsearchable riches 55
O TO BE KEPT FOR JESUS 308
O TO BE LIKE THEE! 358
O WHAT A SAVIOUR 325
O what a wonderful, wonderful 259
O WORD OF GOD INCARNATE 163
O WORSHIP THE KING 24
O yes he cares, I know he 267
O ZION HASTE 399
Oh, dearly, dearly has He 103
Oh, glorious hope O perfect 455
Oh I love to walk with 229
On safe to the rock that 203
Oh the love that sought me 186
Oh what a Saviour that 52
On a hill far away 104
On Christ the solid rock 232
On Jordon's stormy banks 450
On the happy golden shore 448
ON THE VICTORY SIDE 464
One sat alone, beside the 59
Once far from God and 360
Once in sin's dark night 114
ONCE IT WAS THE BLESSING 304
Once my way was dark 40
ONE DAY 337
ONE GOD AND ONE MEDIATOR 346
ONLY A SINNER 191
ONLY A TOUCH 227
ONLY BELIEVE 245
ONLY ONE LIFE 331
ONLY TRUST HIM 439
ONWARD CHRISTIAN SOLDIERS . . . 384
OPEN MY EYES 156
OPENED FOR ME 109
OUR GREAT SAVIOUR 30
Out of my bondage, sorrow 427
Out of the Ivory palaces 362
Out on the highways and 382

PASS ME NOT 431
Peace like a river is 112
PEACE, PERFECT PEACE 189
Peal out the watch-word 315
PENTECOSTAL POWER 157
POWER IN THE BLOOD 125
PRAISE GOD FROM WHOM ALL BLESSINGS FLOW 37
PRAISE HIM! PRAISE HIM! 31
PRAISE THE SAVIOUR, YE WHO KNOW HIM 66
Praise ye the Father 47
PRAISE YE THE TRIUNE GOD 47
Precious name, oh, how sweet 83
Publish good tidings, ... 399

REDEEMED 57
Redeemed, how I love to 57
REJOICE THE LORD IS KING 45
RESCUE THE PERSIHING 412
Revival is my deepest need 218
REVIVAL PRAYER 218
REVIVE US AGAIN 53
RING THE BELLS OF HEAVEN 413
RISE WITH THY RISEN LORD 371
ROCK OF AGES 275
Room for Jesus, King of 434

SAFE IN THE ARMS OF JESUS 440
SATISFIED 209
Satisfied my highest longing 454

GENERAL INDEX

SAVED BY GRACE 449
Saved by grace alone 193
SAVED BY THE BLOOD 72
Saved, I'm saved through 73
Saved, saved my sins are all 72
SAVED, SAVED 73
SAVED, SAVED, SAVED 74
SAVIOUR, BREATHE AN EVENING BLESSING 221
SAVIOUR, LIKE A SHEPHERD LEAD US 236
Saviour, more than life to me 294
Saviour, thy dying love 312
Saviour, 'tis a full surrender 326
Search me, O God 316
SEEKING FOR ME 87
SHALL I EMPTY-HANDED BE? 378
SHOWERS OF BLESSINGS 284
Simply trusting, every day 233
SILENT NIGHT, HOLY NIGHT 90
SINCE JESUS CAME INTO MY HEART . 71
SINCE THE FULLNESS OF HIS LOVE CAME IN 40
Sing, o sing of my redeemer 56
Sing the wondrous love of 443
SINGING I GO 61
Sinners Jesus will receive 437
So I'll cherish the old 104
So precious is Jesus 68
SO SEND I YOU 391
SOFTLY AND TENDERLY 420
Some day you say I will 417
Some through the waters 277
SOMETHING FOR THEE 312
SOMETIME WE'LL UNDERSTAND . . . 249
SPEAK JUST A WORD FOR JESUS . . . 396
SPEAK, LORD, IN THE STILLNESS . . . 217
SPEAK, MY LORD 391
SPIRIT OF GOD, DESCEND UPON MY HEART 150
STAND UP FOR JESUS 368
STANDING ON THE PROMISES 171
Stayed upon Jehovah 265
STEPPING IN THE LIGHT 352
STILL SWEETER EVERY DAY 54
STIR ME, O STIR ME, LORD 389
SUN OF MY SOUL 302
SUNSHINE IN MY SOUL 268
SURELY GOODNESS AND MERCY . . . 286
SWEET BY AND BY 453
SWEET HONEY IN THE ROCK 492
SWEET NAME COME DOWN FROM HEAVEN 63
Sweetest note in seraph song 289

TAKE MORE TIME TO PRAY 495
TAKE MY LIFE AND LET IT BE 314
TAKE THE NAME OF JESUS WITH YOU 83
Take the world but give me 320
Take thou my heart, I would 306
TAKE TIME TO BE HOLY 354
TEACH ME TO PRAY, LORD 210
TELL ME THE STORY OF JESUS 86
Tempted and tried on my 321
THANK YOU LORD 486
THAT BEAUTIFUL NAME 85
THAT'S WHY I LOVE HIM 69
THE BANNER OF THE CROSS 379
THE BATTLE IS THE LORD'S 400
THE BLOOD WILL NEVER LOSE IT'S POWER 126
THE CALL FOR REAPERS 405
THE COMFORTER HAS COME 148
THE CHURCH'S ONE FOUNDATION . . 161
THE FAMILY OF GOD 500
THE FIGHT IS ON 409
THE FUTURE IS EXCITING 324
THE GLORIOUS HOPE 455
THE GLORY OF HIS PRESENCE 225
THE GOD OF ABRAHAM PRAISE 39
The gospel of thy grace 425
THE GREAT PHYSICIAN 289
THE GREATEST THING IS LOVE 182
THE HAVEN OF REST 240
THE KING'S BUSINESS 397
THE LIGHT OF THE WORLD 415
The Lord is my shepherd 351
THE LORD IS RISEN 136
THE LORD'S MY SHEPHERD 293
The Lord's our rock, in 278
THE MASTER HAS COME 385
THE NAME OF JESUS 84
THE OLD BOOK AND THE OLD FAITH 169
THE OLD RUGGED CROSS 104
THE SANDS OF TIME ARE SINKING . . 451
The signs of the times 146
THE SOLID ROCK 232
THE SON OF GOD GOES FORTH TO WAR 393
THE SONG OF THE SOUL SET FREE . . 76
THE SPACIOUS FIRMAMENT 19
THE STAR-SPANGLED BANNER 461
THE STRIFE IS O'ER 111
The trusting heart to 61
The whole world was lost 415
THEN JESUS CAME 59
Then sings my soul 27
There have been names 81
THERE IS A FOUNTAIN 129
THERE IS A GREEN HILL FAR AWAY 103
There's a royal banner 379
There is a stream that 116
There is joy in serving 387
There is joy, joy, joy 387
There is never a day so 82
There is one who loves me 226
There is power, power 125
There is sunshine in my soul 268
There was no arm to save 118
There was one who was 117
There's a land that is fairer 453
THERE'S A SONG IN THE AIR 99

GENERAL INDEX

There's a story ever new 424
THERE'S A WIDENESS IN GOD'S MERCY 207
THERE'S A WONDERFUL NAME 98
There's not a friend like 208
There's within my heart 260
THEY SAY HE IS WONDERFUL 493
THINE IS THE GLORY 134
This friend is real, so real 223
THIS IS MY FATHER'S WORLD 21
This is my story, this is 200
This is the message that I 397
This, this is Christ the king 97
THOU ART CALLING ME, LORD JESUS 153
Thou who knoweth all 212
Thou whose almighty word 406
THOU WILT KEEP HIM IN PERFECT PEACE 263
Though the angry surges 290
THY WILL BE DONE 323
THY WORD HAVE I HID IN MY HEART 165
TILL THE WHOLE WORLD KNOWS . . 395
'TIS MIDNIGHT AND ON OLIVE'S BROW 101
'TIS SO SWEET TO TRUST IN JESUS . . 251
'TIS THE BLESSED HOLY SPIRIT 149
'Tis the grandest theme 235
'Tis the song of a soul 76
TO GOD BE THE GLORY 4
To Jesus every day my 54
TO THE WORK 377
Toiling on, toiling on 377
TRUE-HEARTED, WHOLE-HEARTED . 315
TRUE TO THE END 321
TRUST AND OBEY 234
TRUST HIM 185
Trusting as the moments 233
TRUSTING JESUS 233
Trying to walk in the 352
TURN YOUR EYES UPON JESUS 418

UNDER HIS WINGS 241
UNDERGIRDED 299
UNSEARCHABLE RICHES 55
Up from the grave He arose 133

VERILY, VERILY 52
Verily, verily, I say unto 52
VESSELS FOR THE MASTER'S USE . . 468
VICTORY ALL THE TIME 349
Victory, victory, blessed 349

Walking in sunshine all of 269
WE ARE BY CHRIST REDEEMED 204
We are on the Lord's side 383
WE COME, O CHRIST TO THEE 67
WE GIVE THEE BUT THINE OWN 355
WE HAVE AN ANCHOR 279
We have heard the joyful 388
WE MAY NOT CLIMB THE HEAVENLY STEEPS 329
We praise thee, o God 53
We thank Thee Lord for this our 105
WELCOME HAPPY MORNING 135
WE'RE MARCHING TO ZION 49
WE'VE A STORY TO TELL TO THE NATIONS 381
What a fellowship, what a 206
What a wonderful change 71
WHAT A WONDERFUL SAVIOUR 70
What can wash away my sins 122
WHAT CHILD IS THIS? 97
What tho the way be lonely 288
WHAT WILL YOU DO WITH JESUS? . . 435
When all my labors and trials 441
WHEN HE COMETH 140
WHEN HIS FACE I SEE 454
When I fear my faith 280
When I saw the cleansing 35
WHEN I SURVEY THE WONDROUS CROSS 110
When Jesus comes, the tempter 59
WHEN LOVE SHINES IN 180
When my life's work is 446
When peace like a river 270
WHEN THE ROLL IS CALLED UP YONDER 444
When the trumpet of the Lord 444
When upon life's billows 297
WHEN WE ALL GET TO HEAVEN 443
When we walk with the Lord 234
WHERE HE LEADS ME I'LL FOLLOW . 410
While we pray and while we 443
Who is a pardoning God 20
WHO IS ON THE LORD'S SIDE? 383
Who is this, that like 149
WHOM HAVING NOT SEEN, I LOVE . . 223
"Whosoever heareth", shout 198
WHOSOEVER WILL BELIEVE 425
WHY DO I SING ABOUT JESUS? 51
WHY NOT NOW? 433
Will your anchor hold in the 279
WITH ETERNITY'S VALUES IN VIEW . 499
WONDERFUL GRACE OF JESUS 188
WONDERFUL JESUS 230
Wonderful love that rescued 178
Wonderful love that the father 173
WONDERFUL PEACE 271
WONDERFUL SAVIOUR 34
Wonderful the matchless grace 188
WONDERFUL WORDS OF LIFE 168
WORTHY IS THE LAMB 17
Would you be free from the 125
WOUNDED FOR ME 120

Yea, justified! o blessed 373
Years I spent in vanity 128
Yes, I'll sing the wondrous 60
YE MUST BE BORN AGAIN 416
YESTERDAY, TODAY, FOREVER . . . 257
YIELDED TO GOD 376
You have longed for sweet 319

Add a Song
TO GOD
BE THE GLORY

Add a Song
TO GOD
BE THE GLORY